MA 15300

Indiana University
Purdue University Fort Wayne

College Algebra and Trigonometry I
Second Edition

Connally

To order books or for customer service, please call 1(800)-CALL-WILEY (225-5945).

Printed in the United States of America.

ISBN 978-1-118-16856-1

Printed and bound by EPAC Technologies, Inc.

10 9 8 7 6 5 4 3 2 1

Contents

General Information

1. Why Do I Need College Algebra and Trigonometry?   1

2. The Course Goals for College Algebra and Trigonometry   1

3. The IPFW Baccalaureate Framework   1

4. Prerequisite Skills   2

5. Course Descriptions   3

6. A Team Approach to Problem Solving   3

7. Reading Assignments   3

8. Keys to Success   4

9. Study Time Outside of Class   4

10. Calculator   5

11. Internet Resources and your IPFW Computer Lab Account   5

12. eHW at **ipfw.edu/math**   5

13. Help!   16

Chapter 1. Linear Functions and Change   17

Chapter 2. Functions   77

Chapter 3. Exponential Functions   121

Chapter 4. Logarithmic Functions   167

Chapter 5. Transformations of Functions and Their Graphs   209

Chapter 8. Compositions, Inverses, and Combinations of Functions   259

Chapter 9. Polynomial and Rational Functions   293

Answers to Odd-Numbered Problems   353

Select Chapters from the Student Solutions Manual   383

Index   503

Practice Questions for the Final   515

FUNCTIONS MODELING CHANGE:
A Preparation for Calculus

Third Edition

Produced by the Calculus Consortium and initially funded by a National Science Foundation Grant.

Eric Connally
Harvard University Extension

Deborah Hughes-Hallett
University of Arizona

Andrew M. Gleason
Harvard University

Philip Cheifetz
Nassau Community College

Ann Davidian
Gen. Douglas MacArthur HS

Daniel E. Flath
Macalester College

Brigitte Lahme
Sonoma State University

Patti Frazer Lock
St. Lawrence University

Jerry Morris
Sonoma State University

Karen Rhea
University of Michigan

Ellen Schmierer
Nassau Community College

Pat Shure
University of Michigan

Carl Swenson
Seattle University

Katherine Yoshiwara
Los Angeles Pierce College

Elliot J. Marks

with the assistance of
Frank Avenoso
Nassau Community College

John Wiley & Sons, Inc.

Dedicated to Maria, Ben, Jonah, and Isabel

PUBLISHER	Laurie Rosatone
SENIOR ACQUISITIONS EDITOR	Angela Y. Battle
MARKETING MANAGER	Amy Sell
FREELANCE DEVELOPMENTAL EDITOR	Anne Scanlan-Rohrer
SENIOR PRODUCTION EDITOR	Ken Santor
ASSISTANT EDITOR	Shannon Corliss
MARKETING ASSISTANT	Tara Martinho
COVER DESIGNER	Hope Miller
COVER PHOTO	©Scott Berner/Picture Quest

This book was set in Times Roman by the Consortium using TeX, Mathematica, and the package AsTeX, which was written by Alex Kasman. It was printed and bound by Von Hoffmann Press. The cover was printed by Von Hoffmann Press. The process was managed by Elliot Marks.

This material is based upon work supported by the National Science Foundation under Grant No. DUE-9352905. Opinions expressed are those of the authors and not necessarily those of the Foundation.

ISBN-13 978-0-471-79303-8
ISBN-10 0471-79303-5

Printed in the United States of America

10 9 8 7 6 5 4 3 2 1

STUDENT SOLUTIONS MANUAL

to accompany

Functions
Modeling
Change
A Preparation for Calculus
Third Edition

by
Eric Connally
Harvard University Extension

Deborah Hughes-Hallett
University of Arizona

Andrew M. Gleason
Harvard University

et al.

John Wiley & Sons, Inc.

This material is based upon work supported by the National Science Foundation under Grant No. DUE-9352905. Opinions expressed are those of the authors and not necessarily those of the Foundation.

ISBN-13   978-0-470-10561-0

Printed in the United States of America

10 9 8 7 6 5 4 3 2 1

Printed and bound by Bind-Rite Robbinsville

General Course Information

1. Why Do I Need *College Algebra and Trigonometry*?

Many students take this course because it is required for their degree. But there are better reasons than that!

In this course you will
- create and interpret mathematical models to solve problems presented as real world situations.
- formulate, validate, and analyze solutions to problems using mental, paper and pencil, algebraic, and technology-based techniques as appropriate.
- utilize graphing calculators to find the solution to problems which cannot be solved by pencil and paper, as well as explore mathematical patterns and visualize mathematical ideas.
- build a foundation for quantitative literacy to help you solve problems in and outside of academia.
- learn to make sense of the mathematics you will need, not only for future course work in math and the physical and social sciences, but in any career which requires you to analyze information.

*The above aligns with the goals of the IPFW Baccalaureate Framework (See **Section 3**) and is based on the guidelines of the Mathematical Association of America's subcommittee, Curriculum Renewal Across the First Two Years (CRAFTY). For the full document, see **www.maa.org/cupm/crafty/***

2. The Course Goals for *College Algebra and Trigonometry*

- Highlight the link of mathematics to the real world.
- Develop a wide base of mathematical knowledge, including
  - basic skills and concepts,
  - a functional view of mathematics, including graphical, algebraic, numerical, and contextual viewpoints,
  - properties and applications of some of the basic families of functions
  - geometric visualization,
  - problem solving, predicting, critical thinking, and generalizing.
- Incorporate the use of general academic skills such as
  - communicating mathematics concepts,
  - understanding and using technology, and
  - working collaboratively.

3. The IPFW Baccalaureate Framework

The IPFW faculty have identified six foundations of baccalaureate education. These foundations provide the framework for all baccalaureate degree programs.

Acquisition of Knowledge Students will demonstrate breadth of knowledge across disciplines and depth of knowledge in their chosen discipline. In order to do so, students must demonstrate the requisite information- seeking skills and technological competencies.

Application of Knowledge Students will demonstrate the ability to integrate and apply that knowledge, and, in so doing, demonstrate the skills necessary for life-long learning.

Personal & Professional Values Students will demonstrate the highest levels of personal integrity and professional ethics.

A Sense of Community Students will demonstrate the knowledge and skills necessary to be productive and responsible citizens and leaders in local, regional, national, and international communities. In so doing, students will demonstrate a commitment to free and open inquiry and mutual respect across multiple cultures and perspectives.

Critical Thinking and Problem Solving Students will demonstrate facility and adaptability in their approach to problem solving. In so doing, students will demonstrate critical-thinking abilities and familiarity with quantitative and qualitative reasoning.

Communication Students will demonstrate the written, oral, and multimedia skills necessary to communicate effectively in diverse settings.

The foundations are interdependent, with each one contributing to the integrative and holistic education offered at IPFW.

4. Prerequisite Skills

MA 15300, MA 15400, and MA 15900 are intended for students who have completed two years of high school algebra. The prerequisite for MA 15300 or MA 15900 is completion of Intermediate Algebra MA 11300 with a C or higher or placement by departmental exam. The prerequisite for MA 15400 is MA 15300 with a C or higher or placement by departmental exam. It is assumed that you are proficient in many of the skills mentioned in the sections of the text called **Tools**.

Take a look at the following kinds of problems. If they do not look familiar, perhaps you need to drop the class and take either the prerequisite *Intermediate Algebra* MA 11300, or its prerequisite, *Elementary Intermediate Algebra* MA 10900.

Use algebraic symbols and notation.	**Section 1.1** 30 **Ch 1 Review** 35
Understand function notation, and find the domain and range of a function if given its graph.	**Section 1.1**: 1, 3, 9, 11 **Section 2.1**: 3, 4, 17, 27b, 31 **Section 2.2**: 13
Perform the following activities with lines: a. Graph equations in standard form and slope-intercept form. b. Compute the slope given two points. c. State the slope and vertical-intercept given a linear equation. d. Work with lines which are parallel or perpendicular. e. Write the equation of a line given its slope and another point. f. Write the equation of a line given if given two points. g. Write the equation of a vertical or horizontal line.	**Section 1.5**: 2, 17 **Ch 1 Review**: 19-25 odd **Tools for Ch 1**: 1-25 odd
Solve a system of two linear equations in two variables (having no, one, or many solutions) by graphing, substitution, or elimination.	**Tools for Ch 1**: 33-43 odd
Apply properties of positive integer exponents.	**Tools for Ch 3**: 1-23 odd, 95-111 odd
Apply properties of negative integer or rational exponents.	**Tools for Ch 3**: 25-43 odd, 78-86 odd
Perform multiplication and division with radicals.	**Tools for Ch 3**:: 45-55 odd, 61-75 odd
Change the form of an algebraic expression in factored form by expanding ; reverse the process by factoring.	**Tools for Ch 2:** Expand: 1-25 odd Factor: 29-65 odd
Use algebra to solve the following equations: a. Quadratic with real solutions. b. Fractional leading to a linear or quadratic. c. Polynomial by factoring. d. Radical leading to linear or quadratic.	**Tools for Ch 2:** By Factoring: 77-95 odd By Raising Both Sides to a Power: 83, 105 Fractional Equations: 81, 87-91 odd, 101 **Tools for Ch 3:** Polynomial Equations: 87-91 odd **Tools for Ch 5:** Using the Quadratic Formula: 37-41 odd Use the Best Strategy: 43-55 odd
Complete the square for a quadratic expression.	**Tools for Ch 5**: 1, 4, 13-17 odd, 19, 23, 27
Simplify algebraic fractional expressions	**Tools for Ch 9**: 1-13 odd, 62-66
Solve problems involving basic geometric concepts including the Pythagorean Theorem, formulas for area and perimeter of rectangles, squares, triangles, and circles, and volumes of rectangular prisms and cylinders.	**Section 1.3**: 16, 17 **Ch 1 Review**: 36 **Ch 2 Review**: 42a

Work the above suggested problems to make sure you have the tools you need to succeed.

5. Course Descriptions

MA 15900 (5 credits) presents the concepts of *Precalculus* or *College Algebra and Trigonometry* from four points of view: geometric (graphs), numeric (tables), symbolic (formulas), and written (verbal descriptions). Note: MA 15900 was formerly MA 151. The emphasis is on the mathematical modeling of real-life problems using linear, polynomial, exponential, logarithmic, trigonometric, and rational functions. Topics also include vectors, conic sections, and complex numbers.

The sequence MA 15300 - MA 15400 (3 credits each) is a two semester version of MA 15900. If it has been quite a long time since you've had algebra or trigonometry (or if you have never taken trigonometry), it may be wise to take the two semester sequence. Any degree program which requires MA 15900 will accept credit in successful completion of both MA 15300-MA 15400.

6. A Team Approach to Problem Solving

A primary goal in this course is the ability to work as a functioning member of a team to solve challenging problems and analyze mathematical information. Working in a group not only helps you develop the interpersonal skills required for the workplace, but will help you meet many other course goals as well:
- communicating your reasoning orally,
- actively listening and understanding the reasoning of other team members, and
- creating logical arguments. If you can't explain it, it is likely you don't fully understand it.

Team Roles
Effective groups are organized and have clearly defined roles for its members. Group roles could include:

Manager – encourages all members of the group to participate in the discussion, share their ideas, as well as quiets down someone if he or she is doing too much of the talking, e.g., "I think the group understands what you've been saying; we need to hear some other ideas." The manager keeps everyone on task, e.g. "What you had for lunch isn't relevant.". He or she takes one of the other roles if one of the group members is absent.

Reader – reads the problem aloud to the group. Afterwards, takes on other roles, such as Quality Controller.

Scribe – writes up the group's solution to the problem for presentation to the class, showing the necessary steps to the solution and, if appropriate, writing verbal interpretations of the mathematical concepts in complete sentences.

Quality Controller – double-checks for correctness, capitalizing on the Rule of Four where appropriate.

Clarifier – ensures all participants understand the ideas expressed by other group members, paraphrasing the ideas presented by others and questions everything.

7. Reading Assignments

Students often notice that the text for this course looks different than math textbooks they have used in the past. You might notice the following strengths of this text as opposed to traditional, older math texts:

- **Real world connections**
  - Many concepts are introduced and investigated through simple, realistic applications which are also used by partner disciplines (economics, physical and social sciences, etc.)
- **Multiple perspectives**
  - There is equal emphasis between analytical (symbolic), graphical, numerical, and contextual approaches.
- **Conceptual Understanding**

- Doing the exercises requires an understanding of the material in the text, not searching for a similar worked out exercise in the text and changing the numbers in a "pattern example".
- Supplemented with e-Homework (**Section 12**), which provides virtually unlimited number of worked out examples, students have opportunities to integrate and apply their knowledge in new situations.
- **Problem solving and cooperative learning**
  - Open-ended problems in the text are not cut and dried, providing an opportunity for exploratory learning, use of technology, and small group discussion. Many problems have multiple solution paths.
  - Problems require critical thinking, where you must choose an appropriate mathematical model given a real world situation and interpret what mathematical formulas mean. There is much less emphasis on lower ordered thinking skills such as "plug and chug" or rote memorization.

Compare the above with the Course Goals (**Section 2**) and the IPFW Baccalaureate Framework (**Section 3**).

If you have used a traditional math text in the past, it may have been possible to do relatively well in the course without reading the text before coming to class. In an interactive class setting such as this one, where students work on the material and grapple with the problems together, **it is absolutely essential that you do the reading assignments prior to class.** In fact, the book is written in an informal way to help you make sense of the concepts. Since this may be a new approach, here are some tips to help you read the book before class:

1. Plan some time to do the reading more than once. On the first reading, it is unlikely that you will have a perfect understanding of everything.
2. After you have read it once, try to summarize in your own words the big ideas. Then re-read the section.
3. On the second time through, bring out your graphing calculator, paper, and pencil to work out the examples along with the authors to get a thorough understanding of everything in the section.
4. If something does not make sense, make a note of it to bring it to your instructor, fellow group members, or a tutor at the Tutoring Center (CASA, Kettler G21). Sometimes if you return to it when your mind is fresh, the fog lifts all on its own.

8. Keys to Success

Your behavior is a key ingredient to your learning.

- You are expected to not only attend all class meetings, but participate in your group and contribute to the learning environment of the class as a whole. Travel plans, social functions on campus, appointments with an advisor, non-emergency appointments with your dentist, etc., are never an excuse to miss class.
- Be in your seat and ready to begin at the start of class and do not leave until the class is finished. Sit with your assigned group members.
- Come prepared to be engaged in learning mathematics. The classroom is not a place to read the newspaper, work on homework from other courses, send/receive text messages, or surf the Internet. Once you arrive to class, bring out your graphing calculator. Silence and put away any other electronic devices.
- Listen actively. When your instructor or your fellow students are talking to the class, be respectful, polite, and silent so that people around you can hear. Do not continue working in your group.
- To benefit from an interactive class, come to class prepared, having done the assigned reading and attempted the homework problems so you can contribute to your team. Ask questions if you have trouble as soon as you have difficulty. Use your instructor's office hours or the department's common office hour program.
- Show your work if the solution requires it, as opposed to just writing down an answer. Problem solving is a central focus of this course. Documenting the journey is at least as important as reporting the final destination.

9. Study Time Outside of Class

This course requires a solid effort. During the Fall or Spring Semester, the faculty at IPFW expect you to study a minimum of 6 hours a week outside of class working on mathematics for MA 15300 or MA 15400 and 10 ten hours per week for MA 15900.

10. Calculator

You will be required to use a graphing calculator for activities and assignments in and out of class. This is not optional. The Department of Mathematical Sciences Web Page (**ipfw.edu/math/**) maintains an *Assistance with Graphing Calculators* Website which can help you obtain and use a graphing calculator. The TI-83, TI-83 Plus or TI-84 Plus is strongly recommended. You may use another equivalent calculator* but you will be responsible for understanding how to use it. Your instructor will be most familiar with the TI-83/84 or TI-83/84 Plus and may not be able to offer you help with other calculators.

*Your calculator should have features which enable you to find intersection points, zeros (or roots), and maximum/minimum points of graphs. If you have questions whether your model of calculator is allowed, ask your instructor.

Graphing Calculator Loan Program: You can rent a TI-83 or TI-83 Plus for the semester for a nominal fee from the Indiana University Purdue University Fort Wayne Students' Government Association (IPGSA), located in the Walb Student Union Room 225 (260-481-6586). You get the TI-83 calculator, manual, and unit-to-unit link cable for the entire semester. You must return the calculator at the end of the semester in the same condition you received it or your grades will be encumbered. Supplies are limited and are usually depleted the first week of classes. However, some students may have dropped a class which requires a calculator so one could just be sitting here on a shelf waiting just for you.

11. Internet Resources and your IPFW Computer Lab Account

If your instructor has their own Home Page or uses Blackboard at **http://elearning.ipfw.edu/**, be sure to go there first. In addition, you can access Course Websites as follows:

Go to the Department of Mathematical Sciences Web Page **ipfw.edu/math/** , click on **Course Information** and then on **Math Course Materials** on the left side of the page. Then scroll to find the appropriate course.

Student-access computer labs are located around campus. For a complete list, go to the Information Technology Services Website at **http://ipfw.edu/its/** , click on **Resources & Services** and then **Facilities**. You will should see a link for **Student open access computer labs**. To use the computers in these labs you must have an activated IPFW computer Lab Account, which you received when you enrolled in IPFW. If you no longer have your activation packet, go immediately to the Help Desk at Kettler 206 with a picture ID to obtain a new packet.

12. *eHW* at ipfw.edu/math/

The department has purchased a site license for a Web-based electronic homework (*eHW*) system, which immediately grades your answers and provides worked-out solutions. This gives you many advantages:

- Online homework has been shown to help students develop mastery of those algebraic techniques that are needed for problem solving and mathematical modeling, as well as for later mathematics course work.

- Students sometimes share that they want to learn by watching the teacher do one example after another. This is not the best use of class time. In class, you work in teams to solve problems, communicate your reasoning, and see how mathematics can apply to your lives. Outside of class, online homework can enable you to see patterns through repeated practice, get immediate computer-graded feedback, and keep re-doing the assignment until you get it correct.

- Students have generally responded favorably to online homework when it was piloted previously.

Unsolicited student comments include the following:

- "I flunked this class last semester. This semester, the night before each test, I do online homework over and over just for practice and now I've been getting B's on exams."
- "Handing in regular (paper and pencil) homework is a one shot deal – you miss it and there's no redo. But I can redo *eHW* until I get a 100%. Without *eHW*, I would have failed the class." online assignment."

Students who have responded unfavorably generally did not like *any* kind of math homework, expressed frustration because they did not round numbers correctly, or were not able to enter mathematics in a computer using parentheses. The latter skill is also important when using a graphing calculator and even required for some questions on paper and pencil exams, e.g., $2^{3(x+4)}$ is not the same as 2^{3x+4}.

- When re-doing an assignment to improve your score, you must re-do all of the questions in that assignment, not just the ones you missed. Sometimes the questions do not look exactly like the ones in the previous assignment, but test the same concept. This is an intentional design and not a flaw. Research has shown that if students do an assignment only once, even perfectly, they do not retain the concepts later. It is important to use eHW as a tool for learning, not just for putting a grade in a gradebook.

- You do not need to install any special software to use *eHW* and do not need a home computer. You only need access to a computer with an Internet connection such as those in the open-access labs on campus or, if off-campus, you could use computers in the public library. Some students have used the computers right in The Spot (the IPFW tutoring center in Kettler G21) to work on their *eHW*.

- Once you complete an assignment, your score is immediately recorded in the instructor's *Gradebook*. You need not print anything to submit to your instructor. At any time, you can view your results from past assignments and the worked out solutions by clicking on the *Gradebook* link.

- You do not need to complete an assignment all in one sitting; however, you can only work on one assignment at a time. If you are interrupted during a homework assignment or quiz, you can log back into the system and return to the assignment where you left off. Your interaction with the system is saved as you move from one question to the next. If thunder strikes your computer during the assignment and you lose your connection prior to submitting it, everything up until the last question you were on will be saved.

Getting to the eHW Site
Here is a visual path to get to the eHW site.

1. Go to **ipfw.edu/math/** and click on **e-Homework**.

2. On the **e-Homework** Page, you can purchase an access code if you do not already have one. It is good for an entire year.

6

The link takes you to the Maplesoft Web Store. If this is your first time you have been there, you will need to take a moment to create a membership account with Maplesoft with a userid and a password (which is not your eHW access code). It is vitally important that you **enter your information correctly**.
For example, if George Washington were a student at IPFW, his e-mail might likely be

washg01@students.ipfw.edu

It would **not** be:

washg01@ipfw.edu

A common problem: students have often provided Maplesoft with an incorrect e-mail address. The company then sends the access code to the bogus address, it bounces, and the student never receives what they paid for. Customer Service phone lines then become jammed with students who are irate over a problem they could have avoided. Please be careful when entering your e-mail address.

An access code must be purchased online with a credit card (and not a debit card.)
If you do not have a credit card, purchase a pre-loaded credit card, available at a local supermarket.

Contact Maplesoft customer service at **1-800-267-6583** ext. **240** or by e-mail at <u>custservice@maplesoft.com</u> if you need help purchasing an eHW access code.

3. On the **e-Homework** Page, you can login to the eHW system from any computer connected to the Internet. From there you will be directed to the **Login** page.

    Login page

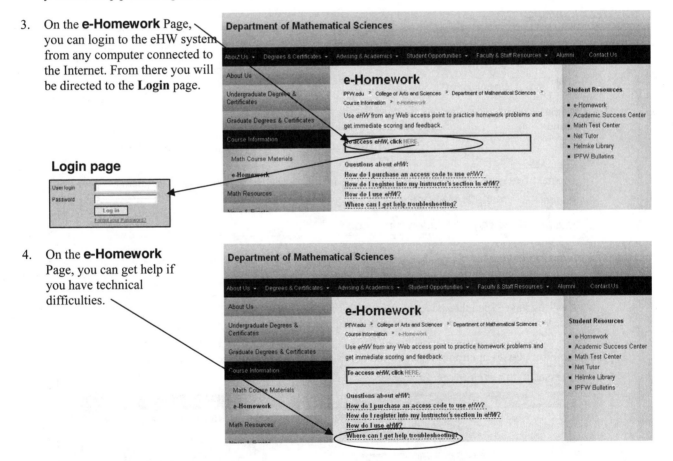

4. On the **e-Homework** Page, you can get help if you have technical difficulties.

Note: When you have trouble, please e-mail **ehwtechsupport@ipfw.edu** describing the problem in as much detail as possible.

How to register in your class in five steps:

1. Purchase an eHW Access code (See previous page).
   On the login screen, enter the login and password you received once you purchased the code.

   It will not be the same as your
   IPFW user account.

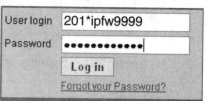
2. Once logged in, you will
   be immediately asked to
   verify your information shown
   in each box below.

   Important!
   You need to change
   the four starred boxes or your
   instructor will not know
   who you are!

   Example:

First Name	George
Last Name	Washington
Display Name	

   This field completes automatically once you type the above.

   Example:
   The next two boxes can each contain a valid e-mail address. Be sure to include ".students."

Student ID	washg01@students.ipfw.edu
Email	washg01@students.ipfw.edu

   If you forget your password, the system will e-mail it to the address you enter here.
   If this address is incorrect, you will not receive it.

   After you have typed the above, click **Submit**.
   Once your changes have been accepted, you will be sent to the **System Homepage**.

3. Click on **Find classes open for registration**. You will then see a list of sections, such as:

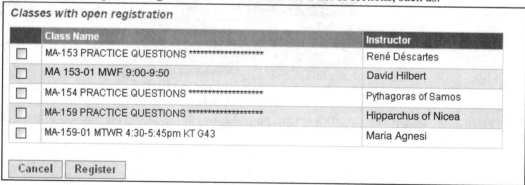

   Check the box for the correct section(s). Be sure to scroll all the way to the bottom to click **Register**.

4. You will then be asked to confirm the class(es) in which you are registering. For example:

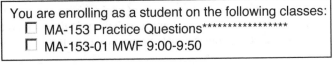

You are enrolling as a student on the following classes:
- ☐ MA-153 Practice Questions*****************
- ☐ MA-153-01 MWF 9:00-9:50

Click **Confirm** to complete the self-registration.

5. That's it! You won't need to do this process again this semester. Click on the link for your section to get to your Class Homepage:

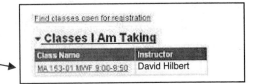

A sample eHW session:

From this link, you will be able to take assignments, view past results in the **Gradebook** in the top left corner, or change your password by clicking the **My Profile** link in the top right corner.

1. Once you are registered in your instructor's course (see previous page), login again to access *eHW*.

   On the login screen, enter your login and password.

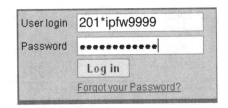

Be sure to keep this access information private from your fellow classmates. Logging in under someone else's account is considered fraudulent behavior, and will be reported to the Dean of Students.

2. Once logged in, click on the link to the course homepage.

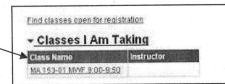

3. Once there, you will see a list of any assignments. Click on the link to your assignment.

Assignment Name	Points	Type	Availability
E-HW0 Syllabus and General Course Info	10.0	Homework/Quiz	Unlimited
E-HW 01 Topics from Chapter	10.0	Homework/Quiz	Unlimited
E-HW 02 Topics from Chapter 2	10.0	Homework/Quiz	Unlimited
E-HW 03 Topics from Section 3.1 and 3.2	10.0	Homework/Quiz	Unlimited
E-HW 04 Selected Topics from Chapter 3	10.0	Homework/Quiz	Unlimited
E-HW05 Topics from Chapter 4	10.0	Homework/Quiz	Unlimited
E-HW06 Topics from Ch 5 (5.1-5.3)	10.0	Homework/Quiz	Unlimited
E-HW07 Section 5.5 and 8.1	10.0	Homework/Quiz	Unlimited
E-HW08 Topics from Ch 9 (9.1-9.3)	10.0	Homework/Quiz	Unlimited
E-HW 09 Asymptotes	10.0	Homework/Quiz	Unlimited
E-HW 10 Rational Functions	10.0	Homework/Quiz	Unlimited

4. The total number of questions in a particular assignment appears in the upper right corner of your screen. The **Assignment Navigation Bar** appears at the top of every page within an assignment. To move between questions use the **Back** and **Next** buttons within the **Assignment Navigation Bar**.

   You can also jump to specific questions you may have skipped by using the **Question Menu** and selecting a specific question number in the drop-down menu.

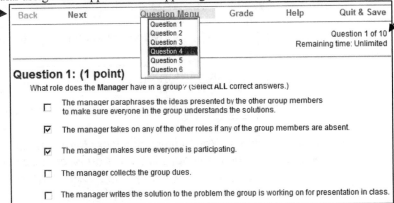

To grade your completed assignment click on the **Grade** link.

To log out of your current assignment to return to complete later, click the **Quit & Save** link.

Important: The only way it will be submitted to your instructor is if you click on **Grade**. You can see your graded assignment later by clicking on the **Gradebook** link. Be careful that you don't just click on **Quit** and miss an assignment deadline. If you can see it in your **Gradebook** link, your instructor can see it as well.

Grading Your Assignment and Viewing Worked Out Solutions:

Once you click on the **Grade** link, if you have not answered any of questions in your assignment, you will be warned and have the opportunity to complete them before grading. If any of your answers include math syntax errors or other input not understood by *eHW*, you will also be warned and have the opportunity to fix those specific questions:

Back	Next	Grade	Help	Quit & Save

Warning: There appear to be errors in your answers to the questions listed below.

- Press the Back button or click on one of the questions in the list to go back and correct your work.
- If you press Grade again, you will get your grade immediately, but the questions listed below will all be graded as wrong.

Question 1: (1 point) The question has not been answered

Question 2: (1 point) Has not been answered yet.

Question 6: (1 point) The formula has no symbols in it.

Question 7: (1 point) You have not filled in all the blanks.

Once you click on **Grade**, you will see your percentage score and the number of questions you answered correctly.

View Details	View Grade	Help	Quit & Save

Thank you
Your assignment is complete. You scored 9 out of 10 (90%).

To view your graded assignment and see any detailed feedback that is available click on the **View Details** link. You will then see your actual assignment with solutions and any detailed feedback, with an option to print.

Working with Math in Responses

You enter formulas using standard mathematical notation similar to that used in a graphing calculator, following the rules for standard order of operations. Some helpful tips follow for entering responses. The most common mistake is parentheses (#2 on the list below) and variable names (#3 below).

Avoiding Common Math Errors

1. ***Exponents:*** Use the caret, ^, for exponentiation, and the letter e for 2.718...

2. ***Parentheses:*** As on a graphing calculator, you must use parentheses. When in doubt, you can use the **Preview** option to see it look the way it would in a math text.

   Examples:

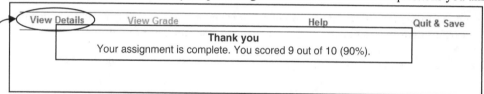

   For $2^{x/13}$, you must type $2\texttt{\^{}(x/13)}$

   not $2\texttt{\^{}x/13}$ ... which would be interpreted as $\dfrac{2^x}{13}$

   For $y = \dfrac{x}{4(x-2)}$, you must type $\texttt{y = x/(4(x-2))}$

   not $\texttt{y = x/4(x-2)}$ ... which would be interpreted as $\frac{x}{4}(x-2)$

3. ***Variable Names:*** You can use any letter for a variable name, but you should always use the same letter that is used in the question. If the question asks you for $\texttt{(t+1)\^{}2}$ then the answer $\texttt{(x+1)\^{}2}$ will be graded wrong. Also, the system is case sensitive. So, if instead of typing $\texttt{(t+1)\^{}2}$ you enter $\texttt{(T+1)\^{}2}$, your answer will be graded wrong.

4. **Multiplication:** You can type an asterisk (i.e. `*`) for multiplication, or just type a letter and a number together (i.e. `2x`).

5. **Square Roots:** The square root function is `sqrt(x)` or you can just type `x^(1/2)` or `x^0.5` instead. Note again that, like on a graphing calculator, `x^1/2` means $\frac{x^1}{2}$.

6. **Absolute Value:** The absolute value function is `abs(x)`, so something like $2|x+1|-3$ would be typed as `2abs(x+1)-3`.

7. **Argument of Functions:** You should always place the argument of a function in parentheses. For example, for $\sqrt{3x}$ you must type `sqrt(3x)`,

   not `sqrt 3x` which would be interpreted as $\sqrt{3}\cdot x$

   Note: The lower level TI calculators (85, 82, and 81) will allow you to enter `sqrt 3x` and `log x/2` without parentheses. Both **eHW** and the higher level TI calculators use the standard convention and require you to put the argument of the function in parentheses in order for your answer to be correctly interpreted.

For MA 159 or MA 154 students especially:

8. **π:** Simply type `Pi` or `pi`. (However, not `PI`.)

9. **Trigonometric Functions:** The names for common mathematical functions (sin, cos, etc.) are just what you would expect. The inverse trig functions are arcsin(x), arccos(x), and arctan(x). Also, trigonometric functions are all set to work in radians.

<u>Using the Preview Option in Responses</u>

Use the **Preview** option to view your response as a typeset mathematics expression. **Preview** demonstrates how the system interprets your entry (inspecting it for misplaced parentheses and other unintended keystrokes).

For example, in the following question, suppose a student types $5/9x+7$ in the box. (Note that this is incorrect.)

> Suppose a student wishes to enter the expression below into a graphing calculator or a computer:
>
> $$\frac{5}{9x+7}$$
>
> Show that you can enter it correctly by typing the expression in the box below.
>
> TIP: Type your answer in the box and click on the **Preview** (🔍) icon to check you typed your answer correctly.
>
> $$\frac{5}{9x+7} = \boxed{\textbf{5/9x+7}}$$
>
> The entry boxes with a small icon beside them are designed to accept numbers or formulas.
> <u>Help</u> I <u>Change Math Entry Mode</u>

After typing $5/9x+7$ in the box and clicking on **Preview** (🔍) a pop-up appears showing how it would appear in "pretty print."

Remember, knowing order of operations is part of the mathematical content of the course, not something extra to satisfy a picky piece of software. Order of precedence is as follows:

Parentheses

Exponents

Multiplication and **D**ivision (from left to right)

Addition and **S**ubtraction (from left to right)

Some students use the mnemonic:

Please

Excuse

My **D**ear

Aunt **S**ally

For example, if you were to compute $8 \div 4 \times 2 + 3$, multiplication and division outrank addition, but multiplication and division are the same rank.

$$8 \div 4 \times 2 + 3 = \frac{8}{4} \times 2 + 3 = 4 + 3 = 7$$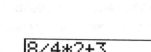

Notice this is what you would obtain from a graphing calculator: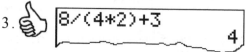

```
8/4*2+3
              7
```

Rules for order of operations are necessary so that a unique value results. Consider the following:

$$8 \div 4 \times 2 + 3 \neq \frac{8}{4 \times 2} + 3 = 1 + 3 = 4$$

$$8 \div 4 \times 2 + 3 \neq \frac{8}{4 \times 2 + 3} = \frac{8}{11}$$

$$8 \div 4 \times 2 + 3 \neq \frac{8}{4} \times (2 + 3) = 2 \times 5 = 10$$

Parentheses outrank all operations. If your intention is to have $\dfrac{8}{4 \times 2} + 3$, the fraction bar serves as a grouping symbol.

The expression $\dfrac{8}{4 \times 2} + 3$ is equivalent to $\dfrac{8}{(4 \times 2)} + 3$.

So if our intention is $\dfrac{8}{4 \times 2} + 3$, we need parentheses: $8 \div (4 \times 2) + 3$.

```
8/(4*2)+3
              4
```

Returning to the example, when you type $5/(9x+7)$
and click on the Preview icon,
a pop-up will confirm that you have
correctly typed the desired expression.

12

Nested Parentheses

To computers and graphing calculators,
brackets such as [or]
or braces such as { or }
are not equivalent to parentheses.

For example, to enter $3^{2/(x+1)}$ you would type $3 \char`\^ (2/(x+1))$

as opposed to $3 \char`\^ (2/[x+1])$.

Using the Symbol Palette in Responses

A symbol palette is also available if you click on **Change Entry Style** () or **Change Math Entry Mode**.

Suppose a student wishes to enter the expression below into a graphing calculator or a computer:

$$\frac{5}{9x + 7}$$

Show that you can enter it correctly by typing the expression in the box below.

TIP: Type your answer in the box and click on the **Preview** ( ) icon to check you typed your answer correctly.

$$\frac{5}{9x + 7}$$

The entry b= [   ] them are designed to accept numbers or formulas.
Help | Change Math Entry Mode

After you click  or click Change Math Entry Mode
you will see a pop-up box
explaining the advantages of Text Mode (default)
and Symbol Mode.

☑ MapleT.A.   [Cancel] [OK]

Equation Editor Modes: You have a choice of two modes for entering answers to math questions:
Text Mode: In text mode, "x squared divided by y" looks like this: $(x\char`\^2)/y$

- Equations are typed in from the keyboard
- Text mode is quick and easy to use in any browser.

Symbol Mode: In symbol mode, "x squared divided by y" looks like this: $\frac{x^2}{y}$

- You need to download a tool to enter equations
- This mode is optimized for Internet Explorer (version 5.0 and later) on Windows and may not work well in other browsers.

Change Equation Editor Mode:

○ Symbol Mode: $\frac{x^2}{y}$

○ Text Mode: $(x\char`\^2)/y$

Important: If you want to work with the current question using the alternate math entry mode, you may need to reload the question after selecting the math entry mode. Return to your question, and use **Next** and **Back** buttons to scroll forward and then back to your question. This forces the system to reload the question using your preferred style of entry.

If you select **Symbol Mode**, you stay in this mode indefinitely unless you change it back to **Text Mode**.

For symbol mode, after downloading a tool, you will see the Equation Editor appear (assuming you have Java installed on your computer.)

Right-click (or **Control**-click on Macintosh) in the box.

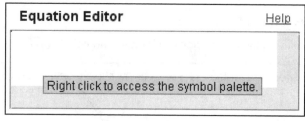

The main palette is displayed.

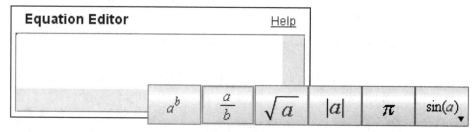

Click a palette to display all symbols in the palette group. Select a symbol/expression. It is displayed in the Equation Editor field.

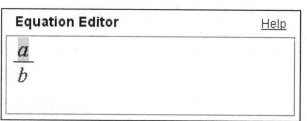

Modify as necessary.

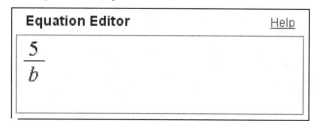

Click **Next** to move to the next question in your assignment.

The system allows you to toggle Math Entry Modes as often as you want, depending on the requirements of the question and your personal preferences. Each time you change the style of math entry, the system remembers your responses on previous questions, and automatically translates them for you. If you move to a previous question (where you have already entered an answer), your response is displayed in the current editor mode.

You can use the following shortcut keys when entering answers in the Equation Editor in **Symbol Mode**. For example, **Ctrl** followed by **Space** completes a symbol.
(If more than one completion option is presented, select the desired symbol.)

Shortcut Characters	Result
Ctrl + Space	symbol completion
^ (caret)	superscript
_ (underscore key)	subscript
/	fraction
Ctrl + '	underscript
Ctrl + Shift + "	overscript
Ctrl + _	pre-subscript
Ctrl + [	scope out
Ctrl +]	scope in
Ctrl + /	return cursor to baseline
Ctrl + Shift + G	Greek mode (next character entered as Greek)
Right-click (Control-click for Macintosh)	display palettes

Rules for Rounding

Standard rules for rounding numbers apply.

For example, suppose we are rounding the following calculations to two decimal places.

```
1.12^2
                1.2544
1.12^8
        2.475963176
1.12^41
        104.2170869
```

Look to the right of the rounding digit, which we have underlined.

If it is 4 or lower, we truncate. So to two decimal places, $1.12^2 \approx 1.25$

If it is 5 or higher, we round up. So to two decimal places, $1.12^8 \approx 2.48$

and to two decimal places, $1.12^{41} \approx 104.22$

What is 1.12^{23} to two decimal places? Since the digit to the right of the rounding digit is 2, we have $1.12^{23} \approx 13.55$.

```
1.12^23
        13.55234726
```

Your calculator mode can be helpful to report answers to a selected number of digits.

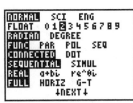

However, use **caution** when doing so! It is easy to forget to change it back to FLOAT and report incorrect results when you need more precision.

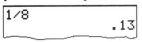

If you want 1/8 reported to full precision and your mode is not set to FLOAT, you could be misled by your calculator!

13. Help!

So you're working your hardest and reading the book. You're doing the assignments and studying every night. But it's just not enough! Where can one find some extra help?

Suggestion 1: Read the book. Really, really read it. Sit down and read it. Carefully. Again and again. It's truly an excellent book.

Suggestion 2: Do lots of individual homework. Understanding material in later chapters typically requires that you understand concepts in previous ones.

Suggestion 3: Recopy your notes.

Suggestion 4: Problem solving requires persistence. If you don't understand something the first time, you're in good company. Even Einstein had trouble and said, "Do not worry about your difficulties in Mathematics. I can assure you mine are still greater." Don't just give up. Take a break and come back and try again!

Suggestion 5: Remember, there's no substitute for daily preparation. Get help as soon as any problems arise. Which takes you to the second column of resources....

Resource 1. Talk to your instructor. Use the office hours.

Resource 2. Use the common office hours (schedule forthcoming) of other instructors who teach the same course.

Resource 3. If you can, meet with your group members outside of class and do your homework together. If this isn't possible, talk with them as soon as you get to class about any assigned problems that gave you trouble.

Resource 4. Use the Center for Academic Support and Advancement (CASA) for tutoring or use drop-in tutoring in Kettler G21.

Resource 5: Use the Web, starting first with the Internet resources listed in this handout.

Chapter One

LINEAR FUNCTIONS AND CHANGE

A function describes how the value of one quantity depends on the value of another. A function can be represented by words, a graph, a formula, or a table of numbers. Section 1.1 gives examples of all four representations and introduces the notation used to represent a function. Section 1.2 introduces the idea of a rate of change.

Sections 1.3–1.6 investigate linear functions, whose rate of change is constant. Section 1.4 gives the equations for a line, and Section 1.5 focuses on parallel and perpendicular lines. In Section 1.6, we see how to approximate a set of data using linear regression.

The Tools Section on page 55 reviews linear equations and the coordinate plane.

1.1   FUNCTIONS AND FUNCTION NOTATION

In everyday language, the word *function* expresses the notion of dependence. For example, a person might say that election results are a function of the economy, meaning that the winner of an election is determined by how the economy is doing. Someone else might claim that car sales are a function of the weather, meaning that the number of cars sold on a given day is affected by the weather.

In mathematics, the meaning of the word *function* is more precise, but the basic idea is the same. A function is a relationship between two quantities. If the value of the first quantity determines exactly one value of the second quantity, we say the second quantity is a function of the first. We make the following definition:

> A **function** is a rule which takes certain numbers as inputs and assigns to each input number exactly one output number. The output is a function of the input.

The inputs and outputs are also called *variables*.

Representing Functions: Words, Tables, Graphs, and Formulas

A function can be described using words, data in a table, points on a graph, or a formula.

Example 1   It is a surprising biological fact that most crickets chirp at a rate that increases as the temperature increases. For the snowy tree cricket (*Oecanthus fultoni*), the relationship between temperature and chirp rate is so reliable that this type of cricket is called the thermometer cricket. We can estimate the temperature (in degrees Fahrenheit) by counting the number of times a snowy tree cricket chirps in 15 seconds and adding 40. For instance, if we count 20 chirps in 15 seconds, then a good estimate of the temperature is $20 + 40 = 60°F$.

The rule used to find the temperature T (in °F) from the chirp rate R (in chirps per minute) is an example of a function. The input is chirp rate and the output is temperature. Describe this function using words, a table, a graph, and a formula.

Solution
- **Words**: To estimate the temperature, we count the number of chirps in fifteen seconds and add forty. Alternatively, we can count R chirps per minute, divide R by four and add forty. This is because there are one-fourth as many chirps in fifteen seconds as there are in sixty seconds. For instance, 80 chirps per minute works out to $\frac{1}{4} \cdot 80 = 20$ chirps every 15 seconds, giving an estimated temperature of $20 + 40 = 60°F$.
- **Table**: Table 1.1 gives the estimated temperature, T, as a function of R, the number of chirps per minute. Notice the pattern in Table 1.1: each time the chirp rate, R, goes up by 20 chirps per minute, the temperature, T, goes up by $5°F$.
- **Graph**: The data from Table 1.1 are plotted in Figure 1.1. For instance, the pair of values $R = 80$, $T = 60$ are plotted as the point P, which is 80 units along the horizontal axis and 60 units up the vertical axis. Data represented in this way are said to be plotted on the *Cartesian plane*. The precise position of P is shown by its coordinates, written $P = (80, 60)$.

Table 1.1   *Chirp rate and temperature*

R, chirp rate (chirps/minute)	T, predicted temperature (°F)
20	45
40	50
60	55
80	60
100	65
120	70
140	75
160	80

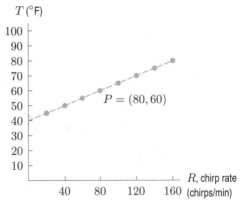

Figure 1.1: Chirp rate and temperature

- **Formula**: A formula is an equation giving T in terms of R. Dividing the chirp rate by four and adding forty gives the estimated temperature, so:

$$\underbrace{\text{Estimated temperature (in °F)}}_{T} = \frac{1}{4} \cdot \underbrace{\text{Chirp rate (in chirps/min)}}_{R} + 40.$$

Rewriting this using the variables T and R gives the formula:

$$T = \frac{1}{4}R + 40.$$

Let's check the formula. Substituting $R = 80$, we have

$$T = \frac{1}{4} \cdot 80 + 40 = 60$$

which agrees with point $P = (80, 60)$ in Figure 1.1. The formula $T = \frac{1}{4}R + 40$ also tells us that if $R = 0$, then $T = 40$. Thus, the dashed line in Figure 1.1 crosses (or intersects) the T-axis at $T = 40$; we say the T-*intercept* is 40.

All the descriptions given in Example 1 provide the same information, but each description has a different emphasis. A relationship between variables is often given in words, as at the beginning of Example 1. Table 1.1 is useful because it shows the predicted temperature for various chirp rates. Figure 1.1 is more suggestive of a trend than the table, although it is harder to read exact values of the function. For example, you might have noticed that every point in Figure 1.1 falls on a straight line that slopes up from left to right. In general, a graph can reveal a pattern that might otherwise go unnoticed. Finally, the formula has the advantage of being both compact and precise. However, this compactness can also be a disadvantage since it may be harder to gain as much insight from a formula as from a table or a graph.

Mathematical Models

When we use a function to describe an actual situation, the function is referred to as a **mathematical model**. The formula $T = \frac{1}{4}R + 40$ is a mathematical model of the relationship between the temperature and the cricket's chirp rate. Such models can be powerful tools for understanding phenomena and making predictions. For example, this model predicts that when the chirp rate is 80 chirps per minute, the temperature is 60°F. In addition, since $T = 40$ when $R = 0$, the model predicts that the chirp rate is 0 at 40°F. Whether the model's predictions are accurate for chirp rates down to 0 and temperatures as low as 40°F is a question that mathematics alone cannot answer; an understanding of the biology of crickets is needed. However, we can safely say that the model does not apply for temperatures below 40°F, because the chirp rate would then be negative. For the range of chirp rates and temperatures in Table 1.1, the model is remarkably accurate.

In everyday language, saying that T is a function of R suggests that making the cricket chirp faster would somehow make the temperature change. Clearly, the cricket's chirping does not cause the temperature to be what it is. In mathematics, saying that the temperature "depends" on the chirp rate means only that knowing the chirp rate is sufficient to tell us the temperature.

Function Notation

To indicate that a quantity Q is a function of a quantity t, we abbreviate

$$Q \text{ is a function of } t \quad \text{to} \quad Q \text{ equals "}f \text{ of } t\text{"}$$

and, using function notation, to

$$Q = f(t).$$

Thus, applying the rule f to the input value, t, gives the output value, $f(t)$. In other words, $f(t)$ represents a value of Q. Here Q is called the *dependent variable* and t is called the *independent variable*. Symbolically,

$$\text{Output} = f(\text{Input})$$

or

$$\text{Dependent} = f(\text{Independent}).$$

We could have used any letter, not just f, to represent the rule.

Example 2   The number of gallons of paint needed to paint a house depends on the size of the house. A gallon of paint typically covers 250 square feet. Thus, the number of gallons of paint, n, is a function of the area to be painted, A ft². We write $n = f(A)$.

(a) Find a formula for f.
(b) Explain in words what the statement $f(10,000) = 40$ tells us about painting houses.

Solution   (a) If $A = 5000$ ft², then $n = 5000/250 = 20$ gallons of paint. In general, n and A are related by the formula

$$n = \frac{A}{250}.$$

(b) The input of the function $n = f(A)$ is an area and the output is an amount of paint. The statement $f(10,000) = 40$ tells us that an area of $A = 10,000$ ft² requires $n = 40$ gallons of paint.

The expressions "Q depends on t" or "Q is a function of t" do *not* imply a cause-and-effect relationship, as the snowy tree cricket example illustrates.

Example 3   Example 1 gives the following formula for estimating air temperature based on the chirp rate of the snowy tree cricket:

$$T = \frac{1}{4}R + 40.$$

In this formula, T depends on R. Writing $T = f(R)$ indicates that the relationship is a function.

Functions Don't Have to Be Defined by Formulas

People sometimes think that functions are always represented by formulas. However, the next example shows a function which is not given by a formula.

Example 4   The average monthly rainfall, R, at Chicago's O'Hare airport is given in Table 1.2, where time, t, is in months and $t = 1$ is January, $t = 2$ is February, and so on. The rainfall is a function of the month, so we write $R = f(t)$. However there is no equation that gives R when t is known. Evaluate $f(1)$ and $f(11)$. Explain what your answers mean.

Table 1.2   *Average monthly rainfall at Chicago's O'Hare airport*

Month, t	1	2	3	4	5	6	7	8	9	10	11	12
Rainfall, R (inches)	1.8	1.8	2.7	3.1	3.5	3.7	3.5	3.4	3.2	2.5	2.4	2.1

Solution   The value of $f(1)$ is the average rainfall in inches at Chicago's O'Hare airport in a typical January. From the table, $f(1) = 1.8$. Similarly, $f(11) = 2.4$ means that in a typical November, there are 2.4 inches of rain at O'Hare.

When Is a Relationship Not a Function?

It is possible for two quantities to be related and yet for neither quantity to be a function of the other.

Example 5   A national park contains foxes that prey on rabbits. Table 1.3 gives the two populations, F and R, over a 12-month period, where $t = 0$ means January 1, $t = 1$ means February 1, and so on.

Table 1.3   *Number of foxes and rabbits in a national park, by month*

t, month	0	1	2	3	4	5	6	7	8	9	10	11
R, rabbits	1000	750	567	500	567	750	1000	1250	1433	1500	1433	1250
F, foxes	150	143	125	100	75	57	50	57	75	100	125	143

(a) Is F a function of t? Is R a function of t?
(b) Is F a function of R? Is R a function of F?

Solution   (a) Both F and R are functions of t. For each value of t, there is exactly one value of F and exactly one value of R. For example, Table 1.3 shows that if $t = 5$, then $R = 750$ and $F = 57$. This means that on June 1 there are 750 rabbits and 57 foxes in the park. If we write $R = f(t)$ and $F = g(t)$, then $f(5) = 750$ and $g(5) = 57$.

(b) No, F is not a function of R. For example, suppose $R = 750$, meaning there are 750 rabbits. This happens both at $t = 1$ (February 1) and at $t = 5$ (June 1). In the first instance, there are 143 foxes; in the second instance, there are 57 foxes. Since there are R-values which correspond to more than one F-value, F is not a function of R.

   Similarly, R is not a function of F. At time $t = 5$, we have $R = 750$ when $F = 57$, while at time $t = 7$, we have $R = 1250$ when $F = 57$ again. Thus, the value of F does not uniquely determine the value of R.

How to Tell if a Graph Represents a Function: Vertical Line Test

What does it mean graphically for y to be a function of x? Look at the graph of y against x. For a function, each x-value corresponds to exactly one y-value. This means that the graph intersects any vertical line at most once. If a vertical line cuts the graph twice, the graph would contain two points with different y-values but the same x-value; this would violate the definition of a function. Thus, we have the following criterion:

> **Vertical Line Test**: If there is a vertical line which intersects a graph in more than one point, then the graph does not represent a function.

Example 6   In which of the graphs in Figures 1.2 and 1.3 could y be a function of x?

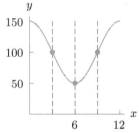

Figure 1.2: Since no vertical line intersects this curve at more than one point, y could be a function of x

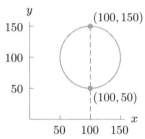

Figure 1.3: Since one vertical line intersects this curve at more than one point, y is not a function of x

Solution   The graph in Figure 1.2 could represent y as a function of x because no vertical line intersects this curve in more than one point. The graph in Figure 1.3 does not represent a function because the vertical line shown intersects the curve at two points.

A graph fails the vertical line test if at least one vertical line cuts the graph more than once, as in Figure 1.3. However, if a graph represents a function, then *every* vertical line must intersect the graph at no more than one point.

Exercises and Problems for Section 1.1

Exercises

Exercises 1–4 use Figure 1.4.

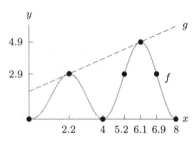

Figure 1.4

1. Find $f(6.9)$

2. Give the coordinates of two points on the graph of g.

3. Solve $f(x) = 0$ for x

4. Solve $f(x) = g(x)$ for x

In Exercises 5–6, write the relationship using function notation (i.e. y is a function of x is written $y = f(x)$).

5. Number of molecules, m, in a gas, is a function of the volume of the gas, v.

6. Weight, w, is a function of caloric intake, c.

7. (a) Which of the graphs in Figure 1.5 represent y as a function of x? (Note that an open circle indicates a point that is not included in the graph; a solid dot indicates a point that is included in the graph.)

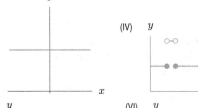

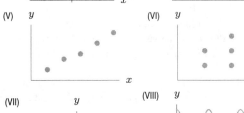

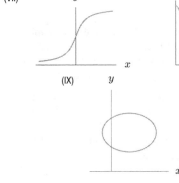

Figure 1.5

(b) Which of the graphs in Figure 1.5 could represent the following situations? Give reasons.

  (i) SAT Math score versus SAT Verbal score for a small number of students.

  (ii) Total number of daylight hours as a function of the day of the year, shown over a period of several years.

(c) Among graphs (I)–(IX) in Figure 1.5, find two which could give the cost of train fare as a function of the time of day. Explain the relationship between cost and time for both choices.

8. Using Table 1.4, graph $n = f(A)$, the number of gallons of paint needed to cover a house of area A. Identify the independent and dependent variables.

Table 1.4

A	0	250	500	750	1000	1250	1500
n	0	1	2	3	4	5	6

9. Use Figure 1.6 to fill in the missing values:

  (a) $f(0) = ?$ **(b)** $f(?) = 0$

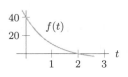

Figure 1.6

10. Use Table 1.5 to fill in the missing values. (There may be more than one answer.)

  (a) $f(0) = ?$ **(b)** $f(?) = 0$
  (c) $f(1) = ?$ **(d)** $f(?) = 1$

Table 1.5

x	0	1	2	3	4
$f(x)$	4	2	1	0	1

11. (a) You are going to graph $p = f(w)$. Which variable goes on the horizontal axis?

(b) If $10 = f(-4)$, give the coordinates of a point on the graph of f.

(c) If 6 is a solution of the equation $f(w) = 1$, give a point on the graph of f.

12. (a) Make a table of values for $f(x) = 10/(1 + x^2)$ for $x = 0, 1, 2, 3$.

(b) What x-value gives the largest $f(x)$ value in your table? How could you have predicted this before doing any calculations?

In Exercises 13–16, label the axes for a sketch to illustrate the given statement.

13. "Over the past century we have seen changes in the population, P (in millions), of the city. . ."

14. "Sketch a graph of the cost of manufacturing q items. . ."

15. "Graph the pressure, p, of a gas as a function of its volume, v, where p is in pounds per square inch and v is in cubic inches."

16. "Graph D in terms of y. . ."

Problems

17. (a) Ten inches of snow is equivalent to about one inch of rain.[1] Write an equation for the amount of precipitation, measured in inches of rain, $r = f(s)$, as a function of the number of inches of snow, s.
  (b) Evaluate and interpret $f(5)$.
  (c) Find s such that $f(s) = 5$ and interpret your result.

18. You are looking at the graph of y, a function of x.

  (a) What is the maximum number of times that the graph can intersect the y-axis? Explain.
  (b) Can the graph intersect the x-axis an infinite number of times? Explain.

19. Let $f(t)$ be the number of people, in millions, who own cell phones t years after 1990. Explain the meaning of the following statements.

  (a) $f(10) = 100.3$ **(b)** $f(a) = 20$
  (c) $f(20) = b$ **(d)** $n = f(t)$

In Problems 20–22, use Table 1.6, which gives values of $v = r(s)$, the eyewall wind profile of a typical hurricane.[2] The eyewall of a hurricane is the band of clouds that surrounds the eye of the storm. The eyewall wind speed v (in mph) is a function of the height above the ground s (in meters).

Table 1.6

s	0	100	200	300	400	500
v	90	110	116	120	121	122

s	600	700	800	900	1000	1100
v	121	119	118	117	116	115

20. Evaluate and interpret $r(300)$.

21. At what altitudes does the eyewall windspeed appear to equal or exceed 116 mph?

22. At what height is the eyewall wind speed greatest?

23. Table 1.7 shows the daily low temperature for a one-week period in New York City during July.

  (a) What was the low temperature on July 19?
  (b) When was the low temperature 73°F?
  (c) Is the daily low temperature a function of the date?
  (d) Is the date a function of the daily low temperature?

Table 1.7

Date	17	18	19	20	21	22	23
Low temp (°F)	73	77	69	73	75	75	70

24. Table 1.8 gives $A = f(d)$, the amount of money in bills of denomination d circulating in US currency in 2005.[3] For example, there were \$60.2 billion worth of \$50 bills in circulation.

  (a) Find $f(100)$. What does this tell you about money?
  (b) Are there more \$1 bills or \$5 bills in circulation?

Table 1.8

Denomination (\$)	1	2	5	10	20	50	100
Circulation (\$bn)	8.4	1.4	9.7	14.8	110.1	60.2	524.5

25. Use the data from Table 1.3 on page 5.

  (a) Plot R on the vertical axis and t on the horizontal axis. Use this graph to explain why you believe that R is a function of t.
  (b) Plot F on the vertical axis and t on the horizontal axis. Use this graph to explain why you believe that F is a function of t.
  (c) Plot F on the vertical axis and R on the horizontal axis. From this graph show that F is not a function of R.
  (d) Plot R on the vertical axis and F on the horizontal axis. From this graph show that R is not a function of F.

26. Since Roger Bannister broke the 4-minute mile on May 6, 1954, the record has been lowered by over sixteen seconds. Table 1.9 shows the year and times (as min:sec) of new world records for the one-mile run.[4]

  (a) Is the time a function of the year? Explain.
  (b) Is the year a function of the time? Explain.
  (c) Let $y(r)$ be the year in which the world record, r, was set. Explain what is meant by the statement $y(3:47.33) = 1981$.
  (d) Evaluate and interpret $y(3:51.1)$.

Table 1.9

Year	Time	Year	Time	Year	Time
1954	3:59.4	1966	3:51.3	1981	3:48.53
1954	3:58.0	1967	3:51.1	1981	3:48.40
1957	3:57.2	1975	3:51.0	1981	3:47.33
1958	3:54.5	1975	3:49.4	1985	3:46.32
1962	3:54.4	1979	3:49.0	1993	3:44.39
1964	3:54.1	1980	3:48.8	1999	3:43.13
1965	3:53.6				

---

[1]http://mo.water.usgs.gov/outreach/rain, accessed May 7, 2006.
[2]Data from the National Hurricane Center, www.nhc.noaa.gov/aboutwindprofile.shtml, last accessed October 7, 2004.
[3]*The World Almanac and Book of Facts*, 2006 (New York), p. 89.
[4]www.infoplease.com/ipsa/A0112924.html, accessed January 15, 2006.

27. Rebecca Latimer Felton of Georgia was the first woman to serve in the US Senate. She took the oath of office on November 22, 1922 and served for just two days. The first woman actually elected to the Senate was Hattie Wyatt Caraway of Arkansas. She was appointed to fill the vacancy caused by the death of her husband, then won election in 1932, was reelected in 1938, and served until 1945. Table 1.10 shows the number of female senators at the beginning of the first session of each Congress.[5]

   (a) Is the number of female senators a function of the Congress's number, c? Explain.
   (b) Is the Congress's number a function of the number of female senators? Explain.
   (c) Let $S(c)$ represent the number of female senators serving in the cth Congress. What does the statement $S(104) = 8$ mean?
   (d) Evaluate and interpret $S(108)$.

Table 1.10

Congress, c	96	98	100	102	104	106	108
Female senators	1	2	2	2	8	9	14

28. A bug starts out ten feet from a light, flies closer to the light, then farther away, then closer than before, then farther away. Finally the bug hits the bulb and flies off. Sketch the distance of the bug from the light as a function of time.

29. A light is turned off for several hours. It is then turned on. After a few hours it is turned off again. Sketch the light bulb's temperature as a function of time.

30. The sales tax on an item is 6%. Express the total cost, C, in terms of the price of the item, P.

31. A cylindrical can is closed at both ends and its height is twice its radius. Express its surface area, S, as a function of its radius, r. [Hint: The surface of a can consists of a rectangle plus two circular disks.]

32. According to Charles Osgood, CBS news commentator, it takes about one minute to read 15 double-spaced typewritten lines on the air.[6]

   (a) Construct a table showing the time Charles Osgood is reading on the air in seconds as a function of the number of double-spaced lines read for $0, 1, 2, \ldots, 10$ lines. From your table, how long does it take Charles Osgood to read 9 lines?
   (b) Plot this data on a graph with the number of lines on the horizontal axis.
   (c) From your graph, estimate how long it takes Charles Osgood to read 9 lines. Estimate how many lines Charles Osgood can read in 30 seconds.
   (d) Construct a formula which relates the time T to n, the number of lines read.

33. Match each story about a bike ride to one of the graphs (i)–(v), where d represents distance from home and t is time in hours since the start of the ride. (A graph may be used more than once.)

   (a) Starts 5 miles from home and rides 5 miles per hour away from home.
   (b) Starts 5 miles from home and rides 10 miles per hour away from home.
   (c) Starts 10 miles from home and arrives home one hour later.
   (d) Starts 10 miles from home and is halfway home after one hour.
   (e) Starts 5 miles from home and is 10 miles from home after one hour.

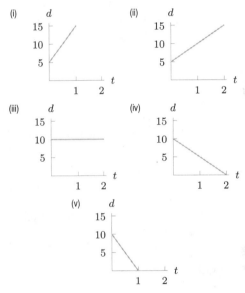

34. A chemical company spends $2 million to buy machinery before it starts producing chemicals. Then it spends $0.5 million on raw materials for each million liters of chemical produced.

   (a) The number of liters produced ranges from 0 to 5 million. Make a table showing the relationship between the number of million liters produced, l, and the total cost, C, in millions of dollars, to produce that number of million liters.
   (b) Find a formula that expresses C as a function of l.

35. The distance between Cambridge and Wellesley is 10 miles. A person walks part of the way at 5 miles per hour, then jogs the rest of the way at 8 mph. Find a formula that expresses the total amount of time for the trip, $T(d)$, as a function of d, the distance walked.

---

[5]www.senate.gov, accessed January 15, 2006.
[6]T. Parker, *Rules of Thumb*, (Boston: Houghton Mifflin, 1983).

36. A person leaves home and walks due west for a time and then walks due north.

   (a) The person walks 10 miles in total. If w represents the (variable) distance west she walks, and D represents her (variable) distance from home at the end of her walk, is D a function of w? Why or why not?

   (b) Suppose now that x is the distance that she walks in total. Is D a function of x? Why or why not?

1.2   RATE OF CHANGE

Sales of digital video disc (DVD) players have been increasing since they were introduced in early 1998. To measure how fast sales were increasing, we calculate a *rate of change* of the form

$$\frac{\text{Change in sales}}{\text{Change in time}}.$$

At the same time, sales of video cassette recorders (VCRs) have been decreasing. See Table 1.11.

Let us calculate the rate of change of DVD player and VCR sales between 1998 and 2003. Table 1.11 gives

$$\begin{array}{l}\text{Average rate of change of DVD} \\ \text{player sales from 1998 to 2003}\end{array} = \frac{\text{Change in DVD player sales}}{\text{Change in time}} = \frac{3050 - 421}{2003 - 1998} \approx 525.8 \; \frac{\text{mn \$/}}{\text{year}}.$$

Thus, DVD player sales increased on average by \$525.8 million per year between 1998 and 2003. See Figure 1.7. Similarly, Table 1.11 gives

$$\begin{array}{l}\text{Average rate of change of VCR sales} \\ \text{from 1998 to 2003}\end{array} = \frac{\text{Change in VCR sales}}{\text{Change in time}} = \frac{407 - 2409}{2003 - 1998} \approx -400.4 \; \frac{\text{mn \$/}}{\text{year}}.$$

Thus, VCR sales decreased on average by \$400.4 million per year between 1998 and 2003. See Figure 1.8.

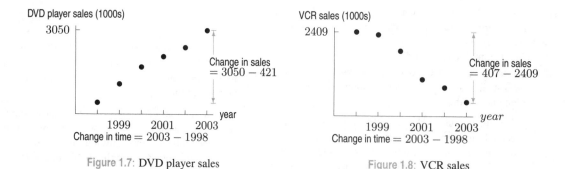

Figure 1.7: DVD player sales

Figure 1.8: VCR sales

Table 1.11   *Annual sales of VCRs and DVD players in millions of dollars*[7]

Year	1998	1999	2000	2001	2002	2003
VCR sales (million $)	2409	2333	1869	1058	826	407
DVD player sales (million $)	421	1099	1717	2097	2427	3050

[7]www.census.gov/prod/2005pubs/06statab/manufact.pdf, accessed January 16, 2006.

Rate of Change of a Function

The rate of change of sales is an example of the rate of change of a function. In general, if $Q = f(t)$, we write ΔQ for a change in Q and Δt for a change in t. We define:[8]

The **average rate of change**, or **rate of change**, of Q with respect to t over an interval is

$$\text{Average rate of change} \atop \text{over an interval} = \frac{\text{Change in } Q}{\text{Change in } t} = \frac{\Delta Q}{\Delta t}.$$

The average rate of change of the function $Q = f(t)$ over an interval tells us how much Q changes, on average, for each unit change in t within that interval. On some parts of the interval, Q may be changing rapidly, while on other parts Q may be changing slowly. The average rate of change evens out these variations.

Increasing and Decreasing Functions

In the previous example, the average rate of change of DVD player sales is positive on the interval from 1998 to 2003 since sales of DVD players increased over this interval. Similarly, the average rate of change of VCR sales is negative on the same interval since sales of VCRs decreased over this interval. The annual sales of DVD players is an example of an *increasing function* and the annual sales of VCRs is an example of a *decreasing function*. In general we say the following:

If $Q = f(t)$ for t in the interval $a \leq t \leq b$,
- f is an **increasing function** if the values of f increase as t increases in this interval.
- f is a **decreasing function** if the values of f decrease as t increases in this interval.

Looking at DVD player sales, we see that an increasing function has a positive rate of change. From the VCR sales, we see that a decreasing function has a negative rate of change. In general:

If $Q = f(t)$,
- If f is an increasing function, then the average rate of change of Q with respect to t is positive on every interval.
- If f is a decreasing function, then the average rate of change of Q with respect to t is negative on every interval.

Example 1   The function $A = q(r) = \pi r^2$ gives the area, A, of a circle as a function of its radius, r. Graph q. Explain how the fact that q is an increasing function can be seen on the graph.

---

[8]The Greek letter Δ, delta, is often used in mathematics to represent change. In this book, we use rate of change to mean average rate of change across an interval. In calculus, rate of change means something called instantaneous rate of change.

Solution   The area increases as the radius increases, so $A = q(r)$ is an increasing function. We can see this in Figure 1.9 because the graph climbs as we move from left to right and the average rate of change, $\Delta A/\Delta r$, is positive on every interval.

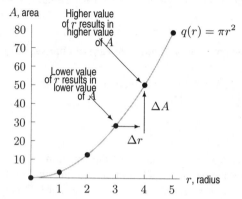

Figure 1.9: The graph of an increasing function, $A = q(r)$, rises when read from left to right

Example 2   Carbon-14 is a radioactive element that exists naturally in the atmosphere and is absorbed by living organisms. When an organism dies, the carbon-14 present at death begins to decay. Let $L = g(t)$ represent the quantity of carbon-14 (in micrograms, μg) in a tree t years after its death. See Table 1.12. Explain why we expect g to be a decreasing function of t. How is this represented on a graph?

Table 1.12   *Quantity of carbon-14 as a function of time*

t, time (years)	0	1000	2000	3000	4000	5000
L, quantity of carbon-14 (μg)	200	177	157	139	123	109

Solution   Since the amount of carbon-14 is decaying over time, g is a decreasing function. In Figure 1.10, the graph falls as we move from left to right and the average rate of change in the level of carbon-14 with respect to time, $\Delta L/\Delta t$, is negative on every interval.

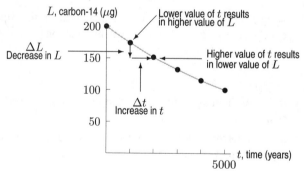

Figure 1.10: The graph of a decreasing function, $L = g(t)$, falls when read from left to right

In general, we can identify an increasing or decreasing function from its graph as follows:

- The graph of an increasing function rises when read from left to right.
- The graph of a decreasing function falls when read from left to right.

Many functions have some intervals on which they are increasing and other intervals on which they are decreasing. These intervals can often be identified from the graph.

Example 3   On what intervals is the function graphed in Figure 1.11 increasing? Decreasing?

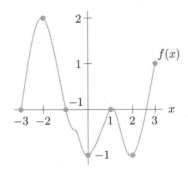

Figure 1.11: Graph of a function which is increasing on some intervals and decreasing on others

Solution   The function appears to be increasing for values of x between -3 and -2, for x between 0 and 1, and for x between 2 and 3. The function appears to be decreasing for x between -2 and 0 and for x between 1 and 2. Using inequalities, we say that f is increasing for $-3 < x < -2$, for $0 < x < 1$, and for $2 < x < 3$. Similarly, f is decreasing for $-2 < x < 0$ and $1 < x < 2$.

Function Notation for the Average Rate of Change

Suppose we want to find the average rate of change of a function $Q = f(t)$ over the interval $a \leq t \leq b$. On this interval, the change in t is given by

$$\Delta t = b - a.$$

At $t = a$, the value of Q is $f(a)$, and at $t = b$, the value of Q is $f(b)$. Therefore, the change in Q is given by

$$\Delta Q = f(b) - f(a).$$

Using function notation, we express the average rate of change as follows:

$$\begin{array}{l} \text{Average rate of change of } Q = f(t) \\ \text{over the interval } a \leq t \leq b \end{array} = \frac{\text{Change in } Q}{\text{Change in } t} = \frac{\Delta Q}{\Delta t} = \frac{f(b) - f(a)}{b - a}.$$

In Figure 1.12, notice that the average rate of change is given by the ratio of the rise, $f(b) - f(a)$, to the run, $b - a$. This ratio is also called the *slope* of the dashed line segment.[9]

---

[9]See Section 1.3 for further discussion of slope.

In the future, we may drop the word "average" and talk about the rate of change over an interval.

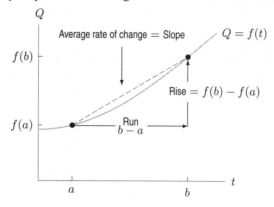

Figure 1.12: The average rate of change is the ratio Rise/Run

In previous examples we calculated the average rate of change from data. We now calculate average rates of change for functions given by formulas.

Example 4   Calculate the average rates of change of the function $f(x) = x^2$ between $x = 1$ and $x = 3$ and between $x = -2$ and $x = 1$. Show your results on a graph.

Solution   Between $x = 1$ and $x = 3$, we have

$$\begin{aligned} \text{Average rate of change of } f(x) \\ \text{over the interval } 1 \leq x \leq 3 \end{aligned} = \frac{\text{Change in } f(x)}{\text{Change in } x} = \frac{f(3) - f(1)}{3 - 1}$$

$$= \frac{3^2 - 1^2}{3 - 1} = \frac{9 - 1}{2} = 4.$$

Between $x = -2$ and $x = 1$, we have

$$\begin{aligned} \text{Average rate of change of } f(x) \\ \text{over the interval } -2 \leq x \leq 1 \end{aligned} = \frac{\text{Change in } f(x)}{\text{Change in } x} = \frac{f(1) - f(-2)}{1 - (-2)}$$

$$= \frac{1^2 - (-2)^2}{1 - (-2)} = \frac{1 - 4}{3} = -1.$$

The average rate of change between $x = 1$ and $x = 3$ is positive because $f(x)$ is increasing on this interval. See Figure 1.13. However, on the interval from $x = -2$ and $x = 1$, the function is partly decreasing and partly increasing. The average rate of change on this interval is negative because the decrease on the interval is larger than the increase.

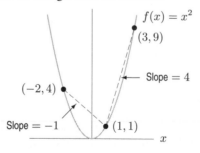

Figure 1.13: Average rate of change of $f(x)$ on an interval is slope of dashed line on that interval

Exercises and Problems for Section 1.2

1. If G is an increasing function, what can you say about $G(3) - G(-1)$?

2. If F is a decreasing function, what can you say about $F(-2)$ compared to $F(2)$?

Exercises 3–7 use Figure 1.14.

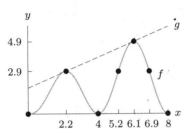

Figure 1.14

3. Find the average rate of change of f for $2.2 \leq x \leq 6.1$.

4. Give two different intervals on which $\Delta f(x)/\Delta x = 0$.

5. What is the average rate of change of g between $x = 2.2$ and $x = 6.1$?

6. What is the relation between the average rate of change of f and the average rate of change of g between $x = 2.2$ and $x = 6.1$?

7. Is the rate of change of f positive or negative on the following intervals?

   (a) $2.2 \leq x \leq 4$ **(b)** $5 \leq x \leq 6$

8. Table 1.11 on page 10 gives the annual sales (in millions) of compact discs and vinyl long playing records. What was the average rate of change of annual sales of each of them between

   (a) 1982 and 1984?   **(b)** 1986 and 1988?
   (c) Interpret these results in terms of sales.

9. Table 1.11 on page 10 shows that CD sales are a function of LP sales. Is it an increasing or decreasing function?

10. Figure 1.15 shows distance traveled as a function of time.

   (a) Find ΔD and Δt between:
      (i) $t = 2$ and $t = 5$ **(ii)** $t = 0.5$ and $t = 2.5$
      (iii) $t = 1.5$ and $t = 3$

   (b) Compute the rate of change, $\Delta D/\Delta t$, and interpret its meaning.

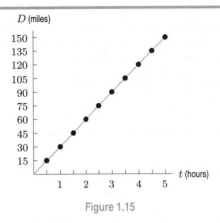

Figure 1.15

11. Table 1.13 shows data for two populations (in hundreds) for five different years. Find the average rate of change of each population over the following intervals.

   (a) 1990 to 2000   **(b)** 1995 to 2007
   (c) 1990 to 2007

Table 1.13

Year	1990	1992	1995	2000	2007
P_1	53	63	73	83	93
P_2	85	80	75	70	65

12. Table 1.14 gives the populations of two cities (in thousands) over a 17-year period.

   (a) Find the average rate of change of each population on the following intervals:
      (i) 1990 to 2000   **(ii)** 1990 to 2007
      (iii) 1995 to 2007

   (b) What do you notice about the average rate of change of each population? Explain what the average rate of change tells you about each population.

Table 1.14

Year	1990	1992	1995	2000	2007
P_1	42	46	52	62	76
P_2	82	80	77	72	65

Problems

13. Because scientists know how much carbon-14 a living organism should have in its tissues, they can measure the amount of carbon-14 present in the tissue of a fossil and then calculate how long it took for the original amount to decay to the current level, thus determining the time of the organism's death. A tree fossil is found to contain 130 μg of carbon-14, and scientists determine from the size of the tree that it would have contained 200 μg of carbon-14 at the time of its death. Using Table 1.12 on page 12, approximately how long ago did the tree die?

14. Table 1.15 shows the number of calories used per minute as a function of body weight for three sports.[10]

(a) Determine the number of calories that a 200-lb person uses in one half-hour of walking.

(b) Who uses more calories, a 120-lb person swimming for one hour or a 220-lb person bicycling for a half-hour?

(c) Does the number of calories used by a person walking increase or decrease as weight increases?

Table 1.15

Activity	100 lb	120 lb	150 lb	170 lb	200 lb	220 lb
Walking	2.7	3.2	4.0	4.6	5.4	5.9
Bicycling	5.4	6.5	8.1	9.2	10.8	11.9
Swimming	5.8	6.9	8.7	9.8	11.6	12.7

15. (a) What is the average rate of change of $g(x) = 2x - 3$ between the points $(-2, -7)$ and $(3, 3)$?

(b) Based on your answer to part (a), is g increasing or decreasing on the given interval? Explain.

(c) Graph the function and determine over what intervals g is increasing and over what intervals g is decreasing.

16. (a) Let $f(x) = 16 - x^2$. Compute each of the following expressions, and interpret each as an average rate of change.

(i) $\dfrac{f(2) - f(0)}{2 - 0}$ (ii) $\dfrac{f(4) - f(2)}{4 - 2}$

(iii) $\dfrac{f(4) - f(0)}{4 - 0}$

(b) Graph $f(x)$. Illustrate each ratio in part (a) by sketching the line segment with the given slope. Over which interval is the average rate of decrease the greatest?

[10]From *1993 World Almanac*.

17. Figure 1.16 shows the graph of the function $g(x)$.

(a) Estimate $\dfrac{g(4) - g(0)}{4 - 0}$.

(b) The ratio in part (a) is the slope of a line segment joining two points on the graph. Sketch this line segment on the graph.

(c) Estimate $\dfrac{g(b) - g(a)}{b - a}$ for $a = -9$ and $b = -1$.

(d) On the graph, sketch the line segment whose slope is given by the ratio in part (c).

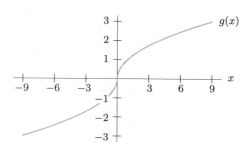

Figure 1.16

For the functions in Problems 18–20:

(a) Find the average rate of change between the points

(i) $(-1, f(-1))$ and $(3, f(3))$

(ii) $(a, f(a))$ and $(b, f(b))$

(iii) $(x, f(x))$ and $(x + h, f(x + h))$

(b) What pattern do you see in the average rate of change between the three pairs of points?

18. $f(x) = 5x - 4$ **19.** $f(x) = \frac{1}{2}x + \frac{5}{2}$

20. $f(x) = x^2 + 1$

21. Find the average rate of change of $f(x) = 3x^2 + 1$ between the points

(a) $(1, 4)$ and $(2, 13)$

(b) (j, k) and (m, n)

(c) $(x, f(x))$ and $(x + h, f(x + h))$

22. The surface of the sun has dark areas known as sunspots, which are cooler than the rest of the sun's surface. The number of sunspots fluctuates with time, as shown in Figure 1.17.

(a) Explain how you know the number of sunspots, s, in year t is a function of t.

(b) Approximate the time intervals on which s is an increasing function of t.

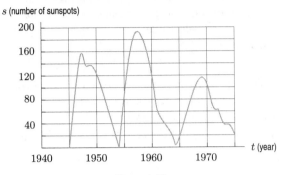

Figure 1.17

23. Table 1.16 gives the amount of garbage, G, in millions of tons, produced[11] in the US in year t.

(a) What is the value of Δt for consecutive entries in this table?

(b) Calculate the value of ΔG for each pair of consecutive entries in this table.

(c) Are all the values of ΔG you found in part (b) the same? What does this tell you?

Table 1.16

t	1960	1970	1980	1990	2000
G	90	120	150	205	234

24. Table 1.17 shows the times, t, in sec, achieved every 10 meters by Carl Lewis in the 100 meter final of the World Championship in Rome in 1987.[12] Distance, d, is in meters.

(a) For each successive time interval, calculate the average rate of change of distance. What is a common name for the average rate of change of distance?

(b) Where did Carl Lewis attain his maximum speed during this race? Some runners are running their fastest as they cross the finish line. Does that seem to be true in this case?

Table 1.17

t	0.00	1.94	2.96	3.91	4.78	5.64
d	0	10	20	30	40	50

t	6.50	7.36	8.22	9.07	9.93	
d	60	70	80	90	100	

25. Table 1.18 gives the average temperature, T, at a depth d, in a borehole in Belleterre, Quebec.[13] Evaluate $\Delta T/\Delta d$ on the the following intervals, and explain what your answers tell you about borehole temperature.

(a) $25 \le d \le 150$
(b) $25 \le d \le 75$
(c) $100 \le d \le 200$

Table 1.18

d, depth (m)	25	50	75	100
T, temp (°C)	5.50	5.20	5.10	5.10
d, depth (m)	125	150	175	200
T, temp (°C)	5.30	5.50	5.75	6.00
d, depth (m)	225	250	275	300
T, temp (°C)	6.25	6.50	6.75	7.00

1.3 LINEAR FUNCTIONS

Constant Rate of Change

In the previous section, we introduced the average rate of change of a function on an interval. For many functions, the average rate of change is different on different intervals. For the remainder of this chapter, we consider functions which have the same average rate of change on every interval. Such a function has a graph which is a line and is called *linear*.

---

[11]www.epa.gov/epaoswer/hon-hw/muncpl/pubs/MSW05rpt.pdf, accessed January 15, 2006.

[12]W. G. Pritchard, "Mathematical Models of Running", *SIAM Review*. 35, 1993, pp. 359–379.

[13]Hugo Beltrami of St. Francis Xavier University and David Chapman of the University of Utah posted this data at http://geophysics.stfx.ca/public/borehole/borehole.html http://geophysics.stfx.ca/public/borehole/borehole.html.

Population Growth

Mathematical models of population growth are used by city planners to project the growth of towns and states. Biologists model the growth of animal populations and physicians model the spread of an infection in the bloodstream. One possible model, a linear model, assumes that the population changes at the same average rate on every time interval.

Example 1   A town of 30,000 people grows by 2000 people every year. Since the population, P, is growing at the constant rate of 2000 people per year, P is a linear function of time, t, in years.

(a) What is the average rate of change of P over every time interval?

(b) Make a table that gives the town's population every five years over a 20-year period. Graph the population.

(c) Find a formula for P as a function of t.

Solution   (a) The average rate of change of population with respect to time is 2000 people per year.

(b) The initial population in year $t = 0$ is $P = 30,000$ people. Since the town grows by 2000 people every year, after five years it has grown by

$$\frac{2000 \text{ people}}{\text{year}} \cdot 5 \text{ years} = 10,000 \text{ people}.$$

Thus, in year $t = 5$ the population is given by

$$P = \text{Initial population} + \text{New population} = 30,000 + 10,000 = 40,000.$$

In year $t = 10$ the population is given by

$$P = 30,000 + \underbrace{2000 \text{ people/year} \cdot 10 \text{ years}}_{20,000 \text{ new people}} = 50,000.$$

Similar calculations for year $t = 15$ and year $t = 20$ give the values in Table 1.19. See Figure 1.18; the dashed line shows the trend in the data.

Table 1.19   *Population over 20 years*

t, years	P, population
0	30,000
5	40,000
10	50,000
15	60,000
20	70,000

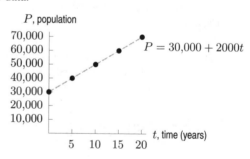

Figure 1.18: Town's population over 20 years

(c) From part (b), we see that the size of the population is given by

$$P = \text{Initial population} + \text{Number of new people}$$
$$= 30,000 + 2000 \text{ people/year} \cdot \text{Number of years},$$

so a formula for P in terms of t is

$$P = 30,000 + 2000t.$$

The graph of the population data in Figure 1.18 is a straight line. The average rate of change of the population over every interval is the same, namely 2000 people per year. Any linear function has the same average rate of change over every interval. Thus, we talk about *the* rate of change of a linear function. In general:

- A **linear function** has a constant rate of change.
- The graph of any linear function is a straight line.

Financial Models

Economists and accountants use linear functions for *straight-line depreciation*. For tax purposes, the value of certain equipment is considered to decrease, or depreciate, over time. For example, computer equipment may be state-of-the-art today, but after several years it is outdated. Straight-line depreciation assumes that the rate of change of value with respect to time is constant.

Example 2   A small business spends $20,000 on new computer equipment and, for tax purposes, chooses to depreciate it to $0 at a constant rate over a five-year period.

(a) Make a table and a graph showing the value of the equipment over the five-year period.
(b) Give a formula for value as a function of time.

Solution   (a) After five years, the equipment is valued at $0. If V is the value in dollars and t is the number of years, we see that

$$\text{Rate of change of value from } t = 0 \text{ to } t = 5 = \frac{\text{Change in value}}{\text{Change in time}} = \frac{\Delta V}{\Delta t} = \frac{-\$20{,}000}{5 \text{ years}} = -\$4000 \text{ per year.}$$

Thus, the value drops at the constant rate of $4000 per year. (Notice that ΔV is negative because the value of the equipment decreases.) See Table 1.20 and Figure 1.19. Since V changes at a constant rate, $V = f(t)$ is a linear function and its graph is a straight line. The rate of change, −$4000 per year, is negative because the function is decreasing and the graph slopes down.

Table 1.20   *Value of equipment depreciated over a 5-year period*

t, year	V, value ($)
0	20,000
1	16,000
2	12,000
3	8,000
4	4,000
5	0

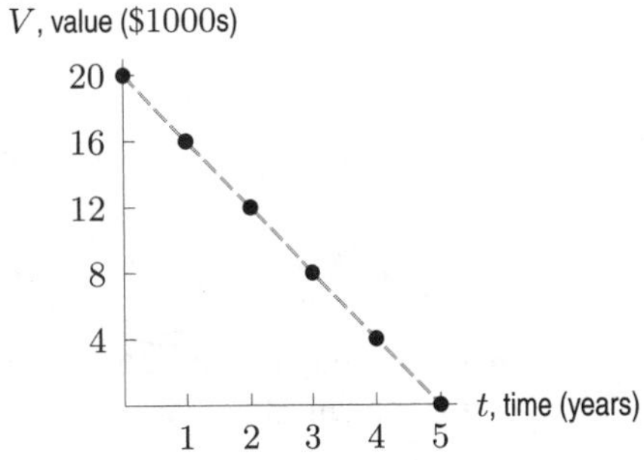

Figure 1.19: Value of equipment depreciated over a 5-year period

(b) After t years have elapsed,

$$\text{Decrease in value of equipment} = \$4000 \cdot \text{Number of years} = \$4000t.$$

The initial value of the equipment is $20,000, so at time t,

$$V = 20{,}000 - 4000t.$$

The total cost of production is another application of linear functions in economics.

A General Formula for the Family of Linear Functions

Example 1 involved a town whose population is growing at a constant rate with formula

$$\underbrace{\text{Current}}_{}\text{population} = \underbrace{\text{Initial}}_{30,000 \text{ people}}\text{population} + \underbrace{\text{Growth}}_{2000 \text{ people per year}}\text{rate} \times \underbrace{\text{Number of}}_{t}\text{years}$$

so

$$P = 30,000 + 2000t.$$

In Example 2, the value, V, as a function of t is given by

$$\underbrace{\text{Total}}_{}\text{cost} = \underbrace{\text{Initial}}_{\$20,000}\text{value} + \underbrace{\text{Change per}}_{-\$4000 \text{ per year}}\text{year} \times \underbrace{\text{Number of}}_{t}\text{years}$$

so

$$V = 20,000 + (-4000)t.$$

Using the symbols x, y, b, m, we see formulas for both of these linear functions follow the same pattern:

$$\underbrace{\text{Output}}_{y} = \underbrace{\text{Initial value}}_{b} + \underbrace{\text{Rate of change}}_{m} \times \underbrace{\text{Input}}_{x}.$$

Summarizing, we get the following results:

If $y = f(x)$ is a linear function, then for some constants b and m:

$$y = b + mx.$$

- m is called the **slope**, and gives the rate of change of y with respect to x. Thus,

$$m = \frac{\Delta y}{\Delta x}.$$

If (x_0, y_0) and (x_1, y_1) are any two distinct points on the graph of f, then

$$m = \frac{\Delta y}{\Delta x} = \frac{y_1 - y_0}{x_1 - x_0}.$$

- b is called the **vertical intercept**, or **y-intercept**, and gives the value of y for $x = 0$. In mathematical models, b typically represents an initial, or starting, value of the output.

Every linear function can be written in the form $y = b + mx$. Different linear functions have different values for m and b. These constants are known as *parameters*.

Example 3   In Example 1, the population function, $P = 30,000 + 2000t$, has slope $m = 2000$ and vertical intercept $b = 30,000$. In Example 2, the value of the computer equipment, $V = 20,000 - 4000t$, has slope $m = -4000$ and vertical intercept $b = 20,000$.

Tables for Linear Functions

A table of values could represent a linear function if the rate of change is constant, for all pairs of points in the table; that is,

$$\text{Rate of change of linear function} = \frac{\text{Change in output}}{\text{Change in input}} = \text{Constant.}$$

Thus, if the value of x goes up by equal steps in a table for a linear function, then the value of y goes up (or down) by equal steps as well. We say that changes in the value of y are *proportional* to changes in the value of x.

Example 4   Table 1.21 gives values of two functions, p and q. Could either of these functions be linear?

Table 1.21   *Values of two functions p and q*

x	50	55	60	65	70
$p(x)$	0.10	0.11	0.12	0.13	0.14
$q(x)$	0.01	0.03	0.06	0.14	0.15

Solution   The value of x goes up by equal steps of $\Delta x = 5$. The value of $p(x)$ also goes up by equal steps of $\Delta p = 0.01$, so $\Delta p/\Delta x$ is a constant. See Table 1.22. Thus, p could be a linear function.

Table 1.22   *Values of $\Delta p/\Delta x$*

x	$p(x)$	Δp	$\Delta p/\Delta x$
50	0.10		
		0.01	0.002
55	0.11		
		0.01	0.002
60	0.12		
		0.01	0.002
65	0.13		
		0.01	0.002
70	0.14		

Table 1.23   *Values of $\Delta q/\Delta x$*

x	$q(x)$	Δq	$\Delta q/\Delta x$
50	0.01		
		0.02	0.004
55	0.03		
		0.03	0.006
60	0.06		
		0.08	0.016
65	0.14		
		0.01	0.002
70	0.15		

In contrast, the value of $q(x)$ does not go up by equal steps. The value climbs by 0.02, then by 0.03, and so on. See Table 1.23. This means that $\Delta q/\Delta x$ is not constant. Thus, q could not be a linear function.

It is possible to have data from a linear function in which neither the x-values nor the y-values go up by equal steps. However the rate of change must be constant, as in the following example.

Example 5   The former Republic of Yugoslavia exported cars called Yugos to the US between 1985 and 1989. The car is now a collector's item.[14] Table 1.24 gives the quantity of Yugos sold, Q, and the price, p, for each year from 1985 to 1988.

(a) Using Table 1.24, explain why Q could be a linear function of p.

(b) What does the rate of change of this function tell you about Yugos?

Table 1.24   *Price and sales of Yugos in the US*

Year	Price in $, p	Number sold, Q
1985	3990	49,000
1986	4110	43,000
1987	4200	38,500
1988	4330	32,000

Solution   (a) We are interested in Q as a function of p, so we plot Q on the vertical axis and p on the horizontal axis. The data points in Figure 1.20 appear to lie on a straight line, suggesting a linear function.

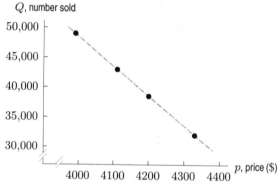

Figure 1.20: Since the data from Table 1.24 falls on a straight line, the table could represent a linear function

To provide further evidence that Q is a linear function, we check that the rate of change of Q with respect to p is constant for the points given. When the price of a Yugo rose from \$3990 to \$4110, sales fell from 49,000 to 43,000. Thus,

$$\Delta p = 4110 - 3990 = 120,$$

$$\Delta Q = 43,000 - 49,000 = -6000.$$

Since the number of Yugos sold decreased, ΔQ is negative. Thus, as the price increased from \$3990 to \$4110,

$$\text{Rate of change of quantity as price increases} = \frac{\Delta Q}{\Delta p} = \frac{-6000}{120} = -50 \text{ cars per dollar.}$$

Next, we calculate the rate of change as the price increased from \$4110 to \$4200 to see if the rate remains constant:

$$\text{Rate of change} = \frac{\Delta Q}{\Delta p} = \frac{38,500 - 43,000}{4200 - 4110} = \frac{-4500}{90} = -50 \text{ cars per dollar,}$$

---

[14]www.inet.hr/~pauric/epov.htm, accessed January 16, 2006.

and as the price increased from \$4200 to \$4330:

$$\text{Rate of change} = \frac{\Delta Q}{\Delta p} = \frac{32,000 - 38,500}{4330 - 4200} = \frac{-6500}{130} = -50 \text{ cars per dollar.}$$

Since the rate of change, -50, is constant, Q could be a linear function of p. Given additional data, $\Delta Q/\Delta p$ might not remain constant. However, based on the table, it appears that the function is linear.

(b) Since ΔQ is the change in the number of cars sold and Δp is the change in price, the rate of change is -50 cars per dollar. Thus the number of Yugos sold decreased by 50 each time the price increased by \$1.

Warning: Not All Graphs That Look Like Lines Represent Linear Functions

The graph of any linear function is a line. However, a function's graph can look like a line without actually being one. Consider the following example.

Example 6

The function $P = 100(1.02)^t$ approximates the population of Mexico in the early 2000s. Here P is the population (in millions) and t is the number of years since 2000. Table 1.25 and Figure 1.21 show values of P over a 5-year period. Is P a linear function of t?

Table 1.25 *Population of Mexico t years after 2000*

t (years)	P (millions)
0	100
1	102
2	104.04
3	106.12
4	108.24
5	110.41

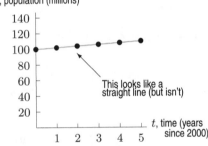

Figure 1.21: Graph of $P = 100(1.02)^t$ over 5-year period: Looks linear (but is not)

Solution

The formula $P = 100(1.02)^t$ is not of the form $P = b + mt$, so P is not a linear function of t. However, the graph of P in Figure 1.21 appears to be a straight line. We check P's rate of change in Table 1.25. When $t = 0$, $P = 100$ and when $t = 1$, $P = 102$. Thus, between 2000 and 2001,

$$\text{Rate of change of population} = \frac{\Delta P}{\Delta t} = \frac{102 - 100}{1 - 0} = 2.$$

For the interval from 2001 to 2002, we have

$$\text{Rate of change} = \frac{\Delta P}{\Delta t} = \frac{104.04 - 102}{2 - 1} = 2.04,$$

and for the interval from 2004 to 2005, we have

$$\text{Rate of change} = \frac{\Delta P}{\Delta t} = \frac{110.41 - 108.24}{5 - 4} = 2.17.$$

Thus, P's rate of change is not constant. In fact, P appears to be increasing at a faster and faster rate. Table 1.26 and Figure 1.22 show values of P over a longer (60-year) period. On this scale, these points do not appear to fall on a straight line. However, the graph of P curves upward so gradually at first that over the short interval shown in Figure 1.21, it barely curves at all. The graphs of many nonlinear functions, when viewed on a small scale, appear to be linear.

Table 1.26   *Population over 60 years*

t (years since 2000)	P (millions)
0	100
10	121.90
20	148.59
30	181.14
40	220.80
50	269.16
60	328.10

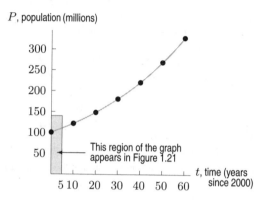

Figure 1.22: Graph of $P = 100(1.02)^t$ over 60 years: Not linear

Exercises and Problems for Section 1.3

Exercises

Which of the tables in Exercises 1–6 could represent a linear function?

1.

x	0	100	300	600
$g(x)$	50	100	150	200

2.

x	0	10	20	30
$h(x)$	20	40	50	55

3.

t	1	2	3	4	5
$g(t)$	5	4	5	4	5

4.

x	0	5	10	15
$f(x)$	10	20	30	40

5.

γ	9	8	7	6	5
$p(\gamma)$	42	52	62	72	82

6.

x	-3	-1	0	3
$j(x)$	5	1	-1	-7

In Exercises 7–10, identify the vertical intercept and the slope, and explain their meanings in practical terms.

7. The population of a town can be represented by the formula $P(t) = 54.25 - \frac{2}{7}t$, where $P(t)$ represents the population, in thousands, and t represents the time, in years, since 1970.

8. A stalactite grows according to the formula $L(t) = 17.75 + \frac{1}{250}t$, where $L(t)$ represents the length of the stalactite, in inches, and t represents the time, in years, since the stalactite was first measured.

9. The profit, in dollars, of selling n items is given by $P(n) = 0.98n - 3000$.

10. A phone company charges according to the formula: $C(n) = 29.99 + 0.05n$, where n is the number of minutes, and $C(n)$ is the monthly phone charge, in dollars.

Problems

11. In 2006, the population of a town was 18,310 and growing by 58 people per year. Find a formula for P, the town's population, in terms of t, the number of years since 2006.

12. The population, $P(t)$, in millions, of a country in year t, is given by the formula $P(t) = 22 + 0.3t$.

(a) Construct a table of values for $t = 0, 10, 20, \ldots, 50$.
(b) Plot the points you found in part (a).
(c) What is the country's initial population?
(d) What is the average rate of change of the population, in millions of people/year?

13. In 2003, the number, N, of cases of SARS (Severe Acute Respiratory Syndrome) reported in Hong Kong[15] was initially approximated by $N = 78.9 + 30.1t$, where t is the number of days since March 17. Interpret the constants 78.9 and 30.1.

14. Table 1.27 shows the cost C, in dollars, of selling x cups of coffee per day from a cart.

(a) Using the table, show that the relationship appears to be linear.
(b) Plot the data in the table.
(c) Find the slope of the line. Explain what this means in the context of the given situation.
(d) Why should it cost $50 to serve zero cups of coffee?

Table 1.27

x	0	5	10	50	100	200
C	50.00	51.25	52.50	62.50	75.00	100.00

15. A woodworker sells rocking horses. His start-up costs, including tools, plans, and advertising, total $5000. Labor and materials for each horse cost $350.

(a) Calculate the woodworker's total cost, C, to make 1, 2, 5, 10, and 20 rocking horses. Graph C against n, the number of rocking horses that he carves.
(b) Find a formula for C in terms of n.
(c) What is the rate of change of the function C? What does the rate of change tell us about the woodworker's expenses?

16. Table 1.28 gives the area and perimeter of a square as a function of the length of its side.

(a) From the table, decide if either area or perimeter could be a linear function of side length.

(b) From the data make two graphs, one showing area as a function of side length, the other showing perimeter as a function of side length. Connect the points.
(c) If you find a linear relationship, give its corresponding rate of change and interpret its significance.

Table 1.28

Length of side	0	1	2	3	4	5	6
Area of square	0	1	4	9	16	25	36
Perimeter of square	0	4	8	12	16	20	24

17. Make two tables, one comparing the radius of a circle to its area, the other comparing the radius of a circle to its circumference. Repeat parts (a), (b), and (c) from Problem 16, this time comparing radius with circumference, and radius with area.

18. Sri Lanka is an island which experienced approximately linear population growth from 1950 to 2000. On the other hand, Afghanistan was torn by warfare in the 1980s and did not experience linear nor near-linear growth.[16]

(a) Table 1.29 gives the population of these two countries, in millions. Which of these two countries is A and which is B? Explain.
(b) What is the approximate rate of change of the linear function? What does the rate of change represent in practical terms?
(c) Estimate the population of Sri Lanka in 1988.

Table 1.29

Year	1950	1960	1970	1980	1990	2000
Population of country A	8.2	9.8	12.4	15.1	14.7	23.9
Population of country B	7.5	9.9	12.5	14.9	17.2	19.2

19. In each case, graph a linear function with the given rate of change. Label and put scales on the axes.

(a) Increasing at 2.1 inches/day
(b) Decreasing at 1.3 gallons/mile

20. A new Toyota RAV4 costs $21,000. The car's value depreciates linearly to $10,500 in three years time. Write a formula which expresses its value, V, in terms of its age, t, in years.

[15] World Health Organisation, www.who.int/csr/sars/country/en
[16] www.census.gov/ipc/www/idbsusum.html, accessed January 12, 2006.

21. Table 1.18 on page 17 gives the temperature-depth profile, $T = f(d)$, in a borehole in Belleterre, Quebec, where T is the average temperature at a depth d.

    (a) Could f be linear?
    (b) Graph f. What do you notice about the graph for $d \geq 150$?
    (c) What can you say about the average rate of change of f for $d \geq 150$?

22. Outside the US, temperature readings are usually given in degrees Celsius; inside the US, they are often given in degrees Fahrenheit. The exact conversion from Celsius, C, to Fahrenheit, F, uses the formula

$$F = \frac{9}{5}C + 32.$$

    An approximate conversion is obtained by doubling the temperature in Celsius and adding $30°$ to get the equivalent Fahrenheit temperature.

    (a) Write a formula using C and F to express the approximate conversion.
    (b) How far off is the approximation if the Celsius temperature is $-5°, 0°, 15°, 30°$?
    (c) For what temperature (in Celsius) does the approximation agree with the actual formula?

23. Tuition cost T (in dollars) for part-time students at Stonewall College is given by $T = 300 + 200C$, where C represents the number of credits taken.

    (a) Find the tuition cost for eight credits.
    (b) How many credits were taken if the tuition was $1700?
    (c) Make a table showing costs for taking from one to twelve credits. For each value of C, give both the tuition cost, T, and the cost per credit, T/C. Round to the nearest dollar.
    (d) Which of these values of C has the smallest cost per credit?
    (e) What does the 300 represent in the formula for T?
    (f) What does the 200 represent in the formula for T?

24. A company finds that there is a linear relationship between the amount of money that it spends on advertising and the number of units it sells. If it spends no money on advertising, it sells 300 units. For each additional $5000 spent, an additional 20 units are sold.

    (a) If x is the amount of money that the company spends on advertising, find a formula for y, the number of units sold as a function of x.
    (b) How many units does the firm sell if it spends $25,000 on advertising? $50,000?

    (c) How much advertising money must be spent to sell 700 units?
    (d) What is the slope of the line you found in part (a)? Give an interpretation of the slope that relates units sold and advertising costs.

25. A report by the US Geological Survey[17] indicates that glaciers in Glacier National Park, Montana, are shrinking. Recent estimates indicate that the area covered by glaciers has decreased from over 25.5 km^2 in 1850 to about 16.6 km^2 in 1995. Let $A = f(t)$ give the area t years after 2000, and assume that $f(t) = 16.2 - 0.062t$. Explain what your answers to the following questions tell you about glaciers.

    (a) Give the slope and A-intercept.
    (b) Evaluate $f(15)$.
    (c) How much glacier area disappears in 15 years?
    (d) Solve $f(t) = 12$.

26. Graph the following function in the window $-10 \leq x \leq 10, -10 \leq y \leq 10$. Is this graph a line? Explain.

$$y = -x \left(\frac{x - 1000}{900} \right)$$

27. Graph $y = 2x + 400$ using the window $-10 \leq x \leq 10, -10 \leq y \leq 10$. Describe what happens, and how you can fix it by using a better window.

28. Graph $y = 200x + 4$ using the window $-10 \leq x \leq 10, -10 \leq y \leq 10$. Describe what happens and how you can fix it by using a better window.

29. Figure 1.23 shows the graph of $y = x^2/1000 + 5$ in the window $-10 \leq x \leq 10, -10 \leq y \leq 10$. Discuss whether this is a linear function.

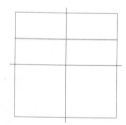

Figure 1.23

30. The cost of a cab ride is given by the function $C = 1.50 + 2d$, where d is the number of miles traveled and C is in dollars. Choose an appropriate window and graph the cost of a ride for a cab that travels no farther than a 10 mile radius from the center of the city.

---

[17]*Glacier Retreat in Glacier National Park, Montana*, http://www.nrmsc.usgs.gov/research/glacier_retreat.htm, accessed October 15, 2003.

31. The graph of a linear function $y = f(x)$ passes through the two points $(a, f(a))$ and $(b, f(b))$, where $a < b$ and $f(a) < f(b)$.

    (a) Graph the function labeling the two points.
    (b) Find the slope of the line in terms of f, a, and b.

32. Let $f(x) = 0.003 - (1.246x + 0.37)$.

(a) Calculate the following average rates of change:

  (i) $\dfrac{f(2) - f(1)}{2 - 1}$ (ii) $\dfrac{f(1) - f(2)}{1 - 2}$

  (iii) $\dfrac{f(3) - f(4)}{3 - 4}$

(b) Rewrite $f(x)$ in the form $f(x) = b + mx$.

1.4 FORMULAS FOR LINEAR FUNCTIONS

To find a formula for a linear function we find values for the slope, m, and the vertical intercept, b in the formula $y = b + mx$.

Finding a Formula for a Linear Function from a Table of Data

If a table of data represents a linear function, we first calculate m and then determine b.

Example 1   A grapefruit is thrown into the air. Its velocity, v, is a linear function of t, the time since it was thrown. A positive velocity indicates the grapefruit is rising and a negative velocity indicates it is falling. Check that the data in Table 1.30 corresponds to a linear function. Find a formula for v in terms of t.

Table 1.30   *Velocity of a grapefruit t seconds after being thrown into the air*

t, time (sec)	1	2	3	4
v, velocity (ft/sec)	48	16	−16	−48

Solution   Figure 1.24 shows the data in Table 1.30. The points appear to fall on a line. To check that the velocity function is linear, calculate the rates of change of v and see that they are constant. From time $t = 1$ to $t = 2$, we have

$$\text{Rate of change of velocity with time} = \frac{\Delta v}{\Delta t} = \frac{16 - 48}{2 - 1} = -32.$$

For the next second, from $t = 2$ to $t = 3$, we have

$$\text{Rate of change} = \frac{\Delta v}{\Delta t} = \frac{-16 - 16}{3 - 2} = -32.$$

You can check that the rate of change from $t = 3$ to $t = 4$ is also -32.

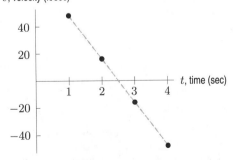

Figure 1.24: Velocity of a grapefruit is a linear function of time

43

A formula for v is of the form $v = b + mt$. Since m is the rate of change, we have $m = -32$ so $v = b - 32t$. The initial velocity (at $t = 0$) is represented by b. We are not given the value of v when $t = 0$, but we can use any data point to calculate b. For example, $v = 48$ when $t = 1$, so

$$48 = b - 32 \cdot 1,$$

which gives

$$b = 80.$$

Thus, a formula for the velocity is $v = 80 - 32t$.

What does the rate of change, m, in Example 1 tell us about the grapefruit? Think about the units:

$$m = \frac{\Delta v}{\Delta t} = \frac{\text{Change in velocity}}{\text{Change in time}} = \frac{-32 \text{ ft/sec}}{1 \text{ sec}} = -32 \text{ ft/sec per second.}$$

The value of m, -32 ft/sec per second, tells us that the grapefruit's velocity is decreasing by 32 ft/sec for every second that goes by. We say the grapefruit is accelerating at -32 ft/sec per second. (The units ft/sec per second are often written ft/sec^2. Negative acceleration is also called deceleration.)[18]

Finding a Formula for a Linear Function from a Graph

We can calculate the slope, m, of a linear function using two points on its graph. Having found m we can use either of the points to calculate b, the vertical intercept.

Example 2   Figure 1.25 shows oxygen consumption as a function of heart rate for two people.
(a) Assuming linearity, find formulas for these two functions.
(b) Interpret the slope of each graph in terms of oxygen consumption.

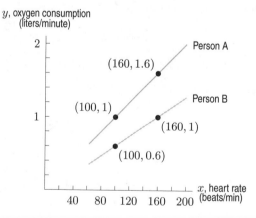

Figure 1.25: Oxygen consumption of two people running on treadmills

---

[18]The notation ft/sec^2 is shorthand for ft/sec per second; it does not mean a "square second" in the same way that areas are measured square feet or square meters.

Solution
(a) Let x be heart rate and let y be oxygen consumption. Since we are assuming linearity, $y = b + mx$. The two points on person A's line, $(100, 1)$ and $(160, 1.6)$, give

$$\text{Slope of } A\text{'s line } = m = \frac{\Delta y}{\Delta x} = \frac{1.6 - 1}{160 - 100} = 0.01.$$

Thus $y = b + 0.01x$. To find b, use the fact that $y = 1$ when $x = 100$:

$$1 = b + 0.01(100)$$
$$1 = b + 1$$
$$b = 0.$$

Alternatively, b can be found using the fact that $x = 160$ if $y = 1.6$. Either way leads to the formula $y = 0.01x$.

For person B, we again begin with the formula $y = b + mx$. In Figure 1.25, two points on B's line are $(100, 0.6)$ and $(160, 1)$, so

$$\text{Slope of } B\text{'s line } = m = \frac{\Delta y}{\Delta x} = \frac{1 - 0.6}{160 - 100} = \frac{0.4}{60} \approx 0.0067.$$

To find b, use the fact that $y = 1$ when $x = 160$:

$$1 = b + (0.4/60) \cdot 160$$
$$1 = b + 1.067$$
$$b = -0.067.$$

Thus, for person B, we have $y = -0.067 + 0.0067x$.
(b) The slope for person A is $m = 0.01$, so

$$m = \frac{\text{Change in oxygen consumption}}{\text{Change in heart rate}} = \frac{\text{Change in liters/min}}{\text{Change in beats/min}} = 0.01 \frac{\text{liters}}{\text{heart beat}}.$$

Every additional heart beat (per minute) for person A translates to an additional 0.01 liters (per minute) of oxygen consumed.

The slope for person B is $m = 0.0067$. Thus, for every additional beat (per minute), person B consumes an additional 0.0067 liter of oxygen (per minute). Since the slope for person B is smaller than for person A, person B consumes less additional oxygen than person A for the same increase in pulse.

What do the y-intercepts of the functions in Example 2 say about oxygen consumption? Often the y-intercept of a function is a starting value. In this case, the y-intercept would be the oxygen consumption of a person whose pulse is zero (i.e. $x = 0$). Since a person running on a treadmill must have a pulse, in this case it makes no sense to interpret the y-intercept this way. The formula for oxygen consumption is useful only for realistic values of the pulse.

Finding a Formula for a Linear Function from a Verbal Description

Sometimes the verbal description of a linear function is less straightforward than those we saw in Section 1.3. Consider the following example.

Example 3   We have $24 to spend on soda and chips for a party. A six-pack of soda costs $3 and a bag of chips costs $2. The number of six-packs we can afford, y, is a function of the number of bags of chips we decide to buy, x.

(a) Find an equation relating x and y.

(b) Graph the equation. Interpret the intercepts and the slope in the context of the party.

Solution   (a) If we spend all $24 on soda and chips, then we have the following equation:

$$\text{Amount spent on chips } + \text{ Amount spent on soda } = \$24.$$

If we buy x bags of chips at $2 per bag, then the amount spent on chips is $\$2x$. Similarly, if we buy y six-packs of soda at $3 per six-pack, then the amount spent on soda is $\$3y$. Thus,

$$2x + 3y = 24.$$

We can solve for y, giving

$$3y = 24 - 2x$$
$$y = 8 - \frac{2}{3}x.$$

This is a linear function with slope $m = -2/3$ and y-intercept $b = 8$.

(b) The graph of this function is a discrete set of points, since the number of bags of chips and the number of six-packs of soda must be (nonnegative) integers.

To find the y-intercept, we set $x = 0$, giving

$$2 \cdot 0 + 3y = 24.$$

So $3y = 24$, giving $y = 8$.

Substituting $y = 0$ gives the x-intercept,

$$2x + 3 \cdot 0 = 24.$$

So $2x = 24$, giving $x = 12$. Thus the points $(0, 8)$ and $(12, 0)$ are on the graph.

The point $(0, 8)$ indicates that we can buy 8 six-packs of soda if we buy no chips. The point $(12, 0)$ indicates that we can buy 12 bags of chips if we buy no soda. The other points on the line describe affordable options between these two extremes. For example, the point $(6, 4)$ is on the line, because

$$2 \cdot 6 + 3 \cdot 4 = 24.$$

This means that if we buy 6 bags of chips, we can afford 4 six-packs of soda.

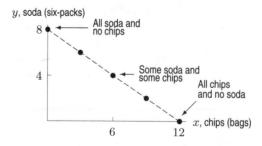

Figure 1.26: Relation between the number of six-packs, y, and the number of bags of chips, x

The points marked in Figure 1.26 represent affordable options. All affordable options lie on or below the line $2x + 3y = 24$. Not all points on the line are affordable options. For example, suppose we purchase one six-pack of soda for $3.00. That leaves $21.00 to spend on chips, meaning we would have to buy 10.5 bags of chips, which is not possible. Therefore, the point $(10.5, 1)$ is not an option, although it is a point on the line $2x + 3y = 24$.

To interpret the slope, notice that

$$m = \frac{\Delta y}{\Delta x} = \frac{\text{Change in number of six-packs}}{\text{Change in number of bags of chips}},$$

so the units of m are six-packs of soda per bags of chips. The fact that $m = -2/3$ means that for each additional 3 bags of chips purchased, we can purchase 2 fewer six-packs of soda. This occurs because 2 six-packs cost $6, the same as 3 bags of chips. Thus, $m = -2/3$ is the rate at which the amount of soda we can buy decreases as we buy more chips.

Alternative Forms for the Equation of a Line

In Example 3, the equation $2x + 3y = 24$ represents a linear relationship between x and y even though the equation is not in the form $y = b + mx$. The following equations represent lines.

- The *slope-intercept form* is
  $$y = b + mx \qquad \text{where } m \text{ is the slope and } b \text{ is the } y\text{-intercept.}$$
- The *point-slope form* is
  $$y - y_0 = m(x - x_0) \quad \text{where } m \text{ is the slope and } (x_0, y_0) \text{ is a point on the line.}$$
- The *standard form* is
  $$Ax + By + C = 0 \qquad \text{where } A, B, \text{ and } C \text{ are constants.}$$

If we know the slope of a line and the coordinates of a point on the line, it is often convenient to use the point-slope form of the equation.

Example 4 Use the point-slope form to find the equation of the line for the oxygen consumption of Person A in Example 2.

Solution In Example 2, we found the slope of person A's line to be $m = 0.01$. Since the point $(100, 1)$ lies on the line, the point-slope form gives the equation

$$y - 1 = 0.01(x - 100).$$

To check that this gives the same equation we got in Example 2, we multiply out and simplify:

$$y - 1 = 0.01x - 1$$
$$y = 0.01x.$$

Alternatively, we could have used the point $(160, 1.6)$ instead of $(100, 1)$, giving

$$y - 1.6 = 0.01(x - 160).$$

Multiplying out again gives $y = 0.01x$.

Exercises and Problems for Section 1.4

Exercises

If possible, rewrite the equations in Exercises 1–9 in slope-intercept form, $y = b + mx$.

1. $5(x + y) = 4$

2. $3x + 5y = 20$

3. $0.1y + x = 18$

4. $5x - 3y + 2 = 0$

5. $y - 0.7 = 5(x - 0.2)$

6. $y = 5$

7. $3x + 2y + 40 = x - y$

8. $x = 4$

9. $\dfrac{x + y}{7} = 3$

Is each function in Exercises 10–15 linear? If so, rewrite it the form $y = b + mx$.

10. $g(w) = -\dfrac{1 - 12w}{3}$

11. $F(P) = 13 - \dfrac{2^{-1}}{4}P$

12. $j(s) = 3s^{-1} + 7$

13. $C(r) = 2\pi r$

14. $h(x) = 3^x + 12$

15. $f(x) = m^2 x + n^2$

Find formulas for the linear functions in Exercises 16–23.

16. Slope -4 and x-intercept 7

17. Slope 3 and y-intercept 8

18. Passes through the points $(-1, 5)$ and $(2, -1)$

19. Slope $2/3$ and passes through the point $(5, 7)$

20. Has x-intercept 3 and y-intercept -5

21. Slope 0.1, passes through $(-0.1, 0.02)$

22. Function f has $f(0.3) = 0.8$ and $f(0.8) = -0.4$

23. Function f has $f(-2) = 7$ and $f(3) = -3$.

Exercises 24–30 give data from a linear function. Find a formula for the function.

24.

Year, t	0	1	2
Value of computer, $V = f(t)$	2000	1500	1000

25.

Price per bottle, p ($)	0.50	0.75	1.00
Number of bottles sold, $q = f(p)$	1500	1000	500

26.

Temperature, $y = f(x)$ (°C)	0	5	20
Temperature, x (°F)	32	41	68

27.

Temperature, $y = f(x)$, (°R)	459.7	469.7	489.7
Temperature, x (°F)	0	10	30

28.

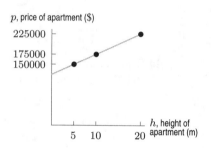

29.

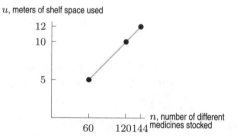

30.

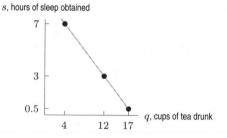

Problems

31. Find the equation of the line l, shown in Figure 1.27, if its slope is $m = 4$.

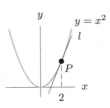

Figure 1.27

32. Find a formula for the line intersecting the graph of $f(x)$ at $x = 1$ and $x = 3$, where

$$f(x) = \frac{10}{x^2 + 1}.$$

33. Find a formula for the linear function $h(t)$ whose graph intersects the graph of $j(t) = 30(0.2)^t$ at $t = -2$ and $t = 1$.

34. Find the equation of the line l in Figure 1.28. The shapes under the line are squares.

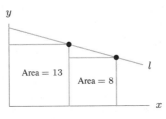

Figure 1.28

35. Find the equation of line l in Figure 1.29.

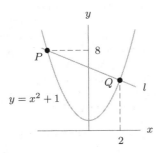

Figure 1.29

36. Find an equation for the line l in Figure 1.30 in terms of the constant A and values of the function f.

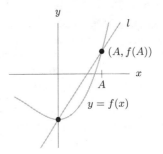

Figure 1.30

37. A bullet is shot straight up into the air from ground level. After t seconds, the velocity of the bullet, in meters per second, is approximated by the formula

$$v = f(t) = 1000 - 9.8t.$$

(a) Evaluate the following: $f(0)$, $f(1)$, $f(2)$, $f(3)$, $f(4)$. Compile your results in a table.

(b) Describe in words what is happening to the speed of the bullet. Discuss why you think this is happening.

(c) Evaluate and interpret the slope and both intercepts of $f(t)$.

(d) The gravitational field near the surface of Jupiter is stronger than that near the surface of the earth, which, in turn, is stronger than the field near the surface of the moon. How is the formula for $f(t)$ different for a bullet shot from Jupiter's surface? From the moon?

38. In a college meal plan you pay a membership fee; then all your meals are at a fixed price per meal.

(a) If 30 meals cost \$152.50 and 60 meals cost \$250, find the membership fee and the price per meal.

(b) Write a formula for the cost of a meal plan, C, in terms of the number of meals, n.

(c) Find the cost for 50 meals.

(d) Find n in terms of C.

(e) Use part (d) to determine the maximum number of meals you can buy on a budget of \$300.

39. John wants to buy a dozen rolls. The local bakery sells sesame and poppy seed rolls for the same price.

(a) Make a table of all the possible combinations of rolls if he buys a dozen, where s is the number of sesame seed rolls and p is the number of poppy seed rolls.

(b) Find a formula for p as a function of s.

(c) Graph this function.

40. A theater manager graphed weekly profits as a function of the number of patrons and found that the relationship was linear. One week the profit was \$11,328 when 1324 patrons attended. Another week 1529 patrons produced a profit of \$13,275.50.

   (a) Find a formula for weekly profit, y, as a function of the number of patrons, x.

   (b) Interpret the slope and the y-intercept.

   (c) What is the break-even point (the number of patrons for which there is zero profit)?

   (d) Find a formula for the number of patrons as a function of profit.

   (e) If the weekly profit was \$17,759.50, how many patrons attended the theater?

41. The demand for gasoline can be modeled as a linear function of price. If the price of gasoline is $p = \$2.10$ per gallon, the quantity demanded in a fixed period is $q = 65$ gallons. If the price rises to \$2.50 per gallon, the quantity demanded falls to 45 gallons in that period.

   (a) Find a formula for q in terms of p.

   (b) Explain the economic significance of the slope of your formula.

   (c) Explain the economic significance of the q-axis and p-axis intercepts.

42. An empty champagne bottle is tossed from a hot-air balloon. Its upward velocity is measured every second and recorded in Table 1.31.

   (a) Describe the motion of the bottle in words. What do negative values of v represent?

   (b) Find a formula for v in terms of t.

   (c) Explain the physical significance of the slope of your formula.

   (d) Explain the physical significance of the t-axis and v-axis intercepts.

Table 1.31

t (sec)	0	1	2	3	4	5
v (ft/sec)	40	8	-24	-56	-88	-120

43. A business consultant works 10 hours a day, 6 days a week. She divides her time between meetings with clients and meetings with co-workers. A client meeting requires 3 hours while a co-worker meeting requires 2 hours. Let x be the number of co-worker meetings the consultant holds during a given week. If y is the number of client meetings for which she has time remaining, then y is a function of x. Assume this relationship is linear and that meetings can be split up and continued on different days.

   (a) Graph the relationship between y and x. [Hint: Consider the maximum number of client and co-worker meetings that can be held.]

   (b) Find a formula for y as a function of x.

   (c) Explain what the slope and the x- and y-intercepts represent in the context of the consultant's meeting schedule.

   (d) A change is made so that co-worker meetings take 90 minutes instead of 2 hours. Graph this situation. Describe those features of this graph that have changed from the one sketched in part (a) and those that have remained the same.

44. The development time, t, of an organism is the number of days required for the organism to mature, and the development rate is defined as $r = 1/t$. In cold-blooded organisms such as insects, the development rate depends on temperature: the colder it is, the longer the organism takes to develop. For such organisms, the degree-day model[19] assumes that the development rate r is a linear function of temperature H (in °C):

$$r = b + kH.$$

   (a) According to the degree-day model, there is a minimum temperature H_{min} below which an organism never matures. Find a formula for H_{min} in terms of the constants b and k.

   (b) Define S as $S = (H - H_{min})t$, where S is the number of degree-days. That is, S is the number of days t times the number of degrees between H and H_{min}. Use the formula for r to show that S is a constant. In other words, find a formula for S that does not involve H. Your formula will involve k.

   (c) A certain organism requires $t = 25$ days to develop at a constant temperature of $H = 20°C$ and has $H_{min} = 15°C$. Using the fact that S is a constant, how many days does it take for this organism to develop at a temperature of 25°C?

   (d) In part (c) we assumed that the temperature H is constant throughout development. If the temperature varies from day to day, the number of degree-days can be accumulated until they total S, at which point the organism completes development. For instance, suppose on the first day the temperature is $H = 20°C$ and that on the next day it is $H = 22°C$. Then for these first two days

Total number of degree days

$$= (20 - 15) \cdot 1 + (22 - 15) \cdot 1 = 12.$$

---

[19]Information drawn from a web site created by Dr. Alexei A. Sharov at the Virginia Polytechnic Institute, http://www.ento.vt.edu/ sharov/PopEcol/popecol.html.

Based on Table 1.32, on what day does the organism reach maturity?

(b) Find the value of S, the number of degree-days required for the organism to mature.

Table 1.32

Day	1	2	3	4	5	6	7	8	9	10	11	12
H (°C)	20	22	27	28	27	31	29	30	28	25	24	26

Table 1.33

H, °C	20	22	24	26	28	30
t, days	14.3	12.5	11.1	10.0	9.1	8.3

45. (Continuation of Problem 44.) Table 1.33 gives the development time t (in days) for an insect as a function of temperature H (in °C).

(a) Find a linear formula for r, the development rate, in terms of H.

46. Describe a linear (or nearly linear) relationship that you have encountered outside the classroom. Determine the rate of change and interpret it in practical terms.

1.5   GEOMETRIC PROPERTIES OF LINEAR FUNCTIONS

Interpreting the Parameters of a Linear Function

The slope-intercept form for a linear function is $y = b + mx$, where b is the y-intercept and m is the slope. The parameters b and m can be used to compare linear functions.

Example 1   With time, t, in years, the populations of four towns, P_A, P_B, P_C and P_D, are given by the following formulas:

$$P_A = 20{,}000 + 1600t, \quad P_B = 50{,}000 - 300t, \quad P_C = 650t + 45{,}000, \quad P_D = 15{,}000(1.07)^t.$$

(a) Which populations are represented by linear functions?

(b) Describe in words what each linear model tells you about that town's population. Which town starts out with the most people? Which town is growing fastest?

Solution   (a) The populations of towns A, B, and C are represented by linear functions because they are written in the form $P = b + mt$. Town D's population does not grow linearly since its formula, $P_D = 15{,}000(1.07)^t$, cannot be expressed in the form $P_D = b + mt$.

(b) For town A, we have

$$P_A = \underbrace{20{,}000}_{b} + \underbrace{1600}_{m} \cdot t,$$

so $b = 20{,}000$ and $m = 1600$. This means that in year $t = 0$, town A has 20,000 people. It grows by 1600 people per year.

For town B, we have

$$P_B = \underbrace{50{,}000}_{b} + \underbrace{(-300)}_{m} \cdot t,$$

so $b = 50{,}000$ and $m = -300$. This means that town B starts with 50,000 people. The negative slope indicates that the population is decreasing at the rate of 300 people per year.

For town C, we have

$$P_C = \underbrace{45{,}000}_{b} + \underbrace{650}_{m} \cdot t,$$

so $b = 45{,}000$ and $m = 650$. This means that town C begins with 45,000 people and grows by 650 people per year.

Town B starts out with the most people, 50,000, but town A, with a rate of change of 1600 people per year, grows the fastest of the three towns that grow linearly.

The Effect of the Parameters on the Graph of a Linear Function

The graph of a linear function is a line. Changing the values of b and m gives different members of the family of linear functions. In summary:

> Let $y = b + mx$. Then the graph of y against x is a line.
> - The y-intercept, b, tells us where the line crosses the y-axis.
> - If the slope, m, is positive, the line climbs from left to right. If the slope, m, is negative, the line falls from left to right.
> - The slope, m, tells us how fast the line is climbing or falling.
> - The larger the magnitude of m (either positive or negative), the steeper the graph of f.

Example 2   (a) Graph the three linear functions P_A, P_B, P_C from Example 1 and show how to identify the values of b and m from the graph.

(b) Graph P_D from Example 1 and explain how the graph shows P_D is not a linear function.

Solution   (a) Figure 1.31 gives graphs of the three functions:

$$P_A = 20{,}000 + 1600t, \qquad P_B = 50{,}000 - 300t, \quad \text{and} \quad P_C = 45{,}000 + 650t.$$

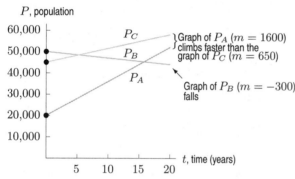

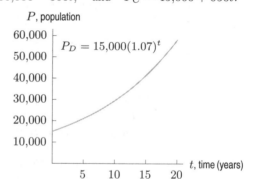

Figure 1.31: Graphs of three linear functions, P_A, P_B, and P_C, showing starting values and rates of climb

Figure 1.32: Graph of $P_D = 15{,}000(1.07)^t$ is not a line

The values of b identified in Example 1 tell us the vertical intercepts. Figure 1.31 shows that the graph of P_A crosses the P-axis at $P = 20{,}000$, the graph of P_B crosses at $P = 50{,}000$, and the graph of P_C crosses at $P = 45{,}000$.

Notice that the graphs of P_A and P_C are both climbing and that P_A climbs faster than P_C. This corresponds to the fact that the slopes of these two functions are positive ($m = 1600$ for P_A and $m = 650$ for P_C) and the slope of P_A is larger than the slope of P_C.

The graph of P_B falls when read from left to right, indicating that population decreases over time. This corresponds to the fact that the slope of P_C is negative ($m = -300$).

(b) Figure 1.32 gives a graph of P_D. Since it is not a line, P_D is not a linear function.

Intersection of Two Lines

To find the point at which two lines intersect, notice that the (x, y)-coordinates of such a point must satisfy the equations for both lines. Thus, in order to find the point of intersection algebraically, solve the equations simultaneously.[20]

---

[20]If you have questions about the algebra in this section, see the Tools Section on page 55.

If linear functions are modeling real quantities, their points of intersection often have practical significance. Consider the next example.

Example 3 The cost in dollars of renting a car for a day from three different rental agencies and driving it d miles is given by the following functions:

$$C_1 = 50 + 0.10d, \qquad C_2 = 30 + 0.20d, \qquad C_3 = 0.50d.$$

(a) Describe in words the daily rental arrangements made by each of these three agencies.
(b) Which agency is cheapest?

Solution (a) Agency 1 charges $50 plus $0.10 per mile driven. Agency 2 charges $30 plus $0.20 per mile. Agency 3 charges $0.50 per mile driven.

(b) The answer depends on how far we want to drive. If we are not driving far, agency 3 may be cheapest because it only charges for miles driven and has no other fees. If we want to drive a long way, agency 1 may be cheapest (even though it charges $50 up front) because it has the lowest per-mile rate.

The three functions are graphed in Figure 1.33. The graph shows that for d up to 100 miles, the value of C_3 is less than C_1 and C_2 because its graph is below the other two. For d between 100 and 200 miles, the value of C_2 is less than C_1 and C_3. For d more than 200 miles, the value of C_1 is less than C_2 and C_3.

By graphing these three functions on a calculator, we can estimate the coordinates of the points of intersection by tracing. To find the exact coordinates, we solve simultaneous equations. Starting with the intersection of lines C_1 and C_2, we set the costs equal, $C_1 = C_2$, and solve for d:

$$50 + 0.10d = 30 + 0.20d$$
$$20 = 0.10d$$
$$d = 200.$$

Thus, the cost of driving 200 miles is the same for agencies 1 and 2. Solving $C_2 = C_3$ gives

$$30 + 0.20d = 0.50d$$
$$0.30d = 30$$
$$d = 100,$$

which means the cost of driving 100 miles is the same for agencies 2 and 3.

Thus, agency 3 is cheapest up to 100 miles. Agency 1 is cheapest for more than 200 miles. Agency 2 is cheapest between 100 and 200 miles. See Figure 1.33. Notice that the point of intersection of C_1 and C_3, $(125, 62.5)$, does not influence our decision as to which agency is the cheapest.

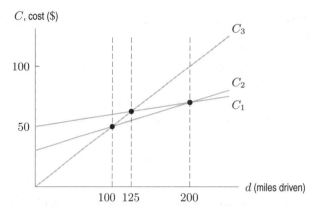

Figure 1.33: Cost of driving a car d miles when renting from three different agencies. Cheapest agency corresponds to the lowest graph for a given d value

Equations of Horizontal and Vertical Lines

An increasing linear function has positive slope and a decreasing linear function has negative slope. What about a line with slope $m = 0$? If the rate of change of a quantity is zero, then the quantity does not change. Thus, if the slope of a line is zero, the value of y must be constant. Such a line is horizontal.

Example 4   Explain why the equation $y = 4$ represents a horizontal line and the equation $x = 4$ represents a vertical line.

Solution   The equation $y = 4$ represents a linear function with slope $m = 0$. To see this, notice that this equation can be rewritten as $y = 4 + 0 \cdot x$. Thus, the value of y is 4 no matter what the value of x is. See Figure 1.34. Similarly, the equation $x = 4$ means that x is 4 no matter what the value of y is. Every point on the line in Figure 1.35 has x equal to 4, so this line is the graph of $x = 4$.

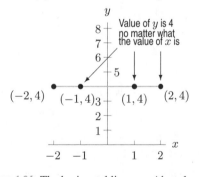

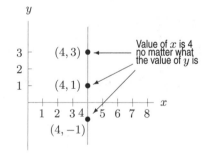

Figure 1.34: The horizontal line $y = 4$ has slope 0   Figure 1.35: The vertical line $x = 4$ has an undefined slope

What is the slope of a vertical line? Figure 1.35 shows three points, $(4, -1)$, $(4, 1)$, and $(4, 3)$ on a vertical line. Calculating the slope, gives

$$m = \frac{\Delta y}{\Delta x} = \frac{3 - 1}{4 - 4} = \frac{2}{0}.$$

The slope is undefined because the denominator, Δx, is 0. The slope of every vertical line is undefined for the same reason. All the x-values on such a line are equal, so Δx is 0, and the denominator of the expression for the slope is 0. A vertical line is not the graph of a function, since it fails the vertical line test. It does not have an equation of the form $y = b + mx$.

In summary,

For any constant k:
- The graph of the equation $y = k$ is a horizontal line and its slope is zero.
- The graph of the equation $x = k$ is a vertical line and its slope is undefined.

Slopes of Parallel and Perpendicular Lines

Figure 1.36 shows two parallel lines. These lines are parallel because they have equal slopes.

Figure 1.36: Parallel lines: l_1 and l_2 have equal slopes

Figure 1.37: Perpendicular lines: l_1 has a positive slope and l_2 has a negative slope

What about perpendicular lines? Two perpendicular lines are graphed in Figure 1.37. We can see that if one line has a positive slope, then any perpendicular line must have a negative slope. Perpendicular lines have slopes with opposite signs.

We show that if l_1 and l_2 are two perpendicular lines with slopes, m_1 and m_2, then m_1 is the negative reciprocal of m_2. If m_1 and m_2 are not zero, we have the following result:

Let l_1 and l_2 be two lines having slopes m_1 and m_2, respectively. Then:
- These lines are parallel if and only if $m_1 = m_2$.
- These lines are perpendicular if and only if $m_1 = -\dfrac{1}{m_2}$.

In addition, any two horizontal lines are parallel and $m_1 = m_2 = 0$. Any two vertical lines are parallel and m_1 and m_2 are undefined. A horizontal line is perpendicular to a vertical line. See Figures 1.38–1.40.

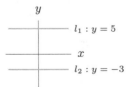

Figure 1.38: Any two horizontal lines are parallel

Figure 1.39: Any two vertical lines are parallel

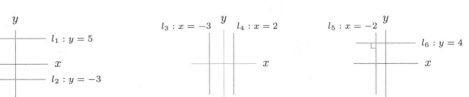

Figure 1.40: A horizontal line and a vertical line are perpendicular

Justification of Formula for Slopes of Perpendicular Lines

Figure 1.41 shows l_1 and l_2, two perpendicular lines with slope m_1 and m_2. Neither line is horizontal or vertical, so m_1 and m_2 are both defined and nonzero. We will show that

$$m_1 = -\frac{1}{m_2},$$

We use the two triangles, $\triangle PQR$ and $\triangle SPR$. We show that $\triangle PQR$ and $\triangle SPR$ are similar by showing that corresponding angles have equal measure. The line PR is horizontal, so $\angle QRP = \angle SRP$ since both are right angles. Since $\triangle QPS$ is a right triangle, $\angle S$ is complementary to $\angle Q$ (that is, $\angle S$ and $\angle Q$ add to $90°$). Since $\triangle QRP$ is a right triangle, $\angle QPR$ is complementary to $\angle Q$. Therefore $\angle S = \angle QPR$. Since two pairs of angles in $\triangle PQR$ and $\triangle SPR$ have equal measure, the third must be equal also; the triangles are similar.

Corresponding sides of similar triangles are proportional. (See Figure 1.42.) Therefore,

$$\frac{\|RS\|}{\|RP\|} = \frac{\|RP\|}{\|RQ\|},$$

where $\|RS\|$ means the length of side RS.

Next, we calculate m_1 using points S and P, and we calculate m_2 using points Q and P. In Figure 1.41, we see that

$$\Delta x = \|RP\|, \quad \Delta y_1 = \|RS\|, \quad \text{and} \quad \Delta y_2 = -\|RQ\|,$$

where Δy_2 is negative because y-values of points on l_2 decrease as x increases. Thus,

$$m_1 = \frac{\Delta y_1}{\Delta x} = \frac{\|RS\|}{\|RP\|} \quad \text{and} \quad m_2 = \frac{\Delta y_2}{\Delta x} = -\frac{\|RQ\|}{\|RP\|}.$$

Therefore, using the result obtained from the similar triangles, we have

$$m_1 = \frac{\|RS\|}{\|RP\|} = \frac{\|RP\|}{\|RQ\|} = -\frac{1}{m_2}.$$

Thus, $m_1 = -1/m_2$.

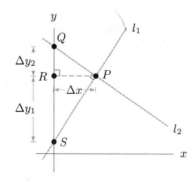

Figure 1.41

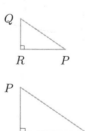

Figure 1.42

Exercises and Problems for Section 1.5

1. Without a calculator, match the functions (a)–(c) to the graphs (i)–(iii).

    (a) $f(x) = 3x + 1$ **(b)** $g(x) = -2x + 1$

    (c) $h(x) = 1$

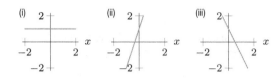

2. Without a calculator, match the equations (a)–(g) to the graphs (I)–(VII).

    (a) $y = x - 5$ **(b)** $-3x + 4 = y$

    (c) $5 = y$ **(d)** $y = -4x - 5$

    (e) $y = x + 6$ **(f)** $y = x/2$

    (g) $5 = x$

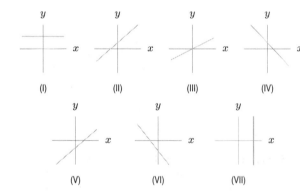

In Exercises 3–5, which line has the greater

(a) Slope?   **(b)** y-intercept?

3. $y = -1 + 2x$, $y = -2 + 3x$

4. $y = 3 + 4x$, $y = 5 - 2x$

5. $y = \frac{1}{4}x$, $y = 1 - 6x$

6. Figure 1.43 gives lines, A, B, C, D, and E. Without a calculator, match each line to f, g, h, u or v:

$$f(x) = 20 + 2x$$
$$g(x) = 20 + 4x$$
$$h(x) = 2x - 30$$
$$u(x) = 60 - x$$
$$v(x) = 60 - 2x$$

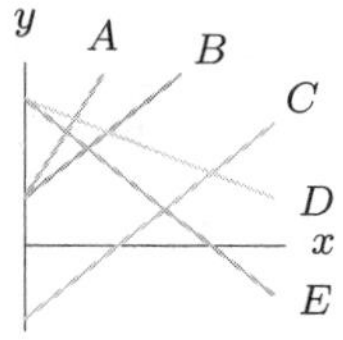

Figure 1.43

7. Without a calculator, match the following functions to the lines in Figure 1.44:

$$f(x) = 5 + 2x$$
$$g(x) = -5 + 2x$$
$$h(x) = 5 + 3x$$
$$j(x) = 5 - 2x$$
$$k(x) = 5 - 3x$$

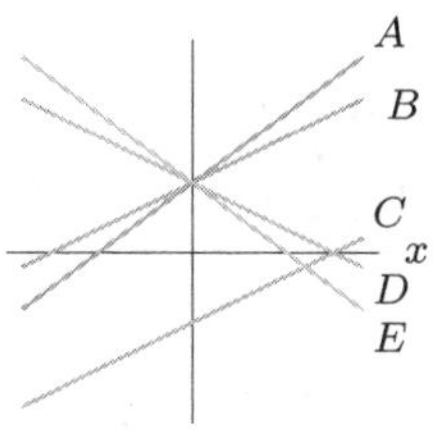

Figure 1.44

8. **(a)** By hand, graph $y = 3$ and $x = 3$.

    (b) Can the equations in part (a) be written in slope-intercept form?

Are the lines in Exercises 9–14 perpendicular? Parallel? Neither?

9. $y = 5x - 7; y = 5x + 8$

10. $y = 4x + 3; y = 13 - \frac{1}{4}x$

11. $y = 2x + 3$ $y = 2x - 7$

12. $y = 4x + 7$ $y = \frac{1}{4}x - 2$

13. $f(q) = 12q + 7; g(q) = \frac{1}{12}q + 96$

14. $2y = 16 - x; 4y = -8 - 2x$

15. Find a formula for the line parallel to the line $y = 20 - 4x$ and containing the point $(3, 12)$.

16. Find the equation of the linear function g whose graph is perpendicular to the line $5x - 3y = 6$; the two lines intersect at $x = 15$.

17. Line l is given by $y = 3 - \frac{2}{3}x$ and point P has coordinates $(6, 5)$.

(a) Find the equation of the line containing P and parallel to l.

(b) Find the equation of the line containing P and perpendicular to l.

(c) Graph the equations in parts (a) and (b).

18. Fill in the missing coordinates for the points in the following figures.

    (a) The triangle in Figure 1.45.
    (b) The parallelogram in Figure 1.46.

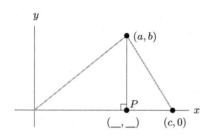

Figure 1.45

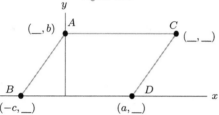

Figure 1.46

19. Using the window $-10 \le x \le 10, -10 \le y \le 10$, graph $y = x$, $y = 10x$, $y = 100x$, and $y = 1000x$.

    (a) Explain what happens to the graphs of the lines as the slopes become large.
    (b) Write an equation of a line that passes through the origin and is horizontal.

20. Graph $y = x + 1$, $y = x + 10$, and $y = x + 100$ in the window $-10 \le x \le 10, -10 \le y \le 10$.

    (a) Explain what happens to the graph of a line, $y = b + mx$, as b becomes large.
    (b) Write a linear equation whose graph cannot be seen in the window $-10 \le x \le 10, -10 \le y \le 10$ because all its y-values are less than the y-values shown.

21. The graphical interpretation of the slope is that it shows steepness. Using a calculator or a computer, graph the function $y = 2x - 3$ in the following windows:

    (a) $-10 \le x \le 10$ by $-10 \le y \le 10$
    (b) $-10 \le x \le 10$ by $-100 \le y \le 100$
    (c) $-10 \le x \le 10$ by $-1000 \le y \le 1000$
    (d) Write a sentence about how steepness is related to the window being used.

22. Find the coordinates of point P in Figure 1.47.

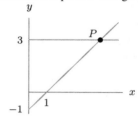

Figure 1.47

23. Estimate the slope of the line in Figure 1.48 and find an approximate equation for the line.

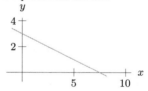

Figure 1.48

24. Line l in Figure 1.49 is parallel to the line $y = 2x + 1$. Find the coordinates of the point P.

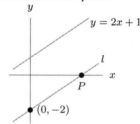

Figure 1.49

25. Find the equation of the line l_2 in Figure 1.50.

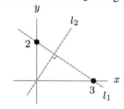

Figure 1.50

In Problems 26–27, what is true about the constant β in the following linear equation if its graph has the given property?

$$y = \frac{x}{\beta - 3} + \frac{1}{6 - \beta}.$$

26. Positive slope, positive y-intercept.

27. Perpendicular to the line $y = (\beta - 7)x - 3$.

28. A circle of radius 2 is centered at the origin and goes through the point $(-1, \sqrt{3})$.

   (a) Find an equation for the line through the origin and the point $(-1, \sqrt{3})$.

   (b) Find an equation for the tangent line to the circle at $(-1, \sqrt{3})$. [Hint: A tangent line is perpendicular to the radius at the point of tangency.]

29. Find an equation for the altitude through point A of the triangle ABC, where A is $(-4, 5)$, B is $(-3, 2)$, and C is $(9, 8)$. [Hint: The altitude of a triangle is perpendicular to the base.]

30. The cost of a Frigbox refrigerator is $950, and it depreciates $50 each year. The cost of an Arctic Air refrigerator is $1200, and it depreciates $100 per year.

   (a) If a Frigbox and an Arctic Air are bought at the same time, when do the two refrigerators have equal value?

   (b) If both refrigerators continue to depreciate at the same rates, what happens to the values of the refrigerators in 20 years time? What does this mean?

31. You need to rent a car and compare the charges of three different companies. Company A charges 20 cents per mile plus $20 per day. Company B charges 10 cents per mile plus $35 per day. Company C charges $70 per day with no mileage charge.

   (a) Find formulas for the cost of driving cars rented from companies A, B, and C, in terms of x, the distance driven in miles in one day.

   (b) Graph the costs for each company for $0 \leq x \leq 500$. Put all three graphs on the same set of axes.

   (c) What do the slope and the vertical intercept tell you in this situation?

   (d) Use the graph in part (b) to find under what circumstances company A is the cheapest? What about Company B? Company C? Explain why your results make sense.

32. You want to choose one long-distance telephone company from the following options.

   • Company A charges $0.37 per minute.
   • Company B charges $13.95 per month plus $0.22 per minute.
   • Company C charges a fixed rate of $50 per month.

Let Y_A, Y_B, Y_C represent the monthly charges using Company A, B, and C, respectively. Let x be the number of minutes per month spent on long distance calls.

   (a) Find formulas for Y_A, Y_B, Y_C as functions of x.

   (b) Figure 1.51 gives the graphs of the functions in part (a). Which function corresponds to which graph?

(c) Find the x-values for which Company B is cheapest.

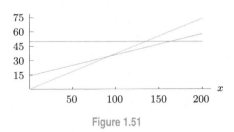

Figure 1.51

33. The solid waste generated each year in the cities of the US is increasing.[21] The solid waste generated, in millions of tons, was 88.1 in 1960 and 234 in 2000. The trend appears linear during this time.

   (a) Construct a formula for the amount of municipal solid waste generated in the US by finding the equation of the line through these two points.

   (b) Use this formula to predict the amount of municipal solid waste generated in the US, in millions of tons, in the year 2020.

34. Fill in the missing coordinates in Figure 1.52. Write an equation for the line connecting the two points. Check your answer by solving the system of two equations.

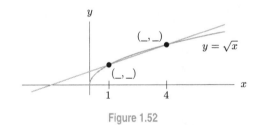

Figure 1.52

35. Two lines are given by $y = b_1 + m_1 x$ and $y = b_2 + m_2 x$, where b_1, b_2, m_1, and m_2 are constants.

   (a) What conditions are imposed on b_1, b_2, m_1, and m_2 if the two lines have no points in common?

   (b) What conditions are imposed on b_1, b_2, m_1, and m_2 if the two lines have all points in common?

   (c) What conditions are imposed on b_1, b_2, m_1, and m_2 if the two lines have exactly one point in common?

   (d) What conditions are imposed on b_1, b_2, m_1, and m_2 if the two lines have exactly two points in common?

---

[21] www.epa.gov/aeposwer/non-hw/muncpl/pubs/MSW05rpt.pdf, accessed January 10, 2006.

36. A commission is a payment made to an employee based on a percentage of sales made. For example, car salespeople earn commission on the selling price of a car. In parts (a)–(d), explain how to choose between the options for different levels of sales.

(a) A weekly salary of $100 or a weekly salary of $50 plus 10% commission.

(b) A weekly salary of $175 plus 7% commission or a weekly salary of $175 plus 8% commission.

(c) A weekly salary of $145 plus 7% commission or a weekly salary of $165 plus 7% commission.

(d) A weekly salary of $225 plus 3% commission or a weekly salary of $180 plus 6% commission.

1.6 FITTING LINEAR FUNCTIONS TO DATA

When real data are collected in the laboratory or the field, they are often subject to experimental error. Even if there is an underlying linear relationship between two quantities, real data may not fit this relationship perfectly. However, even if a data set does not perfectly conform to a linear function, we may still be able to use a linear function to help us analyze the data.

Laboratory Data: The Viscosity of Motor Oil

The viscosity of a liquid, or its resistance to flow, depends on the liquid's temperature. Pancake syrup is a familiar example: straight from the refrigerator, it pours very slowly. When warmed on the stove, its viscosity decreases and it becomes quite runny.

The viscosity of motor oil is a measure of its effectiveness as a lubricant in the engine of a car. Thus, the effect of engine temperature is an important determinant of motor-oil performance. Table 1.34 gives the viscosity, v, of motor oil as measured in the lab at different temperatures, T.

Table 1.34   *The measured viscosity, v, of motor oil as a function of the temperature, T*

T, temperature (°F)	v, viscosity (lbs·sec/in²)
160	28
170	26
180	24
190	21
200	16
210	13
220	11
230	9

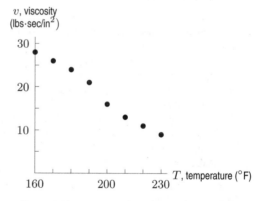

Figure 1.53: The viscosity data from Table 1.34

The *scatter plot* of the data in Figure 1.53 shows that the viscosity of motor oil decreases, approximately linearly, as its temperature rises. To find a formula relating viscosity and temperature, we fit a line to these data points.

Fitting the best line to a set of data is called *linear regression*. One way to fit a line is to draw a line "by eye." Alternatively, many computer programs and calculators compute regression lines. Figure 1.54 shows the data from Table 1.34 together with the computed regression line,

$$v = 75.6 - 0.293T.$$

Notice that none of the data points lie exactly on the regression line, although it fits the data well.

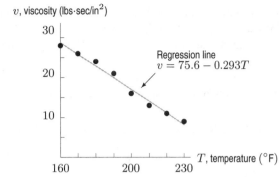

Figure 1.54: A graph of the viscosity data from Table 1.34, together with a regression line (provided by a calculator)

The Assumptions Involved In Finding a Regression Line

When we find a regression line for the data in Table 1.34, we are assuming that the value of v is related to the value of T. However, there may be experimental errors in our measurements. For example, if we measure viscosity twice at the same temperature, we may get two slightly different values. Alternatively, something besides engine temperature could be affecting the oil's viscosity (the oil pressure, for example). Thus, even if we assume that the temperature readings are exact, the viscosity readings include some degree of uncertainty.

Interpolation and Extrapolation

The formula for viscosity can be used to make predictions. Suppose we want to know the viscosity of motor oil at $T = 196°$F. The formula gives

$$v = 75.6 - 0.293 \cdot 196 \approx 18.2 \text{ lb} \cdot \text{sec/in}^2.$$

To see that this is a reasonable estimate, compare it to the entries in Table 1.34. At 190°F, the measured viscosity was 21, and at 200°F, it was 16; the predicted viscosity of 18.2 is between 16 and 21. See Figure 1.55. Of course, if we measured the viscosity at $T = 196°$F in the lab, we might not get exactly 18.2.

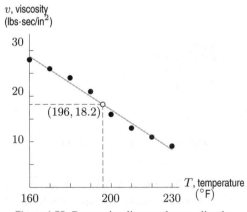

Figure 1.55: Regression line used to predict the viscosity at 196°

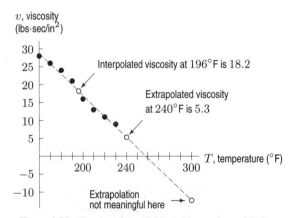

Figure 1.56: The data from Table 1.34 together with the predicted viscosity at $T = 196°$, $T = 240°$, and $T = 300°$

Since the temperature $T = 196°$ is between two temperatures for which v is known (190° and 200°), the estimate of 18.2 is said to be an *interpolation*. If instead we estimate the value of v at a temperature outside the values for T in Table 1.34, our estimate is called an *extrapolation*.

Example 1   Predict the viscosity of motor oil at 240°F and at 300°F.

Solution   At $T = 240°$F, the formula for the regression line predicts that the viscosity of motor oil is

$$v = 75.6 - 0.293 \cdot 240 = 5.3 \text{ lb} \cdot \text{sec/in}^2.$$

This is reasonable. Figure 1.56 shows that the predicted point—represented by an open circle on the graph—is consistent with the trend in the data points from Table 1.34.

On the other hand, at $T = 300°$F the regression-line formula gives

$$v = 75.6 - 0.293 \cdot 300 = -12.3 \text{ lb} \cdot \text{sec/in}^2.$$

This is unreasonable because viscosity cannot be negative. To understand what went wrong, notice that in Figure 1.56, the open circle representing the point $(300, -12.3)$ is far from the plotted data points. By making a prediction at 300°F, we have assumed—incorrectly—that the trend observed in laboratory data extended as far as 300°F.

In general, interpolation tends to be more reliable than extrapolation because we are making a prediction on an interval we already know something about instead of making a prediction beyond the limits of our knowledge.

How Regression Works

How does a calculator or computer decide which line fits the data best? We assume that the value of y is related to the value of x, although other factors could influence y as well. Thus, we assume that we can pick the value of x exactly but that the value of y may be only partially determined by this x-value.

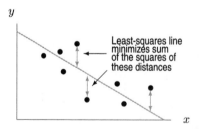

Figure 1.57: A given set of data and the corresponding least-squares regression line

One way to fit a line to the data is shown in Figure 1.57. The line shown was chosen to minimize the sum of the squares of the vertical distances between the data points and the line. Such a line is called a *least-squares line*. There are formulas which a calculator or computer uses to calculate the slope, m, and the y-intercept, b, of the least-squares line.

Correlation

When a computer or calculator calculates a regression line, it also gives a *correlation coefficient*, r. This number lies between -1 and $+1$ and measures how well a particular regression line fits the data. If $r = 1$, the data lie exactly on a line of positive slope. If $r = -1$, the data lie exactly on a line of negative slope. If r is close to 0, the data may be completely scattered, or there may be a non-linear relationship between the variables. (See Figure 1.58.)

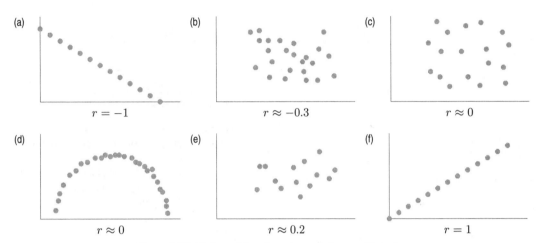

Figure 1.58: Various data sets and correlation coefficients

Example 2   The correlation coefficient for the viscosity data in Table 1.34 on page 44 is $r \approx -0.99$. The fact that r is negative tells us that the regression line has negative slope. The fact that r is close to -1 tells us that the regression line fits the data well.

The Difference between Relation, Correlation, and Causation

It is important to understand that a high correlation (either positive or negative) between two quantities does *not* imply causation. For example, there is a high correlation between children's reading level and shoe size.[22] However, large feet do not cause a child to read better (or vice versa). Larger feet and improved reading ability are both a consequence of growing older.

Notice also that a correlation of 0 does not imply that there is no relationship between x and y. For example, in Figure 1.58(d) there is a relationship between x and y-values, while Figure 1.58(c) exhibits no apparent relationship. Both data sets have a correlation coefficient of $r \approx 0$. Thus a correlation of $r = 0$ usually implies there is no linear relationship between x and y, but this does not mean there is no relationship at all.

---

[22]From *Statistics*, 2ed, by David Freedman. Robert Pisani, Roger Purves, Ani Adhikari, p. 142 (New York: W.W.Norton, 1991).

Exercises and Problems for Section 1.6

1. Match the r values with scatter plots in Figure 1.59.

$$r = -0.98, \quad r = -0.5, \quad r = -0.25,$$

$$r = 0, \quad r = 0.7, \quad r = 1.$$

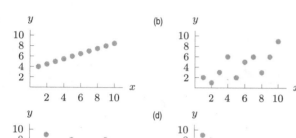

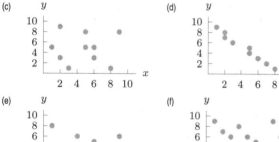

Figure 1.59

2. Table 1.35 shows the number of calories burned per minute by a person walking at 3 mph.

(a) Make a scatter plot of this data.
(b) Draw a regression line by eye.
(c) Roughly estimate the correlation coefficient by eye.

Table 1.35

Body weight (lb)	100	120	150	170	200	220
Calories	2.7	3.2	4.0	4.6	5.4	5.9

3. The rate of oxygen consumption for Colorado beetles increases with temperature. See Table 1.36.

(a) Make a scatter plot of this data.
(b) Draw an estimated regression line by eye.
(c) Use a calculator or computer to find the equation of the regression line. (Alternatively, find the equation of your line in part (b).) Round constants in the equation to the nearest integer.

(d) Interpret the slope and each intercept of the regression equation.
(e) Interpret the correlation between temperature and oxygen rate.

Table 1.36

°C	10	15	20	25	30
Oxygen consumption rate	90	125	200	300	375

4. Table 1.37 shows the IQ of ten students and the number of hours of TV each watches per week.

(a) Make a scatter plot of the data.
(b) By eye, make a rough estimate of the correlation coefficient.
(c) Use a calculator or computer to find the least squares regression line and the correlation coefficient. Your values should be correct to four decimal places.

Table 1.37

IQ	110	105	120	140	100	125	130	105	115	110
TV	10	12	8	2	12	10	5	6	13	3

5. An ecologist tracked 145 deer that were born in 1997. The number of deer, d, living each subsequent year is recorded in Table 1.38.

(a) Make a scatter plot of this data. Let $t = 0$ represent 1997.
(b) Draw by eye a good fitting line and estimate its equation. (Round the coefficients to integers.)
(c) Use a calculator or computer to find the equation of the least squares line. (Round the coefficients to integers.)
(d) Interpret the slope and each intercept of the line.
(e) Interpret the correlation between the year and the number of deer born in 1997 that are still alive.

Table 1.38

Year	1997	1998	1999	2000	2001	2002	2003	2004	2005
Deer	145	144	134	103	70	45	32	22	4

6. Table 1.39 gives the data on hand strength collected from college freshman using a grip meter.

(a) Make a scatter plot of these data treating the strength of the preferred hand as the independent variable.

(b) Draw a line on your scatter plot that is a good fit for these data and use it to find an approximate equation for the regression line.

(c) Using a graphing calculator or computer, find the equation of the least squares line.

(d) What would the predicted grip strength in the non-preferred hand be for a student with a preferred hand strength of 37?

(e) Discuss interpolation and extrapolation using specific examples in relation to this regression line.

(f) Discuss why r, the correlation coefficient, is both positive and close to 1.

(g) Why do the points tend to cluster into two groups on your scatter plot?

Table 1.39   *Hand strength for 20 students in kilograms*

Preferred	28	27	45	20	40	47	28	54	52	21
Nonpreferred	24	26	43	22	40	45	26	46	46	22
Preferred	53	52	49	45	39	26	25	32	30	32
Nonpreferred	47	47	41	44	33	20	27	30	29	29

7. Table 1.40 shows men's and women's world records for swimming distances from 50 meters to 1500 meters.[23]

(a) What values would you add to Table 1.40 to represent the time taken by both men and women to swim 0 meters?

(b) Plot men's time against distance, with time t in seconds on the vertical axis and distance d in meters on the horizontal axis. It is claimed that a straight line models this behavior well. What is the equation for that line? What does its slope represent? On the same graph, plot women's time against distance and find the equation of the straight line that models this behavior well. Is this line steeper or flatter than the men's line? What does that mean in terms of swimming? What are the values of the vertical intercepts? Do these values have a practical interpretation?

(c) On another graph plot the women's times against the men's times, with women's times, w, on the vertical axis and men's times, m, on the horizontal axis. It

should look linear. How could you have predicted this linearity from the equations you found in part (b)? What is the slope of this line and how can it be interpreted? A newspaper reporter claims that the women's records are about 8% slower than the men's. Do the facts support this statement? What is the value of the vertical intercept? Does this value have a practical interpretation?

Table 1.40   *Men's and women's world swimming records*

Distance (m)	50	100	200	400	800	1500
Men (sec)	21.64	47.84	104.06	220.08	458.65	874.56
Women (sec)	24.13	53.62	116.64	243.85	496.22	952.10

8. In baseball, Henry Aaron holds the record for the greatest number of home-runs hit in the major leagues. Table 1.41 shows his cumulative yearly record[24] from the start of his career, 1954, until 1973.

(a) Plot Aaron's cumulative number of home runs H on the vertical axis, and the time t in years along the horizontal axis, where $t = 1$ corresponds to 1954.

(b) By eye draw a straight line that fits these data well and find its equation.

(c) Use a calculator or computer to find the equation of the regression line for these data. What is the correlation coefficient, r, to 4 decimal places? To 3 decimal places? What does this tell you?

(d) What does the slope of the regression line mean in terms of Henry Aaron's home-run record?

(e) From your answer to part (d), how many home-runs do you estimate Henry Aaron hit in each of the years 1974, 1975, 1976, and 1977? If you were told that Henry Aaron retired at the end of the 1976 season, would this affect your answers?

Table 1.41   *Henry Aaron's cumulative home-run record, H, from 1954 to 1973, with t in years since 1953*

t	1	2	3	4	5	6	7	8	9	10
H	13	40	66	110	140	179	219	253	298	342
t	11	12	13	14	15	16	17	18	19	20
H	366	398	442	481	510	554	592	639	673	713

---

[23]Data from "The World Almanac and Book of Facts: 2006," World Almanac Education Group, Inc., New York, 2006.

[24]Adapted from "Graphing Henry Aaron's home-run output" by H. Ringel, The Physics Teacher, January 1974, page 43.

CHAPTER SUMMARY

- **Functions**
  Definition: a rule which takes certain numbers as inputs and assigns to each input exactly one output number.
  Function notation, $y = f(x)$.
  Use of vertical line test.

- **Average rate of change**
  Average rate of change of $Q = f(t)$ on $[a, b]$ is
  $$\frac{\Delta Q}{\Delta t} = \frac{f(b) - f(a)}{b - a}.$$
  Increasing, decreasing functions; identifying from average rate of change.

- **Linear Functions**
  Value of y changes at constant rate.

- **Formulas for Linear Functions**
  Slope-intercept form: $y = b + mx$.
  Point-slope form: $y - y_0 = m(x - x_0)$.
  Standard form: $Ax + By + C = 0$.

- **Properties of Linear Functions**
  Interpretation of slope, vertical and horizontal intercepts.
  Intersection of lines: Solution of equations.
  Parallel lines: $m_1 = m_2$.
  Perpendicular lines: $m_1 = -\dfrac{1}{m_2}$.

- **Fitting Lines to Data**
  Linear regression; correlation. Interpolation, extrapolation; dangers of extrapolation.

REVIEW EXERCISES AND PROBLEMS FOR CHAPTER ONE

Exercises

In Exercises 1–5 a relationship is given between two quantities. Are both quantities functions of the other one, or is one or neither a function of the other? Explain.

1. $7w^2 + 5 = z^2$ **2.** $y = x^4 - 1$ **3.** $m = \sqrt{t}$

4.

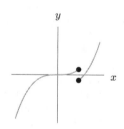

Figure 1.60

5. The number of gallons of gas, g, at \$2 per gallon and the number of pounds of coffee, c, at \$10 per pound that can be bought for a total of \$100.

6. In 2005, you have 40 CDs in your collection. In 2008, you have 120 CDs. In 2012, you have 40. What is the average rate of change in the size of your CD collection between

(a) 2005 and 2008?   (b) 2008 and 2012?
(c) 2005 and 2012?

7. Find the average rate of change of $f(x) = 3x^2 + 1$ between the points

(a) $(1, 4)$ and $(2, 13)$ (b) (j, k) and (m, n)
(c) $(x, f(x))$ and $(x+h, f(x+h))$

In Exercises 8–9, could the table represent a linear function?

8.

λ	1	2	3	4	5
$q(\lambda)$	2	4	8	16	32

9.

t	3	6	9	12	15
$a(t)$	2	4	6	8	10

Problems 10–12 give data from a linear function. Find a formula for the function.

10.

x	200	230	300	320	400
$g(x)$	70	68.5	65	64	60

11.

t	1.2	1.3	1.4	1.5
$f(t)$	0.736	0.614	0.492	0.37

12.

t	5.2	5.3	5.4	5.5
$f(t)$	73.6	61.4	49.2	37

In Exercises 13–14, which line has the greater

(a) Slope?   (b) y-intercept?

13. $y = 7 + 2x$, $y = 8 - 15x$

14. $y = 5 - 2x$, $y = 7 - 3x$

Are the lines in Exercises 15–18 perpendicular? Parallel? Neither?

15. $y = 5x + 2$ $y = 2x + 5$

16. $y = 14x - 2$ $y = -\frac{1}{14}x + 2$

17. $y = 3x + 3$ $y = -\frac{1}{3}x + 3$

18. $7y = 8 + 21x; 9y = 77 - 3x$

Problems

Find formulas for the linear functions in Problems 19–22.

19. The graph of f contains $(-3, -8)$ and $(5, -20)$.

20. $g(100) = 2000$ and $g(400) = 3800$

21. $P = h(t)$ gives the size of a population that begins with 12,000 members and grows by 225 members each year.

22. The graph of h intersects the graph of $y = x^2$ at $x = -2$ and $x = 3$.

23. Find the equation of the line parallel to $3x + 5y = 6$ and passing through the point $(0, 6)$.

24. Find the equation of the line passing through the point $(2, 1)$ and perpendicular to the line $y = 5x - 3$.

25. Find the equations of the lines parallel to and perpendicular to the line $y + 4x = 7$, and through the point $(1, 5)$.

26. You have zero dollars now and the average rate of change in your net worth is $5000 per year. How much money will you have in forty years?

27. A flight costs $10,000 to operate, regardless of the number of passengers. Each ticket costs $127. Express profit, π, as a linear function of the number of passengers, n, on the flight.

28. Table 1.42 gives the ranking r for three different names— Hannah, Alexis, and Madison. Of the three names, which was most popular and which was least popular in

(a) 1995?   **(b)** 2004?

Table 1.42 *Ranking of names—Hannah (r_h), Alexis (r_a), and Madison (r_m)—for girls born between 1995 ($t = 0$) and 2004 ($t = 9$)[25]*

t	0	1	2	3	4	5	6	7	8	9
r_h	7	7	5	2	2	2	3	3	4	5
r_a	14	8	8	6	3	6	5	5	7	11
r_m	29	15	10	9	7	3	2	2	3	3

29. Table 1.42 gives information about the popularity of the names Hannah, Madison, and Alexis. Describe in words what your answers to parts (a)–(c) tell you about these names.

(a) Evaluate $r_m(0) - r_h(0)$.

(b) Evaluate $r_m(9) - r_h(9)$.

(c) Solve $r_m(t) < r_a(t)$.

30. Figure 1.61 gives the depth of the water at Montauk Point, New York, for a day in November.

(a) How many high tides took place on this day?

(b) How many low tides took place on this day?

(c) How much time elapsed in between high tides?

depth of water (feet)

time (hours)

4   8   12   16   20   24

Figure 1.61

31. (a) Is the area, A, of a square a function of the length of one of its sides, s?

(b) Is the area, A, of a rectangle a function of the length of one of its sides, s?

32. A person's blood sugar level at a particular time of the day is partially determined by the time of the most recent meal. After a meal, blood sugar level increases rapidly, then slowly comes back down to a normal level. Sketch a person's blood sugar level as a function of time over the course of a day. Label the axes to indicate normal blood sugar level and the time of each meal.

[25] Data from the SSA website at www.ssa.gov, accessed January 12, 2006.

33. Many people think that hair growth is stimulated by hair-cuts. In fact, there is no difference in the rate hair grows after a haircut, but there *is* a difference in the rate at which hair's ends break off. A haircut eliminates dead and split ends, thereby slowing the rate at which hair breaks. However, even with regular haircuts, hair will not grow to an indefinite length. The average life cycle of human scalp hair is 3-5 years, after which the hair is shed.[26]

Judy trims her hair once a year, when its growth is slowed by split ends. She cuts off just enough to eliminate dead and split ends, and then lets it grow another year. After 5 years, she realizes her hair won't grow any longer. Graph the length of her hair as a function of time. Indicate when she receives her haircuts.

34. At the end of a semester, students' math grades are listed in a table which gives each student's ID number in the left column and the student's grade in the right column. Let N represent the ID number and the G represent the grade. Which quantity, N or G, must necessarily be a function of the other?

35. A price increases 5% due to inflation and is then reduced 10% for a sale. Express the final price as a function of the original price, P.

36. An 8-foot tall cylindrical water tank has a base of diameter 6 feet.

(a) How much water can the tank hold?
(b) How much water is in the tank if the water is 5 feet deep?
(c) Write a formula for the volume of water as a function of its depth in the tank.

37. Figure 1.62 shows the fuel consumption (in miles per gallon, mpg) of a car traveling at various speeds.

(a) How much gas is used on a 300 mile trip at 40 mph?
(b) How much gas is saved by traveling 60 mph instead of 70 mph on a 200 mile trip?
(c) According to this graph, what is the most fuel-efficient speed to travel? Explain.

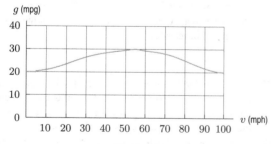

Figure 1.62

38. Academics have suggested that loss of worker productivity can result from sleep deprivation. An article in the Sunday, September 26, 1993, *New York Times* quotes David Poltrack, the senior vice president for planning and research at CBS, as saying that seven million Americans are staying up an hour later than usual to watch talk show host David Letterman. The article goes on to quote Timothy Monk, a professor at the University of Pittsburgh School of Medicine, as saying "... my hunch is that the effect [on productivity due to sleep deprivation among this group] would be in the area of a 10 percent decrement." The article next quotes Robert Solow, a Nobel prize-winning professor of economics at MIT, who suggests the following procedure to estimate the impact that this loss in productivity will have on the US economy — an impact he dubbed "the Letterman loss." First, Solow says, we find the percentage of the work force who watch the program. Next, we determine this group's contribution to the gross domestic product (GDP). Then we reduce the group's contribution by 10% to account for the loss in productivity due to sleep deprivation. The amount of this reduction is "the Letterman loss."

(a) The article estimated that the GDP is $6.325 trillion, and that 7 million Americans watch the show. Assume that the nation's work force is 118 million people and that 75% of David Letterman's audience belongs to this group. What percentage of the work force is in Dave's audience?
(b) What percent of the GDP would be expected to come from David Letterman's audience? How much money would they have contributed if they had not watched the show?
(c) How big is "the Letterman Loss"?

39. There are x male job-applicants at a certain company and y female applicants. Suppose that 15% of the men are accepted and 18% of the women are accepted. Write an expression in terms of x and y representing each of the following quantities:

(a) The total number of applicants to the company.
(b) The total number of applicants accepted.
(c) The percentage of all applicants accepted.

40. You start 60 miles east of Pittsburgh and drive east at a constant speed of 50 miles per hour. (Assume that the road is straight and permits you to do this.) Find a formula for d, your distance from Pittsburgh as a function of t, the number of hours of travel.

---

[26]*Britannica Micropaedia* vol. 5. (Chicago: Encyclopaedia Britannica, Inc., 1989).

Table 1.43 gives the cost, $C(n)$, of producing a certain good as a linear function of n, the number of units produced. Use the table to answer Problems 41–43.

Table 1.43

n (units)	100	125	150	175
$C(n)$ (dollars)	11000	11125	11250	11375

41. Evaluate the following expressions. Give economic interpretations for each.

(a) $C(175)$

(b) $C(175) - C(150)$

(c) $\dfrac{C(175) - C(150)}{175 - 150}$

42. Estimate $C(0)$. What is the economic significance of this value?

43. The *fixed cost* of production is the cost incurred before any goods are produced. The *unit cost* is the cost of producing an additional unit. Find a formula for $C(n)$ in terms of n, given that

$$\text{Total cost} = \text{Fixed cost} + \text{Unit cost} \cdot \text{Number of units}$$

44. Sketch a family of functions $y = -2 - ax$ for five different values of x with $a < 0$.

45. Assume A, B, C are constants with $A \neq 0$, $B \neq 0$. Consider the equation

$$Ax + By = C.$$

(a) Show that $y = f(x)$ is linear. State the slope and the x- and y-intercepts of $f(x)$.

(b) Graph $y = f(x)$, labeling the x- and y-intercepts in terms of A, B, and C, assuming

(i) $A > 0, B > 0, C > 0$

(ii) $A > 0, B > 0, C < 0$

(iii) $A > 0, B < 0, C > 0$

CHECK YOUR UNDERSTANDING

Are the statements in Problems 1–54 true or false? Give an explanation for your answer.

1. $Q = f(t)$ means Q is equal to f times t.

2. A function must be defined by a formula.

3. If $P = f(x)$ then P is called the dependent variable.

4. Independent variables are always denoted by the letter x or t.

5. It is possible for two quantities to be related and yet neither be a function of the other.

6. A function is a rule that takes certain values as inputs and assigns to each input value exactly one output value.

7. It is possible for a table of values to represent a function.

8. If Q is a function of P, then P is a function of Q.

9. The graph of a circle is not the graph of a function.

10. If $n = f(A)$ is the number of angels that can dance on the head of a pin whose area is A square millimeters, then $f(10) = 100$ tells us that 10 angels can dance on the head of a pin whose area is 100 square millimeters.

11. Average speed can be computed by dividing the distance traveled by the time elapsed.

12. The average rate of change of a function Q with respect to t over an interval can be symbolically represented as $\dfrac{\Delta t}{\Delta Q}$.

13. If $y = f(x)$ and as x increases, y increases, then f is an increasing function.

14. If f is a decreasing function, then the average rate of change of f on any interval is negative.

15. The average rate of change of a function over an interval is the slope of a line connecting two points of the graph of the function.

16. The average rate of change of $y = 3x - 4$ between $x = 2$ and $x = 6$ is 7.

17. The average rate of change of $f(x) = 10 - x^2$ between $x = 1$ and $x = 2$ is the ratio $\dfrac{10 - 2^2 - 10 - 1^2}{2 - 1}$.

18. If $y = x^2$ then the slope of the line connecting the point $(2, 4)$ to the point $(3, 9)$ is the same as the slope of the line connecting the point $(-2, 4)$ to the point $(-3, 9)$.

19. A linear function can have different rates of change over different intervals.

20. The graph of a linear function is a straight line.

21. If a line has the equation $3x + 2y = 7$, then the slope of the line is 3.

22. A table of values represents a linear function if $\dfrac{\text{Change in output}}{\text{Change in input}} = \text{constant}$.

23. If a linear function is decreasing, then its slope is negative.

24. If $y = f(x)$ is linear and its slope is negative, then in the expression $\dfrac{\Delta y}{\Delta x}$ either Δx or Δy is negative, but not both.

25. A linear function can have a slope that is zero.

26. If a line has slope 2 and y-intercept -3, then its equation may be written $y = -3x + 2$.

27. The line $3x + 5y = 7$ has slope $3/5$.

28. A line that goes through the point $(-2, 3)$ and whose slope is 4 has the equation $y = 4x + 5$.

29. The line $4x + 3y = 52$ intersects the x-axis at $x = 13$.

30. If $f(x) = -2x + 7$ then $f(2) = 3$.

31. The line that passes through the points $(1, 2)$ and $(4, -10)$ has slope 4.

32. The linear equation $y - 5 = 4(x + 1)$ is equivalent to the equation $y = 4x + 6$.

33. The line $y - 4 = -2(x + 3)$ goes through the point $(4, -3)$.

34. The line whose equation is $y = 3 - 7x$ has slope -7.

35. The line $y = -5x + 8$ intersects the y-axis at $y = 8$.

36. The equation $y = -2 - \frac{2}{3}x$ represents a linear function.

37. The lines $y = 8 - 3x$ and $-2x + 16y = 8$ both cross the y-axis at $y = 8$.

38. The graph of $f(x) = 6$ is a line whose slope is six.

39. The lines $y = -\frac{4}{5}x + 7$ and $4x - 5y = 8$ are parallel.

40. The lines $y = 7 + 9x$ and $y - 4 = -\frac{1}{9}(x + 5)$ are perpendicular.

41. The lines $y = -2x + 5$ and $y = 6x - 3$ intersect at the point $(1, 3)$.

42. If two lines never intersect then their slopes are equal.

43. The equation of a line parallel to the y-axis could be $y = -\frac{3}{4}$.

44. A line parallel to the x-axis has slope zero.

45. The slope of a vertical line is undefined.

46. Fitting the best line to a set of data is called linear regression.

47. The process of estimating a value within the range for which we have data is called interpolation.

48. Extrapolation tends to be more reliable than interpolation.

49. If two quantities have a high correlation then one quantity causes the other.

50. If the correlation coefficient is zero, there is not a relationship between the two quantities.

51. A correlation coefficient can have a value of $-\frac{3}{7}$.

52. A value of a correlation coefficient is always between negative and positive one.

53. A correlation coefficient of one indicates that all the data points lie on a straight line.

54. A regression line is also referred to as a least squares line.

TOOLS FOR CHAPTER ONE: LINEAR EQUATIONS AND THE COORDINATE PLANE

Solving Linear Equations

To solve a linear equation, we isolate the variable.

Example 1   Solve $22 + 1.3t = 31.1$ for t.

Solution   We subtract 22 from both sides. Since $31.1 - 22 = 9.1$, we have

$$1.3t = 9.1.$$

We divide both sides by 1.3, so

$$t = \frac{9.1}{1.3} = 7.$$

Example 2   Solve $3 - [5.4 + 2(4.3 - x)] = 2 - (0.3x - 0.8)$ for x.

Solution   We begin by clearing the innermost parentheses on each side. Using the distributive law, this gives

$$3 - [5.4 + 8.6 - 2x] = 2 - 0.3x + 0.8.$$

Then

$$3 - 14 + 2x = 2 - 0.3x + 0.8$$
$$2.3x = 13.8,$$
$$x = 6.$$

Example 3   Solve $ax = c + bx$ for x. Assume $a \neq b$.

Solution   To solve for x, we first get all the terms involving x on the left side by subtracting bx from both sides

$$ax - bx = c.$$

Factoring on the left, $ax - bx = (a - b)x$, enables us to solve for x by dividing both sides by $(a - b)$:

$$x(a - b) = c$$
$$x = \frac{c}{(a - b)}.$$

Since $a \neq b$, division by $(a - b)$ is possible.

Example 4   Solve for q if $p^2q + r(-q - 1) = 4(p + r)$.

Solution   We first collect all the terms containing q on the left side of the equation.

$$p^2q - rq - r = 4p + 4r$$
$$p^2q - rq = 4p + 5r.$$

To solve for q, we factor and then divide by the coefficient of q.

$$q(p^2 - r) = 4p + 5r$$
$$q = \frac{4p + 5r}{p^2 - r}.$$

Solving Exactly Versus Solving Approximately

Some equations can be solved exactly, often by using algebra. For example, the equation $7x - 1 = 0$ has the exact solution $x = 1/7$. Other equations can be hard or even impossible to solve exactly. However, it is often possible, and sometimes easier, to find an approximate solution to an equation by using a graph or a numerical method on a calculator. The equation $7x - 1 = 0$ has the approximate solution $x \approx 0.14$ (since $1/7 = 0.142857\ldots$). We use the sign $\approx$, meaning approximately equal, when we want to emphasize that we are making an approximation.

Systems of Linear Equations

To solve for two unknowns, we must have two equations—that is, two relationships between the unknowns. Similarly, three unknowns require three equations, and n unknowns (n an integer) require n equations. The group of equations is known as a *system* of equations. To solve the system, we find the *simultaneous* solutions to all equations in the system.

We can solve these equations either by *substitution* (see Example 5) or by *elimination* (see Example 6).

Example 5   Solve for x and y in the following system of equations using substitution.

$$\begin{cases} y + \dfrac{x}{2} = 3 \\ 2(x + y) = 1 - y \end{cases}$$

Solution   Solving the first equation for y, we write $y = 3 - x/2$. Substituting for y in the second equation gives

$$2\left(x + \left(3 - \frac{x}{2}\right)\right) = 1 - \left(3 - \frac{x}{2}\right).$$

Then

$$2x + 6 - x = -2 + \frac{x}{2}$$
$$x + 6 = -2 + \frac{x}{2}$$
$$2x + 12 = -4 + x$$
$$x = -16.$$

Using $x = -16$ in the first equation to find the corresponding y, we have

$$y - \frac{16}{2} = 3$$
$$y = 3 + 8 = 11.$$

Thus, the solution that simultaneously solves both equations is $x = -16$, $y = 11$.

Example 6   Solve for x and y in the following system of equations using elimination.

$$\begin{cases} 8x - 5y = 11 \\ -2x + 10y = -1. \end{cases}$$

Solution   To eliminate y, we observe that if we multiply the first equation by 2, the coefficients of y are -10 and 10:

$$\begin{cases} 16x - 10y = 22 \\ -2x + 10y = -1. \end{cases}$$

Adding these two equations gives

$$14x = 21$$
$$x = 3/2.$$

We can substitute this value for x in either of the original equations to find y. For example

$$8\left(\frac{3}{2}\right) - 5y = 11$$
$$12 - 5y = 11$$
$$-5y = -1$$
$$y = 1/5$$

Thus, the solution is $x = 3/2$, $y = 1/5$,

Intersection of Two Lines

The coordinates of the point of intersection of two lines satisfies the equations of both lines. Thus, the point can be found by solving the equations simultaneously.

Example 7   Find the point of intersection of the lines $y = 3 - \frac{2}{3}x$ and $y = -4 + \frac{3}{2}x$.

Solution   Since the y-values of the two lines are equal at the point of intersection, we have

$$-4 + \frac{3}{2}x = 3 - \frac{2}{3}x.$$

Notice that we have converted a pair of equations into a single equation by eliminating one of the two variables. This equation can be simplified by multiplying both sides by 6:

$$6\left(-4 + \frac{3}{2}x\right) = 6\left(3 - \frac{2}{3}x\right)$$
$$-24 + 9x = 18 - 4x$$
$$13x = 42$$
$$x = \frac{42}{13}.$$

We can evaluate either of the original equations at $x = \dfrac{42}{13}$ to find y. For example, $y = -4 + \dfrac{3}{2}x$ gives

$$y = -4 + \frac{3}{2}\left(\frac{42}{13}\right) = \frac{11}{13}.$$

Therefore, the point of intersection is $\left(\dfrac{42}{13}, \dfrac{11}{13}\right)$. You can check that this point also satisfies the other equation. The lines and their point of intersection are shown in Figure 1.63.

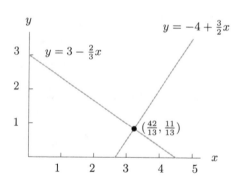

Figure 1.63: Intersection of lines is solution to simultaneous equations

Exercises on Tools for Chapter 1

Solve the equations in Exercises 1–17.

1. $3x = 15$

2. $-2y = 12$

3. $4z = 22$

4. $x + 3 = 10$

5. $y - 5 = 21$

6. $w - 23 = -34$

7. $2x - 5 = 13$

8. $7 - 3y = -14$

9. $13t + 2 = 47$

10. $2x - 5 = 4x - 9$

11. $0.5x - 3 = 7$

12. $17 - 28y = 13y + 24$

13. $\dfrac{5}{3}(y + 2) = \dfrac{1}{2} - y$

14. $3t - \dfrac{2(t-1)}{3} = 4$

15. $2(r + 5) - 3 = 3(r - 8) + 21$

16. $B - 4[B - 3(1 - B)] = 42$

17. $1.06s - 0.01(248.4 - s) = 22.67s$

In Exercises 18–32, solve for the indicated variable.

18. $A = l \cdot w$, for l.

19. $C = 2\pi r$, for r.

20. $I = Prt$, for P.

21. $C = \dfrac{5}{9}(F - 32)$, for F.

22. $l = l_0 + \dfrac{k}{2}w$, for w.

23. $h = v_0 t + \dfrac{1}{2}at^2$, for a.

24. $by - d = ay + c$, for y.

25. $ab + ax = c - ax$, for x.

26. $3xy + 1 = 2y - 5x$, for y.

27. $u(v + 2) + w(v - 3) = z(v - 1)$, for v.

28. $S = \dfrac{rL - a}{r - 1}$, for r.

29. $\dfrac{a - cx}{b + dx} + a = 0$, for x.

30. $\dfrac{At - B}{C - B(1 - 2t)} = 3$, for t.

31. $y'y^2 + 2xyy' = 4y$, for y'.

32. $2x - (xy' + yy') + 2yy' = 0$, for y'.

Solve the systems of equations in Exercises 33–40.

33. $\begin{cases} x + y = 3 \\ x - y = 5 \end{cases}$

34. $\begin{cases} 2x - y = 10 \\ x + 2y = 15 \end{cases}$

35. $\begin{cases} 3x - 2y = 6 \\ y = 2x - 5 \end{cases}$

36. $\begin{cases} x = 7y - 9 \\ 4x - 15y = 26 \end{cases}$

37. $\begin{cases} 2x + 3y = 7 \\ y = -\frac{3}{5}x + 6 \end{cases}$

38. $\begin{cases} 3x - y = 17 \\ -2x - 3y = -4 \end{cases}$

39. $\begin{cases} 2(x + y) = 3 \\ x = y + 3(x - 5) \end{cases}$

40. $\begin{cases} ax + y = 2a \\ x + ay = 1 + a^2 \end{cases}$

Determine the points of intersection for Exercises 41–44.

41.

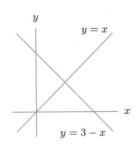

42.

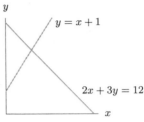

43.

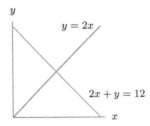

44.

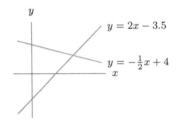

The figures in Problems 45–48 are parallelograms. Find the coordinates of the labeled point(s).

45.

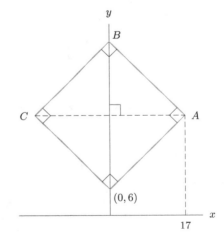

46.

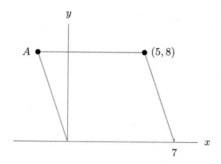

47.

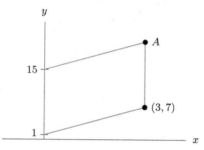

48.

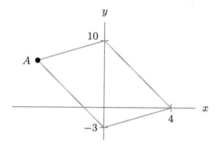

50.

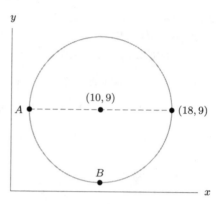

51.

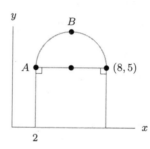

52.

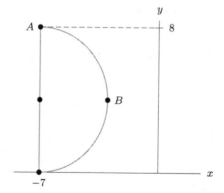

The figures in Problems 49–52 contain a semicircle with the center marked. Find the coordinates of A, a point on the diameter, and B, an extreme point (highest, lowest, or farthest to the right).

49.

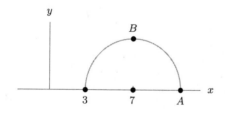

Chapter Two

FUNCTIONS

In this chapter, we investigate properties and notation common to all functions. We begin with a closer look at function notation, including an introduction to inverse functions. The ideas of domain, range, and piecewise defined functions are addressed. Concavity is then introduced and applied to quadratic functions.

The Tools Section on page 99 reviews quadratic equations.

2.1 INPUT AND OUTPUT

Finding Output Values: Evaluating a Function

Evaluating a function means calculating the value of a function's output from a particular value of the input.

In the housepainting example on page 4, the notation $n = f(A)$ indicates that n is a function of A. The expression $f(A)$ represents the output of the function—specifically, the amount of paint required to cover an area of A ft^2. For example $f(20,000)$ represents the number of gallons of paint required to cover a house of 20,000 ft^2.

Example 1   Using the fact that 1 gallon of paint covers 250 ft^2, evaluate the expression $f(20,000)$.

Solution   To evaluate $f(20,000)$, calculate the number of gallons required to cover 20,000 ft^2:

$$f(20,000) = \frac{20,000 \text{ ft}^2}{250 \text{ ft}^2/\text{gallon}} = 80 \text{ gallons of paint.}$$

Evaluating a Function Using a Formula

If we have a formula for a function, we evaluate it by substituting the input value into the formula.

Example 2   The formula for the area of a circle of radius r is $A = q(r) = \pi r^2$. Use the formula to evaluate $q(10)$ and $q(20)$. What do your results tell you about circles?

Solution   In the expression $q(10)$, the value of r is 10, so

$$q(10) = \pi \cdot 10^2 = 100\pi \approx 314.$$

Similarly, substituting $r = 20$, we have

$$q(20) = \pi \cdot 20^2 = 400\pi \approx 1257.$$

The statements $q(10) \approx 314$ and $q(20) \approx 1257$ tell us that a circle of radius 10 cm has an area of approximately 314 cm^2 and a circle of radius 20 cm has an area of approximately 1257 cm^2.

Example 3   Let $g(x) = \dfrac{x^2 + 1}{5 + x}$. Evaluate the following expressions.

(a) $g(3)$ (b) $g(-1)$ (c) $g(a)$

Solution   (a) To evaluate $g(3)$, replace every x in the formula with 3:

$$g(3) = \frac{3^2 + 1}{5 + 3} = \frac{10}{8} = 1.25.$$

(b) To evaluate $g(-1)$, replace every x in the formula with (-1):

$$g(-1) = \frac{(-1)^2 + 1}{5 + (-1)} = \frac{2}{4} = 0.5.$$

(c) To evaluate $g(a)$, replace every x in the formula with a:

$$g(a) = \frac{a^2 + 1}{5 + a}.$$

Evaluating a function may involve algebraic simplification, as the following example shows.

Example 4   Let $h(x) = x^2 - 3x + 5$. Evaluate and simplify the following expressions.

(a) $h(2)$ (b) $h(a - 2)$ (c) $h(a) - 2$ (d) $h(a) - h(2)$

Solution   Notice that x is the input and $h(x)$ is the output. It is helpful to rewrite the formula as

$$\text{Output} = h(\text{Input}) = (\text{Input})^2 - 3 \cdot (\text{Input}) + 5.$$

(a) For $h(2)$, we have Input $= 2$, so

$$h(2) = (2)^2 - 3 \cdot (2) + 5 = 3.$$

(b) In this case, Input $= a - 2$. We substitute and multiply out

$$\begin{aligned}
h(a - 2) &= (a - 2)^2 - 3(a - 2) + 5 \\
&= a^2 - 4a + 4 - 3a + 6 + 5 \\
&= a^2 - 7a + 15.
\end{aligned}$$

(c) First input a, then subtract 2:

$$\begin{aligned}
h(a) - 2 &= a^2 - 3a + 5 - 2 \\
&= a^2 - 3a + 3.
\end{aligned}$$

(d) Since we found $h(2) = 3$ in part (a), we subtract from $h(a)$:

$$\begin{aligned}
h(a) - h(2) &= a^2 - 3a + 5 - 3 \\
&= a^2 - 3a + 2.
\end{aligned}$$

Finding Input Values: Solving Equations

Given an input, we evaluate the function to find the output. Sometimes the situation is reversed; we know the output and we want to find the corresponding input. If the function is given by a formula, the input values are solutions to an equation.

Example 5   Use the cricket function $T = \frac{1}{4}R + 40$, introduced on page 3, to find the rate, R, at which the snowy tree cricket chirps when the temperature, T, is 76°F.

Solution   We want to find R when $T = 76$. Substitute $T = 76$ into the formula and solve the equation

$$76 = \frac{1}{4}R + 40$$

$$36 = \frac{1}{4}R \qquad \text{subtract 40 from both sides}$$

$$144 = R. \qquad \text{multiply both sides by 4}$$

The cricket chirps at a rate of 144 chirps per minute when the temperature is 76°F.

Example 6   Suppose $f(x) = \dfrac{1}{\sqrt{x - 4}}$.

(a) Find an x-value that results in $f(x) = 2$.
(b) Is there an x-value that results in $f(x) = -2$?

Solution   (a) To find an x-value that results in $f(x) = 2$, solve the equation

$$2 = \frac{1}{\sqrt{x - 4}}.$$

Square both sides

$$4 = \frac{1}{x-4}.$$

Now multiply by $(x - 4)$

$$4(x - 4) = 1$$
$$4x - 16 = 1$$
$$x = \frac{17}{4} = 4.25.$$

The x-value is 4.25. (Note that the simplification $(x - 4)/(x - 4) = 1$ in the second step was valid because $x - 4 \neq 0$.)

(b) Since $\sqrt{x - 4}$ is nonnegative if it is defined, its reciprocal, $f(x) = \dfrac{1}{\sqrt{x - 4}}$ is also nonnegative if it is defined. Thus, $f(x)$ is not negative for any x input, so there is no x-value that results in $f(x) = -2$.

In the next example, we solve an equation for a quantity that is being used to model a physical quantity; we must choose the solutions that make sense in the context of the model.

Example 7   Let $A = q(r)$ be the area of a circle of radius r, where r is in cm. What is the radius of a circle whose area is 100 cm²?

Solution   The output $q(r)$ is an area. Solving the equation $q(r) = 100$ for r gives the radius of a circle whose area is 100 cm². Since the formula for the area of a circle is $q(r) = \pi r^2$, we solve

$$q(r) = \pi r^2 = 100$$
$$r^2 = \frac{100}{\pi}$$
$$r = \pm\sqrt{\frac{100}{\pi}} = \pm 5.642.$$

We have two solutions for r, one positive and one negative. Since a circle cannot have a negative radius, we take $r = 5.642$ cm. A circle of area 100 cm² has a radius of 5.642 cm.

Finding Output and Input Values From Tables and Graphs

The following two examples use function notation with a table and a graph respectively.

Example 8   Table 2.1 shows the revenue, $R = f(t)$, received or expected, by the National Football League,[1] NFL, from network TV as a function of the year, t, since 1975.

(a)   Evaluate and interpret $f(25)$.   (b)   Solve and interpret $f(t) = 1159$.

Table 2.1

Year, t (since 1975)	0	5	10	15	20	25	30
Revenue, R (million $)	201	364	651	1075	1159	2200	2200

[1]*Newsweek*, January 26, 1998.

Solution   (a) The table shows $f(25) = 2200$. Since $t = 25$ in the year 2000, we know that NFL's projected revenue from TV was \$2200 million in the year 2000.

(b) Solving $f(t) = 1159$ means finding the year in which TV revenues were \$1159 million; it is $t = 20$. In 1995, NFL's TV revenues were \$1159 million.

Example 9   A man drives from his home to a store and back. The entire trip takes 30 minutes. Figure 2.1 gives his velocity $v(t)$ (in mph) as a function of the time t (in minutes) since he left home. A negative velocity indicates that he is traveling away from the store back to his home.

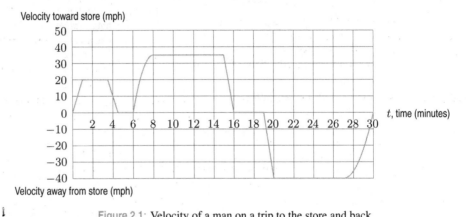

Figure 2.1: Velocity of a man on a trip to the store and back

Evaluate and interpret:

(a) $v(5)$ (b) $v(24)$ (c) $v(8) - v(6)$ (d) $v(-3)$

Solve for t and interpret:

(e) $v(t) = 15$ (f) $v(t) = -20$ (g) $v(t) = v(7)$

Solution   (a) To evaluate $v(5)$, look on the graph where $t = 5$ minutes. Five minutes after he left home, his velocity is 0 mph. Thus, $v(5) = 0$. Perhaps he had to stop at a light.

(b) The graph shows that $v(24) = -40$ mph. After 24 minutes, he is traveling at 40 mph away from the store.

(c) From the graph, $v(8) = 35$ mph and $v(6) = 0$ mph. Thus, $v(8) - v(6) = 35 - 0 = 35$. This shows that the man's speed increased by 35 mph in the interval between $t = 6$ minutes and $t = 8$ minutes.

(d) The quantity $v(-3)$ is not defined since the graph only gives velocities for nonnegative times.

(e) To solve for t when $v(t) = 15$, look on the graph where the velocity is 15 mph. This occurs at $t \approx 0.75$ minute, 3.75 minutes, 6.5 minutes, and 15.5 minutes. At each of these four times the man's velocity was 15 mph.

(f) To solve $v(t) = -20$ for t, we see that the velocity is -20 mph at $t \approx 19.5$ and $t \approx 29$ minutes.

(g) First we evaluate $v(7) \approx 27$. To solve $v(t) = 27$, we look for the values of t making the velocity 27 mph. One such t is of course $t = 7$; the other t is $t \approx 15$ minutes.

Exercises and Problems for Section 2.1

Exercises

In Exercises 1–2, evaluate the function for $x = -7$.

1. $f(x) = x/2 - 1$ **2.** $f(x) = x^2 - 3$

For Exercises 3–6, calculate exactly the values of y when $y = f(4)$ and of x when $f(x) = 6$.

3. $f(x) = \dfrac{6}{2 - x^3}$ **4.** $f(x) = \sqrt{20 + 2x^2}$

5. $f(x) = 4x^{3/2}$ **6.** $f(x) = x^{-3/4} - 2$

7. If $f(x) = 2x+1$, (a) Find $f(0)$ (b) Solve $f(x) = 0$.

8. If $f(t) = t^2 - 4$, (a) Find $f(0)$ (b) Solve $f(t) = 0$.

9. If $g(x) = x^2 - 5x + 6$, (a) Find $g(0)$ (b) Solve $g(x) = 0$.

10. If $g(t) = \dfrac{1}{t + 2} - 1$, (a) Find $g(0)$ (b) Solve $g(t) = 0$.

11. If $f(x) = \dfrac{x}{1 - x^2}$, find $f(-2)$.

12. If $h(x) = ax^2 + bx + c$, find $h(0)$.

13. If $P(t) = 170 - 4t$, find $P(4) - P(2)$.

14. If $g(x) = -\frac{1}{2}x^{1/3}$, find $g(-27)$.

15. Let $h(x) = 1/x$. Find **(a)** $h(x+3)$ **(b)** $h(x) + h(3)$

16. Let $f(x) = \dfrac{2x + 1}{x + 1}$. For what value of x is $f(x) = 0.3$?

17. **(a)** Using Table 2.2, evaluate $f(1)$, $f(-1)$, and $-f(1)$.
    (b) Solve $f(x) = 0$ for x.

Table 2.2

x	-1	0	1	2
$f(x)$	0	-1	2	1

18. **(a)** In Figure 2.2, estimate $f(0)$.
    (b) For what x-value(s) is $f(x) = 0$?
    (c) For what x-value(s) is $f(x) > 0$?

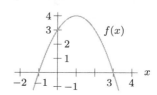

Figure 2.2

19. Let $F = g(t)$ be the number of foxes in a park as a function of t, the number of months since January 1. Evaluate $g(9)$ using Table 1.3 on page 5. What does this tell us about the fox population?

20. Let $F = g(t)$ be the number of foxes in month t in the national park described in Example 5 on page 5. Solve the equation $g(t) = 75$. What does your solution tell you about the fox population?

Problems

21. If $V = \frac{1}{3}\pi r^2 h$ gives the volume of a cylinder, what is the value of V when $r = 3$ inches and $h = 2$ inches? Give units.

22. Let $q(x) = 3 - x^2$. Evaluate and simplify:

  (a) $q(5)$ **(b)** $q(a)$
  (c) $q(a - 5)$ **(d)** $q(a) - 5$
  (e) $q(a) - q(5)$

23. Let $p(x) = x^2 + x + 1$. Find $p(-1)$ and $-p(1)$. Are they equal?

24. Let $f(x) = 3 + 2x^2$. Find $f\left(\dfrac{1}{3}\right)$ and $\dfrac{f(1)}{f(3)}$. Are they equal?

25. Chicago's average monthly rainfall, $R = f(t)$ inches, is given as a function of month, t, in Table 2.3. (January is $t = 1$.) Solve and interpret:

  (a) $f(t) = 3.7$ **(b)** $f(t) = f(2)$

Table 2.3

t	1	2	3	4	5	6	7	8
R	1.8	1.8	2.7	3.1	3.5	3.7	3.5	3.4

26. Let $g(x) = x^2 + x$. Find formulas for the following functions. Simplify your answers.

   (a) $g(-3x)$ **(b)** $g(1-x)$ **(c)** $g(x+\pi)$
   (d) $g(\sqrt{x})$ **(e)** $g(1/(x+1))$ **(f)** $g(x^2)$

27. Let $f(x) = \dfrac{x}{x-1}$.

   (a) Find and simplify

      (i) $f\left(\dfrac{1}{t}\right)$ (ii) $f\left(\dfrac{1}{t+1}\right)$

   (b) Solve $f(x) = 3$.

28. **(a)** Find a point on the graph of $h(x) = \sqrt{x+4}$ whose x-coordinate is 5.
   (b) Find a point on the graph whose y-coordinate is 5.
   (c) Graph $h(x)$ and mark the points in parts (a) and (b).
   (d) Let $p = 2$. Calculate $h(p+1) - h(p)$.

29. Use the graph of $f(x)$ in Figure 2.3 to estimate:

   (a) $f(0)$ **(b)** $f(1)$ **(c)** $f(b)$ **(d)** $f(c)$ **(e)** $f(d)$

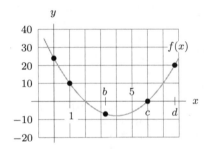

Figure 2.3

30. **(a)** Using Figure 2.4, fill in Table 2.4.

Table 2.4

x	-2	-1	0	1	2	3
$h(x)$						

   (b) Evaluate $h(3) - h(1)$ **(c)** Evaluate $h(2) - h(0)$
   (d) Evaluate $2h(0)$ **(e)** Evaluate $h(1) + 3$

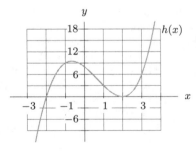

Figure 2.4

31. Let $f(x) = \sqrt{x^2 + 16} - 5$.

   (a) Find $f(0)$
   (b) For what values of x is $f(x)$ zero?
   (c) Find $f(3)$
   (d) What is the vertical intercept of the graph of $f(x)$?
   (e) Where does the graph cross the x-axis?

32. Use the letters a, b, c, d, e, h in Figure 2.5 to answer the following questions.

   (a) What are the coordinates of the points P and Q?
   (b) Evaluate $f(b)$.
   (c) Solve $f(x) = e$ for x.
   (d) Suppose $c = f(z)$ and $z = f(x)$. What is x?
   (e) Suppose $f(b) = -f(d)$. What additional information does this give you?

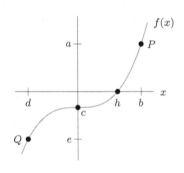

Figure 2.5

33. A ball is thrown up from the ground with initial velocity 64 ft/sec. Its height at time t is

$$h(t) = -16t^2 + 64t.$$

   (a) Evaluate $h(1)$ and $h(3)$. What does this tell us about the height of the ball?
   (b) Sketch this function. Using a graph, determine when the ball hits the ground and the maximum height of the ball.

34. Let $v(t) = t^2 - 2t$ be the velocity, in ft/sec, of an object at time t, in seconds.

   (a) What is the initial velocity, $v(0)$?
   (b) When does the object have a velocity of zero?
   (c) What is the meaning of the quantity $v(3)$? What are its units?

35. Let $s(t) = 11t^2 + t + 100$ be the position, in miles, of a car driving on a straight road at time t, in hours. The car's velocity at any time t is given by $v(t) = 22t + 1$.

(a) Use function notation to express the car's position after 2 hours. Where is the car then?

(b) Use function notation to express the question, "When is the car going 65 mph?"

(c) Where is the car when it is going 67 mph?

36. New York state income tax is based on taxable income, which is part of a person's total income. The tax owed to the state is calculated using the taxable income (not total income). In 2005, for a single person with a taxable income between \$20,000 and \$100,000, the tax owed was \$973 plus 6.85% of the taxable income over \$20,000.

(a) Compute the tax owed by a lawyer whose taxable income is \$68,000.

(b) Consider a lawyer whose taxable income is 80% of her total income, \$$x$, where x is between \$85,000 and \$120,000. Write a formula for $T(x)$, the taxable income.

(c) Write a formula for $L(x)$, the amount of tax owed by the lawyer in part (b).

(d) Use $L(x)$ to evaluate the tax liability for $x = 85,000$ and compare your results to part (a).

37. (a) The Fibonacci sequence is a sequence of numbers that begins 1, 1, 2, 3, 5,.... Each term in the sequence is the sum of the two preceding terms. For example,

$$2 = 1 + 1, \quad 3 = 2 + 1, \quad 5 = 2 + 3, \dots.$$

Based on this observation, complete the following table of values for $f(n)$, the nth term in the Fibonacci sequence.

n	1	2	3	4	5	6	7	8	9	10	11	12
$f(n)$	1	1	2	3	5							

(b) The table of values in part (a) can be completed even though we don't have a formula for $f(n)$. Does the fact that we don't have a formula mean that $f(n)$ is not a function?

(c) Are you able to evaluate the following expressions using parts (a) and (b)? If so, do so; if not, explain why not.

$$f(0), \quad f(-1), \quad f(-2), \quad f(0.5).$$

38. (a) Complete Table 2.5 using

$$f(x) = 2x(x-3) - x(x-5) \quad \text{and} \quad g(x) = x^2 - x.$$

What do you notice? Graph these two functions. Are the two functions the same? Explain.

(b) Complete Table 2.6 using

$$h(x) = x^5 - 5x^3 + 6x + 1 \quad \text{and} \quad j(x) = 2x + 1.$$

What do you notice? Graph these two functions. Are the two functions the same? Explain.

Table 2.5

x	-2	-1	0	1	2
$f(x)$					
$g(x)$					

Table 2.6

x	-2	-1	0	1	2
$h(x)$					
$j(x)$					

39. A psychologist conducts an experiment to determine the effect of sleep loss on job performance. Let $p = f(t)$ be the number of minutes it takes the average person to complete a particular task if they have lost t minutes of sleep, where $t = 0$ means they have had exactly 8 hours of sleep. For instance, $f(60)$ is the amount of time it takes the average person to complete the task after sleeping for only 7 hours. Let $p_0 = f(0)$ and let t_1, t_2, and t_3 be positive constants. Explain what the following statements tell you about sleep loss and job performance.

(a) $f(30) = p_0 + 5$

(b) $f(t_1) = 2p_0$

(c) $f(2t_1) = 1.5f(t_1)$

(d) $f(t_2 + 60) = f(t_2 + 30) + 10$

Problems 40–41 concern $v = r(s)$, the eyewall wind profile of a hurricane at landfall, where v is the eyewall wind speed (in mph) as a function of s, the height (in meters) above the ground. (The eyewall is the band of clouds that surrounds the eye of the storm.) Let s_0 be the height at which the wind speed is greatest, and let $v_0 = r(s_0)$. Interpret the following in terms of the hurricanes.

40. $r(0.5s_0)$

41. $r(s) = 0.75v_0$

2.2   DOMAIN AND RANGE

In Example 4 on page 5, we defined R to be the average monthly rainfall at Chicago's O'Hare airport in month t. Although R is a function of t, the value of R is not defined for every possible value of t. For instance, it makes no sense to consider the value of R for $t = -3$, or $t = 8.21$, or $t = 13$ (since a year has 12 months). Thus, although R is a function of t, this function is defined only for certain values of t. Notice also that R, the output value of this function, takes only the values $\{1.8, 2.1, 2.4, 2.5, 2.7, 3.1, 3.2, 3.4, 3.5, 3.7\}$.

A function is often defined only for certain values of the independent variable. Also, the dependent variable often takes on only certain values. This leads to the following definitions:

> If $Q = f(t)$, then
> - the **domain** of f is the set of input values, t, which yield an output value.
> - the **range** of f is the corresponding set of output values, Q.

Thus, the domain of a function is the set of input values, and the range is the set of output values.

If the domain of a function is not specified, we usually assume that it is as large as possible— that is, all numbers that make sense as inputs for the function. For example, if there are no restrictions, the domain of the function $f(x) = x^2$ is the set of all real numbers, because we can substitute any real number into the formula $f(x) = x^2$. Sometimes, however, we may restrict the domain to suit a particular application. If the function $f(x) = x^2$ is used to represent the area of a square of side x, we restrict the domain to positive numbers.

If a function is being used to model a real-world situation, the domain and range of the function are often determined by the constraints of the situation being modeled, as in the next example.

Example 1   The house painting function $n = f(A)$ in Example 2 on page 4 has domain $A > 0$ because all houses have some positive area. There is a practical upper limit to A because houses cannot be infinitely large, but in principle, A can be as large or as small as we like, as long as it is positive. Therefore we take the domain of f to be $A > 0$.

The range of this function is $n \geq 0$, because we cannot use a negative amount of paint.

Choosing Realistic Domains and Ranges

When a function is used to model a real situation, it may be necessary to modify the domain and range.

Example 2   Algebraically speaking, the formula

$$T = \frac{1}{4}R + 40$$

can be used for all values of R. If we know nothing more about this function than its formula, its domain is all real numbers. The formula for $T = \frac{1}{4}R + 40$ can return any value of T when we choose an appropriate R-value (See Figure 2.6.) Thus, the range of the function is also all real numbers. However, if we use this formula to represent the temperature, T, as a function of a cricket's chirp rate, R, as we did in Example 1 on page 2, some values of R cannot be used. For example, it does not make sense to talk about a negative chirp rate. Also, there is some maximum chirp rate R_{max}

that no cricket can physically exceed. Thus, to use this formula to express T as a function of R, we must restrict R to the interval $0 \leq R \leq R_{\max}$ shown in Figure 2.7.

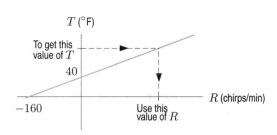

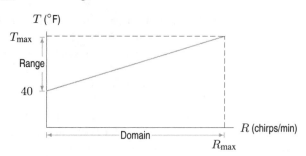

Figure 2.6: Graph showing that any T value can be obtained from some R value

Figure 2.7: Graph showing that if $0 \leq R \leq R_{\max}$, then $40 \leq T \leq T_{\max}$

The range of the cricket function is also restricted. Since the chirp rate is nonnegative, the smallest value of T occurs when $R = 0$. This happens at $T = 40$. On the other hand, if the temperature gets too hot, the cricket will not be able to keep chirping faster. If the temperature $T_{\max}$ corresponds to the chirp rate $R_{\max}$, then the values of T are restricted to the interval $40 \leq T \leq T_{\max}$.

Using a Graph to Find the Domain and Range of a Function

A good way to estimate the domain and range of a function is to examine its graph. The domain is the set of input values on the horizontal axis which give rise to a point on the graph; the range is the corresponding set of output values on the vertical axis.

Example 3   A sunflower plant is measured every day t, for $t \geq 0$. The height, $h(t)$ centimeters, of the plant[2] can be modeled by using the *logistic function*

$$h(t) = \frac{260}{1 + 24(0.9)^t}.$$

(a) Using a graphing calculator or computer, graph the height over 80 days.
(b) What is the domain of this function? What is the range? What does this tell you about the height of the sunflower?

Solution   (a) The logistic function is graphed in Figure 2.8.

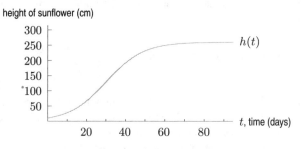

Figure 2.8: Height of sunflower as a function of time

[2] Adapted from H.S. Reed and R.H. Holland, "Growth of an Annual Plant Helianthus" *Proc. Nat. Acad. Sci.*, 5, 1919.

(b) The domain of this function is $t \geq 0$. If we consider the fact that the sunflower dies at some point, then there is an upper bound on the domain, $0 \leq t \leq T$, where T is the day on which the sunflower dies.

To find the range, notice that the smallest value of h occurs at $t = 0$. Evaluating gives $h(0) = 10.4$ cm. This means that the plant was 10.4 cm high when it was first measured on day $t = 0$. Tracing along the graph, $h(t)$ increases. As t-values get large, $h(t)$-values approach, but never reach, 260. This suggests that the range is $10.4 \leq h(t) < 260$. This information tells us that sunflowers typically grow to a height of about 260 cm.

Using a Formula to Find the Domain and Range of a Function

When a function is defined by a formula, its domain and range can often be determined by examining the formula algebraically.

Example 4   State the domain and range of g, where

$$g(x) = \frac{1}{x}.$$

Solution   The domain is all real numbers except those which do not yield an output value. The expression $1/x$ is defined for any real number x except 0 (division by 0 is undefined). Therefore,

$$\text{Domain: all real } x, \quad x \neq 0.$$

The range is all real numbers that the formula can return as output values. It is not possible for $g(x)$ to equal zero, since 1 divided by a real number is never zero. All real numbers except 0 are possible output values, since all nonzero real numbers have reciprocals. Thus

$$\text{Range: all real values,} \quad g(x) \neq 0.$$

The graph in Figure 2.9 indicates agreement with these values for the domain and range.

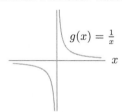

Figure 2.9: Domain and range of $g(x) = 1/x$

Example 5   Find the domain of the function $f(x) = \dfrac{1}{\sqrt{x-4}}$ by examining its formula.

Solution   The domain is all real numbers except those for which the function is undefined. The square root of a negative number is undefined (if we restrict ourselves to real numbers), and so is division by zero. Therefore we need

$$x - 4 > 0.$$

Thus, the domain is all real numbers greater than 4.

$$\text{Domain:} \quad x > 4.$$

In Example 6 on page 63, we saw that for $f(x) = 1/\sqrt{x-4}$, the output, $f(x)$, cannot be negative. Note that $f(x)$ cannot be zero either. (Why?) The range of $f(x) = 1/\sqrt{x-4}$ is $f(x) > 0$. See Problem 16.

Exercises and Problems for Section 2.2

Exercises

In Exercises 1–4, use a graph to find the range of the function on the given domain.

1. $f(x) = \dfrac{1}{x}$, $-2 \le x \le 2$

2. $f(x) = \dfrac{1}{x^2}$, $-1 \le x \le 1$

3. $f(x) = x^2 - 4$, $-2 \le x \le 3$

4. $f(x) = \sqrt{9 - x^2}$, $-3 \le x \le 1$

Graph and give the domain and range of the functions in Exercises 5–12.

5. $f(x) = (x - 4)^3$

6. $f(x) = x^2 - 4$

7. $f(x) = 9 - x^2$

8. $f(x) = x^3 + 2$

9. $f(x) = \sqrt{8 - x}$

10. $f(x) = \sqrt{x - 3}$

11. $f(x) = \dfrac{-1}{(x + 1)^2}$

12. $f(x) = \dfrac{1}{x^2}$

In Exercises 13–14, estimate the domain and range of the function. Assume the entire graph is shown.

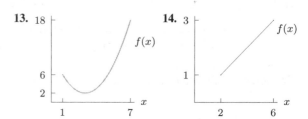

Problems

Find the domain and range of functions in Exercises 15–18 algebraically.

15. $q(x) = \sqrt{x^2 - 9}$

16. $f(x) = \dfrac{1}{\sqrt{x - 4}}$

17. $m(x) = 9 - x$

18. $n(x) = 9 - x^4$

In Exercises 19–24, find the domain and range.

19. $f(x) = -x^2 + 7$

20. $f(x) = \sqrt[3]{x + 77}$

21. $f(x) = x^2 + 2$

22. $f(x) = 1/(x + 1) + 3$

23. $f(x) = x - 3$

24. $f(x) = (x - 3)^2 + 2$

25. Give a formula for a function whose domain is all non-negative values of x except $x = 3$.

26. Give a formula for a function that is undefined for $x = 8$ and for $x < 4$, but is defined everywhere else.

27. A restaurant is open from 2 pm to 2 am each day, and a maximum of 200 clients can fit inside. If $f(t)$ is the number of clients in the restaurant t hours after 2 pm each day, what are a reasonable domain and range for $f(t)$?

28. What is the domain of the function f giving average monthly rainfall at Chicago's O'Hare airport? (See Table 1.2 on page 5)

29. A movie theater seats 200 people. For any particular show, the amount of money the theater makes is a function of the number of people, n, in attendance. If a ticket costs $4.00, find the domain and range of this function. Sketch its graph.

30. A car gets the best mileage at intermediate speeds. Graph the gas mileage as a function of speed. Determine a reasonable domain and range for the function and justify your reasoning.

31. **(a)** Use Table 2.7 to determine the number of calories that a person weighing 200 lb uses in a half–hour of walking.[3]

  (b) Table 2.7 illustrates a relationship between the number of calories used per minute walking and a person's weight in pounds. Describe in words what is true about this relationship. Identify the dependent and independent variables. Specify whether it is an increasing or decreasing function.

  (c) (i) Graph the linear function for walking, as described in part (b), and estimate its equation.

    (ii) Interpret the meaning of the vertical intercept of the graph of the function.

    (iii) Specify a meaningful domain and range for your function.

    (iv) Use your function to determine how many calories per minute a person who weighs 135 lb uses per minute of walking.

Table 2.7   *Calories per minute as a function of weight*

Activity	100 lb	120 lb	150 lb	170 lb	200 lb	220 lb
Walking	2.7	3.2	4.0	4.6	5.4	5.9
Bicycling	5.4	6.5	8.1	9.2	10.8	11.9
Swimming	5.8	6.9	8.7	9.8	11.6	12.7

[3]Source: 1993 World Almanac. Speeds assumed are 3 mph for walking, 10 mph for bicycling, and 2 mph for swimming.

In Exercises 32–33, find the domain and range.

32. $g(x) = a + 1/x$, where a is a constant

33. $q(r) = (x - b)^{1/2} + 6$, where b is a constant

34. The last digit, d, of a phone number is a function of n, its position in the phone book. Table 2.8 gives d for the first 10 listings in the 1998 Boston telephone directory. The table shows that the last digit of the first listing is 3, the last digit of the second listing is 8, and so on. In principle we could use a phone book to figure out other values of d. For instance, if $n = 300$, we could count down to the 300th listing in order to determine d. So we write $d = f(n)$.

(a) What is the value of $f(6)$?

(b) Explain how you could use the phone book to find the domain of f.

(c) What is the range of f?

Table 2.8

n	1	2	3	4	5	6	7	8	9	10
d	3	8	4	0	1	8	0	4	3	5

35. In month $t = 0$, a small group of rabbits escapes from a ship onto an island where there are no rabbits. The island rabbit population, $p(t)$, in month t is given by

$$p(t) = \frac{1000}{1 + 19(0.9)^t}, \quad t \geq 0.$$

(a) Evaluate $p(0)$, $p(10)$, $p(50)$, and explain their meaning in terms of rabbits.

(b) Graph $p(t)$ for $0 \leq t \leq 100$. Describe the graph in words. Does it suggest the growth in population you would expect among rabbits on an island?

(c) Estimate the range of $p(t)$. What does this tell you about the rabbit population?

(d) Explain how you can find the range of $p(t)$ from its formula.

36. Bronze is an alloy or mixture of the metals copper and tin. The properties of bronze depend on the percentage of copper in the mix. A chemist decides to study the properties of a given alloy of bronze as the proportion of copper is varied. She starts with 9 kg of bronze that contain 3 kg of copper and 6 kg of tin and either adds or removes copper. Let $f(x)$ be the percentage of copper in the mix if x kg of copper are added ($x > 0$) or removed ($x < 0$).

(a) State the domain and range of f. What does your answer mean in the context of bronze?

(b) Find a formula in terms of x for $f(x)$.

(c) If the formula you found in part (b) was not intended to represent the percentage of copper in an alloy of bronze, but instead simply defined an abstract mathematical function, what would be the domain and range of this function?

2.3 PIECEWISE DEFINED FUNCTIONS

A function may employ different formulas on different parts of its domain. Such a function is said to be *piecewise defined*. For example, the function graphed in Figure 2.10 has the following formulas:

$$\begin{aligned} y &= x^2 \quad \text{for } x \leq 2 \\ y &= 6 - x \quad \text{for } x > 2 \end{aligned} \quad \text{or more compactly} \quad y = \begin{cases} x^2 & \text{for } x \leq 2 \\ 6 - x & \text{for } x > 2. \end{cases}$$

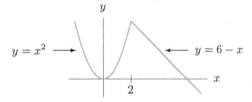

Figure 2.10: Piecewise defined function

Example 1 Graph the function $y = g(x)$ given by the following formulas:

$$g(x) = x + 1 \quad \text{for} \quad x \leq 2 \quad \text{and} \quad g(x) = 1 \quad \text{for} \quad x > 2.$$

Using bracket notation, this function is written:

$$g(x) = \begin{cases} x + 1 & \text{for } x \leq 2 \\ 1 & \text{for } x > 2. \end{cases}$$

Solution

For $x \leq 2$, graph the line $y = x + 1$. The solid dot at the point $(2, 3)$ shows that it is included in the graph. For $x > 2$, graph the horizontal line $y = 1$. See Figure 2.11. The open circle at the point $(2, 1)$ shows that it is not included in the graph. (Note that $g(2) = 3$, and $g(2)$ cannot have more than one value.)

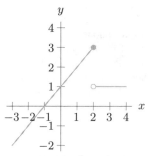

Figure 2.11: Graph of the piecewise defined function g

Example 2   A long-distance calling plan charges 99 cents for any call up to 20 minutes in length and 7 cents for each additional minute or part of a minute.

(a) Use bracket notation to write a formula for the cost, C, of a call as a function of its length t in minutes.
(b) Graph the function.
(c) State the domain and range of the function

Solution

(a) For $0 < t \leq 20$, the value of C is 99 cents. If $t > 20$, we subtract 20 to find the additional minutes and multiply by the rate 7 cents per minute.[4] The cost function in cents is thus

$$C = f(t) = \begin{cases} 99 & \text{for } 0 < t \leq 20 \\ 99 + 7(t - 20) & \text{for } t > 20, \end{cases}$$

or, after simplifying,

$$C = f(t) = \begin{cases} 99 & \text{for } 0 < t \leq 20 \\ 7t - 41 & \text{for } t > 20. \end{cases}$$

(b) See Figure 2.12.
(c) Because negative and zero call lengths do not make sense, the domain is $t > 0$. From the graph, we see that the range is $C \geq 99$.

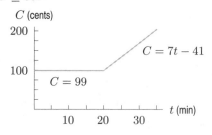

Figure 2.12: Cost of a long-distance phone call

[4]In actuality, most calling plans round the call length to whole minutes or specified fractions of a minute.

Example 3   The Ironman Triathlon is a race that consists of three parts: a 2.4 mile swim followed by a 112 mile bike race and then a 26.2 mile marathon. A participant swims steadily at 2 mph, cycles steadily at 20 mph, and then runs steadily at 9 mph.[5] Assuming that no time is lost during the transition from one stage to the next, find a formula for the distance d, covered in miles, as a function of the elapsed time t in hours, from the beginning of the race. Graph the function.

Solution   For each leg of the race, we use the formula Distance = Rate · Time. First, we calculate how long it took for the participant to cover each of the three parts of the race. The first leg took $2.4/2 = 1.2$ hours, the second leg took $112/20 = 5.6$ hours, and the final leg took $26.2/9 \approx 2.91$ hours. Thus, the participant finished the race in $1.2 + 5.6 + 2.91 = 9.71$ hours.

During the first leg, $t \leq 1.2$ and the speed is 2 mph, so

$$d = 2t \qquad \text{for} \qquad 0 \leq t \leq 1.2.$$

During the second leg, $1.2 < t \leq 1.2 + 5.6 = 6.8$ and the speed is 20 mph. The length of time spent in the second leg is $(t - 1.2)$ hours. Thus, by time t,

$$\text{Distance covered in the second leg} = 20(t - 1.2) \quad \text{for } 1.2 < t \leq 6.8.$$

When the participant is in the second leg, the total distance covered is the sum of the distance covered in the first leg (2.4 miles) plus the part of the second leg that has been covered by time t.

$$d = 2.4 + 20(t - 1.2)$$
$$= 20t - 21.6 \qquad \text{for } 1.2 < t \leq 6.8.$$

In the third leg, $6.8 < t \leq 9.71$ and the speed is 9 mph. Since 6.8 hours were spent on the first two parts of the race, the length of time spent on the third leg is $(t - 6.8)$ hours. Thus, by time t,

$$\text{Distance covered in the third leg} = 9(t - 6.8) \quad \text{for } 6.8 < t \leq 9.71.$$

When the participant is in the third leg, the total distance covered is the sum of the distances covered in the first leg (2.4 miles) and the second leg (112 miles), plus the part of the third leg that has been covered by time t:

$$d = 2.4 + 112 + 9(t - 6.8)$$
$$= 9t + 53.2 \qquad \text{for } 6.8 < t \leq 9.71.$$

The formula for d is different on different intervals of t:

$$d = \begin{cases} 2t & \text{for} & 0 \leq t \leq 1.2 \\ 20t - 21.6 & \text{for} & 1.2 < t \leq 6.8 \\ 9t + 53.2 & \text{for} & 6.8 < t \leq 9.71. \end{cases}$$

Figure 2.13 gives a graph of the distance covered, d, as a function of time, t. Notice the three pieces.

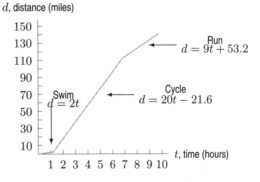

Figure 2.13: Ironman Triathlon: d as a function of t

[5]Data supplied by Susan Reid, Athletics Department, University of Arizona.

The Absolute Value Function

The absolute value of a x, written $|x|$, is defined piecewise

$$\text{For positive } x, \quad |x| = x.$$

$$\text{For negative } x, \quad |x| = -x.$$

(Remember that $-x$ is a positive number if x is a negative number.) For example, if $x = -3$, then

$$|-3| = -(-3) = 3.$$

For $x = 0$, we have $|0| = 0$. This leads to the following two-part definition:

The **Absolute Value Function** is defined by

$$f(x) = |x| = \begin{cases} x & \text{for} \quad x \geq 0 \\ -x & \text{for} \quad x < 0 \end{cases}.$$

Table 2.9 gives values of $f(x) = |x|$ and Figure 2.14 shows a graph of $f(x)$.

Table 2.9   *Absolute value function*

x	$|x|$
-3	3
-2	2
-1	1
0	0
1	1
2	2
3	3

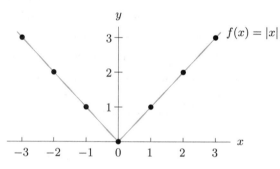

Figure 2.14: Graph of absolute value function

Exercises and Problems for Section 2.3

Exercises

Graph the piecewise defined functions in Exercises 1–4. Use an open circle to represent a point which is not included and a solid dot to indicate a point which is on the graph.

1. $f(x) = \begin{cases} -1, & -1 \leq x < 0 \\ 0, & 0 \leq x < 1 \\ 1, & 1 \leq x < 2 \end{cases}$

2. $f(x) = \begin{cases} x+1, & -2 \leq x < 0 \\ x-1, & 0 \leq x < 2 \\ x-3, & 2 \leq x < 4 \end{cases}$

3. $f(x) = \begin{cases} x+4, & x \leq -2 \\ 2, & -2 < x < 2 \\ 4-x, & x \geq 2 \end{cases}$

4. $f(x) = \begin{cases} x^2, & x \leq 0 \\ \sqrt{x}, & 0 < x < 4 \\ x/2, & x \geq 4 \end{cases}$

For Exercises 5–6, find the domain and range.

5. $G(x) = \begin{cases} x+1 & \text{for} \quad x < -1 \\ x^2 + 3 & \text{for} \quad x \geq -1 \end{cases}$

6. $F(x) = \begin{cases} x^3 & \text{for} \quad x \leq 1 \\ 1/x & \text{for} \quad x > 1 \end{cases}$

In Exercises 7–10, write formulas for the functions.

7.

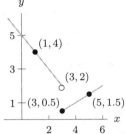

8.

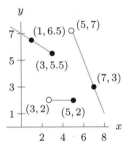

9.

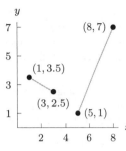

10.

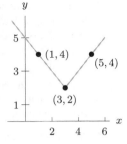

Problems

11. Consider the graph in Figure 2.15. An open circle represents a point which is not included.

(a) Is y a function of x? Explain.

(b) Is x a function of y? Explain.

(c) The domain of $y = f(x)$ is $0 \leq x < 4$. What is the range of $y = f(x)$?

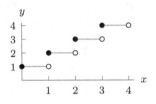

Figure 2.15

12. Many people believe that $\sqrt{x^2} = x$. We will investigate this claim graphically and numerically.

(a) Graph the two functions x and $\sqrt{x^2}$ in the window $-5 \leq x \leq 5$, $-5 \leq y \leq 5$. Based on what you see, do you believe that $\sqrt{x^2} = x$? What function does the graph of $\sqrt{x^2}$ remind you of?

(b) Complete Table 2.10. Based on this table, do you believe that $\sqrt{x^2} = x$? What function does the table for $\sqrt{x^2}$ remind you of? Is this the same function you found in part (a)?

Table 2.10

x	-5	-4	-3	-2	-1	0	1	2	3	4	5
$\sqrt{x^2}$											

(c) Explain how you know that $\sqrt{x^2}$ is the same as the function $|x|$.

(d) Graph the function $\sqrt{x^2} - |x|$ in the window $-5 \leq x \leq 5$, $-5 \leq y \leq 5$. Explain what you see.

13. (a) Graph $u(x) = |x|/x$ in the window $-5 \leq x \leq 5$, $-5 \leq y \leq 5$. Explain what you see.

(b) Complete Table 2.11. Does this table agree with what you found in part (a)?

Table 2.11

x	-5	-4	-3	-2	-1	0	1	2	3	4	5
$|x|/x$											

(c) Identify the domain and range of $u(x)$.

(d) Comment on the claim that $u(x)$ can be written as

$$u(x) = \begin{cases} -1 & \text{if } x < 0, \\ 0 & \text{if } x = 0, \\ 1 & \text{if } x > 0. \end{cases}$$

14. The charge for a taxi ride in New York City is $2.50 for the first $1/4$ of a mile, and $0.40 for each additional $1/4$ of a mile (rounded up to the nearest $1/4$ mile).

(a) Make a table showing the cost of a trip as a function of its length. Your table should start at zero and go up to two miles in $1/4$-mile intervals.

(b) What is the cost for a 1.25-mile trip?

(c) How far can you go for $5.30?

(d) Graph the cost function in part (a).

15. A museum charges $40 for a group of 10 or fewer people. A group of more than 10 people must, in addition to the $40, pay $2 per person for the number of people above 10. For example, a group of 12 pays $44 and a group of 15 pays $50. The maximum group size is 50.

(a) Draw a graph that represents this situation.

(b) What are the domain and range of the cost function?

16. A floor-refinishing company charges $1.83 per square foot to strip and refinish a tile floor for up to 1000 square feet. There is an additional charge of $350 for toxic waste disposal for any job which includes more than 150 square feet of tile.

    (a) Express the cost, y, of refinishing a floor as a function of the number of square feet, x, to be refinished.

    (b) Graph the function. Give the domain and range.

17. A contractor purchases gravel one cubic yard at a time.

    (a) A gravel driveway L yards long and 6 yards wide is to be poured to a depth of 1 foot. Find a formula for $n(L)$, the number of cubic yards of gravel the contractor buys, assuming that he buys 10 more cubic yards of gravel than are needed (to be sure he'll have enough).

    (b) Assuming no driveway is less than 5 yards long, state the domain and range of $n(L)$. Graph $n(L)$ showing the domain and range.

    (c) If the function $n(L)$ did not represent an amount of gravel, but was a mathematical relationship defined by the formula in part (a), what is its domain and range?

18. At a supermarket checkout, a scanner records the prices of the foods you buy. In order to protect consumers, the state of Michigan passed a "scanning law" that says something similar to the following:

    If there is a discrepancy between the price marked on the item and the price recorded by the scanner, the consumer is entitled to receive 10 times the difference between those prices; this amount given must be at least $1 and at most $5. Also, the consumer will be given the difference between the prices, in addition to the amount calculated above.

For example: If the difference is 5¢, you should receive $1 (since 10 times the difference is only 50¢ and you are to receive at least $1), plus the difference of 5¢. Thus, the total you should receive is $1.00 + $0.05 = $1.05,
If the difference is 25¢, you should receive 10 times the difference in addition to the difference, giving $(10)(0.25) + 0.25 = 2.75.
If the difference is 95¢, you should receive $5 (because $10(.95) = 9.50 is more than $5, the maximum penalty), plus 95¢, giving $5 + 0.95 = 5.95.

    (a) What is the lowest possible refund?

    (b) Suppose x is the difference between the price scanned and the price marked on the item, and y is the amount refunded to the customer. Write a formula for y in terms of x. (Hints: Look at the sample calculations.)

    (c) What would the difference between the price scanned and the price marked have to be in order to obtain a $9.00 refund?

    (d) Graph y as a function of x.

19. Many printing presses are designed with large plates that print a fixed number of pages as a unit. Each unit is called a signature. A particular press prints signatures of 16 pages each. Suppose $C(p)$ is the cost of printing a book of p pages, assuming each signature printed costs $0.14.

    (a) What is the cost of printing a book of 128 pages? 129 pages? p pages?

    (b) What are the domain and range of C?

    (c) Graph $C(p)$ for $0 \le p \le 128$.

20. Gore Mountain is a ski resort in the Adirondack mountains in upstate New York. Table 2.12 shows the cost of a weekday ski-lift ticket for various ages and dates.

    (a) Graph cost as a function of age for each time period given. (One graph will serve for times when rates are identical).

    (b) For which age group does the date affect cost?

    (c) Graph cost as a function of date for the age group mentioned in part (b).

    (d) Why does the cost fluctuate as a function of date?

Table 2.12   *Ski-lift ticket prices at Gore Mountain, 1998–1999[6]*

Age	Opening–Dec 12	Dec 13–Dec 24	Dec 25–Jan 3	Jan 4–Jan 15	Jan 16–Jan 18
Up to 6	Free	Free	Free	Free	Free
7–12	$19	$19	$19	$19	$19
13–69	$29	$34	$39	$34	$39
70+	Free	Free	Free	Free	Free

Age	Jan 19–Feb 12	Feb 13–Feb 21	Feb 22–Mar 28	Mar 29–Closing	
Up to 6	Free	Free	Free	Free	
7–12	$19	$19	$19	$19	
13–69	$34	$39	$34	$29	
70+	Free	Free	Free	Free	

---

[6]The Olympic Regional Development Authority.

2.4 COMPOSITE AND INVERSE FUNCTIONS

Composition of Functions

Two functions may be connected by the fact that the output of one is the input of the other. For example, to find the cost, C, in dollars, to paint a room of area A square feet, we need to know the number, n, of gallons of paint required. Since one gallon covers 250 square feet, we have the function $n = f(A) = A/250$. If paint is \$30.50 a gallon, we have the function $C = g(n) = 30.5n$. We substitute $n = f(A)$ into $g(n)$ to find the cost C as a function of A.

Example 1   Find a formula for cost, C, as a function of area, A.

Solution   Since we have

$$C = 30.5n \quad \text{and} \quad n = \frac{A}{250},$$

substituting for n in the formula for C gives

$$C = 30.5 \frac{A}{250} = 0.122A.$$

We say that C is a "function of a function", or *composite function*. If the function giving C in terms of A is called h, so $C = h(A)$, then we write

$$C = h(A) = g(f(A)).$$

The function h is said to be the *composition* of the functions f and g. We say f is the *inside* function and g is the *outside* function. In this example, the composite function $C = h(A) = g(f(A))$ tells us the cost of painting an area of A square feet.

Example 2   The air temperature, T, in °F, is given in terms of the chirp rate, R, in chirps per minute, of a snowy tree cricket by the function

$$T = f(R) = \frac{1}{4}R + 40.$$

Suppose one night we record the chirp rate and find that it varies with time, x, according to the function

$$R = g(x) = 20 + x^2 \qquad \text{where } x \text{ is in hours since midnight and } 0 \leq x \leq 10.$$

Find how temperature varies with time by obtaining a formula for h, where $T = h(x)$.

Solution   Since $f(R)$ is a function of R and $R = g(x)$, we see that g is the inside function and f is the outside function. Thus we substitute $R = g(x)$ into f:

$$T = f(R) = f(g(x)) = \frac{1}{4}g(x) + 40 = \frac{1}{4}(20 + x^2) + 40 = \frac{1}{4}x^2 + 45.$$

Thus, for $0 \leq x \leq 10$, we have

$$T = h(x) = \frac{1}{4}x^2 + 45.$$

Example 3 shows another example of composition.

Example 3   If $f(x) = x^2$ and $g(x) = 2x + 1$, find

(a) $f(g(x))$ (b) $g(f(x))$

Solution   (a) We have
$$f(g(x)) = f(2x + 1) = (2x + 1)^2.$$

(b) We have
$$g(f(x)) = g(x^2) = 2(x^2) + 1 = 2x^2 + 1.$$

Notice that $f(g(x))$ is not equal to $g(f(x))$ in this case.

Inverse Functions

The roles of a function's input and output can sometimes be reversed. For example, the population, P, of birds is given, in thousands, by $P = f(t)$, where t is the number of years since 2007. In this function, t is the input and P is the output. If the population is increasing, knowing the year enables us to calculate the population. Thus we can define a new function, $t = g(P)$, which tells us the value of t given the value of P instead of the other way round. For this function, P is the input and t is the output. The functions f and g are called *inverses* of each other. A function which has an inverse is said to be *invertible*.

The fact that f and g are inverse functions means that they go in "opposite directions." The function f takes t as input and outputs P, while g takes P as input and outputs t.

Inverse Function Notation

In the preceding discussion, there was nothing about the names of the two functions that stressed their special relationship. If we want to emphasize that g is the inverse of f, we call it f^{-1} (read "f-inverse"). To express the fact that the population of birds, P, is a function of time, t, we write
$$P = f(t).$$

To express the fact that the time t is also determined by P, so that t is a function of P, we write
$$t = f^{-1}(P).$$

The symbol f^{-1} is used to represent the function that gives the output t for a given input P.

Warning: The -1 which appears in the symbol f^{-1} for the inverse function is not an exponent. Unfortunately, the notation $f^{-1}(x)$ might lead us to interpret it as $\frac{1}{f(x)}$. The two expressions are not the same in general: $f^{-1}(x)$ is the output when x is fed into the inverse of f, while $\frac{1}{f(x)}$ is the reciprocal of the number we get when x is fed into f.

Example 4   Using $P = f(t)$, where P represents the population, in thousands, of birds on an island and t is the number of years since 2007:

(a) What does $f(4)$ represent?   (b) What does $f^{-1}(4)$ represent?

Solution   (a) The expression $f(4)$ is the bird population (in thousands) in the year 2011.
(b) Since f^{-1} is the inverse function, f^{-1} is a function which takes population as input and returns time as output. Therefore, $f^{-1}(4)$ is the number of years after 2007 at which there were 4,000 birds on the island.

Finding a Formula for the Inverse Function

In the next example, we find the formula for an inverse function.

Example 5 The cricket function, which gives temperature, T, in terms of chirp rate, R, is

$$T = f(R) = \frac{1}{4} \cdot R + 40.$$

Find a formula for the inverse function, $R = f^{-1}(T)$.

Solution The inverse function gives the chirp rate in terms of the temperature, so we solve the following equation for R:

$$T = \frac{1}{4} \cdot R + 40,$$

giving

$$T - 40 = \frac{1}{4} \cdot R$$
$$R = 4(T - 40).$$

Thus, $R = f^{-1}(T) = 4(T - 40)$.

Domain and Range of an Inverse Function

The input values of the inverse function f^{-1} are the output values of the function f. Thus, the domain of f^{-1} is the range of f. For the cricket function, $T = f(R) = \frac{1}{4}R + 40$, if a realistic domain is $0 \le R \le 160$, then the range of f is $40 \le T \le 80$. See Figure 2.16.

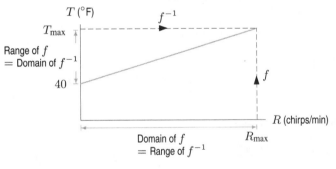

Figure 2.16

A Function and its Inverse Undo Each Other

Example 6 Calculate the composite functions $f^{-1}(f(R))$ and $f(f^{-1}(T))$ for the cricket example. Interpret the results.

Solution Since $f(R) = \frac{1}{4}R + 40.$ and $f^{-1}(T) = 4(T - 40)$, we have

$$f^{-1}(f(R)) = f^{-1}\left(\frac{1}{4} \cdot R + 40\right) = 4\left(\left(\frac{1}{4} \cdot R + 40\right) - 40\right) = R.$$

$$f(f^{-1}(T)) = f(4(T - 40)) = \frac{1}{4}(4(T - 40)) + 40 = T.$$

To interpret these results, we use the fact that $f(R)$ gives the temperature corresponding to chirp rate R, and $f^{-1}(T)$ gives the chirp rate corresponding to temperature T. Thus $f^{-1}(f(R))$ gives the chirp rate at temperature $f(R)$, which is R. Similarly, $f(f^{-1}(T))$ gives the temperature at chirp rate $f^{-1}(T)$, which is T.

Example 6 illustrates the following result, which we see is true in general in Chapter 8.

The functions f and f^{-1} are called inverses because they "undo" each other when composed.

Exercises and Problems for Section 2.4

Exercises

In Exercises 1–4, give the meaning and units of the composite function.

1. $A(f(t))$, where $r = f(t)$ is the radius, in centimeters, of a circle at time t minutes, and $A(r)$ is the area, in square centimeters, of a circle of radius r centimeters.

2. $R(f(p))$, where $Q = f(p)$ is the number of barrels of oil sold by a company when the price is p dollars/barrel and $R(Q)$ is the revenue earned in millions of dollars.

3. $a(g(w))$, where $F = g(w)$ is the force, in newtons, on a rocket when the wind speed is w meters/sec and $a(F)$ is the acceleration, in meters/sec^2, when the force is F newtons.

4. $P(f(t))$, where $l = f(t)$ is the length, in centimeters, of a pendulum at time t minutes, and $P(l)$ is the period, in seconds, of a pendulum of length l.

In Exercises 5–12, use $f(x) = x^2 + 1$, $g(x) = 2x + 3$.

5. $f(g(0))$ 6. $f(g(1))$ 7. $g(f(0))$ 8. $g(f(1))$

9. $f(g(x))$ 10. $g(f(x))$ 11. $f(f(x))$ 12. $g(g(x))$

In Exercises 13–17, give the meaning and units of the inverse function. (Assume f is invertible.)

13. $P = f(t)$ is population in millions in year t.

14. $T = f(H)$ is time in minutes to bake a cake at $H°$F.

15. $N = f(t)$ number of inches of snow in the first t days of January.

16. $V = f(t)$ is the speed in km/hr of an accelerating car t seconds after starting.

17. $I = f(r)$ is the interest earned, in dollars, on a \$10,000 deposit at an interest rate of $r\%$ per year, compounded annually.

In Exercises 18–21, find the inverse function.

18. $y = f(t) = 2t + 3$ 19. $Q = f(x) = x^3 + 3$

20. $y = g(t) = \sqrt{t} + 1$ 21. $P = f(q) = 14q - 2$

22. Use the graph in Figure 2.17 to fill in the missing values:

(a) $f(0) = ?$ (b) $f(?) = 0$
(c) $f^{-1}(0) = ?$ (d) $f^{-1}(?) = 0$

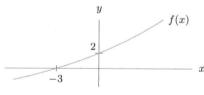

Figure 2.17

23. Use the graph in Figure 2.18 to fill in the missing values:

(a) $f(0) = ?$ (b) $f(?) = 0$
(c) $f^{-1}(0) = ?$ (d) $f^{-1}(?) = 0$

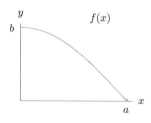

Figure 2.18

Problems

24. Let $n = f(A) = A/250$, where n is the number of gallons of paint and A is the area to be painted. Find a formula for the inverse function $A = g(n)$.

25. Calculate the composite functions $f^{-1}(f(A))$ and $f(f^{-1}(n))$ from Problem 24. Explain the results.

26. Table 2.13 gives values of an invertible function, f.

    (a) Using the table, fill in the missing values:

      (i) $f(0) = ?$ (ii) $f(?) = 0$
      (iii) $f^{-1}(0) = ?$ (iv) $f^{-1}(?) = 0$

    (b) How do the answers to (i)–(iv) in part (a) relate to one another? In particular, how could you have obtained the answers to (iii) and (iv) from the answers to (i) and (ii)?

Table 2.13

x	-2	-1	0	1	2
$f(x)$	5	4	2	0	-3

27. Use the values of the invertible function in Table 2.14 to find as many values of g^{-1} as possible.

Table 2.14

t	1	2	3	4	5
$y = g(t)$	7	12	13	19	22

28. The cost (in dollars) of producing x air conditioners is $C = g(x) = 600 + 45x$. Find a formula for the inverse function $g^{-1}(C)$.

29. The formula $V = f(r) = \frac{4}{3}\pi r^3$ gives the volume of a sphere of radius r. Find a formula for the inverse function, $f^{-1}(V)$, giving radius as a function of volume.

30. The cost, C, in thousands of dollars, of producing q kg of a chemical is given by $C = f(q) = 100 + 0.2q$. Find and interpret

    (a) $f(10)$ **(b)** $f^{-1}(200)$ **(c)** $f^{-1}(C)$

31. The perimeter of a square of side s is given by $P = f(s) = 4s$. Find and interpret

    (a) $f(3)$ **(b)** $f^{-1}(20)$ **(c)** $f^{-1}(P)$

32. The gross domestic product (GDP) of the US is given by $G(t)$ where t is the number of years since 1990 and the units of G are billions of dollars.

    (a) What does $G(11)$ represent?
    (b) What does $G^{-1}(9873)$ represent?

33. The formula for the volume of a cube with side s is $V = s^3$. The formula for the surface area of a cube is $A = 6s^2$.

    (a) Find and interpret the formula for the function $s = f(A)$.
    (b) If $V = g(s)$, find and interpret the formula for $g(f(A))$.

34. Interpret and evaluate $f(100)$ and $f^{-1}(100)$ for the house-painting function, $n = f(A) = A/250$. (See Problem 24.)

35. The cost of producing q thousand loaves of bread is $C(q)$ dollars. Interpret the following statements in terms of bread; give units.

    (a) $C(5) = 653$
    (b) $C^{-1}(80) = 0.62$
    (c) The solution to $C(q) = 790$ is 6.3
    (d) The solution to $C^{-1}(x) = 1.2$ is 150.

36. The area, $A = f(s)$ ft^2, of a square wooden deck is a function of the side s feet. A can of stain costs $\$29.50$ and covers 200 square feet of wood.

    (a) Write the formula for $f(s)$.
    (b) Find a formula for $C = g(A)$, the cost in dollars of staining an area of A ft^2.
    (c) Find and interpret $C = g(f(s))$.
    (d) Evaluate and interpret, giving units:

      (i) $f(8)$ (ii) $g(80)$ (iii) $g(f(10))$

37. The radius, r, in centimeters, of a melting snowball is given by $r = 50 - 2.5t$, where t is time in hours. The snowball is spherical, with volume $V = \frac{4}{3}\pi r^3$ cm^3. Find a formula for $V = f(t)$, the volume of the snowball as a function of time.

38. A circular oil slick is expanding with radius, r in yards, at time t in hours given by $r = 2t - 0.1t^2$, for t in hours, $0 \le t \le 10$. Find a formula for the area in square yards, $A = f(t)$, as a function of time.

39. Carbon dioxide is one of the "greenhouse" gases that are believed to affect global warming. Between January 1998 and January 2003, the concentration of carbon dioxide in the earth's atmosphere increased steadily from 365 parts per million (ppm) to 375 ppm. Let $C(t)$ be the concentration in ppm of carbon dioxide t years after 1998.

    (a) State the domain and range of $C(t)$.
    (b) What is the practical meaning of $C(4)$?
    (c) What does $C^{-1}(370)$ represent?

40. Table 2.15 shows the cost, $C(m)$, of a taxi ride as a function of the number of miles, m, traveled.

   (a) Estimate and interpret $C(3.5)$ in practical terms.
   (b) Assume C is invertible. What does $C^{-1}(3.5)$ mean in practical terms? Estimate $C^{-1}(3.5)$.

   Table 2.15

m	0	1	2	3	4	5
$C(m)$	0	2.50	4.00	5.50	7.00	8.50

41. The perimeter, in meters, of a square whose side is s meters is given by $P = 4s$.

   (a) Write this formula using function notation, where f is the name of the function.
   (b) Evaluate $f(s + 4)$ and interpret its meaning.
   (c) Evaluate $f(s) + 4$ and interpret its meaning.
   (d) What are the units of $f^{-1}(6)$?

2.5   CONCAVITY

Concavity and Rates of Change

The graph of a linear function is a straight line because the average rate of change is a constant. However, not all graphs are straight lines; they may bend up or down. Consider the salary function $S(t)$ shown in Table 2.16 and Figure 2.19, where t is time in years since being hired. Since the rate of change increases with time, the slope of the graph increases as t increases, so the graph bends upward. We say such graphs are *concave up*.

Table 2.16   *Salary: Increasing rate of change*

t (years)	S ($1000s)	Rate of change $\Delta S/\Delta t$
0	40	
		3.2
10	72	
		5.6
20	128	
		10.2
30	230	
		18.1
40	411	

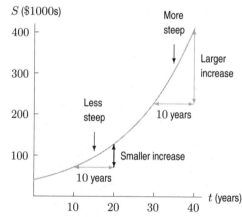

Figure 2.19: Graph of salary function is concave up because rate of change increases

The next example shows that a decreasing function can also be concave up.

Example 1   Table 2.17 shows Q, the quantity of carbon-14 (in μg) in a 200 μg sample remaining after t thousand years. We see from Figure 2.20 that Q is a decreasing function of t, so its rate of change is always negative. What can we say about the concavity of the graph, and what does this mean about the rate of change of the function?

Table 2.17   *Carbon-14: Increasing rate of change*

t (thousand years)	Q (μg)	Rate of change $\Delta Q/\Delta t$
0	200	
		-18.2
5	109	
		-9.8
10	60	
		-5.4
15	33	

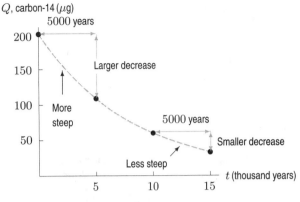

Figure 2.20: Graph of the quantity of carbon-14 is concave up

Solution   The graph bends upward, so it is concave up. Table 2.18 shows that the rate of change of the function is increasing, because the rate is becoming less negative. Figure 2.20 shows how the increasing rate of change can be visualized on the graph: the slope is negative and increasing.

Graphs can bend downward; we call such graphs *concave down*.

Example 2   Table 2.18 gives the distance traveled by a cyclist, Karim, as a function of time. What is the concavity of the graph? Was Karim's speed (that is, the rate of change of distance with respect to time) increasing, decreasing, or constant?

Solution   Table 2.18 shows Karim's speed was decreasing throughout the trip. Figure 2.21 shows how the decreasing speed leads to a decreasing slope and a graph which bends downward; thus the graph is concave down.

Table 2.18   *Karim's distance as a function of time, with the average speed for each hour*

t, time (hours)	d, distance (miles)	Average speed, $\Delta d/\Delta t$ (mph)
0	0	
		20 mph
1	20	
		15 mph
2	35	
		10 mph
3	45	
		7 mph
4	52	
		5 mph
5	57	

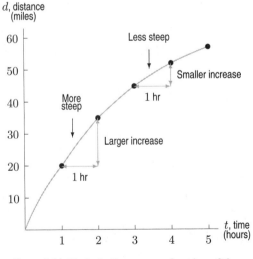

Figure 2.21: Karim's distance as a function of time

Summary: Increasing and Decreasing Functions; Concavity

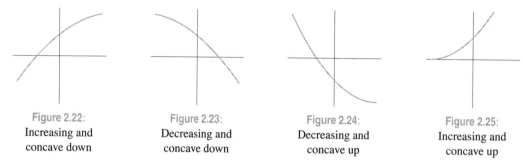

Figure 2.22:
Increasing and
concave down

Figure 2.23:
Decreasing and
concave down

Figure 2.24:
Decreasing and
concave up

Figure 2.25:
Increasing and
concave up

Figures 2.22–2.25 reflect the following relationships between concavity and rate of change:

- If f is a function whose rate of change increases (gets less negative or more positive as we move from left to right[7]), then the graph of f is **concave up**. That is, the graph bends upward.
- If f is a function whose rate of change decreases (gets less positive or more negative as we move from left to right), then the graph of f is **concave down**. That is, the graph bends downward.

If a function has a constant rate of change, its graph is a line and it is neither concave up nor concave down.

Exercises and Problems for Section 2.5

Exercises

Do the graphs of the functions in Exercises 1–8 appear to be concave up, concave down, or neither?

1.

x	0	1	3	6
$f(x)$	1.0	1.3	1.7	2.2

2.

t	0	1	2	3	4
$f(t)$	20	10	6	3	1

3.

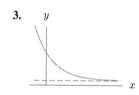

4.

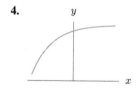

5. $y = x^2$

6. $y = -x^2$

7. $y = x^3, x > 0$

8. $y = x^3, x < 0$

9. Calculate successive rates of change for the function, $p(t)$, in Table 2.19 to decide whether you expect the graph of $p(t)$ to be concave up or concave down.

Table 2.19

t	0.2	0.4	0.6	0.8
$p(t)$	−3.19	−2.32	−1.50	−0.74

10. Calculate successive rates of change for the function, $H(x)$, in Table 2.20 to decide whether you expect the graph of $H(x)$ to be concave up or concave down.

Table 2.20

x	12	15	18	21
$H(x)$	21.40	21.53	21.75	22.02

11. Sketch a graph which is everywhere negative, increasing, and concave down.

12. Sketch a graph which is everywhere positive, increasing, and concave up.

---

[7]In fact, we need to take the average rate of change over an arbitrarily small interval.

Problems

Are the functions in Problems 13–17 increasing or decreasing? What does the scenario tell you about the concavity of the graph modeling it?

13. When money is deposited in the bank, the amount of money increases slowly at first. As the size of the account increases, the amount of money increases more rapidly, since the account is earning interest on the new interest, as well as on the original amount.

14. After a cup of hot chocolate is poured, the temperature cools off very rapidly at first, and then cools off more slowly, until the temperature of the hot chocolate eventually reaches room temperature.

15. When a rumor begins, the number of people who have heard the rumor increases slowly at first. As the rumor spreads, the rate of increase gets greater (as more people continue to tell their friends the rumor), and then slows down again (when almost everyone has heard the rumor).

16. When a drug is injected into a person's bloodstream, the amount of the drug present in the body increases rapidly at first. If the person receives daily injections, the body metabolizes the drug so that the amount of the drug present in the body continues to increase, but at a decreasing rate. Eventually, the quantity levels off at a saturation level.

17. When a new product is introduced, the number of people who use the product increases slowly at first, and then the rate of increase is faster (as more and more people learn about the product). Eventually, the rate of increase slows down again (when most people who are interested in the product are already using it).

18. Match each story with the table and graph which best represent it.

   (a) When you study a foreign language, the number of new verbs you learn increases rapidly at first, but slows almost to a halt as you approach your saturation level.

   (b) You board an airplane in Philadelphia heading west. Your distance from the Atlantic Ocean, in kilometers, increases at a constant rate.

   (c) The interest on your savings plan is compounded annually. At first your balance grows slowly, but its rate of growth continues to increase.

(E)

x	0	5	10	15	20	25
y	20	275	360	390	395	399

(F)

x	0	5	10	15	20	25
y	20	36	66	120	220	400

(G)

x	0	5	10	15	20	25
y	20	95	170	245	320	395

(I)   (II)   (III)

19. Match each of the following descriptions with an appropriate graph and table of values.

   (a) The weight of your jumbo box of Fruity Flakes decreases by an equal amount every week.

   (b) The machinery depreciated rapidly at first, but its value declined more slowly as time went on.

   (c) In free fall, your distance from the ground decreases faster and faster.

   (d) For a while it looked like the decline in profits was slowing down, but then they began declining ever more rapidly.

(E)

x	0	1	2	3	4	5
y	400	384	336	256	144	0

(F)

x	0	1	2	3	4	5
y	400	320	240	160	80	0

(G)

x	0	1	2	3	4	5
y	400	184	98	63	49	43

(H)

x	0	1	2	3	4	5
y	412	265	226	224	185	38

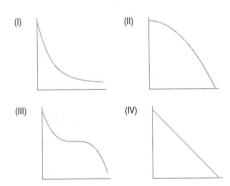

(I)   (II)

(III)   (IV)

20. An incumbent politician running for reelection declared that the number of violent crimes is no longer rising and is presently under control. Does the graph shown in Figure 2.26 support this claim? Why or why not?

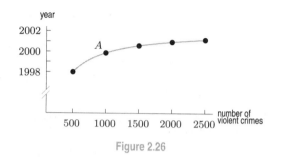

Figure 2.26

21. The rate at which water is entering a reservoir is given for time $t > 0$ by the graph in Figure 2.27. A negative rate means that water is leaving the reservoir. For each of the following statements, give the largest interval on which:

(a) The volume of water is increasing.
(b) The volume of water is constant.
(c) The volume of water is increasing fastest.
(d) The volume of water is decreasing.

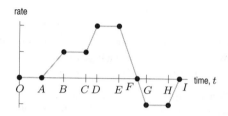

Figure 2.27

22. The relationship between the swimming speed U (in cm/sec) of a salmon to the length l of the salmon (in cm) is given by the function[8]

$$U = 19.5\sqrt{l}.$$

(a) If one salmon is 4 times the length of another salmon, how are their swimming speeds related?
(b) Graph the function $U = 19.5\sqrt{l}$. Describe the graph using words such as increasing, decreasing, concave up, concave down.
(c) Using a property that you described in part (b), answer the question "Do larger salmon swim faster than smaller ones?"
(d) Using a property that you described in part (b), answer the question "Imagine four salmon—two small and two large. The smaller salmon differ in length by 1 cm, as do the two larger. Is the difference in speed between the two smaller fish, greater than, equal to, or smaller than the difference in speed between the two larger fish?"

2.6 QUADRATIC FUNCTIONS

A baseball is "popped" straight up by a batter. The height of the ball above the ground is given by the function $y = f(t) = -16t^2 + 64t + 3$, where t is time in seconds after the ball leaves the bat and y is in feet. See Figure 2.28. Although the path of the ball is straight up and down, the graph of its height as a function of time is concave down. The ball goes up fast at first and then more slowly because of gravity.

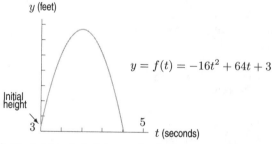

Figure 2.28: The height of a ball t seconds after being "popped up". (Note: This graph does not represent the ball's path)

[8]From K. Schmidt-Nielsen, *Scaling, Why is Animal Size so Important?* (Cambridge: CUP, 1984).

The baseball height function is an example of a *quadratic function*, whose general form is $y = ax^2 + bx + c$.

Finding the Zeros of a Quadratic Function

A natural question to ask is when the ball hits the ground. The graph suggests that $y = 0$ when $t \approx 4$. (See Problem 25 on page 92.) We can phrase the question symbolically: For what value of t does $f(t) = 0$? Input values of t which make the output $f(t) = 0$ are called *zeros* of f. It is easy to find the zeros of a quadratic function if its formula can be factored (see the Tools section to review factoring).

Example 1 Find the zeros of $f(x) = x^2 - x - 6$.

Solution   To find the zeros, set $f(x) = 0$ and solve for x by factoring:

$$x^2 - x - 6 = 0$$
$$(x - 3)(x + 2) = 0.$$

Thus the zeros are $x = 3$ and $x = -2$.

Some quadratic functions can be expressed in *factored form*,

$$q(x) = a(x - r)(x - s),$$

where a, r, and s are constants, $a \neq 0$. Note that r and s are zeros of the function q. The factored form of the function f in Example 1 is $f(x) = (x - 3)(x + 2)$.

We can also find the zeros of a quadratic function by using the quadratic formula. (See the Tools section to review the quadratic formula.)

Example 2 Find the zeros of $f(x) = x^2 - x - 6$ by using the quadratic formula.

Solution   We must solve the equation $x^2 - x - 6 = 0$. For this equation, $a = 1$, $b = -1$, and $c = -6$. Thus

$$x = \frac{-b \pm \sqrt{b^2 - 4ac}}{2a} = \frac{-(-1) \pm \sqrt{(-1)^2 - 4(1)(-6)}}{2(1)}$$
$$= \frac{1 \pm \sqrt{25}}{2} = 3 \text{ or } -2.$$

The zeros are $x = 3$ and $x = -2$, the same as we found by factoring.

The zeros of a function occur at the x-intercepts of its graph. Not every quadratic function has x-intercepts, as we see in the next example.

Example 3 Figure 2.29 shows a graph of $h(x) = -\frac{1}{2}x^2 - 2$. What happens if we try to use algebra to find its zeros?

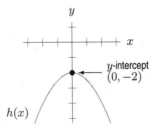

Figure 2.29

Solution

To find the zeros, we solve the equation

$$-\frac{1}{2}x^2 - 2 = 0$$

$$-\frac{1}{2}x^2 = 2$$

$$x^2 = -4$$

$$x = \pm\sqrt{-4}.$$

Since $\sqrt{-4}$ is not a real number, there are no real solutions, so h has no real zeros. This corresponds to the fact that the graph of h in Figure 2.29 does not cross the x-axis.

Concavity and Quadratic Functions

Unlike a linear function, whose graph is a straight line, a quadratic function has a graph which is either concave up or concave down.

Example 4   Let $f(x) = x^2$. Find the average rate of change of f over the intervals of length 2 between $x = -4$ and $x = 4$. What do these rates tell you about the concavity of the graph of f?

Solution

Between $x = -4$ and $x = -2$, we have

$$\frac{\text{Average rate of change}}{\text{of } f} = \frac{f(-2) - f(-4)}{-2 - (-4)} = \frac{(-2)^2 - (-4)^2}{-2 + 4} = -6.$$

Between $x = -2$ and $x = 0$, we have

$$\frac{\text{Average rate of change}}{\text{of } f} = \frac{f(0) - f(-2)}{0 - (-2)} = \frac{0^2 - (-2)^2}{0 + 2} = -2.$$

Between $x = 0$ and $x = 2$, we have

$$\frac{\text{Average rate of change}}{\text{of } f} = \frac{f(2) - f(0)}{2 - 0} = \frac{2^2 - 0^2}{2 - 0} = 2.$$

Between $x = 2$ and $x = 4$, we have

$$\frac{\text{Average rate of change}}{\text{of } f} = \frac{f(4) - f(2)}{4 - 2} = \frac{4^2 - 2^2}{4 - 2} = 6.$$

Since these rates are increasing, we expect the graph of f to be bending upward. Figure 2.30 confirms that the graph is concave up.

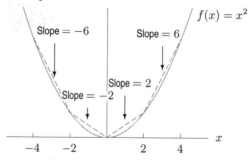

Figure 2.30

Example 5   A high diver jumps off a 10-meter springboard. For h in meters and t in seconds after the diver leaves the board, her height above the water is in Figure 2.31 and given by

$$h = f(t) = -4.9t^2 + 8t + 10.$$

(a) Find and interpret the domain and range of the function and the intercepts of the graph.

(b) Identify the concavity.

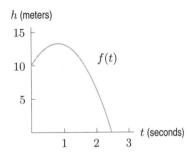

Figure 2.31: Height of diver as a function of time

Solution   (a) The diver enters the water when her height is 0. This occurs when

$$h = f(t) = -4.9t^2 + 8t + 10 = 0.$$

Using the quadratic formula to solve this equation, we find $t = 2.462$ seconds. The domain is the interval of time the diver is in the air, namely $0 \leq t \leq 2.462$. To find the range of f, we look for the largest and smallest outputs for h. From the graph, the diver's maximum height appears to occur at about $t = 1$, so we estimate the largest output value for f to be

$$f(1) = -4.9 \cdot 1^2 + 8 \cdot 1 + 10 = 13.1 \text{ meters}$$

Thus, the range of f is approximately $0 \leq f(t) \leq 13.1$.

The vertical intercept of the graph is

$$f(0) = -4.9 \cdot 0^2 + 8 \cdot 0 + 10 = 10 \text{ meters}.$$

The diver's initial height is 10 meters (the height of the springboard). The horizontal intercept is the point where $f(t) = 0$, which we found in part (a). The diver enters the water approximately 2.462 seconds after leaving the springboard.

(b) In Figure 2.31, we see that the graph is bending downward over its entire domain, so it is concave down. This is confirmed by Table 2.21, which shows that the rate of change, $\Delta h / \Delta t$, is decreasing.

Table 2.21

t (sec)	h (meters)	Rate of change $\Delta h / \Delta t$
0	10	
		5.55
0.5	12.775	
		0.65
1.0	13.100	
		−4.25
1.5	10.975	
		−9.15
2.0	6.400	

Exercises and Problems for Section 2.6

Exercises

Are the functions in Exercises 1–7 quadratic? If so, write the function in the form $f(x) = ax^2 + bx + c$.

1. $f(x) = 2(7 - x)^2 + 1$

2. $L(P) = (P + 1)(1 - P)$

3. $g(m) = m(m^2 - 2m) + 3\left(14 - \dfrac{m^3}{3}\right) + \sqrt{3}m$

4. $h(t) = -16(t - 3)(t + 1)$

5. $R(q) = \dfrac{1}{q^2}(q^2 + 1)^2$

6. $K(x) = 13^2 + 13^x$

7. $T(n) = \sqrt{5} + \sqrt{3n^4} - \sqrt{\dfrac{n^4}{4}}$

8. Find the zeros of $Q(r) = 2r^2 - 6r - 36$ by factoring.

9. Find the zeros of $Q(x) = 5x - x^2 + 3$ using the quadratic formula.

10. Find two quadratic functions with zeros $x = 1, x = 2$.

11. Solve for x using the quadratic formula and demonstrate your solution graphically:

    (a) $6x - \frac{1}{3} = 3x^2$ **(b)** $2x^2 + 7.2 = 5.1x$

12. Without a calculator, graph $y = 3x^2 - 16x - 12$ by factoring and plotting zeros.

In Exercises 13–24, find the zeros (if any) of the function algebraically.

13. $y = (2 - x)(3 - 2x)$ **14.** $y = 2x^2 + 5x + 2$

15. $y = 4x^2 - 4x - 8$ **16.** $y = 7x^2 + 16x + 4$

17. $y = 9x^2 + 6x + 1$ **18.** $y = 6x^2 - 17x + 12$

19. $y = 5x^2 + 2x - 1$ **20.** $y = 3x^2 - 2x + 6$

21. $y = -17x^2 + 23x + 19$ **22.** $y = 89x^2 + 55x + 34$

23. $y = x^4 + 5x^2 + 6$ **24.** $y = x - \sqrt{x} - 12$

Problems

25. Use the quadratic formula to find the time at which the baseball in Figure 2.28 on page 88 hits the ground.

26. Is there a quadratic function with zeros $x = 1$, $x = 2$ and $x = 3$?

27. Determine the concavity of the graph of $f(x) = 4 - x^2$ between $x = -1$ and $x = 5$ by calculating average rates of change over intervals of length 2.

28. Graph a quadratic function which has all the following properties: concave up, y-intercept is -6, zeros at $x = -2$ and $x = 3$.

29. Without a calculator, graph the following function by factoring and plotting zeros:

$$y = -4cx + x^2 + 4c^2 \quad \text{for} \quad c > 0$$

30. A ball is thrown into the air. Its height (in feet) t seconds later is given by $h(t) = 80t - 16t^2$.

    (a) Evaluate and interpret $h(2)$.
    (b) Solve the equation $h(t) = 80$. Interpret your solutions and illustrate them on a graph of $h(t)$.

31. Let $V(t) = t^2 - 4t + 4$ represent the velocity of an object in meters per second.

    (a) What is the object's initial velocity?
    (b) When is the object not moving?
    (c) Identify the concavity of the velocity graph.

32. The percentage of schools with interactive videodisc players[9] each year from 1992 to 1996 is shown in Table 2.22. If x is in years since 1992, show that this data set can be approximated by the quadratic function $p(x) = -0.8x^2 + 8.8x + 7.2$. What does this model predict for the year 2004? How good is this model for predicting the future?

Table 2.22

Year	1992	1993	1994	1995	1996
Percentage	8	14	21	29.1	29.3

[9]Data from R. Famighetti, ed. *The World Almanac and Book of Facts: 1999*. (New Jersey: Funk and Wagnalls, 1998).

33. Let $f(x) = x^2$ and $g(x) = x^2 + 2x - 8$.

(a) Graph f and g in the window $-10 \leq x \leq 10$, $-10 \leq y \leq 10$. How are the two graphs similar? How are they different?

(b) Graph f and g in the window $-10 \leq x \leq 10$, $-10 \leq y \leq 100$. Why do the two graphs appear more similar on this window than on the window from part (a)?

(c) Graph f and g in the window $-20 \leq x \leq 20$, $-10 \leq y \leq 400$, the window $-50 \leq x \leq 50$, $-10 \leq y \leq 2500$, and the window $-500 \leq x \leq 500$, $-2500 \leq y \leq 250,000$. Describe the change in appearance of f and g on these three successive windows.

34. A relief package is dropped from a moving airplane. Since the package is initially released with a forward horizontal velocity, it follows a parabolic path (instead of dropping straight down). Figure 2.32 shows the height of the package, h, in km, as a function of the horizontal distance, d, in meters, it has traveled since it was dropped.

(a) From what height was the package released?

(b) How far away from the spot above which it was released does the package hit the ground?

(c) Write a formula for $h(d)$. [Hint: The package starts falling at the highest point on the parabola].

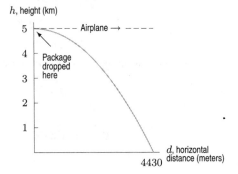

Figure 2.32

35. (a) Fit a quadratic function to the first three data points in Table 2.23. Use the fifth point as a check.

(b) Find the formula for a linear function that passes through the second two data points.

(c) Compare the value of the linear function at $x = 3$ to the value of the quadratic at $x = 3$.

(d) Compare the values of the linear and quadratic functions at $x = 50$.

(e) For approximately what x values do the quadratic and linear function values differ by less than 0.05? Using a calculator or computer, graph both functions on the same axes and estimate an answer.

Table 2.23

x	0	1	2	3	50
y	1.0	3.01	5.04	7.09	126.0

CHAPTER SUMMARY

- **Input and Output**
  Evaluating functions: finding $f(a)$ for given a.
  Solving equations: finding x if $f(x) = b$ for given b.

- **Domain and Range**
  Domain: set of input values.
  Range: set of output values
  Piecewise functions: different formulas on different intervals.

- **Inverse functions**
  If $y = f(x)$, then $f^{-1}(y) = x$.
  Evaluating $f^{-1}(b)$. Interpretation of $f^{-1}(b)$. Formula for $f^{-1}(y)$ given formula for $f(x)$.

- **Concavity**
  Concave up: increasing rate of change.
  Concave down: decreasing rate of change.

- **Quadratic Functions**
  Standard form for quadratic functions:

  $$f(x) = ax^2 + bx + c, \quad a \neq 0.$$

  Factored form gives zeros r, s of quadratic:

  $$f(x) = a(x - r)(x - s).$$

  Quadratic formula:

  $$x = \frac{-b \pm \sqrt{b^2 - 4ac}}{2a}.$$

REVIEW EXERCISES AND PROBLEMS FOR CHAPTER TWO

Exercises

If $p(r) = r^2 + 5$, evaluate the expressions in Exercises 1–2.

1. $p(7)$ **2.** $p(x) + p(8)$

3. Let $h(x) = x^2 + bx + c$. Evaluate and simplify:

   (a) $h(1)$ **(b)** $h(b+1)$

4. If $g(x) = x\sqrt{x} + 100x$, evaluate without a calculator

   (a) $g(100)$ **(b)** $g(4/25)$ **(c)** $g(1.21 \cdot 10^4)$

5. Find the zeros of $s(l) = 7l - l^2$.

6. **(a)** How can you tell from the graph of a function that an x-value is not in the domain? Sketch an example.
   (b) How can you tell from the formula for a function that an x-value is not in the domain? Give an example.

In Exercises 7–10, state the domain and range.

7. $h(x) = x^2 + 8x$ **8.** $f(x) = \sqrt{x - 4}$

9. $r(x) \quad = \quad$ **10.** $g(x) = \dfrac{4}{4 + x^2}$
$\dfrac{}{\sqrt{4 - \sqrt{x - 4}}}$

11. Let $g(x) = x^2 + x$. Evaluate and simplify the following.

   (a) $-3g(x)$ **(b)** $g(1) - x$
   (c) $g(x) + \pi$ **(d)** $\sqrt{g(x)}$
   (e) $g(1)/(x+1)$ **(f)** $(g(x))^2$

12. Let $f(x) = 1 - x$. Evaluate and simplify the following.

   (a) $2f(x)$ **(b)** $f(x) + 1$ **(c)** $f(1 - x)$
   (d) $(f(x))^2$ **(e)** $f(1)/x$ **(f)** $\sqrt{f(x)}$

In Exercises 13–14, let $f(x) = 3x - 7$, $g(x) = x^3 + 1$ to find a formula for the function.

13. $f(g(x))$ **14.** $g(f(x))$

In Exercises 15–16, find the inverse function.

15. $y = f(x) = 3x - 7$ **16.** $y = g(x) = x^3 + 1$

17. Use the graph in Figure 2.33 to fill in the missing values:

   (a) $f(0) = ?$ **(b)** $f(?) = 0$
   (c) $f^{-1}(0) = ?$ **(d)** $f^{-1}(?) = 0$

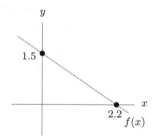

Figure 2.33

In Exercises 18–20, let $P = f(t)$ be the population, in millions, of a country at time t in years and let $E = g(P)$ be the daily electricity consumption, in megawatts, when the population is P. Give the meaning and units of the function. Assume both f and g are invertible.

18. $g(f(t))$ **19.** $f^{-1}(P)$ **20.** $g^{-1}(E)$

Problems

In Figure 2.34, show the coordinates of the point(s) representing the statements in Problems 21–24.

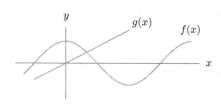

Figure 2.34

21. $f(0) = 2$

22. $f(-3) = f(3) = f(9) = 0$

23. $f(2) = g(2)$

24. $g(x) > f(x)$ for $x > 2$

In Problems 25–27, if $f(x) = \dfrac{ax}{a + x}$, find and simplify

25. $f(a)$ **26.** $f(1 - a)$ **27.** $f\left(\dfrac{1}{1 - a}\right)$

28. (a) Find the side, $s = f(d)$, of a square as function of its diagonal d.
(b) Find the area, $A = g(s)$, of a square as function of its side s.
(c) Find the area $A = h(d)$ as a function of d.
(d) What is the relation between f, g, and h?

29. The cost of producing q thousand loaves of bread is $C(q)$ dollars. Interpret the following statements in terms of bread; give units.

(a) $C(5) = 653$
(b) $C^{-1}(80) = 0.62$
(c) The solution to $C(q) = 790$ is 6.3
(d) The solution to $C^{-1}(x) = 1.2$ is 150.

In Exercises 30–32, let $H = f(t) = \frac{5}{9}(t - 32)$, where H is temperature in degrees Celsius and t is in degrees Fahrenheit.

30. Find and interpret the inverse function, $f^{-1}(H)$.

31. Using the results of Exercise 30, evaluate and interpret:

(a) $f(0)$ **(b)** $f^{-1}(0)$
(c) $f(100)$ **(d)** $f^{-1}(100)$

32. The temperature, $t = g(n) = 68 + 10 \cdot 2^{-n}$, in degrees Fahrenheit of a room is a function of the number, n, of hours that the air conditioner has been running. Find and interpret $f(g(n))$. Give units.

33. The period, T, of a pendulum of length l is given by $T = f(l) = 2\pi\sqrt{l/g}$, where g is a constant. Find a formula for $f^{-1}(T)$ and explain its meaning.

34. The area, in square centimeters, of a circle whose radius is r cm is given by $A = \pi r^2$.

(a) Write this formula using function notation, where f is the name of the function.
(b) Evaluate $f(0)$.
(c) Evaluate and interpret $f(r + 1)$.
(d) Evaluate and interpret $f(r) + 1$.
(e) What are the units of $f^{-1}(4)$?

35. An epidemic of influenza spreads through a city. Figure 2.35 is the graph of $I = f(w)$, where I is the number of individuals (in thousands) infected w weeks after the epidemic begins.

(a) Evaluate $f(2)$ and explain its meaning in terms of the epidemic.
(b) Approximately how many people were infected at the height of the epidemic? When did that occur? Write your answer in the form $f(a) = b$.
(c) Solve $f(w) = 4.5$ and explain what the solutions mean in terms of the epidemic.
(d) The graph used $f(w) = 6w(1.3)^{-w}$. Use the graph to estimate the solution of the inequality

$6w(1.3)^{-w} \geq 6$. Explain what the solution means in terms of the epidemic.

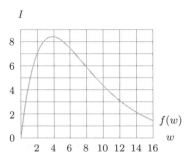

Figure 2.35

36. Let t be time in seconds and let $r(t)$ be the rate, in gallons/second, that water enters a reservoir:

$$r(t) = 800 - 40t.$$

(a) Evaluate the expressions $r(0), r(15), r(25)$, and explain their physical significance.
(b) Graph $y = r(t)$ for $0 \leq t \leq 30$, labeling the intercepts. What is the physical significance of the slope and the intercepts?
(c) For $0 \leq t \leq 30$, when does the reservoir have the most water? When does it have the least water?
(d) What are the domain and range of $r(t)$?

37. Suppose that $f(x)$ is invertible and that both f and f^{-1} are defined for all values of x. Let $f(2) = 3$ and $f^{-1}(5) = 4$. Evaluate the following expressions, or, if the given information is insufficient, write unknown.

(a) $f^{-1}(3)$ **(b)** $f^{-1}(4)$ **(c)** $f(4)$

38. Suppose that $j(x) = h^{-1}(x)$ and that both j and h are defined for all values of x. Let $h(4) = 2$ and $j(5) = -3$. Evaluate if possible:

(a) $j(h(4))$ **(b)** $j(4)$ **(c)** $h(j(4))$
(d) $j(2)$ **(e)** $h^{-1}(-3)$ **(f)** $j^{-1}(-3)$
(g) $h(5)$ **(h)** $(h(-3))^{-1}$ **(i)** $(h(2))^{-1}$

39. Values of f and g are given in Table 2.24.

(a) Evaluate $f(1)$ and $g(3)$.
(b) Describe in full sentences the patterns you see in the values for each function.
(c) Assuming that the patterns you observed in part (b) hold true for all values of x, calculate $f(5), f(-2)$, $g(5)$, and $g(-2)$.
(d) Find possible formulas for $f(x)$ and $g(x)$.

Table 2.24

x	-1	0	1	2	3	4
$f(x)$	-4	-1	2	5	8	11
$g(x)$	4	1	0	1	4	9

40. Let $k(x) = 6 - x^2$.

(a) Find a point on the graph of $k(x)$ whose x-coordinate is -2.

(b) Find two points on the graph whose y-coordinates are -2.

(c) Graph $k(x)$ and locate the points in parts (a) and (b).

(d) Let $p = 2$. Calculate $k(p) - k(p - 1)$.

41. Let $f(a)$ be the cost in dollars of a pounds of organic apples at the Gourmet Garage in New York City in January 2006. What do the following statements tell you? What are the units of each of the numbers?

(a) $f(2) = 4.98$ (b) $f(0.5) = 1.25$

(c) $f^{-1}(0.62) = 0.25$ (d) $f^{-1}(12.45) = 5$

42. Let $t(x)$ be the time required, in seconds, to melt 1 gram of a compound at $x°C$.

(a) Express the following statement as an equation using $t(x)$: It takes 272 seconds to melt 1 gram of the compound at $400°C$.

(b) Explain the following equations in words:

    (i) $t(800) = 136$ (ii) $t^{-1}(68) = 1600$

(c) Above a certain temperature, doubling the temperature, x, halves the melting time. Express this fact with an equation involving $t(x)$.

43. Table 2.25 shows $N(s)$, the number of sections of Economics 101, as a function of s, the number of students in the course. If s is between two numbers listed in the table, then $N(s)$ is the higher number of sections.

Table 2.25

s	50	75	100	125	150	175	200
$N(s)$	4	4	5	5	6	6	7

(a) Evaluate and interpret:

    (i) $N(150)$ (ii) $N(80)$ (iii) $N(55.5)$

(b) Solve for s and interpret:

    (i) $N(s) = 4$ (ii) $N(s) = N(125)$

Problems 44–45 concern studies which indicate that as carbon dioxide (CO_2) levels rise, hurricanes will become more intense.[10] Hurricane intensity is measured in terms of the minimum central pressure (in mb): the lower the pressure, the more powerful the storm. Since warm ocean waters fuel hurricanes, P is a decreasing function of H, sea surface temperature in $°C$. Let $P = n(H)$ be the hurricane-intensity function for present-day CO_2 levels, and let $P = N(H)$ be the hurricane-intensity function for future projected CO_2 levels. If H_0 is the average temperature in the Caribbean Sea, what do the following quantities tell you about hurricane intensity?

44. $N(H_0) - n(H_0)$ **45.** $n(H_0 + 1) - n(H_0)$

46. Table 2.26 shows the population, P, in millions, of Ireland[11] at various times between 1780 and 1910, with t in years since 1780.

(a) When was the population increasing? Decreasing?

(b) For each successive time interval, construct a table showing the average rate of change of the population.

(c) From the table you constructed in part (b), when is the graph of the population concave up? Concave down?

(d) When was the average rate of change of the population the greatest? The least? How is this related to part (c)? What does this mean in human terms?

(e) Graph the data in Table 2.26 and join the points by a curve to show the trend in the data. From this graph identify where the curve is increasing, decreasing, concave up and concave down. Compare your answers to those you got in parts (a) and (c). Identify the region you found in part (d).

(f) Something catastrophic happened in Ireland between 1780 and 1910. When? What happened in Ireland at that time to cause this catastrophe?

Table 2.26   *The population of Ireland from 1780 to 1910, where $t = 0$ corresponds to 1780*

t	0	20	40	60	70	90	110	130
P	4.0	5.2	6.7	8.3	6.9	5.4	4.7	4.4

---

[10] Journal of Climate, September 14, 2004, pages 3477–3495.

[11] Adapted from D. N. Burghes and A. D. Wood, Ellis Horwood, *Mathematical Models in the Social, Management and Life Science*, p. 104 (Ellis Horwood, 1980).

47. The surface area of a cylindrical aluminum can is a measure of how much aluminum the can requires. If the can has radius r and height h, its surface area A and its volume V are given by the equations:

$$A = 2\pi r^2 + 2\pi rh \quad \text{and} \quad V = \pi r^2 h.$$

(a) The volume, V, of a 12 oz cola can is 355 cm³. A cola can is approximately cylindrical. Express its surface area A as a function of its radius r, where r is measured in centimeters. [Hint: First solve for h in terms of r.]

(b) Graph $A = s(r)$, the surface area of a cola can whose volume is 355 cm³, for $0 \leq r \leq 10$.

(c) What is the domain of $s(r)$? Based on your graph, what, approximately, is the range of $s(r)$?

(d) The manufacturers wish to use the least amount of aluminum (in cm²) necessary to make a 12 oz cola can. Use your answer in (c) to find the minimum amount of aluminum needed. State the values of r and h that minimize the amount of aluminum used.

(e) The radius of a real 12 oz cola can is about 3.25 cm. Show that real cola cans use more aluminum than necessary to hold 12 oz of cola. Why do you think real cola cans are made to this way?

CHECK YOUR UNDERSTANDING

Are the statements in Problems 1–51 true or false? Give an explanation for your answer.

1. If $f(t) = 3t^2 - 4$ then $f(2) = 0$.

2. If $f(x) = x^2 - 9x + 10$ then $f(b) = b^2 - 9b + 10$.

3. If $f(x) = x^2$ then $f(x+h) = x^2 + h^2$.

4. If $q = \dfrac{1}{\sqrt{z^2 + 5}}$ then the values of z that make $q = \frac{1}{3}$ are $z = \pm 2$.

5. If $W = \dfrac{t+4}{t-4}$ then when $t = 8$, $W = 1$.

6. If $f(t) = t^2 + 64$ then $f(0) = 64$.

7. If $f(x) = 0$ then $x = 0$.

8. If $f(x) = x^2 + 2x + 7$ then $f(-x) = f(x)$.

9. If $g(x) = \dfrac{3}{\sqrt{x^2 + 4}}$ then $g(x)$ can never be zero.

10. If $h(p) = -6p + 9$ then $h(3) + h(4) = h(7)$.

11. The domain of a function is the set of input values.

12. If a function is being used to model a real world situation, the domain and range are often determined by the constraints of the situation being modeled.

13. The domain of $f(x) = \dfrac{4}{x-3}$ consists of all real numbers x, $x \neq 0$.

14. If $f(x) = \sqrt{2-x}$, the domain of f consists of all real numbers $x \geq 2$.

15. The range of $f(x) = \dfrac{1}{x}$ is all real numbers.

16. The range of $y = 4 - \dfrac{1}{x}$ is $0 < y < 4$.

17. If $f(x) = \frac{2}{5}x + 6$ and its domain is $15 \leq x \leq 20$ then the range of f is $12 \leq x \leq 14$.

18. The domain of $f(x) = \dfrac{x}{\sqrt{x^2 + 1}}$ is all real numbers.

19. The graph of the absolute value function $y = |x|$ has a V shape.

20. The domain of $f(x) = |x|$ is all real numbers.

21. If $f(x) = |x|$ and $g(x) = |-x|$ then for all x, $f(x) = g(x)$.

22. If $f(x) = |x|$ and $g(x) = -|x|$ then for all x, $f(x) = g(x)$.

23. If $y = \dfrac{x}{|x|}$ then $y = 1$ for $x \neq 0$.

24. If $f(x) = \begin{cases} 3 & \text{if } x < 0 \\ x^2 & \text{if } 0 \leq x \leq 4 \,, \\ 7 & \text{if } x > 4 \end{cases}$ then $f(3) = 0$.

25. Let $f(x) = \begin{cases} x & \text{if } x < 0 \\ x^2 & \text{if } 0 \leq x \leq 4 \\ -x & \text{if } x > 4 \end{cases}$ If $f(x) = 4$ then $x = 2$.

26. If $f(3) = 5$ and f is invertible, then $f^{-1}(3) = 1/5$.

27. If $h(7) = 4$ and h is invertible, then $h^{-1}(4) = 7$.

28. If $f(x) = \frac{3}{4}x - 6$ then $f^{-1}(8) = 0$.

29. If $R = f(S) = \frac{2}{3}S + 8$ then $S = f^{-1}(R) = \frac{3}{2}(R - 8)$.

30. In general $f^{-1}(x) = (f(x))^{-1}$.

31. If $f(x) = \dfrac{x}{x+1}$ then $f(t^{-1}) = \dfrac{1/t}{1/t + 1}$.

32. The units of the output of a function are the same as the units of output of its inverse.

33. The functions $f(x) = 2x + 1$ and $g(x) = \frac{1}{2}x - 1$ are inverses.

34. If $q = f(x)$ is the quantity of rice in tons required to feed x million people for a year and $p = g(q)$ is the cost, in dollars, of q tons of rice, then $g(f(x))$ is the dollar cost of feeding x million people for a year.

35. If $f(t) = t+2$ and $g(t) = 3t$, then $g(f(t)) = 3(t+2) = 3t + 6$.

36. A fireball has radius $r = f(t)$ meters t seconds after an explosion. The volume of the ball is $V = g(r)$ meter^3 when it has radius r meters. Then the units of measurement of $g(f(t))$ are meter^3/sec.

37. If the graph of a function is concave up, then the average rate of change of a function over an interval of length 1 increases as the interval moves from left to right.

38. The function f in the table could be concave up.

x	-2	0	2	4
$f(x)$	5	6	8	12

39. The function g in the table could be concave down.

t	-1	1	3	5
$g(t)$	9	8	6	3

40. A straight line is concave up.

41. A function can be both decreasing and concave down.

42. If a function is concave up, it must be increasing.

43. The quadratic function $f(x) = x(x + 2)$ is in factored form.

44. If $f(x) = (x + 1)(x + 2)$, then the zeros of f are 1 and 2.

45. A quadratic function whose graph is concave up has a maximum.

46. All quadratic equations have the form $f(x) = ax^2$.

47. If the height above the ground of an object at time t is given by $s(t) = at^2 + bt + c$, then $s(0)$ tells us when the object hits the ground.

48. To find the zeros of $f(x) = ax^2 + bx + c$, solve the equation $ax^2 + bx + c = 0$ for x.

49. Every quadratic equation has two real solutions.

50. There is only one quadratic function with zeros at $x = -2$ and $x = 2$.

51. A quadratic function has exactly two zeros.

TOOLS FOR CHAPTER 2: QUADRATIC EQUATIONS

Expanding an Expression

The *distributive property* for real numbers a, b, and c tells us that

$$a(b + c) = ab + ac,$$

and

$$(b + c)a = ba + ca.$$

We use the distributive property and the rules of exponents to multiply algebraic expressions involving parentheses. This process is sometimes referred to as *expanding* the expression.

Example 1 Multiply the following expressions and simplify.

    (a) $\;3x^2\left(x + \dfrac{1}{6}x^{-3}\right)$ (b) $\;\left((2t)^2 - 5\right)\sqrt{t}$

Solution   (a) $3x^2\left(x + \dfrac{1}{6}x^{-3}\right) = \left(3x^2\right)(x) + \left(3x^2\right)\left(\dfrac{1}{6}x^{-3}\right) = 3x^3 + \dfrac{1}{2}x^{-1}$

           (b) $\left((2t)^2 - 5\right)\sqrt{t} = (2t)^2(\sqrt{t}) - 5\sqrt{t} = \left(4t^2\right)\left(t^{1/2}\right) - 5t^{1/2} = 4t^{5/2} - 5t^{1/2}$

If there are two terms in each factor, then there are four terms in the product:

$$(a + b)(c + d) = a(c + d) + b(c + d) = ac + ad + bc + bd.$$

The following special cases of the above product occur frequently. Learning to recognize their forms aids in factoring.

$$(a + b)(a - b) = a^2 - b^2$$
$$(a + b)^2 = a^2 + 2ab + b^2$$
$$(a - b)^2 = a^2 - 2ab + b^2$$

Example 2 Expand the following and simplify by gathering like terms.

    (a) $\;(5x^2 + 2)(x - 4)$ (b) $\;(2\sqrt{r} + 2)(4\sqrt{r} - 3)$ (c) $\;\left(3 - \dfrac{1}{2}x\right)^2$

Solution   (a) $\left(5x^2 + 2\right)(x - 4) = \left(5x^2\right)(x) + \left(5x^2\right)(-4) + (2)(x) + (2)(-4) = 5x^3 - 20x^2 + 2x - 8$

           (b) $(2\sqrt{r} + 2)(4\sqrt{r} - 3) = (2)(4)(\sqrt{r})^2 + (2)(-3)(\sqrt{r}) + (2)(4)(\sqrt{r}) + (2)(-3) = 8r + 2\sqrt{r} - 6$

           (c) $\left(3 - \dfrac{1}{2}x\right)^2 = 3^2 - 2(3)\left(\dfrac{1}{2}x\right) + \left(-\dfrac{1}{2}x\right)^2 = 9 - 3x + \dfrac{1}{4}x^2$

Factoring

To write an expanded expression in factored form, we "un-multiply" the expression. Some techniques for factoring are given in this section. We can check factoring by remultiplying.

Removing a Common Factor

It is sometimes useful to factor out the same factor from each of the terms in an expression. This is basically the distributive law in reverse:

$$ab + ac = a(b + c).$$

One special case is removing a factor of -1, which gives

$$-a - b = -(a + b)$$

Another special case is

$$(a - b) = -(b - a)$$

Example 3   Factor the following:

(a) $\dfrac{2}{3}x^2y + \dfrac{4}{3}xy$ (b) $(2p+1)p^3 - 3p(2p+1)$ (c) $-\dfrac{s^2t}{8w} - \dfrac{st^2}{16w}$

Solution   (a) $\dfrac{2}{3}x^2y + \dfrac{4}{3}xy = \dfrac{2}{3}xy(x+2)$

(b) $(2p+1)p^3 - 3p(2p+1) = (p^3 - 3p)(2p+1) = p(p^2 - 3)(2p+1)$
(Note that the expression $(2p+1)$ was one of the factors common to both terms.)

(c) $-\dfrac{s^2t}{8w} - \dfrac{st^2}{16w} = -\dfrac{st}{8w}\left(s + \dfrac{t}{2}\right).$

Grouping Terms

Even though all the terms may not have a common factor, we can sometimes factor by first grouping the terms and then removing a common factor.

Example 4   Factor $x^2 - hx - x + h$.

Solution $x^2 - hx - x + h = \left(x^2 - hx\right) - (x - h) = x(x - h) - (x - h) = (x - h)(x - 1)$

Factoring Quadratics

One way to factor quadratics is to mentally multiply out the possibilities.

Example 5   Factor $t^2 - 4t - 12$.

Solution   If the quadratic factors, it will be of the form

$$t^2 - 4t - 12 = (t + ?)(t + ?).$$

We are looking for two numbers whose product is -12 and whose sum is -4. By trying combinations, we find

$$t^2 - 4t - 12 = (t - 6)(t + 2).$$

Example 6   Factor $4 - 2M - 6M^2$.

Solution   By a similar method as in the previous example, we find $4 - 2M - 6M^2 = (2 - 3M)(2 + 2M)$.

Perfect Squares and the Difference of Squares

Recognition of the special products $(x + y)^2$, $(x - y)^2$ and $(x + y)(x - y)$ in expanded form is useful in factoring. Reversing the results in the last section, we have

$$a^2 + 2ab + b^2 = (a + b)^2,$$
$$a^2 - 2ab + b^2 = (a - b)^2, \quad .$$
$$a^2 - b^2 = (a - b)(a + b).$$

When we can see that terms in an expression we want to factor are squares, it often makes sense to look for one of these forms. The difference of squares identity (the third one listed above) is especially useful.

Example 7   Factor: (a) $16y^2 - 24y + 9$ (b) $25S^2R^4 - T^6$ (c). $x^2(x - 2) + 16(2 - x)$

Solution   (a) $16y^2 - 24y + 9 = (4y - 3)^2$
(b) $25S^2R^4 - T^6 = \left(5SR^2\right)^2 - \left(T^3\right)^2 = \left(5SR^2 - T^3\right)\left(5SR^2 + T^3\right)$
(c) $x^2(x - 2) + 16(2 - x) = x^2(x - 2) - 16(x - 2) = (x - 2)\left(x^2 - 16\right) = (x - 2)(x - 4)(x + 4)$

Solving Quadratic Equations

Example 8   Give exact and approximate solutions to $x^2 = 3$.

Solution   The exact solutions are $x = \pm\sqrt{3}$; approximate ones are $x \approx \pm 1.73$, or $x \approx \pm 1.732$, or $x \approx \pm 1.73205$. (since $\sqrt{3} = 1.732050808\ldots$). Notice that the equation $x^2 = 3$ has only two exact solutions, but many possible approximate solutions, depending on how much accuracy is required.

Solving by Factoring

Some equations can be put into factored form such that the product of the factors is zero. Then we solve by using the fact that if $a \cdot b = 0$, then either a or b (or both) is zero.

Example 9   Solve $(x + 1)(x + 3) = 15$ for x.

Solution   Do not make the mistake of setting $x + 1 = 15$ and $x + 3 = 15$. It is not true that $a \cdot b = 15$ means that $a = 15$ or $b = 15$ (or both). (Although it is true that if $a \cdot b = 0$, then $a = 0$ or $b = 0$, or both.) So, we must expand the left-hand side and set the equation equal to zero:

$$x^2 + 4x + 3 = 15,$$
$$x^2 + 4x - 12 = 0.$$

Then, factoring gives

$$(x - 2)(x + 6) = 0.$$

Thus $x = 2$ and $x = -6$ are solutions.

Example 10   Solve $2(x + 3)^2 = 5(x + 3)$.

Solution You might be tempted to divide both sides by $(x + 3)$. However, if you do this you will overlook one of the solutions. Instead, write

$$2(x+3)^2 - 5(x+3) = 0$$
$$(x+3)\left(2(x+3) - 5\right) = 0$$
$$(x+3)(2x + 6 - 5) = 0$$
$$(x+3)(2x + 1) = 0.$$

Thus, $x = -\dfrac{1}{2}$ and $x = -3$ are solutions.

Solving with the Quadratic Formula

Alternatively, we can solve the equation $ax^2 + bx + c = 0$ by using the quadratic formula:

$$x = \frac{-b \pm \sqrt{b^2 - 4ac}}{2a}.$$

The quadratic formula is derived by completing the square for $y = ax^2 + bx + c$. See page 239 in Tools for Chapter 5.

Example 11 Solve $11 + 2x = x^2$.

Solution The equation is

$$-x^2 + 2x + 11 = 0.$$

The expression on the left does not factor using integers, so we use

$$x = \frac{-2 + \sqrt{4 - 4(-1)(11)}}{2(-1)} = \frac{-2 + \sqrt{48}}{-2} = \frac{-2 + \sqrt{16 \cdot 3}}{-2} = \frac{-2 + 4\sqrt{3}}{-2} = 1 - 2\sqrt{3},$$

$$x = \frac{-2 - \sqrt{4 - 4(-1)(11)}}{2(-1)} = \frac{-2 - \sqrt{48}}{-2} = \frac{-2 - \sqrt{16 \cdot 3}}{-2} = \frac{-2 - 4\sqrt{3}}{-2} = 1 + 2\sqrt{3}.$$

The exact solutions are $x = 1 - 2\sqrt{3}$ and $x = 1 + 2\sqrt{3}$.

The decimal approximations to these numbers $x = 1 - 2\sqrt{3} = -2.464$ and $x = 1 + 2\sqrt{3} = 4.464$ are approximate solutions to this equation. The approximate solutions could be found directly from a graph or calculator.

Exercises on Tools for Chapter 2

For Exercises 1–18, expand and simplify.

1. $3(x + 2)$

2. $5(x - 3)$

3. $2(3x - 7)$

4. $-4(y + 6)$

5. $12(x + y)$

6. $-7(5x - 8y)$

7. $x(2x + 5)$

8. $3z(2x - 9z)$

9. $-10r(5r + 6rs)$

10. $x(3x - 8) + 2(3x - 8)$

11. $5z(x - 2) - 3(x - 2)$

12. $(x + 1)(x + 3)$

13. $(x - 2)(x + 6)$

14. $(5x - 1)(2x - 3)$

15. $(x + 2)(3x - 8)$

16. $(y + 1)(z + 3)$

17. $(12y - 5)(8w + 7)$

18. $(5z - 3)(x - 2)$

Multiply and write the expressions in Problems 19–27 without parentheses. Gather like terms.

19. $-(x - 3) - 2(5 - x)$

20. $(x - 5)6 - 5(1 - (2 - x))$

21. $\left(3x - 2x^2\right)4 + (5 + 4x)(3x - 4)$

22. $\left(t^2 + 1\right)50t - \left(25t^2 + 125\right)2t$

23. $P(p - 3q)^2$

24. $\left(A^2 - B^2\right)^2$

25. $4(x - 3)^2 + 7$

26. $-\left(\sqrt{2x} + 1\right)^2$

27. $u\left(u^{-1} + 2^u\right)2^u$

For Exercises 28–76, factor completely if possible.

28. $2x + 6$

29. $3y + 15$

30. $5z - 30$

31. $4t - 6$

32. $10w - 25$

33. $u^2 - 2u$

34. $3u^4 - 4u^3$

35. $3u^7 + 12u^2$

36. $12x^3y^2 - 18x$

37. $14r^4s^2 - 21rst$

38. $x^2 + 3x + 2$

39. $x^2 + 3x - 2$

40. $x^2 - 3x + 2$

41. $x^2 - 3x - 2$

42. $x^2 + 2x + 3$

43. $x^2 - 2x - 3$

44. $x^2 - 2x + 3$

45. $x^2 + 2x - 3$

46. $2x^2 + 5x + 2$

47. $3x^2 - x - 4$

48. $2x^2 - 10x + 12$

49. $x^2 + 3x - 28$

50. $x^3 - 2x^2 - 3x$

51. $x^3 + 2x^2 - 3x$

52. $ac + ad + bc + bd$

53. $x^2 + 2xy + 3xz + 6yz$

54. $x^2 - 1.4x - 3.92$

55. $a^2x^2 - b^2$

56. $\pi r^2 + 2\pi rh$

57. $B^2 - 10B + 24$

58. $c^2 + x^2 - 2cx$

59. $x^2 + y^2$

60. $a^4 - a^2 - 12$

61. $(t + 3)^2 - 16$

62. $x^2 + 4x + 4 - y^2$

63. $a^3 - 2a^2 + 3a - 6$

64. $b^3 - 3b^2 - 9b + 27$

65. $c^2d^2 - 25c^2 - 9d^2 + 225$

66. $hx^2 + 12 - 4hx - 3x$

67. $r(r - s) - 2(s - r)$

68. $y^2 - 3xy + 2x^2$

69. $x^2e^{-3x} + 2xe^{-3x}$

70. $t^2e^{5t} + 3te^{5t} + 2e^{5t}$

71. $(s + 2t)^2 - 4p^2$

72. $P(1 + r)^2 + P(1 + r)^2r$

73. $x^2 - 6x + 9 - 4z^2$

74. $dk + 2dm - 3ek - 6em$

75. $\pi r^2 - 2\pi r + 3r - 6$

76. $8gs - 12hs + 10gm - 15hm$

Solve the equations in Exercises 77–108.

77. $x^2 + 7x + 6 = 0$

78. $y^2 - 5y - 6 = 0$

79. $2w^2 + w - 10 = 0$

80. $4s^2 + 3s - 15 = 0$

81. $\dfrac{2}{x} + \dfrac{3}{2x} = 8$

82. $\dfrac{3}{x - 1} + 1 = 5$

83. $\sqrt{y - 1} = 13$

84. $\sqrt{5y + 3} = 7$

85. $\sqrt{2x - 1} + 3 = 9$

86. $\dfrac{21}{z - 5} - \dfrac{13}{z^2 - 5z} = 3$

87. $-16t^2 + 96t + 12 = 60$

88. $r^3 - 6r^2 = 5r - 30$

89. $g^3 - 4g = 3g^2 - 12$

90. $8 + 2x - 3x^2 = 0$

91. $2p^3 + p^2 - 18p - 9 = 0$

92. $N^2 - 2N - 3 = 2N(N - 3)$

93. $\dfrac{1}{64}t^3 = t$

94. $x^2 - 1 = 2x$

95. $4x^2 - 13x - 12 = 0$

96. $60 = -16t^2 + 96t + 12$

97. $n^5 + 80 = 5n^4 + 16n$

98. $5a^3 + 50a^2 = 4a + 40$

99. $y^2 + 4y - 2 = 0$

100. $\dfrac{2}{z - 3} + \dfrac{7}{z^2 - 3z} = 0$

101. $\dfrac{x^2 + 1 - 2x^2}{(x^2 + 1)^2} = 0$

102. $4 - \dfrac{1}{L^2} = 0$

103. $2 + \dfrac{1}{q + 1} - \dfrac{1}{q - 1} = 0$

104. $\sqrt{r^2 + 24} = 7$

105. $\dfrac{1}{\sqrt[3]{x}} = -2$

106. $3\sqrt{x} = \dfrac{1}{2}x$

107. $10 = \sqrt{\dfrac{v}{7\pi}}$

108. $\dfrac{(3x + 4)(x - 2)}{(x - 5)(x - 1)} = 0$

In Exercises 109–112, solve for the indicated variable.

109. $T = 2\pi\sqrt{\dfrac{l}{g}}$, for l.

110. $Ab^5 = C$, for b.

111. $|2x + 1| = 7$, for x.

112. $\dfrac{x^2 - 5mx + 4m^2}{x - m} = 0$, for x

Solve the systems of equations in Exercises 113–117.

113. $\begin{cases} y = 2x - x^2 \\ y = -3 \end{cases}$

114. $\begin{cases} y = 1/x \\ y = 4x \end{cases}$

115. $\begin{cases} x^2 + y^2 = 36 \\ y = x - 3 \end{cases}$

116. $\begin{cases} y = 4 - x^2 \\ y - 2x = 1 \end{cases}$

117. $\begin{cases} y = x^3 - 1 \\ y = e^x \end{cases}$

118. Let ℓ be the line of slope 3 passing through the origin. Find the points of intersection of the line ℓ and the parabola whose equation is $y = x^2$. Sketch the line and the parabola, and label the points of intersection.

Determine the points of intersection for Problems 119–120.

119.

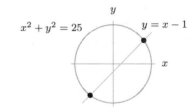

120.

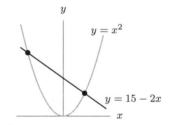

Chapter Three

EXPONENTIAL FUNCTIONS

Exponential functions represent quantities that increase or decrease at a constant percent rate. In contrast to linear functions, in which a constant amount is added per unit input, an exponential function involves multiplication by a constant factor for each unit increase in input value. Examples include the balance of a savings account, the size of some populations, and the quantity of a chemical that decays radioactively.

The Tools Section on page 146 reviews the properties of exponents.

3.1 INTRODUCTION TO THE FAMILY OF EXPONENTIAL FUNCTIONS

Growing at a Constant Percent Rate

Linear functions represent quantities that change at a constant rate. In this section we introduce functions that change at a constant *percent* rate, the *exponential functions*.

Salary Raises

Example 1   After graduation from college, you will probably be looking for a job. Suppose you are offered a job at a starting salary of $40,000 per year. To strengthen the offer, the company promises annual raises of 6% per year for at least the first five years after you are hired. Let's compute your salary for the first few years.

If t represents the number of years since the beginning of your contract, then for $t = 0$, your salary is $40,000. At the end of the first year, when $t = 1$, your salary increases by 6% so

$$\text{Salary when } t = 1 = \text{Original salary } + 6\% \text{ of Original salary}$$
$$= 40000 + 0.06 \cdot 40000$$
$$= 42400 \text{ dollars.}$$

After the second year, your salary again increases by 6%, so

$$\text{Salary when } t = 2 = \text{Former salary } + 6\% \text{ of Former salary}$$
$$= 42400 + 0.06 \cdot 42400$$
$$= 44944 \text{ dollars.}$$

Notice that your raise is higher in the second year than in the first since the second 6% increase applies both to the original $40,000 salary and to the $2400 raise given in the first year.

Salary calculations for four years have been rounded and recorded in Table 3.1. At the end of the third and fourth years your salary again increases by 6%, and your raise is larger each year. Not only are you given the 6% increase on your original salary, but your raises earn raises as well.

Table 3.1 *Raise amounts and resulting salaries for a person earning 6% annual salary increases*

Year	Raise amount ($)	Salary ($)
0		40000.00
1	2400.00	42400.00
2	2544.00	44944.00
3	2696.64	47640.64
4	2858.44	50499.08

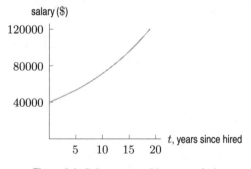

Figure 3.1: Salary over a 20-year period

Figure 3.1 shows salary over a 20-year period assuming that the annual increase remains 6%. Since the rate of change of your salary (in dollars per year) is not constant, the graph of this function is not a line. The salary increases at an increasing rate, giving the graph its upward curve.

122

Population Growth

Exponential functions provide a reasonable model for many growing populations.

Example 2   During the early 2000s, the population of Mexico increased at a constant annual percent rate of 2%. Since the population grew by the same percent each year, it can be modeled by an exponential function.

Let's calculate the population of Mexico for the first few years after 2000. In 2000, the population was 100 million. The population grew by 2%, so

$$\text{Population in 2001} = \text{Population in 2000} + 2\% \text{ of Population in 2000}$$
$$= 100 + 0.02(100)$$
$$= 100 + 2 = 102 \text{ million.}$$

Similarly,

$$\text{Population in 2002} = \text{Population in 2001} + 2\% \text{ of Population in 2001}$$
$$= 102 + 0.02(102)$$
$$= 102 + 2.04 = 104.04 \text{ million.}$$

The calculations for years 2000 through 2004 have been rounded and recorded in Table 3.2. The population of Mexico increased by slightly more each year than it did the year before, because each year the increase is 2% of a larger number.

Table 3.2   *Calculated values for the population of Mexico*

Year	ΔP, increase in population	P, population (millions)
2000	—	100
2001	2	102
2002	2.04	104.04
2003	2.08	106.12
2004	2.12	108.24

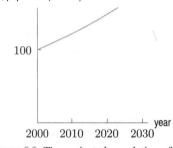

Figure 3.2: The projected population of Mexico, assuming 2% annual growth

Figure 3.2 gives a graph of the population of Mexico over a 30-year period, assuming a 2% annual growth rate. Notice that this graph curves upward like the graph in Figure 3.1.

Radioactive Decay

Exponential functions can also model decreasing quantities. A quantity which decreases at a constant percent rate is said to be decreasing exponentially.

Example 3   Carbon-14 is used to estimate the age of organic compounds. Over time, radioactive carbon-14 decays into a stable form. The decay rate is 11.4% every 1000 years. For example, if we begin with a 200 microgram (μg) sample of carbon-14 then

$$\begin{aligned}\text{Amount remaining}\atop\text{after 1000 years} &= \text{Initial amount} - 11.4\% \text{ of Initial amount}\\ &= 200 - 0.114 \cdot 200\\ &= 177.2.\end{aligned}$$

Similarly,

$$\begin{aligned}\text{Amount remaining}\atop\text{after 2000 years} &= \text{Amount remaining}\atop\text{after 1000 years} - 11.4\% \text{ of }\ \text{Amount remaining}\atop\text{after 1000 years}\\ &= 177.2 - 0.114(177.2) \approx 156.999,\end{aligned}$$

and

$$\begin{aligned}\text{Amount remaining}\atop\text{after 3000 years} &= \text{Amount remaining}\atop\text{after 2000 years} - 11.4\% \text{ of }\ \text{Amount remaining}\atop\text{after 2000 years}\\ &= 156.999 - 0.114 \cdot 156.999 \approx 139.101.\end{aligned}$$

These calculations are recorded in Table 3.3. During each 1000-year period, the amount of carbon-14 that decays is smaller than in the previous period. This is because we take 11.4% of a smaller quantity each time.

Table 3.3 *The amount of carbon-14 remaining over time*

Years elapsed	Amount decayed (μg)	Amount remaining (μg)
0	—	200.0
1000	22.8	177.2
2000	20.2	156.999
3000	17.898	139.101

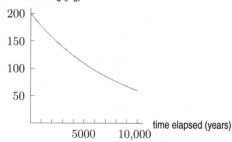

Figure 3.3: Amount of carbon-14 over 10,000 years

Figure 3.3 shows the amount of carbon-14 left from a 200 μg sample over 10,000 years. Because the amount decreases by a smaller amount over each successive time interval, the graph is not linear but bends upward.

Growth Factors and Percent Growth Rates

The Growth Factor of an Increasing Exponential Function

The salary in Example 1 increases by 6% every year. We say that the annual percent growth rate is 6%. But there is another way to think about the growth of this salary. We know that each year,

$$\text{New salary} = \text{Old salary} + 6\% \text{ of Old salary}.$$

We can rewrite this as follows:

$$\text{New salary} = 100\% \text{ of Old salary} + 6\% \text{ of Old salary}.$$

So

$$\text{New salary} = 106\% \text{ of Old salary}.$$

Since $106\% = 1.06$, we have

$$\text{New salary} = 1.06 \cdot \text{Old salary}.$$

We call the 1.06 the *annual growth factor*.

The Growth Factor of a Decreasing Exponential Function

In Example 3, the carbon-14 changes by -11.4% every 1000 years. The negative growth rate tells us that the quantity of carbon-14 decreases over time. We have

$$\text{New amount} = \text{Old amount} - 11.4\% \text{ of Old amount},$$

which can be rewritten as

$$\text{New amount} = 100\% \text{ of Old amount} - 11.4\% \text{ of Old amount}.$$

So,

$$\text{New amount} = 88.6\% \text{ of Old amount}.$$

Since $88.6\% = 0.886$, we have

$$\text{New amount} = 0.886 \cdot \text{Old amount}.$$

Hence the growth factor is 0.886 per millennium. The fact that the growth factor is less than 1 indicates that the amount of carbon-14 is decreasing, since multiplying a quantity by a factor between 0 and 1 decreases the quantity.

Although it may sound strange to refer to the growth factor, rather than decay factor, of a decreasing quantity, we will use growth factor to describe both increasing and decreasing quantities.

A General Formula for the Family of Exponential Functions

Because it grows at a constant percentage rate each year, the salary, S, in Example 1 is an example of an exponential function. We want a formula for S in terms of t, the number of years since being hired. Since the annual growth factor is 1.06, we know that for each year,

$$\text{New salary} = \text{Previous salary} \cdot 1.06.$$

Thus, after one year, or when $t = 1$,

$$S = \underbrace{40{,}000}_{\text{Previous salary}} \cdot 1.06.$$

Similarly, when $t = 2$,

$$S = \underbrace{40{,}000(1.06)}_{\text{Previous salary}} \cdot 1.06 = 40{,}000(1.06)^2.$$

Here there are *two* factors of 1.06 because the salary has increased by 6% twice. When $t = 3$,

$$S = \underbrace{40{,}000(1.06)^2}_{\text{Previous salary}} \cdot 1.06 = 40{,}000(1.06)^3$$

and continues in this pattern so that after t years have elapsed,

$$S = 40{,}000 \underbrace{(1.06)(1.06) \ldots (1.06)}_{t \text{ factors of } 1.06} = 40{,}000(1.06)^t.$$

After t years the salary has increased by a factor of 1.06 a total of t times. Thus,

$$S = 40{,}000(1.06)^t.$$

These results, which are summarized in Table 3.4, are the same as in Table 3.1. Notice that in this formula we assume that t is an integer, $t \geq 0$, since the raises are given only once a year.

Table 3.4   *Salary after t years*

t (years)	S, salary (\$)
0	40,000
1	$40{,}000(1.06) = 42{,}400.00$
2	$40{,}000(1.06)^2 = 44{,}944.00$
3	$40{,}000(1.06)^3 = 47{,}640.64$
t	$40{,}000(1.06)^t$

This salary formula can be written as

$$S = \text{Initial salary} \cdot (\text{Growth factor})^t.$$

In general, we have:

An **exponential function** $Q = f(t)$ has the formula

$$f(t) = ab^t, \quad b > 0,$$

where a is the initial value of Q (at $t = 0$) and b, the base, is the growth factor: $b > 1$ gives exponential growth, $0 < b < 1$ gives exponential decay. The growth factor is given by

$$b = 1 + r$$

where r is the decimal representation of the percent rate of change.

The constants a and b are called *parameters.*. The base b is restricted to positive values because if $b < 0$ then b^t is undefined for some exponents t, for example, $t = 1/2$.

Every function in the form $f(t) = ab^t$ with the input, t, in the exponent is an exponential function, provided $a \neq 0$. Note that if $b = 1$, then $f(t) = a \cdot 1^t = a$ and $f(t)$ is a constant, so when $b = 1$, the function is generally not considered exponential. Graphs showing exponential growth and decay are in Figures 3.4 and 3.5. Notice that in both cases the graph is concave up.

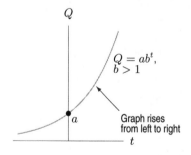

Figure 3.4: Exponential growth: $b > 1$

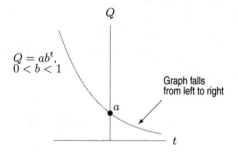

Figure 3.5: Exponential decay: $0 < b < 1$

Example 4   Use the formula $S = 40{,}000(1.06)^t$ to calculate your salary after 4 years, 12 years, and 40 years.

Solution   After 4 years, $t = 4$, and we have

$$S = 40{,}000(1.06)^4 \approx \$50{,}499.08.$$

Notice that this agrees with Table 3.1 on page 106. After 12 years, $t = 12$, and we have

$$S = 40{,}000(1.06)^{12} \approx \$80{,}487.86.$$

After 12 years, the salary has more than doubled from the initial salary of $\$40{,}000$. When $t = 40$ we have

$$S = 40{,}000(1.06)^{40} \approx \$411{,}428.72.$$

Thus if you work for 40 years and consistently earn 6% annual raises, your salary will be over $400,000 a year.

Example 5   Carbon-14 decays at a rate of 11.4% every 1000 years. Write a formula for the quantity, Q, of a 200 μg sample remaining as a function of time, t, in thousands of years.

Solution   The growth factor of carbon-14 over 1000 years is $1 - 0.114 = 0.886$. Originally, there are 200 μg, so the quantity remaining after t thousand years is given by

$$Q = 200(0.886)^t.$$

Example 6   Using Example 2 on page 107, find a formula for P, the population of Mexico (in millions), in year t where $t = 0$ represents the year 2000.

Solution   In 2000, the population of Mexico was 100 million, and it was growing at a constant 2% annual rate. The growth factor is $b = 1 + 0.02 = 1.02$, and $a = 100$, so

$$P = 100(1.02)^t.$$

Because the growth factor may change eventually, this formula may not give accurate results for large values of t.

Example 7   What does the formula $P = 100(1.02)^t$ predict when $t = 0$? When $t = -5$? What do these values tell you about the population of Mexico?

Solution   If $t = 0$, then , since $(1.02)^0 = 1$, we have

$$P = 100(1.02)^0 = 100.$$

This makes sense because $t = 0$ stands for 2000, and in 2000 the population was 100 million. When $t = -5$ we have

$$P = 100(1.02)^{-5} \approx 90.573.$$

To make sense of this number, we must interpret the year $t = -5$ as five years before 2000; that is, as the year 1995. If the population of Mexico had been growing at a 2% annual rate from 1995 onward, then it was 90.573 million in 1995.

Example 8   On August 2, 1988, a US District Court judge imposed a fine on the city of Yonkers, New York, for defying a federal court order involving housing desegregation.[1] The fine started at $100 for the first day and was to double daily until the city chose to obey the court order.

(a) What was the daily percent growth rate of the fine?
(b) Find a formula for the fine as a function of t, the number of days since August 2, 1988.
(c) If Yonkers waited 30 days before obeying the court order, what would the fine have been?

[1]*The Boston Globe,* August 27, 1988.

Solution   (a) Since the fine increased each day by a factor of 2, the fine grew exponentially with growth factor $b = 2$. To find the percent growth rate, we set $b = 1 + r = 2$, from which we find $r = 1$, or 100%. Thus the daily percent growth rate is 100%. This makes sense because when a quantity increases by 100%, it doubles in size.

(b) If t is the number of days since August 2, the formula for the fine, P in dollars, is

$$P = 100 \cdot 2^t.$$

(c) After 30 days, the fine is $P = 100 \cdot 2^{30} \approx 1.074 \cdot 10^{11}$ dollars, or $107,374,182,400.

Exercises and Problems for Section 3.1

Exercises

What is the growth factor in Exercises 1–4? Assume time is measured in the units given.

1. Water usage is increasing by 3% per year.

2. A city grows by 28% per decade.

3. A diamond mine is depleted by 1% per day.

4. A forest shrinks 80% per century.

In Exercises 5–10, you start with 500 items. How many do you have after the following change?

5. 10% increase   6. 100% increase

7. 1% decrease   8. 42% decrease

9. 42% increase followed by 42% decrease

10. 42% decrease followed by 42% increase

In Exercises 11–14, give the starting value a, the growth factor b, and the growth rate r if $Q = ab^t = a(1 + r)^t$.

11. $Q = 1750(1.593)^t$ 12. $Q = 34.3(0.788)^t$

13. $Q = 79.2(1.002)^t$ 14. $Q = 0.0022(2.31)^{-3t}$

15. Without a calculator or computer, match each exponential formula to one of the graphs I–VI.

(a) $10(1.2)^t$ (b) $10(1.5)^t$ (c) $20(1.2)^t$
(d) $30(0.85)^t$ (e) $30(0.95)^t$ (f) $30(1.05)^t$

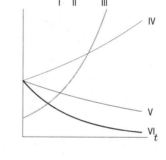

16. The populations, P, of six towns with time t in years are given by.

(i) $P = 1000(1.08)^t$ (ii) $P = 600(1.12)^t$
(iii) $P = 2500(0.9)^t$ (iv) $P = 1200(1.185)^t$
(v) $P = 800(0.78)^t$ (vi) $P = 2000(0.99)^t$

(a) Which towns are growing in size? Which are shrinking?

(b) Which town is growing the fastest? What is the annual percent growth rate for that town?

(c) Which town is shrinking the fastest? What is the annual percent "decay" rate for that town?

(d) Which town has the largest initial population (at $t = 0$)? Which town has the smallest?

17. A quantity increases from 10 to 12. By what percent has it increased? Now suppose that it had increased from 100 to 102. What is the percent increase in this case?

18. An investment decreases by 5% per year for 4 years. By what total percent does it decrease?

Problems

19. Find a formula for $P = f(t)$, the size of a population that begins in year $t = 0$ with 2200 members and decreases at a 3.2% annual rate.

20. The value $$V$ of an investment in year t is given by $V = 2500(1.0325)^t$. Describe the investment in words.

21. In 2006, the cost of a train ticket from Boston to New York was $73. Assume that the price rises by 10% per year. Make a table showing the price of tickets each year until 2010.

22. In 2006, the population of a country was 70 million and growing at a rate of 1.9% per year. Assuming the percentage growth rate remains constant, express the population, P, as a function of t, the number of years after 2006.

23. The mass, Q, of a sample of Tritium (a radioactive isotope of Hydrogen), decays at a rate of 5.626% per year. Write a function giving the mass of a 726 gram sample after a time, t, in years. Graph this decay function.

24. Every year, a lake becomes more polluted, and 2% fewer organisms can live in it. If in 2010 there are one million organisms, write an equation relating O, the number of organisms, to time, t, in years since 2010.

25. The value, V, of a $100,000 investment that earns 3% annual interest is given by $V = f(t)$ where t is in years. How much is the investment worth in 3 years?

26. The amount (in milligrams) of a drug in the body t hours after taking a pill is given by $A(t) = 25(0.85)^t$.

   (a) What is the initial dose given?
   (b) What percent of the drug leaves the body each hour?
   (c) What is the amount of drug left after 10 hours?
   (d) After how many hours is there less than 1 milligram left in the body?

27. **(a)** The annual inflation rate is 3.5% per year. If a movie ticket costs $7.50, find a formula for p, the price of the ticket t years from today, assuming that movie tickets keep up with inflation.
   (b) According to your formula, how much will movie tickets cost in 20 years?

28. In the year 2004, a total of 7.9 million passengers took a cruise vacation.[2] The global cruise industry has been growing at approximately 10% per year for the last decade; assume that this growth rate continues.

   (a) Write a formula to approximate the number, N, of cruise passengers (in millions) t years after 2004.
   (b) How many cruise passengers are predicted in the year 2010? Approximately how many passengers went on a cruise in the year 2000?

29. A typical cup of coffee contains about 100 mg of caffeine and every hour approximately 16% of the amount of caffeine in the body is metabolized and eliminated.

   (a) Write C, the amount of caffeine in the body in mg as a function of t, the number of hours since the coffee was consumed.
   (b) How much caffeine is in the body after 5 hours?

30. Radioactive gallium-67 decays by 1.48% every hour; there are 100 milligrams initially.

   (a) Find a formula for the amount of gallium-67 remaining after t hours.
   (b) How many milligrams are left after 24 hours? After 1 week?

31. In 2005 the number of people infected by a virus was P_0. Due to a new vaccine, the number of infected people has decreased by 20% each year since 2005. In other words, only 80% as many people are infected each year as were infected the year before. Find a formula for $P = f(n)$, the number of infected people n years after 2005. Graph $f(n)$. Explain, in terms of the virus, why the graph has the shape it does.

32. You owe $2000 on a credit card. The card charges 1.5% monthly interest on your balance, and requires a minimum monthly payment of 2.5% of your balance. All transactions (payments and interest charges) are recorded at the end of the month. You make only the minimum required payment every month and incur no additional debt.

   (a) Complete Table 3.5 for a twelve-month period.
   (b) What is your unpaid balance after one year has passed? At that time, how much of your debt have you paid off? How much money in interest charges have you paid your creditors?

Table 3.5

Month	Balance	Interest	Minimum payment
0	$2000.00	$30.00	$50.00
1	$1980.00	$29.70	$49.50
2	$1960.20		
⋮			

33. Polluted water is passed through a series of filters. Each filter removes 85% of the remaining impurities. Initially, the untreated water contains impurities at a level of 420 parts per million (ppm). Find a formula for L, the remaining level of impurities, after the water has been passed through a series of n filters.

34. The UN Food and Agriculture Organization estimates that 4.2% of the world's natural forests existing in 1990 were gone by the end of the decade. In 1990, the world's forest cover stood at 3843 million hectares.[3]

   (a) How many million hectares of natural forests were lost during the 1990s?

---

[2]The Worldwatch Institute, *Vital Signs* 2005 (New York: W.W. Norton & Company, 2002), p. 100.
[3]The Worldwatch Institute, *Vital Signs* 2002 (New York: W.W. Norton & Company, 2002), p. 104.

(b) How many million hectares of natural forests existed in the year 2000?

(c) Write an exponential formula approximating the number of million hectares of natural forest in the world t years after 1990.

(d) What was the annual percent decay rate during the 1990s?

35. The *Home* section of many Sunday newspapers includes a mortgage table similar to Table 3.6. The table gives the monthly payment per $1000 borrowed for loans at various interest rates and time periods. Determine the monthly payment on a

(a) $60,000 mortgage at 8% for fifteen years.

(b) $60,000 mortgage at 8% for thirty years.

(c) $60,000 mortgage at 10% for fifteen years.

(d) Over the life of the loan, how much money would be saved on a 15-year mortgage of $60,000 if the rate were 8% instead of 10%?

(e) Over the life of the loan, how much money would be saved on an 8% mortgage of $60,000 if the term of the loan was fifteen years rather than thirty years?

Table 3.6

Interest rate (%)	15-year loan	20-year loan	25-year loan	30-year loan
8.00	9.56	8.37	7.72	7.34
8.50	9.85	8.68	8.06	7.69
9.00	10.15	9.00	8.40	8.05
9.50	10.45	9.33	8.74	8.41
10.00	10.75	9.66	9.09	8.78
10.50	11.06	9.99	9.45	9.15
11.00	11.37	10.33	9.81	9.53
11.50	11.69	10.67	10.17	9.91

36. Every year, teams from 64 colleges qualify to compete in the NCAA basketball playoffs. For each round, every team is paired with an opponent. A team is eliminated from the tournament once it loses a round. So, at the end of a round, only one half the number of teams move on to the next round. Let $N(r)$ be the number of teams remaining in competition after r rounds of the tournament have been played.

(a) Find a formula for $N(r)$ and graph $y = N(r)$.

(b) How many rounds does it take to determine the winner of the tournament?

37. Figure 3.6 is the graph of $f(x) = 4 \cdot b^x$. Find the slope of the line segment PQ in terms of b.

Figure 3.6

38. A one-page letter is folded into thirds to go into an envelope. If it were possible to repeat this kind of tri-fold 20 times, how many miles thick would the letter be? (A stack of 150 pieces of stationery is one inch thick; 1 mile = 5280 feet.)

39. Let P be the number of students in a school district, N be the size of the tax base (in households), and r be the average annual tax rate (in $/household).

(a) Find a formula for R, the total tax revenue, in terms of N and r.

(b) Find a formula for A, the average revenue per student.

(c) Suppose the tax base goes up by 2% and the tax rate is raised by 3%. Find formulas for the new tax base and tax rate in terms of N and r.

(d) Using your answer to part (c), find a formula for the new total tax revenue in terms of R. By what percent did R increase?

(e) Over the time period in part (c), the student population rises by 8%. Find a formula for the new average revenue in terms of A. Did the average revenue rise or fall? By how much?

Use Figure 3.7 in Problems 40–43.

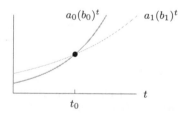

Figure 3.7

40. Which is greater, a_0 or a_1?

41. Which is greater, b_0 or b_1?

42. What happens to t_0 if a_0 is increased while the other quantities remain fixed?

43. What happens to t_0 if b_1 is decreased while the other quantities remain fixed?

3.2 COMPARING EXPONENTIAL AND LINEAR FUNCTIONS

The exponential function $Q = ab^t$ represents a quantity changing at a constant percent rate. In this section we compare exponential and linear models and we fit exponential models to data from tables and graphs.

Identifying Linear and Exponential Functions From a Table

Table 3.7 gives values of a linear and an exponential functions. Notice that the value of x changes by equal steps of $\Delta x = 5$. The function f is linear because the difference between consecutive values of $f(x)$ is constant: $f(x)$ increases by 15 each time x increases by 5.

Table 3.7   *Two functions, one linear and one exponential*

x	20	25	30	35	40	45
$f(x)$	30	45	60	75	90	105
$g(x)$	1000	1200	1440	1728	2073.6	2488.32

On the other hand, the difference between consecutive values of $g(x)$ is *not* constant:

$$1200 - 1000 = 200$$
$$1440 - 1200 = 240$$
$$1728 - 1440 = 288.$$

Thus, g is not linear. However, the *ratio* of consecutive values of $g(x)$ is constant:

$$\frac{1200}{1000} = 1.2, \quad \frac{1440}{1200} = 1.2, \quad \frac{1728}{1440} = 1.2,$$

and so on. Note that $1200 = 1.2(1000)$, $1440 = 1.2(1200)$, $1728 = 1.2(1440)$. Thus, each time x increases by 5, the value of $g(x)$ increases by a factor of 1.2. This pattern of constant ratios is indicative of exponential functions. In general:

For a table of data that gives y as a function of x and in which Δx is constant:
- If the *difference* of consecutive y-values is constant, the table could represent a linear function.
- If the *ratio* of consecutive y-values is constant, the table could represent an exponential function.

Finding a Formula for an Exponential Function

To find a formula for the exponential function in Table 3.7, we must determine the values of a and b in the formula $g(x) = ab^x$. The table tells us that $ab^{20} = 1000$ and that $ab^{25} = 1200$. Taking the ratio gives

$$\frac{ab^{25}}{ab^{20}} = \frac{1200}{1000} = 1.2.$$

Notice that the value of a cancels in this ratio, so

$$\frac{ab^{25}}{ab^{20}} = b^5 = 1.2.$$

We solve for b by raising each side to the $(1/5)^{\text{th}}$ power:

$$(b^5)^{1/5} = b = 1.2^{1/5} \approx 1.03714.$$

Now that we have the value of b, we can solve for a. Since $g(20) = ab^{20} = 1000$, we have

$$a(1.03714)^{20} = 1000$$

$$a = \frac{1000}{1.03714^{20}} \approx 482.253.$$

Thus, a formula for g is $g(x) = 482.253(1.037)^x$. (Note: We could have used $g(25)$ or any other value from the table to find a.)

Modeling Linear and Exponential Growth Using Two Data Points

If we are given two data points, we can fit either a line or an exponential function to the points. The following example compares the predictions made by a linear model and an exponential model fitted to the same data.

Example 1   At time $t = 0$ years, a species of turtle is released into a wetland. When $t = 4$ years, a biologist estimates there are 300 turtles in the wetland. Three years later, the biologist estimates there are 450 turtles. Let P represent the size of the turtle population in year t.

(a) Find a formula for $P = f(t)$ assuming linear growth. Interpret the slope and P-intercept of your formula in terms of the turtle population.

(b) Now find a formula for $P = g(t)$ assuming exponential growth. Interpret the parameters of your formula in terms of the turtle population.

(c) In year $t = 12$, the biologist estimates that there are 900 turtles in the wetland. What does this indicate about the two population models?

Solution   (a) Assuming linear growth, we have $P = f(t) = b + mt$, and

$$m = \frac{\Delta P}{\Delta t} = \frac{450 - 300}{7 - 4} = \frac{150}{3} = 50.$$

Calculating b gives

$$300 = b + 50 \cdot 4$$
$$b = 100,$$

so $P = f(t) = 100 + 50t$. This formula tells us that 100 turtles were originally released into the wetland and that the number of turtles increases at the constant rate of 50 turtles per year.

(b) Assuming exponential growth, we have $P = g(t) = ab^t$. The values of a and b are calculated from the ratio

$$\frac{ab^7}{ab^4} = \frac{450}{300},$$

so

$$b^3 = 1.5.$$

Thus,

$$b = (1.5)^{1/3} \approx 1.145.$$

Using the fact that $g(4) = ab^4 = 300$ to find a gives

$$a(1.145)^4 = 300$$

$$a = \frac{300}{1.145^4} \approx 175, \quad \text{Rounding to the nearest whole turtle}$$

so $P = g(t) = 175(1.145)^t$. This formula tells us that 175 turtles were originally released into the wetland and the number increases at about 14.5% per year.

(c) In year $t = 12$, there are approximately 900 turtles. The linear function from part (a) predicts

$$P = 100 + 50 \cdot 12 \doteq 700 \text{ turtles.}$$

The exponential formula from part (b), however, predicts

$$P = 175(1.145)^{12} \approx 889 \text{ turtles.}$$

The fact that 889 is closer to the observed value of 900 turtles suggests that, during the first 12 years, exponential growth is a better model of the turtle population than linear growth. The two models are graphed in Figure 3.8.

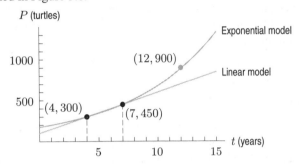

Figure 3.8: Comparison of the linear and exponential models of the turtle population

Similarities and Differences between Linear and Exponential Functions

In some ways the general formulas for linear and exponential functions are similar. If y is a linear function of x and x is a positive integer, we can write $y = b + mx$ as

$$y = b + \underbrace{m + m + m + \ldots + m}_{x \text{ times}}.$$

Similarly, if y is an exponential function of x, so that $y = a \cdot b^x$ and x is a positive integer, we can write

$$y = a \cdot \underbrace{b \cdot b \cdot b \cdot \ldots \cdot b}_{x \text{ times}}.$$

So linear functions involve repeated sums whereas exponential functions involve repeated products. In both cases, x determines the number of repetitions.

There are other similarities between the formulas for linear and exponential functions. The slope m of a linear function gives the rate of change of a physical quantity and the y-intercept gives the starting value. Similarly, in $y = a \cdot b^x$, the value of b gives the growth factor and a gives the starting value.

Example 2   The following tables contain values from an exponential or linear function. For each table, decide if the function is linear or exponential, and find a possible formula for the function.

(a)

x	$f(x)$
0	65
1	75
2	85
3	95
4	105

(b)

x	$g(x)$
0	400
1	600
2	900
3	1350
4	2025

Solution

(a) The function values increase by 10 as x increases by 1, so this is a linear function with slope $m = 10$. Since $f(0) = 65$, the vertical intercept is 65. A possible formula is

$$f(x) = 65 + 10x.$$

(b) The function is not linear, since $g(x)$ increases by different amounts as x increases by 1. To determine whether g might be exponential, we look at ratios of consecutive values:

$$\frac{600}{400} = 1.5, \quad \frac{900}{600} = 1.5, \quad \frac{1350}{900} = 1.5, \quad \frac{2025}{1350} = 1.5.$$

Each time x increases by 1, the value of $g(x)$ increases by a factor of 1.5. This is an exponential function with growth factor 1.5. Since $g(0) = 400$, the vertical intercept is 400. A possible formula is

$$g(x) = 400(1.5)^x.$$

Exponential Growth Will Always Outpace Linear Growth in the Long Run

Figure 3.8 shows the graphs of the linear and exponential models for the turtle population from Example 1. The graphs highlight the fact that, although these two graphs remain fairly close for the first ten or so years, the exponential model predicts explosive growth later on.

It can be shown that an exponentially increasing quantity will, in the long run, always outpace a linearly increasing quantity. This fact led the 19th-century clergyman and economist, Thomas Malthus, to make some rather gloomy predictions, which are illustrated in the next example.

Example 3

The population of a country is initially 2 million people and is increasing at 4% per year. The country's annual food supply is initially adequate for 4 million people and is increasing at a constant rate adequate for an additional 0.5 million people per year.

(a) Based on these assumptions, in approximately what year will this country first experience shortages of food?

(b) If the country doubled its initial food supply, would shortages still occur? If so, when? (Assume the other conditions do not change).

(c) If the country doubled the rate at which its food supply increases, in addition to doubling its initial food supply, would shortages still occur? If so, when? (Again, assume the other conditions do not change.)

Solution

Let P represent the country's population (in millions) and N the number of people the country can feed (in millions). The population increases at a constant percent rate, so it can be modeled by an exponential function. The initial population is $a = 2$ million people and the annual growth factor is $b = 1 + 0.04 = 1.04$, so a formula for the population is

$$P = 2(1.04)^t.$$

In contrast, the food supply increases by a constant amount each year and is therefore modeled by a linear function. The initial food supply is adequate for $b = 4$ million people and the growth rate is $m = 0.5$ million per year, so the number of people that can be fed is

$$N = 4 + 0.5t.$$

(a) Figure 3.9(a) gives the graphs of P and N over a 105-year span. For many years, the food supply is far in excess of the country's needs. However, after about 78 years the population has begun to grow so rapidly that it catches up to the food supply and then outstrips it. After that time, the country will suffer from shortages.

(b) If the country can initially feed eight million people rather than four, the formula for N is

$$N = 8 + 0.5t.$$

However, as we see from Figure 3.9(b), this measure only buys the country three or four extra years with an adequate food supply. After 81 years, the population is growing so rapidly that the head start given to the food supply makes little difference.

(c) If the country doubles the rate at which its food supply increases, from 0.5 million per year to 1.0 million per year, the formula for N is

$$N = 8 + 1.0t.$$

Unfortunately the country still runs out of food eventually. Judging from Figure 3.9(c), this happens in about 102 years.

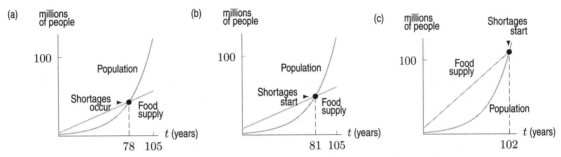

Figure 3.9: These graphs illustrate the fact that an exponentially growing population eventually outstrips a linearly growing food supply

Malthus believed that populations increase exponentially while food production increases linearly. The last example explains his gloomy predictions: Malthus believed that any population eventually outstrips its food supply, leading to famine and war.

Exercises and Problems for Section 3.2

Exercises

1. The following formulas give the populations (in 1000s) of four different cities, A, B, C, and D, where t is in years. Which are changing exponentially? Describe in words how each of these populations is changing over time. Graph those that are exponential.

$$P_A = 200 + 1.3t, \quad P_B = 270(1.021)^t,$$
$$P_C = 150(1.045)^t, \quad P_D = 600(0.978)^t.$$

2. A population has size 5000 at time $t = 0$, with t in years.

(a) If the population decreases by 100 people per year, find a formula for the population, P, at time t.

(b) If the population decreases by 8% per year, find a formula for the population, P, at time t.

3. A population has size 100 at time $t = 0$, with t in years.

(a) If the population grows by 10 people per year, find a formula for the population, P, at time t.

(b) If the population grows by 10% per year, find a formula for the population, P, at time t.

(c) Graph both functions on the same axes.

4. In an environment with unlimited resources and no predators, a population tends to grow by the same percentage each year. Should a linear or exponential function be used to model such a population? Why?

5. Determine whether the function whose values are in Table 3.8 could be exponential.

Table 3.8

x	1	2	4	5	8	9
$f(x)$	4096	1024	64	16	0.25	0.0625

The tables in Problems 6–9 contain values from an exponential or a linear function. In each problem:

(a) Decide if the function is linear or exponential.

(b) Find a possible formula for each function and graph it.

6.

x	$f(x)$
0	12.5
1	13.75
2	15.125
3	16.638
4	18.301

7.

x	$g(x)$
0	0
1	2
2	4
3	6
4	8

8.

x	$h(x)$
0	14
1	12.6
2	11.34
3	10.206
4	9.185

9.

x	$i(x)$
0	18
1	14
2	10
3	6
4	2

Problems

10. Explain the difference between linear and exponential growth. That is, without writing down any formulas, describe how linear and exponential functions progress differently from one value to the next.

In Problems 11–16, find formulas for the exponential functions satisfying the given conditions.

11. $h(0) = 3$ and $h(1) = 15$

12. $f(3) = -3/8$ and $f(-2) = -12$

13. $g(1/2) = 4$ and $g(1/4) = 2\sqrt{2}$

14. $g(0) = 5$ and $g(-2) = 10$

15. $g(1.7) = 6$ and $g(2.5) = 4$

16. $f(1) = 4$ and $f(3) = d$

17. Suppose $f(-3) = 5/8$ and $f(2) = 20$. Find a formula for f assuming it is:

(a) Linear   **(b)** Exponential

For Problems 18–23, find formulas for the exponential functions.

18.

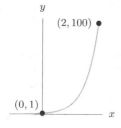

19.

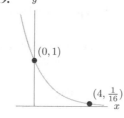

20.

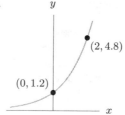

21.

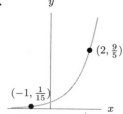

22.

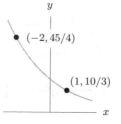

23.

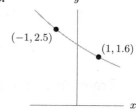

24. Find possible formulas for the functions in Figure 3.10.

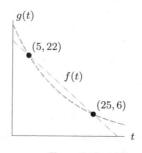

Figure 3.10

25. Find formulas for the exponential functions in Figure 3.11.

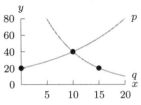

Figure 3.11

In Problems 26–29, could the function be linear or exponential or is it neither? Write possible formulas for the linear or exponential functions.

26.

r	1	3	7	15	31
$p(r)$	13	19	31	55	103

27.

x	6	9	12	18	24
$q(x)$	100	110	121	146.41	177.16

28.

x	10	12	15	16	18
$f(x)$	1	2	4	8	16

29.

t	1	2	3	4	5
$g(t)$	512	256	128	64	32

30. Let $p(x) = 2 + x$ and $q(x) = 2^x$. Estimate the values of x such that $p(x) < q(x)$.

31. Let $P(t)$ be the population of a country, in millions, t years after 1990, with $P(7) = 3.21$ and $P(13) = 3.75$.

   (a) Find a formula for $P(t)$ assuming it is linear. Describe in words the country's annual population growth given this assumption.

   (b) Find a formula for $P(t)$ assuming it is exponential. Describe in words the country's annual population growth given this assumption.

32. What is the value of the population at the end of 10 years, given each of the following assumptions? Graph each population against time.

   (a) A population decreases linearly and the decrease is 10% in the first year.

   (b) A population decreases exponentially at the rate of 10% a year.

33. Figure 3.12 shows the balance, P, in a bank account.

   (a) Find a possible formula for $P = f(t)$ assuming the balance grows exponentially.

   (b) What was the initial balance?

   (c) What annual interest rate does the account pay?

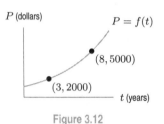

Figure 3.12

34. The number of asthma sufferers in the world was about 84 million in 1990 and 130 million in 2001.[4] Let N represent the number of asthma sufferers (in millions) worldwide t years after 1990.

   (a) Write N as a linear function of t. What is the slope? What does it tell you about asthma sufferers?

   (b) Write N as an exponential function of t. What is the growth factor? What does it tell you about asthma sufferers?

   (c) How many asthma sufferers are predicted worldwide in the year 2010 with the linear model? With the exponential model?

35. Table 3.9 gives the approximate number of cell phone subscribers, S, worldwide.[5]

   (a) Explain how you know an exponential function fits the data. Find a formula for S in terms of t, the number of years since 1995.

   (b) Interpret the growth rate in terms of cell phone subscribers.

   (c) In 2004, there were 1340 million subscribers.[6] Does this fit the pattern?

Table 3.9

Year	1995	1996	1997	1998	1999	2000
Subscribers (m.)	91	138	210	320	485	738

---

[4]www.who.int/inf-fs/en/fact206.html, August 24, 2002.
[5]The Worldwatch Institute, *Vital Signs* 2002 (New York: W.W. Norton & Company, 2002), p. 84.
[6]*The World Almanac and Book of Facts 2006*, p. 380 (New York).

36. A 1987 treaty to protect the ozone layer produced dramatic declines in global production, P, of chlorofluorocarbons (CFCs). See Figure 3.13.[7] Find a formula for P as an exponential function of the number of years, t, since 1989. What was the annual percent decay rate?

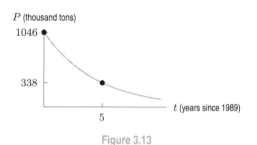

Figure 3.13

37. In 1940, there were about 10 brown tree snakes per square mile on the island of Guam, and in 2002, there were about 20,000 per square mile.[8] Find an exponential formula for the number, N, of brown tree snakes per square mile on Guam t years after 1940. What was, on average, the annual percent increase in the population during this period?

38. Match the stories in (a)–(e) with the formulas in (i)–(v). In each case, state what the variables represent. Assume that the constants P_0, r, B, A are all positive.

(a) The percent of a lake's surface covered by algae, initially at 35%, was halved each year since the passage of anti-pollution laws.

(b) The amount of charge on a capacitor in an electric circuit decreases by 30% every second.

(c) Polluted water is passed through a series of filters. Each filter removes all but 30% of the remaining impurities from the water.

(d) In 1950, the population of a town was 3000 people. Over the course of the next 50 years, the town grew at a rate of 10% per decade.

(e) In 1950, the population of a town was 3000 people. Over the course of the next 50 years, the town grew at a rate of 250 people per year.

(i) $f(x) = P_0 + rx$ (ii) $g(x) = P_0(1+r)^x$

(iii) $h(x) = B(0.7)^x$ (iv) $j(x) = B(0.3)^x$
(v) $k(x) = A(2)^{-x}$

39. A 2006 Lexus costs \$61,055 and the car depreciates a total of 46% during its first 7 years.

(a) Suppose the depreciation is exponential. Find a formula for the value of the car at time t.

(b) Suppose instead that the depreciation is linear. Find a formula for the value of the car at time t.

(c) If this were your car and you were trading it in after 4 years, which depreciation model would you prefer (exponential or linear)?

40. On November 27, 1993, the *New York Times* reported that wildlife biologists have found a direct link between the increase in the human population in Florida and the decline of the local black bear population. From 1953 to 1993, the human population increased, on average, at a rate of 8% per year, while the black bear population decreased at a rate of 6% per year. In 1953 the black bear population was 11,000.

(a) The 1993 human population of Florida was 13 million. What was the human population in 1953?

(b) Find the black bear population for 1993.

(c) Had this trend continued,[9] when would the black bear population have numbered less than 100?

41. Suppose the city of Yonkers is offered two alternative fines by the judge. (See Example 8 on page 111.)

Penalty A: \$1 million on August 2 and the fine increases by \$10 million each day thereafter.

Penalty B: 1¢ on August 2 and the fine doubles each day thereafter.

(a) If the city of Yonkers plans to defy the court order until the end of the month (August 31), compare the fines incurred under Penalty A and Penalty B.

(b) If t represents the number of days after August 2, express the fine incurred as a function of t under

(i) Penalty A   (ii) Penalty B

(c) Assume your formulas in part (b) holds for $t \geq 0$, is there a time such that the fines incurred under both penalties are equal? If so, estimate that time.

3.3   GRAPHS OF EXPONENTIAL FUNCTIONS

As with linear functions, an understanding of the significance of the parameters a and b in the formula $Q = ab^t$ helps us analyze and compare exponential functions.

---

[7]These numbers reflect the volume of the major CFCs multiplied by their respective ozone-depleting potentials (ODPs), as reported by the United Nations Environmental Programme Ozone Secretariat. See hq.uncp.org/ozone.

[8]*Science News*, Vol. 162, August 10, 2002, p. 85.

[9]Since 1993, the black bear population has in fact remained stable: www.myfwc.com/bear, accessed January 5, 2006.

Graphs of the Exponential Family: The Effect of the Parameter a

In the formula $Q = ab^t$, the value of a tells us where the graph crosses the Q-axis, since a is the value of Q when $t = 0$. In Figure 3.14 each graph has the same value of b but different values of a and thus different vertical intercepts.

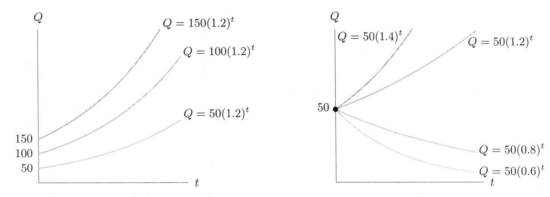

Figure 3.14: Graphs of $Q = a(1.2)^t$ for $a = 50, 100,$ and 150 Figure 3.15: Graphs of $Q = 50b^t$ for $b = 0.6, 0.8, 1.2$ and 1.4

Graphs of the Exponential Family: The Effect of the Parameter b

The growth factor, b, is called the *base* of an exponential function. Provided a is positive, if $b > 1$, the graph climbs when read from left to right, and if $0 < b < 1$, the graph falls when read from left to right.

Figure 3.15 shows how the value of b affects the steepness of the graph of $Q = ab^t$. Each graph has a different value of b but the same value of a (and thus the same Q-intercept). For $b > 1$, the greater the value of b, the more rapidly the graph rises. For $0 < b < 1$, the smaller the value of b, the more rapidly the graph falls. In every case, however, the graph is concave up.

Horizontal Asymptotes

The t-axis is a *horizontal asymptote* for the graph of $Q = ab^t$, because Q approaches 0 as t gets large, either positively or negatively. For exponential decay, such as $Q = f(t) = a(0.6)^t$ in Figure 3.15, the value of Q approaches 0 as t gets large and positive. We write

$$Q \to 0 \quad \text{as} \quad t \to \infty.$$

This means that Q is as close to 0 as we like for all sufficiently large values of t. We say that the *limit* of Q as t goes to infinity is 0, and we write

$$\lim_{t \to \infty} f(t) = 0.$$

For exponential growth, the value of Q approaches zero as t grows more negative. See Figure 3.28. In this case, we write

$$Q \to 0 \quad \text{as} \quad t \to -\infty.$$

This means that Q is as close to 0 as we like for all sufficiently large negative values of t. Using limit notation, we write

$$\lim_{t \to -\infty} f(t) = 0.$$

We make the following definition:

> The horizontal line $y = k$ is a **horizontal asymptote** of a function, f, if the function values get arbitrarily close to k as x gets large (either positively or negatively or both). We describe this behavior using the notation
>
> $$f(x) \to k \qquad \text{as} \qquad x \to \infty$$
>
> or
>
> $$f(x) \to k \qquad \text{as} \qquad x \to -\infty.$$
>
> Alternatively, using limit notation, we write
>
> $$\lim_{x \to \infty} f(x) = k \quad \text{or} \quad \lim_{x \to -\infty} f(x) = k$$

Example 1   A capacitor is the part of an electrical circuit that stores electric charge. The quantity of charge stored decreases exponentially with time. Stereo amplifiers provide a familiar example: When an amplifier is turned off, the display lights fade slowly because it takes time for the capacitors to discharge. (Thus, it can be unsafe to open a stereo or a computer immediately after it is turned off.)

If t is the number of seconds after the circuit is switched off, suppose that the quantity of stored charge (in micro-coulombs) is given by

$$Q = 200(0.9)^t, \quad t \geq 0,$$

(a) Describe in words how the stored charge changes over time.

(b) What quantity of charge remains after 10 seconds? 20 seconds? 30 seconds? 1 minute? 2 minutes? 3 minutes?

(c) Graph the charge over the first minute. What does the horizontal asymptote of the graph tell you about the charge?

Solution   (a) The charge is initially 200 micro-coulombs. Since $b = 1 + r = 0.9$, we have $r = -0.10$, which means that the charge level decreases by 10% each second.

(b) Table 3.10 gives the value of Q at $t = 0, 10, 20, 30, 60, 120,$ and 180. Notice that as t increases, Q gets closer and closer to, but does not quite reach, zero. The charge stored by the capacitor is getting smaller, but never completely vanishes.

(c) Figure 3.16 shows Q over a 60-second interval. The horizontal asymptote at $Q = 0$ corresponds to the fact that the charge gets very small as t increases. After 60 seconds, for all practical purposes, the charge is zero.

Table 3.10   *Charge (in micro-coulombs) stored by a capacitor over time*

t (seconds)	Q, charge level
0	200
10	69.736
20	24.315
30	8.478
60	0.359
120	0.000646
180	0.00000116

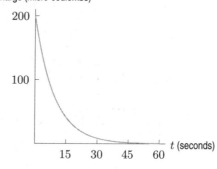

Figure 3.16: The charge stored by a capacitor over one minute

Solving Exponential Equations Graphically

We are often interested in solving equations involving exponential functions. In the following examples, we do this graphically. In Section 4.1, we will see how to solve equations using logarithms.

Example 2   In Example 8 on page 111, the fine, P, imposed on the city of Yonkers is given by $P = 100 \cdot 2^t$ where t is the number of days after August 2. In 1988, the annual budget of the city was $337 million. If the city chose to disobey the court order, at what point would the fine have wiped out the entire annual budget?

Solution   We need to find the day on which the fine reaches $337 million. That is, we must solve the equation

$$100 \cdot 2^t = 337{,}000{,}000.$$

Using a computer or graphing calculator we can graph $P = 100 \cdot 2^t$ to find the point at which the fine reaches 337 million. From Figure 3.17, we see that this occurs between $t = 21$ and $t = 22$. At day $t = 21$, August 23, the fine is:

$$P = 100 \cdot 2^{21} = 209{,}715{,}200$$

or just over $200 million. On day $t = 22$, the fine is

$$P = 100 \cdot 2^{22} = 419{,}430{,}400$$

or almost $420 million—quite a bit more than the city's entire annual budget!

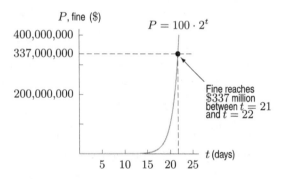

Figure 3.17: The fine imposed on Yonkers exceeds $337 million after 22 days

Example 3   A 200 μg sample of carbon-14 decays according to the formula

$$Q = 200(0.886)^t$$

where t is in thousands of years. Estimate when there is 25 μg of carbon-14 left.

Solution   We must solve the equation

$$200(0.886)^t = 25.$$

At the moment, we cannot find a formula for the solution to this equation. However, we can estimate the solution graphically. Figure 3.18 shows a graph of $Q = 200(0.886)^t$ and the line $Q = 25$. The amount of carbon-14 decays to 25 micrograms at $t \approx 17.180$. Since t is measured in thousands of years, this means in about 17,180 years.

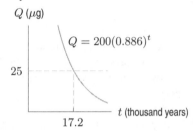

Figure 3.18: Solving the equation $200(0.886)^t = 25$

Fitting Exponential Functions to Data

The data in Table 3.11 gives population data for the Houston Metro Area since 1900. In Section 1.6, we saw how to fit a linear function to data, but Figure 3.19 suggests that it may make more sense to fit an exponential function using *exponential regression*.

Table 3.11   *Population (in thousands) of Houston Metro Area, t years after 1900*

t	N	t	N
0	184	60	1583
10	236	70	2183
20	332	80	3122
30	528	90	3733
40	737	100	4672
50	1070		

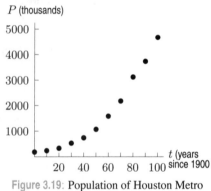

Figure 3.19: Population of Houston Metro Area

One algorithm used by a calculator or computer gives the best fitting exponential function as

$$P = 183.5(1.035)^t.$$

Other algorithms may give different formulas. Figure 3.20 shows this function and the data.

Since the base of this exponential function is 1.035, the population was increasing at a rate of about 3.5% per year between 1900 and 2000.

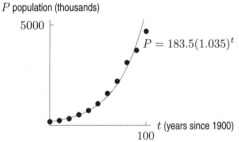

Figure 3.20: The population data since 1900 together with an exponential model

Exercises and Problems for Section 3.3

Exercises

1. (a) Make a table of values for $f(x) = 2^x$ for $x = -3, -2, -1, 0, 1, 2, 3$.
   (b) Graph $f(x)$. Describe the graph in words.

2. (a) Make a table of values for $f(x) = \left(\frac{1}{2}\right)^x$ for $x = -3, -2, -1, 0, 1, 2, 3$.
   (b) Graph $f(x)$. Describe the graph in words.

3. The graphs of $f(x) = (1.1)^x$, $g(x) = (1.2)^x$, and $h(x) = (1.25)^x$ are in Figure 3.21. Explain how you can match these formulas and graphs without a calculator.

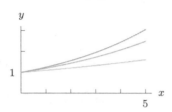

Figure 3.21

4. The graphs of $f(x) = (0.7)^x$, $g(x) = (0.8)^x$, and $h(x) = (0.85)^x$ are in Figure 3.22. Explain how you can match these formulas and graphs without a calculator.

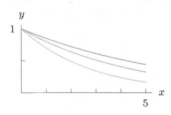

Figure 3.22

For Exercises 5–8, use Figure 3.23. Assume the equations for A, B, C, and D can all be written in the form $y = ab^t$.

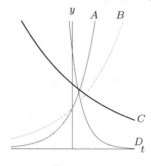

Figure 3.23

5. Which function has the largest value for a?

6. Which two functions have the same value for a?

7. Which function has the smallest value for b?

8. Which function has the largest value for b?

9. Solve $y = 46(1.1)^x$ graphically for x if $y = 91$.

10. Solve $p = 22(0.87)^q$ graphically for q if $p = 10$.

11. Solve $4m = 17(2.3)^w$ graphically for w if $m = 12$.

12. Solve $P/7 = (0.6)^t$ graphically for t if $P = 2$.

13. If $b > 1$, what is the horizontal asymptote of $y = ab^t$ as $t \to -\infty$?

14. If $0 < b < 1$, what is the horizontal asymptote of $y = ab^t$ as $t \to \infty$?

Problems

15. The city of Baltimore has been declining in population for the last fifty years.[10] In the year 2000, the population of Baltimore was 651 thousand and declining at a rate of 0.75% per year. If this trend continues:

   (a) Give a formula for the population of Baltimore, P, in thousands, as a function of years, t, since 2000.
   (b) What is the predicted population in 2010?
   (c) To two decimal places, estimate t when the population is 550 thousand.

16. Let $P = f(t) = 1000(1.04)^t$ be the population of a community in year t.

   (a) Evaluate $f(0)$ and $f(10)$. What do these expressions represent in terms of the population?
   (b) Using a calculator or a computer, find appropriate viewing windows on which to graph the population for the first 10 years and for the first 50 years. Give the viewing windows you used and sketch the resulting graphs.
   (c) If the percentage growth rate remains constant, approximately when will the population reach 2500 people?

---

[10]*The World Almanac and Book of Facts 2006*, p. 480 (New York).

17. Suppose y, the number of cases of a disease, is reduced by 10% each year.

    (a) If there are initially 10,000 cases, express y as a function of t, the number of years elapsed.

    (b) How many cases will there be 5 years from now?

    (c) How long does it take to reduce the number of cases to 1000?

18. The earth's atmospheric pressure, P, in terms of height above sea level is often modeled by an exponential decay function. The pressure at sea level is 1013 millibars and that the pressure decreases by 14% for every kilometer above sea level.

    (a) What is the atmospheric pressure at 50 km?

    (b) Estimate the altitude h at which the pressure equals 900 millibars.

19. Consider the exponential functions graphed in Figure 3.24 and the six constants a, b, c, d, p, q.

    (a) Which of these constants are definitely positive?

    (b) Which of these constants are definitely between 0 and 1?

    (c) Which of these constants could be between 0 and 1?

    (d) Which two of these constants are definitely equal?

    (e) Which one of the following pairs of constants could be equal?

$$a \text{ and } p \qquad b \text{ and } d \qquad b \text{ and } q \qquad d \text{ and } q$$

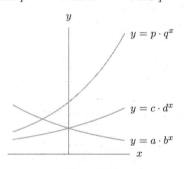

Figure 3.24

Problems 20–21 use Figure 3.25, where y_0 is the y-coordinate of the point of intersection of the graphs. Describe what happens to y_0 if the following changes are made, assuming the other quantities remain the same.

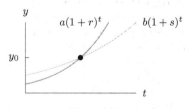

Figure 3.25

20. r is increased   **21.** a is increased

Problems 22–23 use Figure 3.26, where t_0 is the t-coordinate of the point of intersection of the graphs. Describe what happens to t_0 if the following changes are made, assuming the other quantities remain the same.

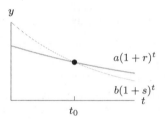

Figure 3.26

22. b is decreased   **23.** r is increased

24. For which value(s) of a and b is $y = ab^x$ an increasing function? A decreasing function? Concave up?

25. Write a paragraph that compares the function $f(x) = a^x$, where $a > 1$, and $g(x) = b^x$, where $0 < b < 1$. Include graphs in your answer.

26. Set a window of $-4 \le x \le 4, -1 \le y \le 6$ and graph the following functions using several different values of a for each. Include some values of a with $a < 1$.

    (a) $y = a2^x$, $0 < a < 5$.

    (b) $y = 2a^x$, $0 < a < 5$.

In Problems 27–30, graph $f(x)$, a function defined for all real numbers and satisfying the condition.

27. $f(x) \to 5$ as $x \to \infty$

28. $f(x) \to 2$ as $x \to -\infty$ and $f(x) \to -1$ as $x \to \infty$

29. $\lim_{x \to -\infty} f(x) = 3$

30. $\lim_{x \to -\infty} f(x) = 0$ and $\lim_{x \to \infty} f(x) = -\infty$

In Problems 31–32, assume that all important features are shown in the graph of $y = f(x)$. Estimate

  (a) $\lim_{x \to -\infty} f(x)$ **(b)** $\lim_{x \to \infty} f(x)$

31. 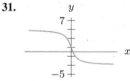   **32.**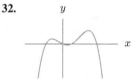

33. Find **(a)** $\lim_{x \to \infty} 7(0.8)^x$ **(b)** $\lim_{t \to -\infty} 5(1.2)^t$

(c) $\lim_{t \to \infty} 0.7(1 - (0.2)^t)$

34. If the exponential function ab^x has the property that $\lim_{x \to \infty} ab^x = 0$, what can you say about the value of b?

In Problems 35–36, graph the function to find horizontal asymptotes.

35. $f(x) = 8 - 2^x$ **36.** $f(x) = 3^{-x^2} + 2$

37. Suppose you use your calculator to graph $y = 1.04^{5x}$. You correctly enter $y = 1.04\char`^(5x)$ and see the graph in Figure 3.27. A friend graphed the function by entering $y = 1.04\char`^5x$ and said, "The graph is a straight line, so I must have the wrong window." Explain why changing the window will not correct your friend's error.

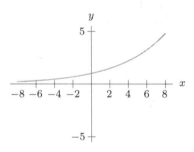

Figure 3.27

38. The population of a colony of rabbits grows exponentially. The colony begins with 10 rabbits; five years later there are 340 rabbits.

(a) Give a formula for the population of the colony of rabbits as a function of the time.

(b) Use a graph to estimate how long it takes for the population of the colony to reach 1000 rabbits.

39. Table 3.12 shows global wind energy generating capacity, W (in megawatts), as a function of the number of years, t, since 1995.[11]

(a) Plot the data and explain why it is reasonable to approximate these data with an exponential function.

(b) Use a calculator or computer to fit an exponential function to these data.

(c) What annual percent growth rate does the exponential model show?

Table 3.12

t	0	1	2	3	4
W	4780	6070	7640	10,150	13,930

t	5	6	7	8	9
W	18,450	24,930	32,037	39,664	47,760

40. Sales of energy-efficient compact fluorescent lamps in China have been growing approximately exponentially. Table 3.13 shows the sales in millions.[12]

(a) Use a calculator or computer to find the exponential regression function for sales, S (in millions), as a function of the number of years, t, since 1994.

(b) Plot the function with the data. Does it appear to fit the data well?

(c) What annual percent growth rate does the exponential model show?

(d) If this growth rate continues, what sales are predicted in the year 2010?

Table 3.13

Year	1994	1996	1998	2000	2002	2003
Sales (millions)	20	30	60	125	295	440

41. What are the domain and range of the exponential function $Q = ab^t$ where a and b are both positive constants?

42. The functions $f(x) = (\frac{1}{2})^x$ and $g(x) = 1/x$ are similar in that they both tend toward zero as x becomes large. Using a calculator, determine which function, f or g, approaches zero faster.

43. Let f be a piecewise-defined function given by

$$f(x) = \begin{cases} 2^x, & x < 0 \\ 0, & x = 0 \\ 1 - \frac{1}{2}x, & x > 0. \end{cases}$$

(a) Graph f for $-3 \le x \le 4$.

(b) The domain of $f(x)$ is all real numbers. What is its range?

(c) What are the intercepts of f?

(d) What happens to $f(x)$ as $x \to \infty$ and $x \to -\infty$?

(e) Over what intervals is f increasing? Decreasing?

---

[11]The Worldwatch Institute, *Vital Signs* 2005 (New York: W.W. Norton & Company, 2005), p. 35.

[12]Nadel, S. and Hong, "Market Data on Efficient Lighting," Right Light 6 Conference, Session 8, May, 2005.

44. Three scientists, working independently of each other, arrive at the following formulas to model the spread of a species of mussel in a system of fresh water lakes:

$$f_1(x) = 3(1.2)^x, \quad f_2(x) = 3(1.21)^x, \quad f_3(x) = 3.01(1.2)^x,$$

where $f_n(x)$, $n = 1, 2, 3$, is the number of individual mussels (in 1000s) predicted by model number n to be living in the lake system after x months have elapsed.

(a) Graph these three functions for $0 \leq x \leq 60$, $0 \leq y \leq 40,000$.

(b) The graphs of these three models do not seem all that different from each other. But do the three functions make significantly different predictions about the future mussel population? To answer this, graph the difference function, $f_2(x) - f_1(x)$, of the population sizes predicted by models 1 and 2, as well as the difference functions, $f_3(x) - f_1(x)$ and $f_3(x) - f_2(x)$. (Use the same window as in part (a).)

(c) Based on your graphs in part (b), discuss the assertion that all three models are in good agreement as far as long-range predictions of mussel population are concerned. What conclusions can you draw about exponential functions in general?

3.4   CONTINUOUS GROWTH AND THE NUMBER e

If $1.00 is invested in a bank account that pays 100% interest once a year, then, assuming no other deposits or withdrawals, after one year we have

$$\$1.00(1 + 100\%) = \$2.00.$$

If $1.00 is invested in a bank account that pays 50% interest twice a year, then, since $50\% = 100\%/2$, we have

$$\text{Balance after first six months} = \$1.00\left(1 + \frac{100\%}{2}\right) = \$1.50$$

$$\text{Balance after second six months} = \$1.50\left(1 + \frac{100\%}{2}\right) = \$1.00\left(1 + \frac{100\%}{2}\right)^2 = \$2.25.$$

The balance is larger because interest earned in the first six months itself earns interest in the second six months.

Similarly, if $1.00 is invested in a bank account that pays 25% interest 4 times a year, then after one year, since $25\% = 100\%/4$, we have

$$\text{Balance} = \$1.00\left(1 + \frac{100\%}{4}\right)^4 = \$2.441406.$$

Table 3.14 shows the balance after one year as the interest is calculated more and more frequently.

Table 3.14   *Approximate balance for various frequencies*

Frequency	Approximate balance
1 (annually)	$2.00
2 (semi-annually)	$2.25
4 (quarterly)	$2.441406
12 (monthly)	$2.613035
365 (daily)	$2.714567

As the frequency increases, the balance increases, because the interest earns more interest. How large can the balance grow? Table 3.15 shows balances for computations made each hour, each minute, and each second. It appears that the balance never gets larger than 2.7182. In fact, as the frequency of computation increases, the balance approaches 2.71828182.... This irrational number, introduced by Euler[13] in 1727, is so important that it is given a special name, e.

Table 3.15   *Approximate balance for greater frequencies*

Frequency	Approximate balance
8760 (hourly)	$2.718127
525,600 (each minute)	$2.718279
31,536,000 (each second)	$2.718282

The Number e

The number $e = 2.71828182\ldots$ is often used for the base, b, of the exponential function. Base e is called the *natural base*. This may seem mysterious, as what could possibly be natural about using an irrational base such as e? The answer is that the formulas of calculus are much simpler if e is used as the base for exponentials. Some of the remarkable properties of the number e are introduced in Problems 25–28 on page 135. Since $2 < e < 3$, the graph of $Q = e^t$ lies between the graphs of $Q = 3^t$ and $Q = 2^t$. See Figure 3.28.

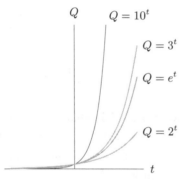

Figure 3.28: Graphs of exponential functions with various bases

Exponential Functions with Base e Represent Continuous Growth

Any positive base b can be written as a power of e:

$$b = e^k.$$

If $b > 1$, then k is positive; if $0 < b < 1$, then k is negative. The function $Q = ab^t$ can be rewritten in terms of e:

$$Q = ab^t = a\left(e^k\right)^t = ae^{kt}.$$

The constant k is called the *continuous growth rate*. In general:

> For the exponential function $Q = ab^t$, the **continuous growth rate**, k, is given by solving $e^k = b$. Then
> $$Q = ae^{kt}.$$
>
> If a is positive,
> - If $k > 0$, then Q is increasing.
> - If $k < 0$, then Q is decreasing.

---

[13]Leonhard Euler (1707-1783), a Swiss mathematician, introduced e, $f(x)$ notation, π, and i (for $\sqrt{-1}$).

The value of the continuous growth rate, k, may be given as a decimal or a percent. If t is in years, for example, then the units of k are given per year; if t is in minutes, then k is given per minute.

Example 1   Give the continuous growth rate of each of the following functions and graph each function:
$$P = 5e^{0.2t}, \qquad Q = 5e^{0.3t}, \qquad \text{and} \quad R = 5e^{-0.2t}.$$

Solution   The function $P = 5e^{0.2t}$ has a continuous growth rate of 20%, and $Q = 5e^{0.3t}$ has a continuous 30% growth rate. The function $R = 5e^{-0.2t}$ has a continuous growth rate of -20%. The negative sign in the exponent tells us that R is decreasing instead of increasing.

Because $a = 5$ in all three formulas, all three functions cross the vertical axis at 5. Note that the graphs of these functions in Figure 3.29 have the same shape as the exponential functions in Section 3.3. They are concave up and have horizontal asymptotes of $y = 0$. (Note that $P \to 0$ and $Q \to 0$ as $t \to -\infty$, whereas $R \to 0$ as $t \to \infty$.)

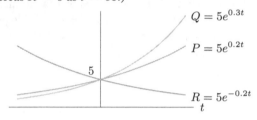

Figure 3.29: Exponential functions with different continuous growth rates

Example 2   A population increases from 7.3 million at a continuous rate of 2.2% per year. Write a formula for the population, and estimate graphically when the population reaches 10 million.

Solution   We express the formula in base e since the continuous growth rate is given. If P is the population (in millions) in year t, then
$$P = 7.3e^{0.022t}.$$

See Figure 3.30. We see that $P = 10$ when $t \approx 14.3$. Thus, it takes about 14.3 years for the population to reach 10 million.

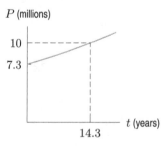

Figure 3.30

Example 3   Caffeine leaves the body at a continuous rate of 17% per hour. How much caffeine is left in the body 8 hours after drinking a cup of coffee containing 100 mg of caffeine?

Solution   If A is the amount of caffeine in the body t hours after drinking the coffee, then
$$A = 100e^{-0.17t}.$$

After 8 hours, we have $A = 100e^{-0.17(8)} = 25.67$ mg.

The Difference Between Annual and Continuous Growth Rates

If $P = P_0(1.07)^t$, with t in years, we say that P is growing at an *annual* rate of 7%. If $P = P_0e^{0.07t}$, with t in years, we say that P is growing at a *continuous* rate of 7% per year. Since $e^{0.07} = 1.0725\ldots$, we can rewrite $P_0e^{0.07t} = P_0(1.0725)^t$. In other words, a 7% continuous rate and a 7.25% annual rate generate the same increases in P. We say the two rates are equivalent.

We can check that $e^{0.0677} = 1.07\ldots$, so a 7% annual growth rate is equivalent to a 6.77% continuous growth rate. The continuous growth rate is always smaller than the equivalent annual rate.

The bank account example at the start of this section reminds us why a quantity growing at continuous rate of 7% per year increases faster than a quantity growing at an annual rate of 7%: In the continuous case, the interest earns more interest.

Example 4   In November 2005, the Wells Fargo Bank offered interest at a 2.323% continuous yearly rate.[14] Find the equivalent annual rate.

Solution   Since $e^{0.02323} = 1.0235$, the equivalent annual rate is 2.35%. As expected, the equivalent annual rate is larger than the continuous yearly rate.

Exercises and Problems for Section 3.4

Exercises

1. Without a calculator, match the functions $y = e^x$, $y = 2e^x$, and $y = 3e^x$ to the graphs in Figure 3.31.

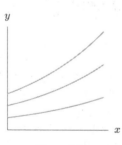

Figure 3.31

2. Without a calculator, match the functions $y = 2^x$, $y = 3^x$, and $y = e^x$ with the graphs in Figure 3.32.

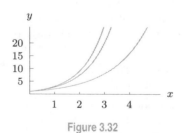

Figure 3.32

3. Without a calculator, match the functions (a)–(d) with the graphs (I)–(IV) in Figure 3.33.

(a) $e^{0.25t}$ **(b)** $(1.25)^t$ **(c)** $(1.2)^t$ **(d)** $e^{0.3t}$

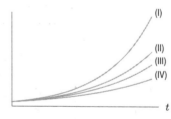

Figure 3.33

4. Without graphing on a calculator, match the functions (a)–(d) with the graphs (I)–(IV) in Figure 3.34.

(a) 1.5^x **(b)** $e^{0.45x}$ **(c)** $e^{0.47x}$ **(d)** $e^{0.5x}$

Figure 3.34

---

[14]http://money.cnn.com/2005/11/30/debt/informa_rate.

5. Without a calculator, match the functions $y = e^x$, $y = e^{-x}$, and $y = -e^x$ to the graphs in Figure 3.35.

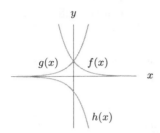

Figure 3.35

6. Without a calculator, match each formula to one of the graphs (I)–(IV) in Figure 3.36.

(a) $e^{-0.01t}$ (b) $e^{0.05t}$ (c) $e^{-0.10t}$ (d) $e^{0.20t}$

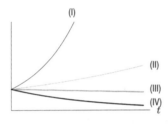

Figure 3.36

7. Without a calculator, match the functions (a)–(d) with the graphs (I)–(IV) in Figure 3.37.

(a) $y = e^x$ (b) $y = e^{-x}$

(c) $y = e^{-2x}$ (d) $y = e^{-3x}$

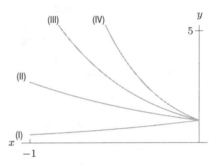

Figure 3.37

8. At time t in years, the value, V, of an investment of $1000 is given by $V = 1000e^{0.02t}$. When is the investment worth $3000?

9. How long does it take an investment to double if it grows according to the formula $V = 537e^{0.015t}$? Assume t is in years.

Problems

10. Without a calculator, arrange the following quantities in ascending order:

(a) $3^{2.2}$, $e^{2.2}$, $(\sqrt{2})^{2.2}$
(b) $3^{-2.2}$, $e^{-2.2}$

In Problems 11–14, find the limits.

11. $\lim_{x \to \infty} e^{-3x}$

12. $\lim_{t \to -\infty} 5e^{0.07t}$

13. $\lim_{t \to \infty} (2 - 3e^{-0.2t})$

14. $\lim_{t \to -\infty} 2e^{-0.1t+6}$

15. If $\lim_{t \to \infty} ae^{kt} = \infty$, what can you say about the values of a and k?

16. From time $t = 0$, with t in years, a $1200 deposit in a bank account grows according to the formula

$$B = 1200e^{0.03t}.$$

(a) What is the balance in the account at the end of 100 years?

(b) When does the balance first go over $50,000?

17. Calculate the amount of money in a bank account if $2000 is deposited for 15 years at an interest rate of

(a) 5% annually
(b) 5% continuously per year

18. A population of 3.2 million grows at a constant percentage rate.

(a) What is the population one century later if there is:
   (i) An annual growth rate of 2%
   (ii) A continuous growth rate of 2% per year
(b) Explain how you can tell which of the answers would be larger before doing the calculations.

19. A population is 25,000 in year $t = 0$ and grows at a continuous rate of 7.5% per year.

(a) Find a formula for $P(t)$, the population in year t.
(b) By what percent does the population increase each year? Why is this more than 7.5%?

20. A population grows from its initial level of 22,000 at a continuous growth rate of 7.1% per year.

   (a) Find a formula for $P(t)$, the population in year t.

   (b) By what percent does the population increase each year?

21. A radioactive substance decays at a continuous rate of 14% per year, and 50 mg of the substance is present in the year 2000.

   (a) Write a formula for the amount present, A (in mg), t years after 2000.

   (b) How much will be present in the year 2010?

   (c) Estimate when the quantity drops below 5 mg.

22. In 2004, the gross world product, W, (total output in goods and services) was 54.7 trillion dollars and growing at a continuous rate of 3.8% per year.[15] Write a formula for W, in trillions of dollars, as a function of years, t, since 2004. Estimate the value of t when the gross world product is predicted to reach 80 trillion dollars.

23. World poultry production was 77.2 million tons in the year 2004 and increasing at a continuous rate of 1.6% per year.[16] Assume that this growth rate continues.

   (a) Write an exponential formula for world poultry production, P, in million tons, as a function of the number of years, t, since 2004.

   (b) Use the formula to estimate world poultry production in the year 2010.

   (c) Use a graph to estimate the year in which world poultry production goes over 90 million tons.

24. What can you say about the value of the constants a, k, b, l in Figure 3.38?

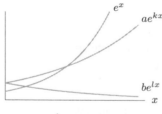

Figure 3.38

25. This problem explores the value of $(1+1/n)^n$ for integer values of n as n gets large.

   (a) Use a calculator or computer to evaluate $(1+1/n)^n$, correct to seven decimal places, for $n = 1000$,

10,000, 100,000, and 1,000,000. Does $(1 + 1/n)^n$ appear to be an increasing or decreasing function of n?

   (b) The limit of the sequence of values in part (a) is $e = 2.718281828\ldots$. What power of 10 is needed to give a value of e correct to 6 decimal places?

   (c) What happens if you evaluate $(1 + 1/n)^n$ using much larger values of n? For example, try $n = 10^{16}$ on a calculator.

26. This problem uses a calculator or computer to explore graphically the value of $(1 + 1/x)^x$ as x gets large.

   (a) Graph $y = (1 + 1/x)^x$ for $1 \leq x \leq 10$.

   (b) Are the values of y in part (a) increasing or decreasing?

   (c) Do the values of y in part (a) appear to approach a limiting value?

   (d) Graph $y = (1 + 1/x)^x$, for $1 \leq x \leq 100$, and then for $1 \leq x \leq 1000$. Do the y values appear to approach a limiting value? If so, approximately what is it?

   (e) Graph $y = (1 + 1/x)^x$ and $y = e$ on the same axes, for $1 \leq x \leq 10,000$. What does the graph suggest?

   (f) By checking $x = 10,000$, $x = 20,000$, and so on, decide how large (as a multiple of 10,000) x should be to give a value of e correct to 4 decimal places.

27. **(a)** Using a computer or calculator, graph $f(x) = 2^x$.

   (b) Find the slope of the line tangent to f at $x = 0$ to an accuracy of two decimals. [Hint: Zoom in on the graph until it is indistinguishable from a line and estimate the slope using two points on the graph.]

   (c) Find the slope of the line tangent to $g(x) = 3^x$ at $x = 0$ to an accuracy of two decimals.

   (d) Find b (to two decimals) such that the line tangent to the function $h(x) = b^x$ at $x = 0$ has slope 1.

28. With more terms giving a better approximation, it can be shown that

$$e = 1 + \frac{1}{1} + \frac{1}{1 \cdot 2} + \frac{1}{1 \cdot 2 \cdot 3} + \frac{1}{1 \cdot 2 \cdot 3 \cdot 4} + \cdots.$$

   (a) Use a calculator to sum the five terms shown.

   (b) Find the sum of the first seven terms.

   (c) Compare your sums with the calculator's displayed value for e (which you can find by entering $e^\wedge 1$) and state the number of correct digits in the five and seven term sum.

   (d) How many terms of the sum are needed in order to give a nine decimal digit approximation equal to the calculator's displayed value for e?

---

[15]The Worldwatch Institute, *Vital Signs 2005* (New York: W.W. Norton & Company, 2005), p. 45.

[16]The Worldwatch Institute, *Vital Signs 2005* (New York: W.W. Norton & Company, 2005), p. 24.

3.5 COMPOUND INTEREST

What is the difference between a bank account that pays 12% interest once per year and one that pays 1% interest every month? Imagine we deposit $1000 into the first account. Then, after 1 year, we have (assuming no other deposits or withdrawals)

$$\$1000(1.12) = \$1120.$$

But if we deposit $1000 into the second account, then after 1 year, or 12 months, we have

$$\$1000 \underbrace{(1.01)(1.01)\ldots(1.01)}_{\text{12 months of 1\% monthly interest}} = 1000(1.01)^{12} = \$1126.83.$$

Thus, we earn $6.83 more in the second account than in the first. To see why this happens, notice that the 1% interest we earn in January itself earns interest at a rate of 1% per month. Similarly, the 1% interest we earn in February earns interest, and so does the interest earned in March, April, May, and so on. The extra $6.83 comes from interest earned on interest. This effect is known as *compounding*. We say that the first account earns 12% interest *compounded annually* and the second account earns 12% interest *compounded monthly*.

Nominal Versus Effective Rate

The expression 12% compounded monthly means that interest is added twelve times per year and that $12\%/12 = 1\%$ of the current balance is added each time. We refer to the 12% as the *nominal rate* (nominal means "in name only"). When the interest is compounded more frequently than once a year, the account effectively earns more than the nominal rate. Thus, we distinguish between nominal rate and *effective annual rate*, or *effective rate*. The effective annual rate tells you how much interest the investment actually earns.

Example 1   What are the nominal and effective annual rates of an account paying 12% interest, compounded annually? Compounded monthly?

Solution   Since an account paying 12% annual interest, compounded annually, grows by exactly 12% in one year, we see that its nominal rate is the same as its effective rate: both are 12%.

    The account paying 12% interest, compounded monthly, also has a nominal rate of 12%. On the other hand, since it pays 1% interest every month, after 12 months, its balance increases by a factor of

$$\underbrace{(1.01)(1.01)\ldots(1.01)}_{\text{12 months of 1\% monthly growth}} = 1.01^{12} \approx 1.1268250.$$

Thus, effectively, the account earns 12.683% interest in a year.

Example 2   What is the effective annual rate of an account that pays interest at the nominal rate of 6% per year, compounded daily? Compounded hourly?

Solution   Since there are 365 days in a year, daily compounding pays interest at the rate of

$$\frac{6\%}{365} = 0.0164384\% \text{ per day.}$$

Thus, the daily growth factor is

$$1 + \frac{0.06}{365} = 1.000164384.$$

If at the beginning of the year the account balance is P, after 365 days the balance is

$$P \cdot \underbrace{\left(1 + \frac{0.06}{365}\right)^{365}}_{\substack{\text{365 days of} \\ \text{0.0164384\% daily interest}}} = P \cdot (1.0618313).$$

Thus, this account earns interest at the effective annual rate of 6.18313%.

Notice that daily compounding results in a higher rate than yearly compounding (6.183% versus 6%), because with daily compounding the interest has the opportunity to earn interest.

If interest is compounded hourly, since there are $24 \cdot 365$ hours in a year, the balance at year's end is

$$P \cdot \left(1 + \frac{0.06}{24 \cdot 365}\right)^{24 \cdot 365} = P \cdot (1.0618363).$$

The effective rate is now 6.18363% instead of 6.18313%—that is, just slightly better than the rate of the account that compounds interest daily. The effective rate increases with the frequency of compounding.

To summarize:

> If interest at an annual rate of r is compounded n times a year, then r/n times the current balance is added n times a year. Therefore, with an initial deposit of $\$P$, the balance t years later is
> $$B = P \cdot \left(1 + \frac{r}{n}\right)^{nt}.$$
> Note that r is the nominal rate; for example, $r = 0.05$ if the annual rate is 5%.

Continuous Compounding and the Number e

In Example 2 we calculated the effective interest rates for two accounts with a 6% per year nominal interest rate, but different compounding periods. We see that the account with more frequent compounding earns a higher effective rate, though the increase is small.

This suggests that compounding more and more frequently—every minute or every second or many times per second—would increase the effective rate still further. As we saw in Section 3.4, there is a limit to how much more an account can earn by increasing the frequency of compounding.

Table 3.16   *Effect of increasing the frequency of compounding*

Compounding frequency	Annual growth factor	Effective annual rate
Annually	1.0600000	6%
Monthly	1.0616778	6.16778%
Daily	1.0618313	6.18313%
Hourly	1.0618363	6.18363%
$\vdots$	$\vdots$	$\vdots$
Continuously	$e^{0.06} \approx 1.0618365$	6.18365%

Table 3.16 shows several compounding periods with their annual growth factors and effective annual rates. As the compounding periods become shorter, the growth factor approaches $e^{0.06}$. Using a calculator, we check that

$$e^{0.06} \approx 1.0618365,$$

which is the final value for the annual growth factors in Table 3.16. If an account with a 6% nominal interest rate delivers this effective yield, we say that the interest has been *compounded continuously*.

In general:

> If interest on an initial deposit of $\$P$ is *compounded continuously* at an annual rate r, the balance t years later can be calculated using the formula
>
> $$B = Pe^{rt}.$$
>
> Again, r is the nominal rate, and, for example, $r = 0.06$ when the annual rate is 6%.

It is important to realize that the functions $B = Pe^{0.06t}$ and $B = P(1.0618365)^t$ both give the balance in a bank account growing at a continuous rate of 6% per year. These formulas both represent the *same* exponential function—they just describe it in different ways.[17]

Example 3   Which is better: An account that pays 8% annual interest compounded quarterly or an account that pays 7.95% annual interest compounded continuously?

Solution   The account that pays 8% interest compounded quarterly pays 2% interest 4 times a year. Thus, in one year the balance is

$$P(1.02)^4 \approx P(1.08243),$$

which means the effective annual rate is 8.243%.

The account that pays 7.95% interest compounded continuously has a year-end balance of

$$Pe^{0.0795} \approx P(1.08275),$$

so the effective annual rate is 8.275%. Thus, 7.95% compounded continuously pays more than 8% compounded quarterly.

---

[17]Actually, this is not precisely true, because we rounded off when we found $b = 1.0618365$. However, we can find b to as many digits as we want, and to this extent the two formulas are the same.

Exercises and Problems for Section 3.5

In Exercises 1–4, what is the balance after 1 year if an account containing $500 earns the stated yearly nominal interest, compounded

(a) Annually   (b) Weekly (52 weeks per year)

(c) Every minute (525,600 per year)

(d) Continuously?

1. 1%   **2.** 3%   **3.** 5%   **4.** 8%

5. The same amount of money is deposited into two different bank accounts paying the same nominal rate, one compounded annually and the other compounded continuously. Which curve in Figure 3.39 corresponds to which compounding method? What is the initial deposit?

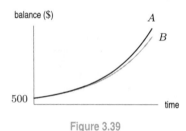

balance ($)

A

B

500

time

Figure 3.39

6. Find the effective annual yield and the continuous growth rate if $Q = 5500\,e^{0.19\,t}$.

7. If $5000 is deposited in an account paying a nominal interest rate of 4% per year, how much is in the account 10 years later if interest is compounded

(a) Annually?

(b) Continuously?

8. Suppose $1000 is deposited into an account paying interest at a nominal rate of 8% per year. Find the balance three years later if the interest is compounded

(a) Monthly   (b) Weekly

(c) Daily   (d) Continuously

9. Find the effective annual rate if $1000 is deposited at 5% annual interest, compounded continuously.

10. A bank pays interest at the nominal rate of 4.2% per year. What is the effective annual yield if compounding is:

(a) Annual   (b) Monthly   (c) Continuous

In Problems 11–14, what are the nominal and effective annual rates for an account paying the stated annual interest, compounded

(a) Annually?   (b) Quarterly?

(c) Daily?   (d) Continuously?

11. 1%   **12.** 100%   **13.** 3%   **14.** 6%

15. A bank account pays 6% annual interest. As the number of compounding periods increases, the effective interest rate earned also rises.

(a) Find the annual interest rate earned by the account if the interest is compounded:

   (i) Quarterly   (ii) Monthly

   (iii) Weekly   (iv) Daily

(b) Evaluate $e^{0.06}$, where $e = 2.71828\ldots$ Explain what your result tells you about the bank account.

16. If you need $25,000 six years from now, what is the minimum amount of money you need to deposit into a bank account that pays 5% annual interest, compounded:

(a) Annually   (b) Monthly   (c) Daily

(d) Your answers get smaller as the number of times of compounding increases. Why is this so?

17. Suppose $300 was deposited into one of five bank accounts and t is time in years. For each verbal description (i)–(v), state which formulas (a)–(e) could represent it.

(a) $B = 300(1.2)^t$ (b) $B = 300(1.12)^t$

(c) $B = 300(1.06)^{2t}$ (d) $B = 300(1.06)^{t/2}$

(e) $B = 300(1.03)^{4t}$

  (i) This investment earned 12% annually, compounded annually.

 (ii) This investment earned, on average, more than 1% each month.

(iii) This investment earned 12% annually, compounded semi-annually.

(iv) This investment earned, on average, less than 3% each quarter.

 (v) This investment earned, on average, more than 6% every 6 months.

18. Three different investments are given.

   (a) Find the balance of each of the investments after the two-year period.
   (b) Rank them from best to worst in terms of rate of return. Explain your reasoning.

   - Investment A: $875 deposited at 13.5% per year compounded daily for 2 years.
   - Investment B: $1000 deposited at 6.7% per year compounded continuously for 2 years.
   - Investment C: $1050 deposited at 4.5% per year compounded monthly for 2 years.

19. Rank the following three bank deposit options from best to worst.

   - Bank A: 7% compounded daily
   - Bank B: 7.1% compounded monthly
   - Bank C: 7.05% compounded continuously

20. Which is better, an account paying 5.3% interest compounded continuously or an account paying 5.5% interest compounded annually? Justify your answer.

21. If the balance, M, at time t in years, of a bank account that compounds its interest payments monthly is given by

$$M = M_0(1.07763)^t.$$

   (a) What is the effective annual rate for this account?

   (b) What is the nominal annual rate?

22. A sum of $850 is invested for 10 years and the interest is compounded quarterly. There is $1000 in the account at the end of 10 years. What is the nominal annual rate?

23. In the 1980s a northeastern bank experienced an unusual robbery. Each month an armored car delivered cash deposits from local branches to the main office, a trip requiring only one hour. One day, however, the delivery was six hours late. This delay turned out to be a scheme devised by an employee to defraud the bank. The armored car drivers had lent the money, a total of approximately $200,000,000, to arms merchants who then used it as collateral against the purchase of illegal weapons. The interest charged for this loan was 20% per year compounded continuously. How much was the fee for the six-hour period?

24. An investment grows by 3% per year for 10 years. By what percent does it increase over the 10-year period?

25. An investment grows by 30% over a 5-year period. What is its effective annual percent growth rate?

26. An investment decreases by 60% over a 12-year period. At what effective annual percent rate does it decrease?

CHAPTER SUMMARY

- **Exponential Functions**
  Value of $f(t)$ changes at constant percent rate with respect to t.

- **General Formula for Exponential Functions**
  Exponential function: $f(t) = ab^t$, $b > 0$.
  f increasing for $b > 1$, decreasing for $0 < b < 1$.
     Growth factor: $b = 1 + r$.
     Growth rate: r, percent change as a decimal.

- **Comparing Linear and Exponential Functions**
  An increasing exponential function eventually overtakes any linear function.

- **Graphs of Exponential Functions**
  Concavity; asymptotes; effect of parameters a and b.
  Solving exponential equations graphically; fitting expo-

nential functions to data.

- **The Number e**
  Continuous growth: $f(t) = ae^{kt}$.
  f is increasing for $k > 0$, decreasing for $k < 0$.
     Continuous growth rate: k.

- **Compound Interest**
  For compounding n times per year, balance,
  $$B = P\left(1 + \frac{r}{n}\right)^{nt}.$$
  For continuous compounding, $B = Pe^{kt}$.
  Nominal rate, r or k, versus effective rate earned over one year.

- **Horizontal Asymptotes and Limits to Infinity**

REVIEW EXERCISES AND PROBLEMS FOR CHAPTER THREE

Exercises

Are the functions in Exercises 1–9 exponential? If so, write the function in the form $f(t) = ab^t$.

1. $g(w) = 2\left(2^{-w}\right)$

2. $m(t) = (2 \cdot 3^t)^3$

3. $f(x) = \dfrac{3^{2x}}{4}$

4. $G(t) = 3(t)^t$

5. $q(r) = \dfrac{-4}{3^r}$

6. $j(x) = 2^x 3^x$

7. $Q(t) = 8^{t/3}$

8. $K(x) = \dfrac{2^x}{3 \cdot 3^x}$

9. $p(r) = 2^r + 3^r$

10. A town has population 3000 people at year $t = 0$. Write a formula for the population, P, in year t if the town

 (a) Grows by 200 people per year.
 (b) Grows by 6% per year.
 (c) Grows at a continuous rate of 6% per year.
 (d) Shrinks by 50 people per year.
 (e) Shrinks by 4% per year.
 (f) Shrinks at a continuous rate of 4% per year.

11. The following formulas each describe the size of an animal population, P, in t years since the start of the study. Describe the growth of each population in words.

 (a) $P = 200(1.028)^t$ (b) $P = 50e^{-0.17t}$
 (c) $P = 1000(0.89)^t$ (d) $P = 600e^{0.20t}$
 (e) $P = 2000 - 300t$ (f) $P = 600 + 50t$

12. If $f(x) = 12 + 20x$ and $g(x) = \frac{1}{2} \cdot 3^x$, for what values of x is $g(x) < f(x)$?

For Exercises 13–18, find a formula for the exponential function.

13.

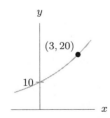

14.

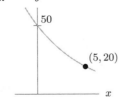

15.

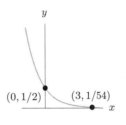

16.

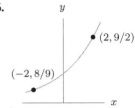

17.

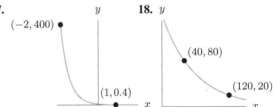

18.

19. Without a calculator, match each of the formulas to one of the graphs in Figure 3.40.

 (a) $y = 0.8^t$ (b) $y = 5(3)^t$
 (c) $y = -6(1.03)^t$ (d) $y = 15(3)^{-t}$
 (e) $y = -4(0.98)^t$ (f) $y = 82(0.8)^{-t}$

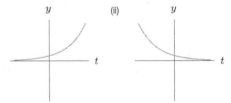
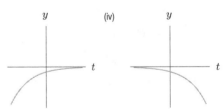

Figure 3.40

20. Without a calculator, match each of the following formulas to one of the graphs in Figure 3.40.

 (a) $y = 8.3e^{-t}$ (b) $y = 2.5e^t$ (c) $y = -4e^{-t}$

Problems

In Problems 21–25, graph $f(x)$, a function defined for all real numbers and satisfying the condition.

21. $f(x) \to 3$ as $x \to -\infty$

22. $\lim_{x \to \infty} f(x) = 5$

23. $\lim_{x \to -\infty} f(x) = 2$ and $\lim_{x \to \infty} f(x) = -1$

24. $f(x) \to 0$ as $x \to -\infty$ and $f(x) \to -\infty$ as $x \to \infty$

25. $f(x)$ has a horizontal asymptote of $y = 5$.

Find the limits in Problems 26–31.

26. $\lim_{x \to \infty} 257(0.93)^x$ **27.** $\lim_{t \to \infty} 5.3 e^{-0.12t}$

28. $\lim_{x \to -\infty} (15 - 5e^{3x})$ **29.** $\lim_{t \to -\infty} (21(1.2)^t + 5.1)$

30. $\lim_{x \to \infty} (7.2 - 2e^{3x})$ **31.** $\lim_{x \to -\infty} (5e^{-7x} + 1.5)$

32. An account pays interest at a nominal rate of 8% per year. Find the effective annual yield if interest is compounded

(a) Monthly   (b) Weekly

(c) Daily   (d) Continuously

33. Find $g(t) = ab^t$ if $g(10) = 50$ and $g(30) = 25$.

34. Find a formula for $f(x)$, an exponential function such that $f(-8) = 200$ and $f(30) = 580$.

35. Suppose that $f(x)$ is exponential and that $f(-3) = 54$ and $f(2) = \frac{2}{9}$. Find a formula for $f(x)$.

36. Find a formula for $f(x)$, an exponential function such that $f(2) = 1/27$ and $f(-1) = 27$.

37. Find the equation of an exponential curve through the points $(-1, 2)$, $(1, 0.3)$.

Find possible formulas for the functions in Problems 38–40.

38. V gives the value of an account that begins in year $t = 0$ with $12,000 and earns 4.2% annual interest, compounded continuously.

39. The exponential function $p(t)$ given that $p(20) = 300$ and $p(50) = 40$.

40. The linear function $q(x)$ whose graph intersects the graph of $y = 5000e^{-x/40}$ at $x = 50$ and $x = 150$.

41. An investment worth $V = 2500$ in year $t = 0$ earns 4.2% annual interest, compounded continuously. Find a formula for V in terms of t.

42. A population is represented by $P = 12,000e^{-0.122t}$. Give the values of a, k, b, and r, where $P = ae^{kt} = ab^t$. What do these values tell you about the population?

Decide whether the functions in Problems 43–45 could be approximately linear, approximately exponential, or are neither. For those that could be nearly linear or nearly exponential, find a formula.

43.

t	3	10	14
$Q(t)$	7.51	8.7	9.39

44.

t	5	9	15
$R(t)$	2.32	2.61	3.12

45.

t	5	12	16
$S(t)$	4.35	6.72	10.02

46. In January 2005, the population of California was 36.8 million and growing at an annual rate of 1.3%. Assume that growth continues at the same rate.

(a) By how much will the population increase between 2005 and 2030? Between 2030 and 2055?

(b) Explain how you can tell before doing the calculations which of the two answers in part (a) is larger.

47. There were 178.8 million licensed drivers in the US in 1989 and 187.2 million in 1999.[18] Find a formula for the number, N of licensed drivers in the US as a function of t, the number of years since 1989, assuming growth is

(a) Linear   (b) Exponential

48. The population of a small town increases by a growth factor of 1.134 over a two-year period.

(a) By what percent does the town increase in size during the two-year period?

(b) If the town grows by the same percent each year, what is its annual percent growth rate?

[18] *The World Almanac* 2002 (New York: World Almanac Education Group, Inc., 2002), p. 228.

49. If t is in years, the formulas for dollar balances of two different bank accounts are:

$$f(t) = 1100(1.05)^t \quad \text{and} \quad g(t) = 1500e^{0.05t}.$$

(a) Describe in words the bank account modeled by f.

(b) Describe the account modeled by g. State the effective annual yield.

50. Accion is a non-profit microlending organization which makes small loans to entrepreneurs who do not qualify for bank loans.[19] A New York woman who sells clothes from a cart has the choice of a $1000 loan from Accion to be repaid by $1160 a year later and a $1000 loan from a loan shark with an annual interest rate of 22%, compounded annually.

(a) What is the annual interest rate charged by Accion?

(b) To pay off the loan shark for a year's loan of $1000, how much would the woman have to pay?

(c) Which loan is a better deal for the woman? Why?

Problems 51–54 use Figure 3.41, which show $f(x) = ab^x$ and $g(x) = cd^x$ on three different scales. Their point of intersection is marked.

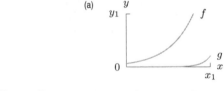

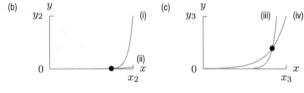

Figure 3.41

51. Which is larger, a or c?

52. Which is larger, b or d?

53. Rank in order from least to greatest: x_1, x_2, x_3.

54. Match f and g to the graphs labeled (i)–(iv) in (b) and (c).

55. Find the annual growth rates of a quantity which:

(a) Doubles in size every 7 years

(b) Triples in size every 11 years

(c) Grows by 3% per month

(d) Grows by 18% every 5 months

56. In 1995, the population of a town was 18,500 and it grew by 250 people by the end of the year. By 2005, its population had reached 22,500.

(a) Can this population be best described by a linear or an exponential model, or neither? Explain.

(b) If possible, find a formula for $P(t)$, the population t years after 1995.

57. In 1995, the population of a town was 20,000, and it grew by 4.14% that year. By 2005, the town's population had reached 30,000.

(a) Can this population be best described by a linear or an exponential model, or neither? Explain.

(b) If possible, find a formula for $P(t)$, this population t years after 1995.

58. Forty percent of a radioactive substance decays in five years. By what percent does the substance decay each year?

59. Table 3.17 shows the concentration of theophylline, a common asthma drug, in the blood stream as a function of time after injection of a 300 mg initial dose.[20] It is claimed that this data set is consistent with an exponential decay model $C = ab^t$ where C is the concentration and t is the time.

(a) Estimate the values of a and b, using ratios to estimate b. How good is this model?

(b) Use a calculator or computer to find the exponential regression function for concentration as a function of time. Compare answers from parts (a) and (b).

Table 3.17

Time (hours)	0	1	3	5	7	9
Concentration (mg/l)	12.0	10.0	7.0	5.0	3.5	2.5

60. Figure 3.42 gives the voltage, $V(t)$, across a circuit element at time t seconds. For $t < 0$, the voltage is a constant 80 volts; for $t \geq 0$, the voltage decays exponentially.

(a) Find a piecewise formula for $V(t)$.

(b) At what value of t will the voltage reach 0.1?

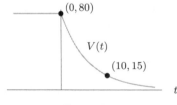

Figure 3.42

---

[19]www.accion.org.

[20]Based on D. N. Burghes, I. Huntley, and J. McDonald, *Applying Mathematics*. (Ellis Horwood, 1982).

61. Hong Kong shifted from British to Chinese rule in 1997. Figure 3.43 shows[21] the number of people who emigrated from Hong Kong during each of the years from 1980 to 1992.

   (a) Find an exponential function that approximates the data.
   (b) What does the model predict about the number of emigrants in 1997?
   (c) Briefly explain why this model is or is not useful to predict emigration in the year 2010.

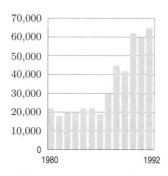

Figure 3.43

62. The annual inflation rate, r, for a five-year period is given in Table 3.18.

   (a) By what total percent did prices rise between the start of 2000 and the end of 2004?
   (b) What is the average annual inflation rate for this time period?
   (c) At the beginning of 2000, a shower curtain costs $20. Make a prediction for the good's cost at the beginning of 2010, using the average inflation rate found in part (b).

Table 3.18

t	2000	2001	2002	2003	2004
r	3.4%	2.8%	1.6%	2.3%	2.7%

63. Before the AIDS epidemic, Botswana[22] had a rapidly growing population as shown in Table 3.19. In 2005, the population started falling.

   (a) Fit an exponential growth model, $P = ab^t$, to this data set, where P is the population in millions and t measures the years since 1975 in 5-year intervals— so $t = 1$ corresponds to 1980. Estimate a and b. Plot the data set and $P = ab^t$ on the same graph.

   (b) Starting from 1975, how long does it take for the population of Botswana to double? When is the population of Botswana projected to exceed 214 million, the 1975 population of the US?

Table 3.19

Year	1975	1980	1985	1990
Population (millions)	0.755	0.901	1.078	1.285

64. It is a well-documented fact that the earning power of men is higher than that of women.[23] Table 3.20 gives the median income of year-round full-time workers in the US in dollars.

   (a) Plot the data and connect the points.
   (b) Let t be the year. Construct two functions of the form $W(t) = ae^{b(t-1950)}$, one each for the men's and women's earning power data.
   (c) Graph the two functions from 1950 to 2000 and again from 2000 to 2080.
   (d) Do the graphs in part (c) predict women's salaries will catch up with men's? If so, when?
   (e) Comment on your predictions in part (d).

Table 3.20

Year	1950	1960	1970	1980	1990	2000
Female	953	1261	2237	4920	10,070	16,063
Male	2570	4080	6670	12,530	20,293	28,343

65. According to a letter to the *New York Times* on April 10, 1993, "... the probability of [a driver's] involvement in a single-car accident increases exponentially with increasing levels of blood alcohol." The letter goes on to state that when a driver's blood-alcohol content (BAC) is 0.15, the risk of such an accident is about 25 times greater than for a nondrinker.

   (a) Let p_0 be a nondrinker's probability of being involved in a single-car accident. Let $f(x)$ be the probability of an accident for a driver whose blood alcohol level is x. Find a formula for $f(x)$. (This only makes sense for some values of x.)

[21] Adapted from the *New York Times* July 5, 1995.
[22] *World Population Growth and Aging* by N. Keyfitz, University of Chicago Press, 1990.
[23] *The World Almanac and Book of Facts 2006*, p. 84.

(b) At the time of the letter, the legal definition of intoxication was a BAC of 0.1 or higher. According to your formula for $f(x)$, how many times more likely to be involved in a single-car accident was a driver at the legal limit than a nondrinker?

(c) Suppose that new legislation is proposed to change the definition of legal intoxication. The new definition states that a person is legally intoxicated when their likelihood of involvement in a single-car accident is three times that of a non-drinker. To what BAC would the new definition of legal intoxication correspond?

CHECK YOUR UNDERSTANDING

Are the statements in Problems 1–32 true or false? Give an explanation for your answer.

1. Exponential functions are functions that increase or decrease at a constant percent rate.

2. The independent variable in an exponential function is always found in the exponent.

3. If $y = 40(1.05)^t$ then y is an exponential function of t.

4. The following table shows a function that could be exponential.

x	1	2	4	5	6
y	1	2	4	7	11

5. If your salary, S, grows by 4% each year, then $S = S_0(0.04)^t$ where t is in years.

6. If $f(t) = 4(2)^t$ then $f(2) = 64$.

7. If $f(t) = 3(\frac{2}{5})^t$ then f is a decreasing function.

8. If $Q = f(t) = 1000(0.5)^t$ then when $Q = 125, t = 3$.

9. If $Q = f(t) = ab^t$ then a is the initial value of Q.

10. If we are given two data points, we can find a linear function and an exponential function that go through these points.

11. A population that has 1000 members and decreases at 10% per year can be modeled as $P = 1000(0.10)^t$.

12. A positive increasing exponential function always becomes larger than any increasing linear function in the long run.

13. A possible formula for an exponential function that passes through the point $(0, 1)$ and the point $(2, 10)$ is $y = 4.5t + 1$.

14. If a population increases by 50% each year, then in two years it increases by 100%.

15. In the formula $Q = ab^t$, the value of a tells us where the graph crosses the Q-axis.

16. In the formula $Q = ab^t$, if $a > 1$, the graph always rises as we read from left to right.

17. The symbol e represents a constant whose value is approximately 2.71828.

18. If $f(x) \to k$ as $x \to \infty$ we say that the line $y = k$ is a horizontal asymptote.

19. Exponential graphs are always concave up.

20. If there are 110 grams of a substance initially and its decay rate is 3% per minute, then the amount after t minutes is $Q = 110(0.03)^t$ grams.

21. If a population had 200 members at time zero and was growing a 4% per year, then the population size after t years can be expressed as $P = 200(1.04)^t$.

22. If $P = 5e^{0.2t}$, we say the continuous growth rate of the function is 2%.

23. If $P = 4e^{-0.90t}$, we say the continuous growth rate of the function is 10%.

24. If $Q = 3e^{0.2t}$, then when $t = 5, Q = 3$.

25. If $Q = Q_0 e^{kt}$, with Q_0 positive and k negative, then Q is decreasing.

26. If an investment earns 5% compounded monthly, its effective rate will be more than 5%.

27. If a $500 investment earns 6% per year, compounded quarterly, we can find the balance after three years by evaluating the formula $B = 500(1 + \frac{6}{4})^{3 \cdot 4}$.

28. If interest on a $2000 investment is compounded continuously at 3% per year, the balance after five years is found by evaluating the formula $B = 2000e^{(0.03)(5)}$.

29. Investing $10,000 for 20 years at 5% earns more if interest is compounded quarterly than if it is compounded annually.

30. Investing $P for T years always earns more if interest is compounded continuously than if it is compounded annually.

31. There is no limit to the amount a twenty-year $10,000 investment at 5% interest can earn if the number of times the interest is compounded becomes greater and greater.

32. If you put $1000 into an account that earns 5.5% compounded continuously, then it takes about 18 years for the investment to grow to $2000.

TOOLS FOR CHAPTER 3: EXPONENTS

We list the definition and properties that are used to manipulate exponents.

Definition of Zero, Negative, and Fractional Exponents

If m and n are positive integers:[24]

- $a^0 = 1$
- $a^{-n} = \dfrac{1}{a^n}$
- $a^{1/n} = \sqrt[n]{a}$, the nth root of a
- $a^{m/n} = \sqrt[n]{a^m} = (\sqrt[n]{a})^m$

Properties of Exponents

- $a^m \cdot a^n = a^{m+n}$ For example, $2^4 \cdot 2^3 = (2 \cdot 2 \cdot 2 \cdot 2) \cdot (2 \cdot 2 \cdot 2) = 2^7$.
- $\dfrac{a^m}{a^n} = a^{m-n}, a \neq 0$ For example, $\dfrac{2^4}{2^3} = \dfrac{2 \cdot 2 \cdot 2 \cdot 2}{2 \cdot 2 \cdot 2} = 2^1$.
- $(a^m)^n = a^{mn}$ For example, $(2^3)^2 = 2^3 \cdot 2^3 = 2^6$.
- $(ab)^n = a^n b^n$
- $\left(\dfrac{a}{b}\right)^n = \dfrac{a^n}{b^n}, \quad b \neq 0$

Be aware of the following notational conventions:

$$ab^n = a(b^n), \qquad \text{but } ab^n \neq (ab)^n,$$
$$-b^n = -(b^n), \qquad \text{but } -b^n \neq (-b)^n,$$
$$-ab^n = (-a)(b^n).$$

For example, $-2^4 = -(2^4) = -16$, but $(-2)^4 = (-2)(-2)(-2)(-2) = +16$. Also, be sure to realize that for $n \neq 1$,

$$(a+b)^n \neq a^n + b^n \qquad \text{Power of a sum} \neq \text{Sum of powers.}$$

Example 1   Evaluate without a calculator:

(a) $(27)^{2/3}$ (b) $(4)^{-3/2}$ (c) $8^{1/3} - 1^{1/3}$

Solution   (a) We have $(27)^{2/3} = \sqrt[3]{27^2} = \sqrt[3]{729} = 9$, or, equivalently, $(27)^{2/3} = \left(27^{1/3}\right)^2 = \left(\sqrt[3]{27}\right)^2 = 3^2 = 9$.

(b) We have $(4)^{-3/2} = (2)^{-3} = \dfrac{1}{2^3} = \dfrac{1}{8}$.

(c) We have $8^{1/3} - 1^{1/3} = 2 - 1 = 1$.

---

[24]We assume that the base is restricted to the values for which the power is defined.

Example 2   Use the rules of exponents to simplify the following:

(a) $\dfrac{100x^2y^4}{5x^3y^2}$ (b) $\dfrac{y^4(x^3y^{-2})^2}{2x^{-1}}$ (c) $\sqrt[3]{-8x^6}$ (d) $\left(\dfrac{M^{1/5}}{3N^{-1/2}}\right)^2$

Solution   (a) We have

$$\frac{100x^2y^4}{5x^3y^2} = 20(x^{2-3})(y^{4-2}) = 20x^{-1}y^2 = \frac{20y^2}{x}.$$

(b) We have

$$\frac{y^4\left(x^3y^{-2}\right)^2}{2x^{-1}} = \frac{y^4x^6y^{-4}}{2x^{-1}} = \frac{y^{(4-4)}x^{(6-(-1))}}{2} = \frac{y^0x^7}{2} = \frac{x^7}{2}.$$

(c) We have

$$\sqrt[3]{-8x^6} = \sqrt[3]{-8}\cdot\sqrt[3]{x^6} = -2x^2.$$

(d) We have

$$\left(\frac{M^{1/5}}{3N^{-1/2}}\right)^2 = \frac{\left(M^{1/5}\right)^2}{\left(3N^{-1/2}\right)^2} = \frac{M^{2/5}}{3^2N^{-1}} = \frac{M^{2/5}N}{9}.$$

Example 3   Solve for x:

(a) $\dfrac{10x^7}{4x^2} = 37$ (b) $\dfrac{x^2}{3x^5} = 10$ (c) $\sqrt{9x^5} = 10$

Solution   (a) We have

$$\frac{10x^7}{4x^2} = 37$$
$$2.5x^5 = 37$$
$$x^5 = 14.8$$
$$x = (14.8)^{1/5} = 1.714.$$

(b) We have

$$\frac{x^2}{3x^5} = 10$$
$$\frac{1}{3}x^{-3} = 10$$
$$\frac{1}{x^3} = 30$$
$$x^3 = \frac{1}{30}$$
$$x = \left(\frac{1}{30}\right)^{1/3} = 0.322.$$

(c) We have

$$\sqrt{9x^5} = 10$$
$$3x^{5/2} = 10$$
$$x^{5/2} = \frac{10}{3}$$
$$x = \left(\frac{10}{3}\right)^{2/5} = 1.619.$$

Exercises to Tools for Chapter 3

For Exercises 1–43, evaluate without a calculator.

1. 4^3

2. $(-5)^2$

3. 11^2

4. 10^4

5. $(-1)^{12}$

6. $(-1)^{13}$

7. $\dfrac{5^3}{5^2}$

8. $\dfrac{5^3}{5}$

9. $\dfrac{10^8}{10^5}$

10. $\dfrac{6^4}{6^4}$

11. 8^0

12. $\sqrt{4}$

13. $\sqrt{4^2}$

14. $\sqrt{4^3}$

15. $\sqrt{4^4}$

16. $\sqrt{(-4)^2}$

17. $\dfrac{1}{7^{-2}}$

18. $\dfrac{2^7}{2^3}$

19. $(-1)^{445}$

20. -11^2

21. $(-2)3^2$

22. $\left(5^0\right)^3$

23. $2.1\left(10^3\right)$

24. $32^{1/5}$

25. $16^{1/2}$

26. $16^{1/4}$

27. $16^{3/4}$

28. $16^{5/4}$

29. $16^{5/2}$

30. $100^{5/2}$

31. $\sqrt[3]{-125}$

32. $\sqrt{(-4)^2}$

33. $(-1)^3\sqrt{36}$

34. $(0.04)^{1/2}$

35. $(-8)^{2/3}$

36. 3^{-1}

37. 3^{-2}

38. $3^{-3/2}$

39. 25^{-1}

40. 25^{-2}

41. $25^{-3/2}$

42. $(1/27)^{-1/3}$

43. $(0.125)^{1/3}$

Simplify the expressions in Exercises 44–77 and leave without radicals if possible. Assume all variables are positive.

44. $\sqrt{x^4}$

45. $\sqrt{y^8}$

46. $\sqrt{w^8 z^4}$

47. $\sqrt{x^5 y^4}$

48. $\sqrt{16x^3}$

49. $\sqrt{49w^9}$

50. $\sqrt{25x^3 z^4}$

51. $\sqrt{r^2}$

52. $\sqrt{r^3}$

53. $\sqrt{r^4}$

54. $\sqrt{36t^2}$

55. $\sqrt{64s^7}$

56. $\sqrt{50x^4 y^6}$

57. $\sqrt{48u^{10}v^{12}y^5}$

58. $\sqrt{8m}\sqrt{2m^3}$

59. $\sqrt{6s^2 t^3 v^5}\sqrt{6st^5 v^3}$

60. $(0.1)^2\left(4xy^2\right)^2$

61. $3\left(3^{x/2}\right)^2$

62. $\left(4L^{2/3}P\right)^{3/2}(P)^{-3/2}$

63. $7\left(5w^{1/2}\right)\left(2w^{1/3}\right)$

64. $\left(S\sqrt{16xt^2}\right)^2$

65. $\sqrt{e^{2x}}$

66. $(3AB)^{-1}\left(A^2 B^{-1}\right)^2$

67. $e^{kt}\cdot e^3\cdot e$

68. $\sqrt{M+2}(2+M)^{3/2}$

69. $\left(3x\sqrt{x^3}\right)^2$

70. $x^e\left(x^e\right)^2$

71. $\left(y^{-2}e^y\right)^2$

72. $\dfrac{4x^{(3\pi+1)}}{x^2}$

73. $\dfrac{4A^{-3}}{(2A)^{-4}}$

74. $\dfrac{a^{n+1}3^{n+1}}{a^n 3^n}$

75. $\dfrac{12u^3}{3\left(uv^2 w^4\right)^{-1}}$

76. $\left(a^{-1}+b^{-1}\right)^{-1}$

77. $\left(\dfrac{35(2b + 1)^9}{7(2b + 1)^{-1}} \right)^2$ (Do not expand $(2b + 1)^9$.)

If possible, evaluate the quantities in Exercises 78–86. Check your answers with a calculator.

78. $(-32)^{3/5}$ **79.** $-32^{3/5}$ **80.** $-625^{3/4}$

81. $(-625)^{3/4}$ **82.** $(-1728)^{4/3}$ **83.** $64^{-3/2}$

84. $-64^{3/2}$ **85.** $(-64)^{3/2}$ **86.** $81^{5/4}$

In Exercises 87–92, solve for x.

87. $\dfrac{10x^5}{x^2} = 2$ **88.** $\dfrac{5x^3}{x^5} = 125$

89. $\sqrt{4x^3} = 5$ **90.** $7x^4 = 20x^2$

91. $5x^{-2} = 500$ **92.** $2(x + 2)^3 = 100$

In Exercises 93–94, use algebra to find the point of intersection.

93.

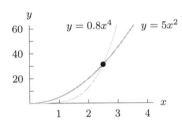

94.

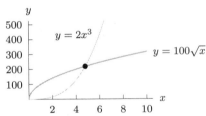

Are the statements in Exercises 95–104 true or false.?

95. $t^3 t^4 = t^{12}$ **96.** $x^2 y^5 = (xy)^{10}$

97. $(p^3)^8 = p^{11}$ **98.** $5u^2 + 5u^3 = 10u^5$

99. $(3r)^2 9s^2 = 81r^2 s^2$ **100.** $\sqrt[3]{-64b^3 c^6} = -4bc^2$

101. $\dfrac{m^8}{2m^2} = \dfrac{1}{2}m^4$ **102.** $5z^{-4} = \dfrac{1}{5z^4}$

103. $-4w^2 - 3w^3 = -w^2(4 + 3w)$

104. $(u + v)^{-1} = \dfrac{1}{u} + \dfrac{1}{v}$

Solve the equations in Problems 105–106 in terms of r and s given that

$$2^r = 5 \quad \text{and} \quad 2^s = 7.$$

105. $2^x = 35.$ **106.** $2^x = 140.$

Let $2^a = 5$ and $2^b = 7$. Using exponent rules, solve the equations in Problems 107–112 in terms of a and b.

107. $5^x = 32$ **108.** $7^x = \dfrac{1}{8}$

109. $25^x = 64$ **110.** $14^x = 16$

111. $5^x = 7$ **112.** $0.4^x = 49$

Chapter Four

LOGARITHMIC FUNCTIONS

In this chapter, we introduce the inverse of exponential functions, logarithmic functions. We study the properties of logarithms and use logarithms to solve exponential equations; logarithms are used to calculate doubling time and half-life. We also look at log scales, and we see how logs are used to linearize data.

The Tools Section on page 189 reviews the properties of logarithms.

4.1 LOGARITHMS AND THEIR PROPERTIES

What is a Logarithm?

Suppose that a population grows according to the formula $P = 10^t$, where P is the colony size at time t, in hours. When will the population be 2500? We want to solve the following equation for t:

$$10^t = 2500.$$

In Section 3.2, we used a graphical method to approximate t. This time, we introduce a function which returns precisely the exponent of 10 we need.

Since $10^3 = 1000$ and $10^4 = 10,000$, and $1000 < 2500 < 10,000$, the exponent we are looking for is between 3 and 4. But how do we find the exponent exactly?

To answer this question, we define the *common logarithm function*, or simply the *log function*, written $\log_{10} x$, or $\log x$, as follows.

If x is a positive number,

$$\log x \text{ is the exponent of 10 that gives } x.$$

In other words, if

$$y = \log x \qquad \text{then} \qquad 10^y = x.$$

For example, $\log 100 = 2$, because 2 is the exponent of 10 that gives 100, or $10^2 = 100$.

To solve the equation $10^t = 2500$, we must find the power of 10 that gives 2500. Using the log button on a calculator, we can approximate this exponent. We find

$$\log 2500 \approx 3.398, \quad \text{which means that} \quad 10^{3.398} \approx 2500.$$

As predicted, this exponent is between 3 and 4. The precise exponent is $\log 2500$; the approximate value is 3.398. Thus, it takes roughly 3.4 hours for the population to reach 2500.

Example 1   Rewrite the following statements using exponents instead of logs.

(a) $\log 100 = 2$ (b) $\log 0.01 = -2$ (c) $\log 30 = 1.477$

Solution   For each statement, we use the fact that if $y = \log x$ then $10^y = x$.
(a) $2 = \log 100$ means that $10^2 = 100$.
(b) $-2 = \log 0.01$ means that $10^{-2} = 0.01$.
(c) $1.477 = \log 30$ means that $10^{1.477} = 30$. (Actually, this is only an approximation. Using a calculator, we see that $10^{1.477} = 29.9916\ldots$ and that $\log 30 = 1.47712125\ldots$.)

Example 2   Rewrite the following statements using logs instead of exponents.

(a) $10^5 = 100,000$ (b) $10^{-4} = 0.0001$ (c) $10^{0.8} = 6.3096$.

Solution   For each statement, we use the fact that if $10^y = x$, then $y = \log x$.

(a) $10^5 = 100{,}000$ means that $\log 100{,}000 = 5$.

(b) $10^{-4} = 0.0001$ means that $\log 0.0001 = -4$.

(c) $10^{0.8} = 6.3096$ means that $\log 6.3096 = 0.8$. (This, too, is only an approximation because $10^{0.8}$ actually equals $6.30957344\ldots$.)

Logarithms Are Exponents

Note that logarithms are just exponents! Thinking in terms of exponents is often a good way to answer a logarithm problem.

Example 3   Without a calculator, evaluate the following, if possible:

(a) $\log 1$ (b) $\log 10$ (c) $\log 1{,}000{,}000$

(d) $\log 0.001$ (e) $\log \dfrac{1}{\sqrt{10}}$ (f) $\log(-100)$

Solution

(a) We have $\log 1 = 0$, since $10^0 = 1$.

(b) We have $\log 10 = 1$, since $10^1 = 10$.

(c) Since $1{,}000{,}000 = 10^6$, the exponent of 10 that gives $1{,}000{,}000$ is 6. Thus, $\log 1{,}000{,}000 = 6$.

(d) Since $0.001 = 10^{-3}$, the exponent of 10 that gives 0.001 is -3. Thus, $\log 0.001 = -3$.

(e) Since $1/\sqrt{10} = 10^{-1/2}$, the exponent of 10 that gives $1/\sqrt{10}$ is $-\frac{1}{2}$. Thus $\log(1/\sqrt{10}) = -\frac{1}{2}$.

(f) Since 10 to any power is positive, -100 cannot be written as a power of 10. Thus, $\log(-100)$ is undefined.

Logarithmic and Exponential Functions are Inverses

The operation of taking a logarithm "undoes" the exponential function; the logarithm and the exponential are inverse functions. For example, $\log(10^6) = 6$ and $10^{\log 6} = 6$. In particular

> For any N,
> $$\log(10^N) = N$$
> and for $N > 0$,
> $$10^{\log N} = N.$$

Example 4   Evaluate without a calculator: (a) $\log\left(10^{8.5}\right)$ (b) $10^{\log 2.7}$ (c) $10^{\log(x+3)}$

Solution   Using $\log(10^N) = N$ and $10^{\log N} = N$, we have:

(a) $\log\left(10^{8.5}\right) = 8.5$ (b) $10^{\log 2.7} = 2.7$ (c) $10^{\log(x+3)} = x + 3$

You can check the first two results on a calculator.

Properties of Logarithms

In Chapter 3, we saw how to solve exponential equations such as $100 \cdot 2^t = 337{,}000{,}000$, graphically. To use logarithms to solve these equations, we use the properties of logarithms, which are justified on page 156.

Properties of the Common Logarithm
- By definition, $y = \log x$ means $10^y = x$.
- In particular,
$$\log 1 = 0 \quad \text{and} \quad \log 10 = 1.$$
- The functions 10^x and $\log x$ are inverses, so they "undo" each other:
$$\log(10^x) = x \qquad \text{for all } x,$$
$$10^{\log x} = x \qquad \text{for } x > 0.$$
- For a and b both positive and any value of t,
$$\log(ab) = \log a + \log b$$
$$\log\left(\frac{a}{b}\right) = \log a - \log b$$
$$\log(b^t) = t \cdot \log b.$$

We can now use logarithms to solve the equation that we solved graphically in Section 3.2.

Example 5 Solve $100 \cdot 2^t = 337{,}000{,}000$ for t.

Solution Dividing both sides of the equation by 100 gives
$$2^t = 3{,}370{,}000.$$
Taking logs of both sides gives
$$\log\left(2^t\right) = \log(3{,}370{,}000).$$
Since $\log(2^t) = t \cdot \log 2$, we have
$$t \log 2 = \log(3{,}370{,}000),$$
so, solving for t, we have
$$t = \frac{\log(3{,}370{,}000)}{\log 2} = 21.684.$$
In Example 2 on page 125, we found the graphical approximation of between 21 and 22 days as the time for the Yonkers fine to exceed the city's annual budget.

The Natural Logarithm

When e is used as the base for exponential functions, computations are easier with the use of another logarithm function, called log base e. The log base e is used so frequently that it has its own notation: $\ln x$, read as the *natural log of* x. We make the following definition:

For $x > 0$,

$$\ln x \text{ is the power of } e \text{ that gives } x$$

or, in symbols,

$$\ln x = y \quad \text{means} \quad e^y = x,$$

and y is called the **natural logarithm** of x.

Just as the functions 10^x and $\log x$ are inverses, so are e^x and $\ln x$. The function $\ln x$ has similar properties to the common log function:

Properties of the Natural Logarithm
- By definition, $y = \ln x$ means $x = e^y$.
- In particular,
$$\ln 1 = 0 \quad \text{and} \quad \ln e = 1.$$
- The functions e^x and $\ln x$ are inverses, so they "undo" each other:
$$\ln(e^x) = x \qquad \text{for all } x$$
$$e^{\ln x} = x \qquad \text{for } x > 0.$$
- For a and b both positive and any value of t,
$$\ln(ab) = \ln a + \ln b$$
$$\ln\left(\frac{a}{b}\right) = \ln a - \ln b$$
$$\ln(b^t) = t \cdot \ln b.$$

Example 6 Solve for x:
(a) $5e^{2x} = 50$
(b) $3^x = 100$.

Solution (a) We first divide both sides by 5 to obtain

$$e^{2x} = 10.$$

Taking the natural log of both sides, we have

$$\ln(e^{2x}) = \ln 10$$
$$2x = \ln 10$$
$$x = \frac{\ln 10}{2} \approx 1.151.$$

(b) Taking natural logs of both sides,

$$\ln(3^x) = \ln 100$$
$$x \ln 3 = \ln 100$$
$$x = \frac{\ln 100}{\ln 3} \approx 4.192.$$

Misconceptions and Calculator Errors Involving Logs

It is important to know how to use the properties of logarithms. It is equally important to recognize statements that are *not* true. Beware of the following:

- $\log(a + b)$ is not the same as $\log a + \log b$
- $\log(a - b)$ is not the same as $\log a - \log b$
- $\log(ab)$ is not the same as $(\log a)(\log b)$
- $\log\left(\dfrac{a}{b}\right)$ is not the same as $\dfrac{\log a}{\log b}$
- $\log\left(\dfrac{1}{a}\right)$ is not the same as $\dfrac{1}{\log a}$.

There are no formulas to simplify either $\log(a+b)$ or $\log(a-b)$. Also the expression $\log 5x^2$ is not the same as $2 \cdot \log 5x$, because the exponent, 2, applies only to the x and not to the 5. However, it is correct to write

$$\log 5x^2 = \log 5 + \log x^2 = \log 5 + 2\log x.$$

Using a calculator to evaluate expressions like $\log\left(\frac{17}{3}\right)$ requires care. On some calculators, entering $\log 17/3$ gives 0.410, which is incorrect. This is because the calculator assumes that you mean $(\log 17)/3$, which is not the same as $\log(17/3)$. Notice also that

$$\frac{\log 17}{\log 3} \approx \frac{1.230}{0.477} \approx 2.579,$$

which is not the same as either $(\log 17)/3$ or $\log(17/3)$. Thus, the following expressions are all different.

$$\log\frac{17}{3} \approx 0.753, \qquad \frac{\log 17}{3} \approx 0.410, \qquad \text{and} \qquad \frac{\log 17}{\log 3} \approx 2.579.$$

Justification of $\log(a \cdot b) = \log a + \log b$ and $\log(a/b) = \log a - \log b$

If a and b are both positive, we can write $a = 10^m$ and $b = 10^n$, so $\log a = m$ and $\log b = n$. Then, the product $a \cdot b$ can be written

$$a \cdot b = 10^m \cdot 10^n = 10^{m+n}.$$

Therefore $m + n$ is the power of 10 needed to give $a \cdot b$, so

$$\log(a \cdot b) = m + n,$$

which gives

$$\log(a \cdot b) = \log a + \log b.$$

Similarly, the quotient a/b can be written as

$$\frac{a}{b} = \frac{10^m}{10^n} = 10^{m-n}.$$

Therefore $m - n$ is the power of 10 needed to give a/b, so

$$\log\left(\frac{a}{b}\right) = m - n,$$

and thus

$$\boxed{\log\left(\frac{a}{b}\right) = \log a - \log b.}$$

Justification of $\log(b^t) = t \cdot \log b$

Suppose that b is positive, so we can write $b = 10^k$ for some value of k. Then

$$b^t = (10^k)^t.$$

We have rewritten the expression b^t so that the base is a power of 10. Using a property of exponents, we can write $(10^k)^t$ as 10^{kt}, so

$$b^t = (10^k)^t = 10^{kt}.$$

Therefore kt is the power of 10 which gives b^t, so

$$\log(b^t) = kt.$$

But since $b = 10^k$, we know $k = \log b$. This means

$$\log(b^t) = (\log b)t = t \cdot \log b.$$

Thus, for $b > 0$ we have

$$\boxed{\log\left(b^t\right) = t \cdot \log b.}$$

Exercises and Problems for Section 4.1

Exercises

Rewrite the statements in Exercises 1–6 using exponents instead of logs.

1. $\log 19 = 1.279$

2. $\log 4 = 0.602$

3. $\ln 26 = 3.258$

4. $\ln(0.646) = -0.437$

5. $\log P = t$

6. $\ln q = z$

Rewrite the statements in Exercises 7–10 using logs.

7. $10^8 = 100{,}000{,}000$

8. $e^{-4} = 0.0183$

9. $10^v = \alpha$

10. $e^a = b$

Solve the equations in Exercises 11–18 using logs.

11. $2^x = 11$

12. $(1.45)^x = 25$

13. $e^{0.12x} = 100$

14. $10 = 22(0.87)^q$

15. $48 = 17(2.3)^w$

16. $2/7 = (0.6)^{2t}$

17. $0.00012 = 0.001^{m/2}$

18. $500 = 25(1.1)^{3x}$

19. Evaluate without a calculator.

   (a) $\log 1$ **(b)** $\log 0.1$ **(c)** $\log(10^0)$

   (d) $\log\sqrt{10}$ **(e)** $\log(10^5)$ **(f)** $\log(10^2)$

   (g) $\log\left(\dfrac{1}{\sqrt{10}}\right)$ **(h)** $10^{\log 100}$ **(i)** $10^{\log 1}$

   (j) $10^{\log(0.01)}$

20. Evaluate without a calculator.

   (a) $\ln 1$ **(b)** $\ln e^0$ **(c)** $\ln e^5$

   (d) $\ln\sqrt{e}$ **(e)** $e^{\ln 2}$ **(f)** $\ln\left(\dfrac{1}{\sqrt{e}}\right)$

Problems

21. Evaluate 10^n for $n = 3$, $n = 3.5$, $n = 3.48$, $n = 3.477$, and $n = 3.47712$. Based on your answer, estimate the value of $\log 3000$.

22. Given that $10^{1.3} \approx 20$, approximate the value of $\log 200$ without using a calculator.

23. Evaluate without a calculator.

(a) $\log(\log 10)$
(b) $\sqrt{\log 100} - \log \sqrt{100}$
(c) $\log(\sqrt{10}\sqrt[3]{10}\sqrt[5]{10})$
(d) $1000^{\log 3}$
(e) $0.01^{\log 2}$
(f) $\dfrac{1}{\log(1/\log \sqrt[10]{10})}$

24. Express the following in terms of x without logs.

(a) $\log 100^x$
(b) $1000^{\log x}$
(c) $\log 0.001^x$

25. Express the following in terms of x without natural logs.

(a) $\ln e^{2x}$
(b) $e^{\ln(3x+2)}$
(c) $\ln\left(\dfrac{1}{e^{5x}}\right)$
(d) $\ln \sqrt{e^x}$

26. True or false?

(a) $\log AB = \log A + \log B$
(b) $\dfrac{\log A}{\log B} = \log A - B$
(c) $\log A \log B = \log A + \log B$
(d) $p \cdot \log A = \log A^p$
(e) $\log \sqrt{x} = \frac{1}{2} \log x$
(f) $\sqrt{\log x} = \log(x^{1/2})$

27. True or false?

(a) $\ln(ab^t) = t \ln(ab)$
(b) $\ln(1/a) = -\ln a$
(c) $\ln a \cdot \ln b = \ln(a + b)$
(d) $\ln a - \ln b = \dfrac{\ln a}{\ln b}$

28. Suppose that $x = \log A$ and that $y = \log B$. Write the following expressions in terms of x and y.

(a) $\log(AB)$
(b) $\log(A^3 \cdot \sqrt{B})$
(c) $\log(A - B)$
(d) $\dfrac{\log A}{\log B}$
(e) $\log \dfrac{A}{B}$
(f) AB

29. Let $p = \log m$ and $q = \log n$. Write the following expressions in terms of p and/or q without using logs.

(a) m
(b) n^3
(c) $\log(mn^3)$
(d) $\log \sqrt{m}$

30. Let $p = \ln m$ and $q = \ln n$. Write the following expressions in terms of p and/or q without using logs.

(a) $\ln(nm^4)$
(b) $\ln\left(\dfrac{1}{n}\right)$
(c) $\dfrac{\ln m}{\ln n}$
(d) $\ln(n^3)$

31. A graph of $P = 25(1.075)^t$ is given in Figure 4.1.

(a) What is the initial value of P (when $t = 0$)? What is the percent growth rate?
(b) Use the graph to estimate the value of t when $P = 100$.
(c) Use logs to find the exact value of t when $P = 100$.

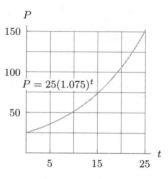

Figure 4.1

32. A graph of $Q = 10e^{-0.15t}$ is given in Figure 4.2.

(a) What is the initial value of Q (when $t = 0$)? What is the continuous percent decay rate?
(b) Use the graph to estimate the value of t when $Q = 2$.
(c) Use logs to find the exact value of t when $Q = 2$.

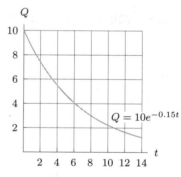

Figure 4.2

33. Find a possible formula for the exponential function S in Figure 4.3, if $R(x) = 5.1403(1.1169)^x$.

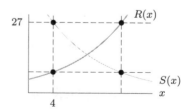

Figure 4.3

174

In Problems 34–50, solve the equations exactly for x or t.

34. $5(1.031)^x = 8$

35. $4(1.171)^x = 7(1.088)^x$

36. $3\log(2x + 6) = 6$

37. $3 \cdot 2^x + 8 = 25$

38. $e^{x+4} = 10$

39. $e^{x+5} = 7 \cdot 2^x$

40. $b^x = c$

41. $ab^x = c$

42. $Pa^x = Qb^x$

43. $Pe^{kx} = Q$

44. $121e^{-0.112t} = 88$

45. $58e^{4t+1} = 30$

46. $17e^{0.02t} = 18e^{0.03t}$

47. $44e^{0.15t} = 50(1.2)^t$

48. $\log(1 - x) - \log(1 + x) = 2$

49. $\log(2x + 5) \cdot \log(9x^2) = 0$

50. $\sqrt{\log \sqrt[3]{x} - \log \sqrt[4]{x}} = \dfrac{1}{2}$

51. Solve each of the following equations exactly for x.

   (a) $e^{2x} + e^{2x} = 1$ **(b)** $2e^{3x} + e^{3x} = b$

52. Suppose $0 < A < AB < 1 < B$. Rank the following in order from least to greatest:

$$0, \log A, \log B, \log A + \log B, \log(B^A).$$

53. Suppose $\log A < 0 < \log AB < 1 < \log B$. Rank the following in order from least to greatest:

$$0, \ 1, \ 100, \ A, \ A^2B^2, \ B^2.$$

54. Three students try to solve the equation

$$11 \cdot 3^x = 5 \cdot 7^x.$$

The first student finds that $x = \dfrac{\log(11/5)}{\log(7/3)}$. The second finds that $x = \dfrac{\log(5/11)}{\log(3/7)}$. The third finds that $x = \dfrac{\log 11 - \log 5}{\log 7 - \log 3}$. Which student (or students) is (are) correct? Explain.

4.2   LOGARITHMS AND EXPONENTIAL MODELS

The log function is often useful when answering questions about exponential models. Because logarithms "undo" the exponential functions, we use them to solve many exponential equations.

Example 1   In Example 3 on page 125 we solved the equation $200(0.886^t) = 25$ graphically, where t is in thousands of years. We found that a 200 microgram sample of carbon-14 decays to 25 micrograms in approximately 17,200 years. Now solve $200(0.886)^t = 25$ using logarithms.

Solution   First, isolate the power on one side of the equation

$$200(0.886^t) = 25$$
$$0.886^t = 0.125.$$

Take the log of both sides, and use the fact that $\log(0.886^t) = t \log 0.886$. Then

$$\log(0.886^t) = \log 0.125$$
$$t \log 0.886 = \log 0.125$$

so

$$t = \frac{\log 0.125}{\log 0.886} \approx 17.18 \text{ thousand years.}$$

This answer is close to the value we found from the graph, 17,200.

Example 2   The US population, P, in millions, is currently growing according to the formula[1]

$$P = 299e^{0.009t},$$

where t is in years since 2006. When is the population predicted to reach 350 million?

[1] Based on data from www.census.gov and www.cia.gov/cia/publications/factbook, accessed July 31, 2006.

Solution   We want to solve the following equation for t:

$$299e^{0.009t} = 350.$$

Dividing by 299 gives

$$e^{0.009t} = \frac{350}{299}$$

So $0.009t$ is the power of e which gives $350/299$. Thus, by the definition of the natural log,

$$0.009t = \ln\left(\frac{350}{299}\right).$$

Solving for t and evaluating $\ln(350/299)$ on a calculator gives

$$t = \frac{\ln(350/299)}{0.009} = 17.5 \text{ years.}$$

The US population is predicted to reach 350 million during the year 2024.

Example 3   The population of City A begins with 50,000 people and grows at 3.5% per year. The population of City B begins with a larger population of 250,000 people but grows at the slower rate of 1.6% per year. Assuming that these growth rates hold constant, will the population of City A ever catch up to the population of City B? If so, when?

Solution   If t is time measured in years and P_A and P_B are the populations of these two cities, then

$$P_A = 50{,}000(1.035)^t \qquad \text{and} \qquad P_B = 250{,}000(1.016)^t.$$

We want to solve the equation

$$50{,}000(1.035)^t = 250{,}000(1.016)^t.$$

We first get the exponential terms together by dividing both sides of the equation by $50{,}000(1.016)^t$:

$$\frac{(1.035)^t}{(1.016)^t} = \frac{250{,}000}{50{,}000} = 5.$$

Since $\dfrac{a^t}{b^t} = \left(\dfrac{a}{b}\right)^t$, this gives

$$\left(\frac{1.035}{1.016}\right)^t = 5.$$

Taking logs of both sides and using $\log b^t = t \log b$, we have

$$\log\left(\frac{1.035}{1.016}\right)^t = \log 5$$

$$t \log\left(\frac{1.035}{1.016}\right) = \log 5$$

$$t = \frac{\log 5}{\log(1.035/1.016)} \approx 86.865.$$

Thus, the cities' populations will be equal in just under 87 years. To check this, notice that when $t = 86.865$,

$$P_A = 50{,}000(1.035)^{86.865} = 992{,}575$$

and

$$P_B = 250{,}000(1.016)^{86.865} = 992{,}572.$$

The answers are not exactly equal because we rounded off the value of t. Rounding can introduce significant errors, especially when logs and exponentials are involved. Using $t = 86.86480867$, the computed values of P_A and P_B agree to three decimal places.

Doubling Time

Eventually, any exponentially growing quantity doubles, or increases by 100%. Since its percent growth rate is constant, the time it takes for the quantity to grow by 100% is also a constant. This time period is called the *doubling time*.

Example 4   (a) Find the time needed for the turtle population described by the function $P = 175(1.145)^t$ to double its initial size.

(b) How long does this population take to quadruple its initial size? To increase by a factor of 8?

Solution   (a) The initial size is 175 turtles; doubling this gives 350 turtles. We need to solve the following equation for t:

$$175(1.145)^t = 350$$
$$1.145^t = 2$$
$$\log\left(1.145^t\right) = \log 2$$
$$t \cdot \log 1.145 = \log 2$$
$$t = \frac{\log 2}{\log 1.145} \approx 5.119 \text{ years.}$$

We check this by noting that

$$175(1.145)^{5.119} = 350,$$

which is double the initial population. In fact, at any time it takes the turtle population about 5.119 years to double in size.

(b) Since the population function is exponential, it increases by 100% every 5.119 years. Thus it doubles its initial size in the first 5.119 years, quadruples its initial size in two 5.119 year periods, or 10.238 years, and increases by a factor of 8 in three 5.119 year periods, or 15.357 years. We check this by noting that

$$175(1.145)^{10.238} = 700,$$

or 4 times the initial size, and that

$$175(1.145)^{15.357} = 1400,$$

or 8 times the initial size.

Example 5   A population doubles in size every 20 years. What is its continuous growth rate?

Solution   We are not given the initial size of the population, but we can solve this problem without that information. Let the symbol P_0 represent the initial size of the population. We have $P = P_0 e^{kt}$. After 20 years, $P = 2P_0$, and so

$$P_0 e^{k \cdot 20} = 2P_0$$
$$e^{20k} = 2$$
$$20k = \ln 2 \qquad \text{Taking ln of both sides}$$
$$k = \frac{\ln 2}{20} \approx 0.03466.$$

Thus, the population grows at the continuous rate of 3.466% per year.

Half-Life

Just as an exponentially growing quantity doubles in a fixed amount of time, an exponentially decaying quantity decreases by a factor of 2 in a fixed amount of time, called the *half-life* of the quantity.

Example 6   Carbon-14 decays radioactively at a constant annual rate of 0.0121%. Show that the half-life of carbon-14 is about 5728 years.

Solution   We are not given an initial amount of carbon-14, but we can solve this problem without that information. Let the symbol Q_0 represent the initial quantity of carbon-14 present. The growth rate is -0.000121 because carbon-14 is decaying. So the growth factor is $b = 1 - 0.000121 = 0.999879$. Thus, after t years the amount left will be

$$Q = Q_0(0.999879)^t.$$

We want to find how long it takes for the quantity to drop to half its initial level. Thus, we need to solve for t in the equation

$$\frac{1}{2}Q_0 = Q_0(0.999879)^t.$$

Dividing each side by Q_0, we have

$$\frac{1}{2} = 0.999879^t.$$

Taking logs

$$\log \frac{1}{2} = \log\left(0.999879^t\right)$$
$$\log 0.5 = t \cdot \log 0.999879$$
$$t = \frac{\log 0.5}{\log 0.999879} \approx 5728.143.$$

Thus, no matter how much carbon-14 there is initially, after about 5728 years, half will remain.

Similarly, we can determine the growth rate given the half-life or doubling time.

Example 7   The quantity, Q, of a substance decays according to the formula $Q = Q_0 e^{-kt}$, where t is in minutes. The half-life of the substance is 11 minutes. What is the value of k?

Solution   We know that after 11 minutes, $Q = \frac{1}{2}Q_0$. Thus, solving for k, we get

$$Q_0 e^{-k \cdot 11} = \frac{1}{2}Q_0$$
$$e^{-11k} = \frac{1}{2}$$
$$-11k = \ln \frac{1}{2}$$
$$k = \frac{\ln(1/2)}{-11} \approx 0.06301,$$

so $k = 0.063$ per minute. This substance decays at the continuous rate of 6.301% per minute.

Converting Between $Q = ab^t$ and $Q = ae^{kt}$

Any exponential function can be written in either of the two forms:

$$Q = ab^t \quad \text{or} \quad Q = ae^{kt}.$$

If $b = e^k$, so $k = \ln b$, the two formulas represent the same function.

Example 8   Convert the exponential function $P = 175(1.145)^t$ to the form $P = ae^{kt}$.

Solution   Since the new formula represents the same function, we want $P = 175$ when $t = 0$. Thus, substituting $t = 0$, gives $175 = ae^{k(0)} = a$, so $a = 175$. The parameter a in both functions represents the initial population. For all t,

$$175(1.145)^t = 175(e^k)^t,$$

so we must find k such that

$$e^k = 1.145.$$

Therefore k is the power of e which gives 1.145. By the definition of ln, we have

$$k = \ln 1.145 \approx 0.1354.$$

Therefore,

$$P = 175e^{0.1354t}.$$

Example 9   Convert the formula $Q = 7e^{0.3t}$ to the form $Q = ab^t$.

Solution   Using the properties of exponents,

$$Q = 7e^{0.3t} = 7(e^{0.3})^t.$$

Using a calculator, we find $e^{0.3} \approx 1.3499$, so

$$Q = 7(1.3499)^t.$$

Example 10   Assuming t is in years, find the continuous and annual percent growth rates in Examples 8 and 9.

Solution   In Example 8, the annual percent growth rate is 14.5% and the continuous percent growth rate per year is 13.54%. In Example 9, the continuous percent growth rate is 30% and the annual percent growth rate is 34.985%.

Example 11   Find the continuous percent growth rate of $Q = 200(0.886)^t$, where t is in thousands of years.

Solution   Since this function describes exponential decay, we expect a negative value for k. We want

$$e^k = 0.886.$$

Solving for k gives

$$k = \ln(0.886) = -0.12104.$$

So we have $Q = 200e^{-0.12104t}$ and the continuous growth rate is -12.104% per thousand years.

Exponential Growth Problems That Cannot Be Solved By Logarithms

Some equations with the variable in the exponent cannot be solved using logarithms.

Example 12   With t in years, the population of a country (in millions) is given by $P = 2(1.02)^t$, while the food supply (in millions of people that can be fed) is given by $N = 4 + 0.5t$. Determine the year in which the country first experiences food shortages.

Solution   The country starts to experience shortages when the population equals the number of people that can be fed—that is, when $P = N$. We attempt to solve the equation $P = N$ by using logs:

$$2(1.02)^t = 4 + 0.5t$$
$$1.02^t = 2 + 0.25t \qquad \text{Dividing by 2}$$
$$\log 1.02^t = \log(2 + 0.25t)$$
$$t \log 1.02 = \log(2 + 0.25t).$$

Unfortunately, we cannot isolate t, so, this equation cannot be solved using logs. However, we can approximate the solution of the original equation numerically or graphically, as shown in Figure 4.4. The two functions, P and N, are equal when $t \approx 199.381$. Thus, it will be almost 200 years before shortages occur.

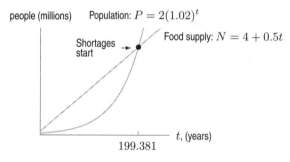

Figure 4.4: Finding the intersection of linear and exponential graphs

Exercises and Problems for Section 4.2

Exercises

In Exercises 1–8, give the starting value a, the growth rate r, and the continuous growth rate k.

1. $Q = 230(1.182)^t$

2. $Q = 0.181 \left(e^{0.775}\right)^t$

3. $Q = 0.81(2)^t$

4. $Q = 5 \cdot 2^{t/8}$

5. $Q = 12.1 \cdot 10^{-0.11t}$

6. $Q = 40e^{(t-5)/12}$

7. $Q = 2e^{(1-3t/4)}$

8. $Q = 2^{-(t-5)/3}$

In Exercises 9–12, convert to the form $Q = ae^{kt}$.

9. $Q = 4 \cdot 7^t$

10. $Q = 2 \cdot 3^t$

11. $Q = 4 \cdot 8^{1.3t}$

12. $Q = 973 \cdot 6^{2.1t}$

In Exercises 13–16, convert to the form $Q = ab^t$.

13. $Q = 4e^{7t}$

14. $Q = 0.3e^{0.7t}$

15. $Q = \dfrac{14}{5}e^{0.03t}$

16. $Q = e^{-0.02t}$

For Exercises 17–18, write the exponential function in the form $y = ab^t$. Find b accurate to four decimal places. If t is measured in years, give the percent annual growth or decay rate and the continuous percent growth or decay rate per year.

17. $y = 25e^{0.053t}$

18. $y = 100e^{-0.07t}$

For Exercises 19–20, write the exponential function in the form $y = ae^{kt}$. Find k accurate to four decimal places. If t is measured in years, give the percent annual growth rate and the continuous percent growth rate per year.

19. $y = 6000(0.85)^t$

20. $y = 5(1.12)^t$

Find the doubling time in Exercises 21–24.

21. A population growing according to $P = P_0 e^{0.2t}$.

22. A city is growing by 26% per year.

23. A bank account is growing by 2.7% per year.

24. A company's profits are increasing by an annual growth factor of 1.12.

Find the half-lives of the substances in Exercises 25–27.

25. Tritium, which decays at a rate of 5.471% per year.

26. Einsteinium-253, which decays at a rate of 3.406% per day.

27. A radioactive substance that decays at a continuous rate of 11% per minute.

Problems

In Problems 28–30, find a formula for the exponential function.

28. $V = f(t)$ gives the value after t years of $2500 invested at 3.25% annual interest, compounded quarterly (four times per year).

29. The graph of g contains $(-50, 20)$ and $(120, 70)$.

30. $V = h(t)$ gives the value of an item initially worth $10,000 that loses half its value every 5 years.

31. A population grows from 11000 to 13000 in three years. Assuming the growth is exponential, find the:

    (a) Annual growth rate   **(b)** Continuous growth rate

    (c) Why are your answers to parts (a) and (b) different?

32. A population doubles in size every 15 years. Assuming exponential growth, find the

    (a) Annual growth rate   **(b)** Continuous growth rate

33. A population increases from 5.2 million at an annual rate of 3.1%. Find the continuous growth rate.

34. If 17% of a radioactive substance decays in 5 hours, what is the half-life of the substance?

35. Sketch the exponential function $y = u(t)$ given that it has a starting value of 0.8 and a doubling time of 12 years. Label the axes and indicate the scale.

Solve the equations in Problems 36–41 if possible. Give an exact solution if there is one.

36. $1.7(2.1)^{3x} = 2(4.5)^x$ **37.** $3^{4\log x} = 5$

38. $5(1.044)^t = t + 10$ **39.** $12(1.221)^t = t + 3$

40. $10e^{3t} - e = 2e^{3t}$

41. $\log x + \log(x - 1) = \log 2$

42. Use algebra to show that the time it takes for a quantity growing exponentially to double is independent of the starting quantity and the time. To do this, let d represent the time it takes for P to double. Show that if P becomes $2P$ at time $t + d$, then d depends only on the growth factor b, but not on the starting quantity a and time t. (Assume $P \neq 0$.)

43. The US census projects the population of the state of Washington using the function $N(t) = 5.4e^{0.013t}$, where $N(t)$ is in millions and t is in years since 1995.

    (a) What is the population's continuous growth rate?

    (b) What is the population of Washington in year $t = 0$?

    (c) How many years is it before the population triples?

    (d) In what year does this model indicate a population of only one person? Is this reasonable or unreasonable?

44. The voltage V across a charged capacitor is given by $V(t) = 5e^{-0.3t}$ where t is in seconds.

    (a) What is the voltage after 3 seconds?

    (b) When will the voltage be 1?

    (c) By what percent does the voltage decrease each second?

45. A colony of bacteria grows exponentially. The colony begins with 3 bacteria, but 3 hours after the beginning of the experiment, it has grown to 100 bacteria.

    (a) Give a formula for the number of bacteria as a function of time.

    (b) How long does it take for the colony to triple in size?

46. In July 2005, the Internet was linked by a global network of about 353.2 million host computers.[2] The number of host computers has been growing approximately exponentially and was about 36.7 million in July 1998.

    (a) Find a formula for the number, N, of internet host computers as an exponential function of t, the number of years since July 1998, using the form $N = ae^{kt}$.

    (b) At what continuous annual percent rate does N increase?

    (c) What is the doubling time?

47. The number of cases of sepsis, an immune response to infection or trauma, has been growing exponentially and has doubled in this country in the last 5 years.[3]

    (a) Find the continuous annual percent growth rate in the number of cases.

    (b) If this growth rate continues, how many years will it take for the number of cases to triple?

48. The half-life of iodine-123 is about 13 hours. You begin with 50 grams of iodine-123.

    (a) Write an equation that gives the amount of iodine-123 remaining after t hours.

    (b) Determine the number of hours needed for your sample to decay to 10 grams.

---

[2]www.isc.org/ds/, accessed January 11, 2006.

[3]"Improvement seen in Recognizing, Treating Sepsis", Watertown Daily Times, September 25, 2002.

49. Scientists observing owl and hawk populations collect the following data. Their initial count for the owl population is 245 owls, and the population grows by 3% per year. They initially observe 63 hawks, and this population doubles every 10 years.

(a) Find a formula for the size of the population of owls in terms of time t.
(b) Find a formula for the size of the population of hawks in terms of time t.
(c) Use a graph to find how long it will take for these populations to be equal in number.

50. Figure 4.5 shows the graphs of the exponential functions f and g, and the linear function, h.

(a) Find formulas for f, g, and h.
(b) Find the exact value(s) of x such that $f(x) = g(x)$.
(c) Estimate the value(s) of x such that $f(x) = h(x)$.

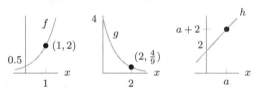

Figure 4.5

51. In 1991, the body of a man was found in melting snow in the Alps of Northern Italy. An examination of the tissue sample revealed that 46% of the carbon-14 present in his body at the time of his death had decayed. The half-life of carbon-14 is approximately 5728 years. How long ago did this man die?

52. In a country where inflation is a concern, prices have risen by 40% over a 5-year period.

(a) By what percent do the prices rise each year?
(b) How long does it take for prices to rise by 5%?
(c) Use a continuous growth rate to model inflation by a function of the form $P = P_0 e^{rt}$.

53. A person's blood alcohol content (BAC) is a measure of how much alcohol is in the blood stream. When the person stops drinking, the BAC declines over time as the alcohol is metabolized. If Q is the amount of alcohol and Q_0 the initial amount, then $Q = Q_0 e^{-t/\tau}$, where τ is known as the *elimination time*. How long does it take for a person's BAC to drop from 0.10 to 0.04 if the elimination time is 2.5 hours?

54. The probability of a transistor failing within t months is given by $P(t) = 1 - e^{-0.016t}$.

(a) What is the probability of failure within the first 6 months? Within the second six months?
(b) Within how many months will the probability of failure be 99.99%?

55. You deposit $4000 into an account that earns 6% annual interest, compounded annually. A friend deposits $3500 into an account that earns 5.95% annual interest, compounded continuously. Will your friend's balance ever equal yours? If so, when?

56. (a) Find the time required for an investment to triple in value if it earns 4% annual interest, compounded continuously.
(b) Now find the time required assuming that the interest is compounded annually.

57. The temperature, H, in °F, of a cup of coffee t hours after it is set out to cool is given by the equation:

$$H = 70 + 120(1/4)^t.$$

(a) What is the coffee's temperature initially (that is, at time $t = 0$)? After 1 hour? 2 hours?
(b) How long does it take the coffee to cool down to 90°F? 75°F?

58. The size of a population, P, of toads t years after it is introduced into a wetland is given by

$$P = \frac{1000}{1 + 49(1/2)^t}.$$

(a) How many toads are there in year $t = 0$? $t = 5$? $t = 10$?
(b) How long does it take for the toad population to reach 500? 750?
(c) What is the maximum number of toads that the wetland can support?

Problems 59–60 use Figure 4.6, where t_0 is the t-coordinate of the point of intersection of the graphs. Describe what happens to t_0 if the following changes are made, assuming the other quantities remain the same.

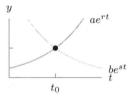

Figure 4.6

59. a is increased

60. s is decreased

61. In Figure 4.6, suppose that a and b are fixed and r increases. Describe how s changes if t_0 remains unchanged.

4.3 THE LOGARITHMIC FUNCTION

The Graph, Domain, and Range of the Common Logarithm

In Section 4.1 we defined the log function (to base 10) for all positive numbers. In other words,

Domain of $\log x$ is all positive numbers.

By considering its graph in Figure 4.7, we determine the range of $y = \log x$. The log graph crosses the x-axis at $x = 1$, because $\log 1 = \log(10^0) = 0$. The graph climbs to $y = 1$ at $x = 10$, because $\log 10 = \log(10^1) = 1$. In order for the log graph to climb to $y = 2$, the value of x must reach 100, or 10^2, and in order for it to climb to $y = 3$, the value of x must be 10^3, or 1000. To reach the modest height of $y = 20$ requires x to equal 10^{20}, or 100 billion billion! The log function increases so slowly that it often serves as a benchmark for other slow-growing functions. Nonetheless, the graph of $y = \log x$ eventually climbs to any value we choose.

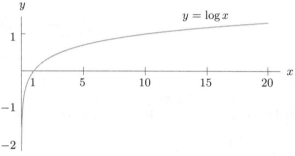

Figure 4.7: The log function grows very rapidly for $0 < x < 1$ and very slowly for $x > 1$. It has a vertical asymptote at $x = 0$ but never touches the y-axis.

Although x cannot equal zero in the log function, we can choose $x > 0$ to be as small as we like. As x decreases toward zero, the values of $\log x$ get large and negative. For example,

$$\log 0.1 \ = \ \log 10^{-1} = -1,$$
$$\log 0.01 \ = \ \log 10^{-2} = -2,$$
$$\vdots \qquad\qquad \vdots$$
$$\log 0.0000001 \ = \ \log 10^{-7} = -7,$$

and so on. So, small positive values of x give exceedingly large negative values of y. Thus,

Range of $\log x$ is all real numbers.

The log function is increasing and its graph is concave down, since its rate of change is decreasing.

Graphs of the Inverse Functions $y = \log x$ and $y = 10^x$

The fact that $y = \log x$ and $y = 10^x$ are inverses means that their graphs are related. Looking at Tables 4.1 and 4.2, we see that the point $(0.01, -2)$ is on the graph of $y = \log x$ and the point

$(-2, 0.01)$ is on the graph of $y = 10^x$. In general, if the point (a, b) is on the graph of $y = \log x$, the point (b, a) is on the graph of $y = 10^x$. Thus, the graph of $y = \log x$ is the graph of $y = 10^x$ with x and y-axes interchanged. If the x- and y-axes have the same scale, this is equivalent to reflecting the graph of $y = 10^x$ across the diagonal line $y = x$. See Figure 4.8.

Table 4.1 *Log function*

x	$y = \log x$
0.01	-2
0.1	-1
1	0
10	1
100	2
1000	3

Table 4.2 *Exponential function*

x	$y = 10^x$
-2	0.01
-1	0.1
0	1
1	10
2	100
3	1000

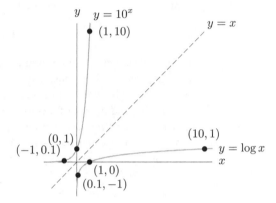

Figure 4.8: The functions $y = \log x$ and $y = 10^x$ are inverses of one another

Asymptotes

In Section 3.3 we saw that the graph of an exponential function has a horizontal asymptote. In Figure 4.8, we see that $y = 10^x$ has horizontal asymptote $y = 0$, because

$$\text{as } x \to -\infty, \quad 10^x \to 0.$$

Correspondingly, as x gets closer to zero, $y = \log x$ takes on larger and larger negative values. We write

$$\text{as } x \to 0^+, \quad f(x) \to -\infty.$$

The notation $x \to 0^+$ is read "x approaches zero from the right" and means that we are choosing smaller and smaller positive values of x—that is, we are sliding toward $x = 0$ through small positive values. We say the graph of the log function $y = \log x$ has a *vertical asymptote* of $x = 0$.

To describe vertical asymptotes in general, we use the notation

$$x \to a^+$$

to mean that x slides toward a from the right (that is, through values larger than a) and

$$x \to a^-$$

to mean that x slides toward a from the left (that is, through values smaller than a).

If $f(x) \to \infty$ as $x \to a^+$, we say the *limit* of $f(x)$ as x approaches a from the right is infinity,[4] and write

$$\lim_{x \to a^+} f(x) = \infty.$$

If $f(x) \to \infty$ as $x \to a^-$, we write

$$\lim_{x \to a^-} f(x) = \infty.$$

---

[4]Some authors say that these limits do not exist.

If both $\lim_{x \to a^+} f(x) = \infty$ and $\lim_{x \to a^-} f(x) = \infty$, we say the limit of $f(x)$ as x approaches a is infinity, and write

$$\lim_{x \to a} f(x) = \infty.$$

Similarly, we can write

$$\lim_{x \to a^+} f(x) = -\infty \quad \text{or} \quad \lim_{x \to a^-} f(x) = -\infty \quad \text{or} \quad \lim_{x \to a} f(x) = -\infty.$$

We summarize the information about both horizontal and vertical asymptotes:

> Let $y = f(x)$ be a function and let a be a finite number.
> - The graph of f has a **horizontal asymptote** of $y = a$ if
>
> $$\lim_{x \to \infty} f(x) = a \quad \text{or} \quad \lim_{x \to -\infty} f(x) = a \quad \text{or both.}$$
>
> - The graph of f has a **vertical asymptote** of $x = a$ if
>
> $$\lim_{x \to a^+} f(x) = \infty \quad \text{or} \quad \lim_{x \to a^+} f(x) = -\infty \quad \text{or} \quad \lim_{x \to a^-} f(x) = \infty \quad \text{or} \quad \lim_{x \to a^-} f(x) = -\infty.$$

Notice that the process of finding a vertical asymptote is different from the process for finding a horizontal asymptote. Vertical asymptotes occur where the function values grow larger and larger, either positively or negatively, as x approaches a finite value (i.e. where $f(x) \to \infty$ or $f(x) \to -\infty$ as $x \to a$.) Horizontal asymptotes are determined by whether the function values approach a finite number as x takes on large positive or large negative values (i.e., as $x \to \infty$ or $x \to -\infty$).

Graph of Natural Logarithm

In addition to similar algebraic properties, the natural log and the common log have similar graphs.

Example 1   Graph $y = \ln x$ for $0 < x < 10$.

Solution   Values of $\ln x$ are in Table 4.3. Like the common log, the natural log is only defined for $x > 0$ and has a vertical asymptote at $x = 0$. The graph is slowly increasing and concave down.

Table 4.3   *Values of* $\ln x$ *(rounded)*

x	$\ln x$
0	Undefined
1	0
2	0.7
e	1
3	1.1
4	1.4
$\vdots$	$\vdots$

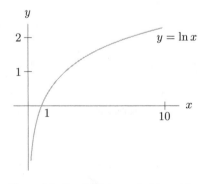

Figure 4.9: Graph of the natural logarithm

The functions $y = \ln x$ and $y = e^x$ are inverses. If the scales on the axes are the same, their graphs are reflections of one another across the line $y = x$. See Figure 4.10.

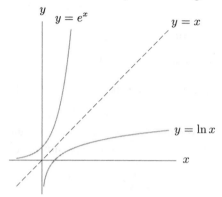

Figure 4.10: The functions $y = \ln x$ and $y = e^x$ are inverses of one another

Chemical Acidity

Logarithms are useful in measuring quantities whose magnitudes vary widely, such as acidity (pH), sound (decibels), and earthquakes (the Richter scale). In chemistry, the acidity of a liquid is expressed using pH. The acidity depends on the hydrogen ion concentration in the liquid (in moles per liter); this concentration is written $[H^+]$. The greater the hydrogen ion concentration, the more acidic the solution. The pH is defined as:

$$pH = -\log[H^+].$$

Example 2   The hydrogen ion concentration of seawater is $[H^+] = 1.1 \cdot 10^{-8}$. Estimate the pH of seawater. Then check your answer with a calculator.

Solution   We want to estimate $pH = -\log(1.1 \cdot 10^{-8})$. Since $1.1 \cdot 10^{-8} \approx 10^{-8}$ and $\log 10^{-8} = -8$, we know that

$$pH = -\log(1.1 \cdot 10^{-8}) \approx -(-8) = 8.$$

Using a calculator, we have

$$pH = -\log(1.1 \cdot 10^{-8}) = 7.959.$$

Example 3   A vinegar solution has a pH of 3. Determine the hydrogen ion concentration.

Solution   Since $3 = -\log[H^+]$, we have $-3 = \log[H^+]$. This means that $10^{-3} = [H^+]$. So the hydrogen ion concentration is 10^{-3} moles per liter.

Logarithms and Orders of Magnitude

We often compare sizes or quantities by computing their ratios. If A is twice as tall as B, then

$$\frac{\text{Height of } A}{\text{Height of } B} = 2.$$

If one object is 10 times heavier than another, we say it is an *order of magnitude* heavier. If one quantity is two factors of 10 greater than another, we say it is two orders of magnitude greater, and so on. For example, the value of a dollar is two orders of magnitude greater than the value of a penny, because we have

$$\frac{\$1}{\$0.01} = 100 = 10^2.$$

The order of magnitude is the logarithm of their ratio.

Example 4   The sound intensity of a refrigerator motor is 10^{-11} watts/cm^2. A typical school cafeteria has sound intensity of 10^{-8} watts/cm^2. How many orders of magnitude more intense is the sound of the cafeteria?

Solution   To compare the two intensities, we compute their ratio:

$$\frac{\text{Sound intensity of cafeteria}}{\text{Sound intensity of refrigerator}} = \frac{10^{-8}}{10^{-11}} = 10^{-8-(-11)} = 10^3.$$

Thus, the sound intensity of the cafeteria is 1000 times greater than the sound intensity of the refrigerator. The log of this ratio is 3. We say that the sound intensity of the cafeteria is three orders of magnitude greater than the sound intensity of the refrigerator.

Decibels

The intensity of audible sound varies over an enormous range. The range is so enormous that we consider the logarithm of the sound intensity. This is the idea behind the *decibel* (abbreviated dB). To measure a sound in decibels, the sound's intensity, I, is compared to the intensity of a standard benchmark sound, I_0. The intensity of I_0 is defined to be 10^{-16} watts/cm^2, roughly the lowest intensity audible to humans. The comparison between a sound intensity I and the benchmark sound intensity I_0 is made as follows:

$$\text{Noise level in decibels} = 10 \cdot \log\left(\frac{I}{I_0}\right).$$

For instance, let's find the decibel rating of the refrigerator in Example 4. First, we find how many orders of magnitude more intense the refrigerator sound is than the benchmark sound:

$$\frac{I}{I_0} = \frac{\text{Sound intensity of refrigerator}}{\text{Benchmark sound intensity}} = \frac{10^{-11}}{10^{-16}} = 10^5.$$

Thus, the refrigerator's intensity is 5 orders of magnitude more than I_0, the benchmark intensity. We have

$$\text{Decibel rating of refrigerator} = 10 \cdot \underbrace{\text{Number of orders of magnitude}}_{5} = 50 \text{ dB}.$$

Note that 5, the number of orders of magnitude, is the log of the ratio I/I_0. We use the log function because it "counts" the number of powers of 10. Thus if N is the decibel rating, then

$$N = 10 \log\left(\frac{I}{I_0}\right).$$

Example 5   (a) If a sound doubles in intensity, by how many units does its decibel rating increase?

(b) Loud music can measure 110 dB whereas normal conversation measures 50 dB. How many times more intense is loud music than normal conversation?

Solution   (a) Let I be the sound's intensity before it doubles. Once doubled, the new intensity is $2I$. The decibel rating of the original sound is $10\log(I/I_0)$, and the decibel rating of the new sound is $10\log(2I/I_0)$. The difference in decibel ratings is given by

$$\text{Difference in decibel ratings} = 10\log\left(\frac{2I}{I_0}\right) - 10\log\left(\frac{I}{I_0}\right)$$

$$= 10\left(\log\left(\frac{2I}{I_0}\right) - \log\left(\frac{I}{I_0}\right)\right) \qquad \text{Factoring out 10}$$

$$= 10\cdot\log\left(\frac{2I/I_0}{I/I_0}\right) \qquad \text{Using the property } \log a - \log b = \log(a/b)$$

$$= 10\cdot\log 2 \qquad \text{Canceling } I/I_0$$

$$\approx 3.010\text{ dB} \qquad \text{Because } \log 2 \approx 0.3.$$

Thus, if the sound intensity is doubled, the decibel rating goes up by approximately 3 dB.

(b) If I_M is the sound intensity of loud music, then

$$10\log\left(\frac{I_M}{I_0}\right) = 110\text{ dB}.$$

Similarly, if I_C is the sound intensity of conversation, then

$$10\log\left(\frac{I_C}{I_0}\right) = 50\text{ dB}.$$

Computing the difference of the decibel ratings gives

$$10\log\left(\frac{I_M}{I_0}\right) - 10\log\left(\frac{I_C}{I_0}\right) = 60.$$

Dividing by 10 gives

$$\log\left(\frac{I_M}{I_0}\right) - \log\left(\frac{I_C}{I_0}\right) = 6$$

$$\log\left(\frac{I_M/I_0}{I_C/I_0}\right) = 6 \qquad \text{Using the property } \log b - \log a = \log(b/a)$$

$$\log\left(\frac{I_M}{I_C}\right) = 6 \qquad \text{Canceling } I_0$$

$$\frac{I_M}{I_C} = 10^6 \qquad \log x = 6 \text{ means that } x = 10^6.$$

So $I_M = 10^6 I_C$, which means that loud music is 10^6 times, or one million times, as intense as normal conversation.

Exercises and Problems for Section 4.3

Exercises

1. What is the equation of the asymptote of the graph of $y = 10^x$? Of the graph of $y = 2^x$? Of the graph of $y = \log x$?

2. What is the equation for the asymptote of the graph of $y = e^x$? Of the graph of $y = e^{-x}$? Of the graph of $y = \ln x$?

3. Without a calculator, match the functions $y = 10^x$, $y = e^x$, $y = \log x$, $y = \ln x$ with the graphs in Figure 4.11.

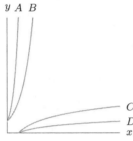

Figure 4.11

4. Without a calculator, match the functions $y = 2^x$, $y = e^{-x}$, $y = 3^x$, $y = \ln x$, $y = \log x$ with the graphs in Figure 4.12.

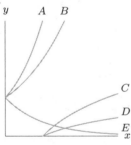

Figure 4.12

5. What is the value (if any) of the following?
(a) 10^{-x} as $x \to \infty$ (b) $\log x$ as $x \to 0^+$

6. What is the value (if any) of the following?
(a) e^x as $x \to -\infty$ (b) $\ln x$ as $x \to 0^+$

Graph the functions in Problems 7–10. Label all asymptotes and intercepts.

7. $y = 2 \cdot 3^x + 1$ **8.** $y = -e^{-x}$

9. $y = \log(x - 4)$ **10.** $y = \ln(x + 1)$

In Problems 11–12, graph the function. Identify any vertical asymptotes. State the domain of the function.

11. $y = 2\ln(x - 3)$ **12.** $y = 1 - \ln(2 - x)$

In Exercises 13–17, find the hydrogen ion concentration, $[H^+]$, for the substances.[5] [Hint: pH $= -\log[H^+]$.]

13. Lye, with a pH of 13.

14. Battery acid, with a pH of 1.

15. Baking soda, with a pH of 8.3.

16. Tomatoes, with a pH of 4.5.

17. Hydrochloric acid, with a pH of 0.

18. Find (a) $\lim\limits_{x \to 0^+} \log x$ (b) $\lim\limits_{x \to 0^-} \ln(-x)$

Problems

19. Match the statements (a)–(d) with the functions (I)–(IV).

(a) $\lim\limits_{x \to 0^+} f(x) = -\infty$ (b) $\lim\limits_{x \to 0^-} f(x) = 0$
(c) $\lim\limits_{x \to \infty} f(x) = \infty$ (d) $\lim\limits_{x \to -\infty} f(x) = 0$

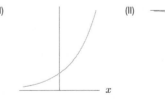
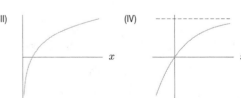

[5]Data from www.miamisci.org/ph/hhoh.html

20. Match the graphs (a)–(c) to one of the functions $r(x)$, $s(x)$, $t(x)$ whose values are in the tables.

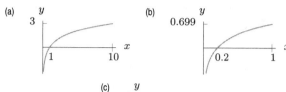

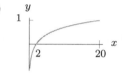

x	2	4	10
$r(x)$	1	1.301	1.699

x	0.5	5	10
$s(x)$	−0.060	0.379	0.699

x	0.1	2	100
$t(x)$	−3	0.903	6

21. Immediately following the gold medal performance of the US women's gymnastic team in the 1996 Olympic Games, an NBC commentator, John Tesh, said of one team member: "Her confidence and performance have grown logarithmically." He clearly thought this was an enormous compliment. Is it a compliment? Is it realistic?

In Problems 22–27, find possible formulas for the functions using logs or exponentials.

22.
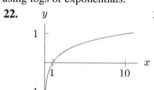

23.
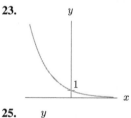

24.
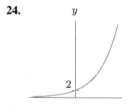

25.
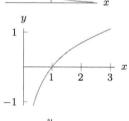

26.
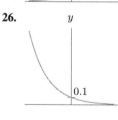

27.
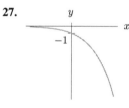

Find the domain of the functions in Problems 28–31.

28. $h(x) = \ln(x^2)$

29. $g(x) = (\ln x)^2$

30. $f(x) = \ln(\ln x)$

31. $k(x) = \ln(x - 3)$

32. (a) Using the definition of pH on page 170, find the concentrations of hydrogen ions in solutions with

  (i) pH $= 2$ (ii) pH $= 4$ (iii) pH $= 7$

(b) A high concentration of hydrogen ions corresponds to an acidic solution. From your answer to part (a), decide if solutions with high pHs are more or less acidic than solutions with low pHs.

33. (a) A 12 oz cup of coffee contains about $2.41 \cdot 10^{18}$ hydrogen ions. What is the concentration (moles/liter) of hydrogen ions in a 12 oz cup of coffee? [Hint: One liter equals 30.3 oz. One mole of hydrogen ions equals $6.02 \cdot 10^{23}$ hydrogen ions.]

(b) Based on your answer to part (a) and the formula for pH, what is the pH of a 12 oz cup of coffee?

34. (a) The pH of lemon juice is about 2.3. What is the concentration of hydrogen ions in lemon juice?

(b) A person squeezes 2 oz of lemon juice into a cup. Based on your answer to part (a), how many hydrogen ions does this juice contain?

35. Sound A measures 30 decibels and sound B is 5 times as loud as sound A. What is the decibel rating of sound B to the nearest integer?

36. (a) Let D_1 and D_2 represent the decibel ratings of sounds of intensity I_1 and I_2, respectively. Using log properties, find a simplified formula for the difference between the two ratings, $D_2 - D_1$, in terms of the two intensities, I_1 and I_2. (Decibels are introduced on page 171.)

(b) If a sound's intensity doubles, how many decibels louder does the sound become?

37. The magnitude of an earthquake is measured relative to the strength of a "standard" earthquake, whose seismic waves are of size W_0. The magnitude, M, of an earthquake with seismic waves of size W is defined to be

$$M = \log \left(\frac{W}{W_0} \right).$$

The value of M is called the *Richter scale* rating of the strength of an earthquake.

(a) Let M_1 and M_2 represent the magnitude of two earthquakes whose seismic waves are of sizes W_1 and W_2, respectively. Using log properties, find a simplified formula for the difference $M_2 - M_1$ in terms of W_1 and W_2.

(b) The 1989 earthquake in California had a rating of 7.1 on the Richter scale. How many times larger were the seismic waves in the March 2005 earthquake off the coast of Sumatra, which measured 8.7 on the Richter scale? Give your answer to the nearest integer.

38. The average time T, in milliseconds (ms), it takes a person to move a mouse cursor a distance D across a computer screen to a target button of length S is given by *Fitts' Law*, which states that $T = a + b \log(D/S + 1)$, where a and b are constants.[6]

  (a) Briefly explain why it does not matter what units are used for S and D, provided the units are the same. Why is it useful for a formula concerning computer screens not to be based on fixed sizes?

  (b) The cursor is moved 15 cm to a target of length 3 cm. Letting $a = 50$ and $b = 500$, estimate the time required to complete this operation.

  (c) Graph T for $S = 3$ cm and for $0 \le D \le 20$.

  (d) What is the T-intercept of the graph in part (c)? What does this tell you about cursor movement?

  (e) Suppose the distance moved, D, is doubled and the target length S stays the same. Without knowing the values of D and S, but assuming $a = 50$ and $b = 500$, what can you say about the change in T, the time required?

4.4 LOGARITHMIC SCALES

The Solar System and Beyond

Table 4.4 gives the distance from the sun to a number of different astronomical objects. The planet Mercury is 58,000,000 km from the sun, that earth is 149,000,000 km from the sun, and that Pluto is 5,900,000,000 km, or almost 6 billion kilometers from the sun. The table also gives the distance to Proxima Centauri, the star closest to the sun, and to the Andromeda Galaxy, the spiral galaxy closest to our own galaxy, the Milky Way.

Table 4.4   *Distance from the sun to various astronomical objects*

Object	Distance (million km)		
Mercury	58	Saturn	1426
Venus	108	Uranus	2869
Earth	149	Neptune	4495
Mars	228	Pluto	5900
Jupiter	778	Proxima Centauri	$4.1 \cdot 10^{7}$
		Andromeda Galaxy	$2.4 \cdot 10^{13}$

Linear Scales

We can represent the information in Table 4.4 graphically in order to get a better feel for the distances involved. Figure 4.13 shows the distance from the sun to the first five planets on a *linear scale*, which means that the evenly spaced units shown in the figure represent equal distances. In this case, each unit represents 100 million kilometers.

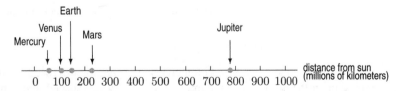

Figure 4.13: The distance from the sun of the first five planets (in millions of kilometers)

---

[6]Raskin, J, *The Humane Interface* (Reading: Addison Wesley, 2000), p 93. Jef Raskin designed the Apple Macintosh computer using, among other resources, mathematical formulas such as Fitts' Law.

The drawback of Figure 4.13 is that the scale is too small to show all of the astronomical distances described by the table. For example, to show the distance to Pluto on this scale would require over six times as much space on the page. Even worse, assuming that each 100 million km unit on the scale measures half an inch on the printed page, we would need 3 miles of paper to show the distance to Proxima Centauri!

You might conclude that we could fix this problem by choosing a larger scale. In Figure 4.14 each unit on the scale is 1 billion kilometers. Notice that all five planets shown by Figure 4.13 are crowded into the first unit of Figure 4.14; even so, the distance to Pluto barely fits. The distances to the other objects certainly don't fit. For instance, to show the Andromeda Galaxy, Figure 4.14 would have to be almost 200,000 miles long. Choosing an even larger scale will not improve the situation.

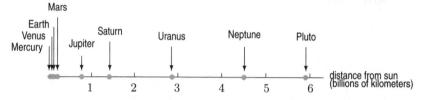

Figure 4.14: The distance to all nine planets (in billions of kilometers)

Logarithmic Scales

We conclude that the data in Table 4.4 cannot easily be represented on a linear scale. If the scale is too small, the more distant objects do not fit; if the scale is too large, the less distant objects are indistinguishable. The problem is not that the numbers are too big or too small; the problem is that the numbers vary too greatly in size.

We consider a different type of scale on which equal distances are not evenly spaced. All the objects from Table 4.4 are represented in Figure 4.15. The nine planets are still cramped, but it is possible to tell them apart. Each tick mark on the scale in Figure 4.15 represents a distance ten times larger than the one before it. This kind of scale is called *logarithmic*.

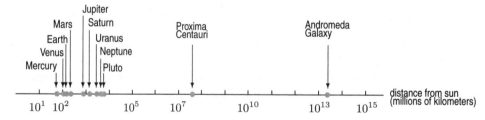

Figure 4.15: The distance from the sun (in millions of kilometers)

How Do We Plot Data on a Logarithmic Scale?

A logarithmic scale is marked with increasing powers of 10: 10^1, 10^2, 10^3, and so on. Notice that even though the distances in Figure 4.15 are not evenly spaced, the exponents are evenly spaced. Therefore the distances in Figure 4.15 are spaced according to their logarithms.

In order to plot the distance to Mercury, 58 million kilometers, we use the fact that

$$10 < 58 < 100,$$

so Mercury's distance is between 10^1 and 10^2, as shown in Figure 4.15. To plot Mercury's distance more precisely, calculate $\log 58 = 1.763$, so $10^{1.763} = 58$, and use 1.763 to represent Mercury's position. See Figure 4.16.

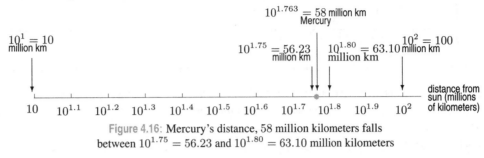

Figure 4.16: Mercury's distance, 58 million kilometers falls between $10^{1.75} = 56.23$ and $10^{1.80} = 63.10$ million kilometers

Example 1   Where should Saturn be on the logarithmic scale? What about the Andromeda Galaxy?

Solution   Saturn's distance is 1426 million kilometers, so we want the exponent of 10 that gives 1426, which is

$$\log 1426 \approx 3.154119526.$$

Thus $10^{3.154} \approx 1426$, so we use 3.154 to indicate Saturn's distance.

Similarly, the distance to the Andromeda Galaxy is $2.4 \cdot 10^{13}$ million kilometers, and since

$$\log(2.4 \cdot 10^{13}) \approx 13.38,$$

we use 13.38 to represent the galaxy's distance. See Figure 4.17.

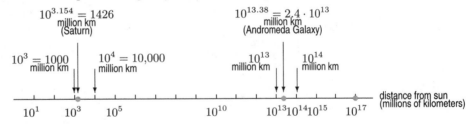

Figure 4.17: Saturn's distance is $10^{3.154}$ and the Andromeda Galaxy's distance is $10^{13.38}$

Logs of Small Numbers

The history of the world, like the distance to the stars and planets, involves numbers of vastly different sizes. Table 4.5 gives the ages of certain events[7] and the logarithms of their ages. The logarithms have been used to plot the events in Figure 4.18.

Table 4.5   *Ages of various events in earth's history and logarithms of the ages*

Event	Age (millions of years)	log (age)	Event	Age (millions of years)	log (age)
Man emerges	1	0	Rise of dinosaurs	245	2.39
Ape man fossils	5	0.70	Vertebrates appear	570	2.76
Rise of cats, dogs, pigs	37	1.57	First plants	2500	3.40
Demise of dinosaurs	67	1.83	Earth forms	4450	3.65

[7]*CRC Handbook*, 75th ed. 14-8.

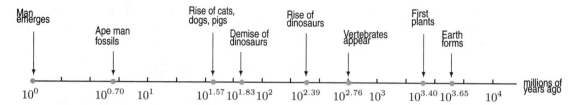

Figure 4.18: Logarithmic scale showing the ages of various events (in millions of years ago)

The events described by Table 4.5 all happened at least 1 million years ago. How do we indicate events which occurred less than 1 million years ago on the log scale?

Example 2   Where should the building of the pyramids be indicated on the log scale?

Solution   The pyramids were built about 5000 years ago, or

$$\frac{5000}{1{,}000{,}000} = 0.005 \text{ million years ago.}$$

Notice that 0.005 is between 0.001 and 0.01, that is,

$$10^{-3} < 0.005 < 10^{-2}.$$

Since

$$\log 0.005 \approx -2.30,$$

we use -2.30 for the pyramids. See Figure 4.19.

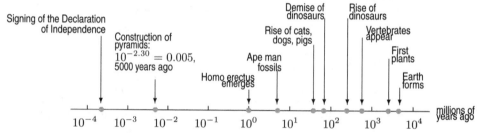

Figure 4.19: Logarithmic scale showing the ages of various events. Note that events that are less than 1 million years old are indicated by negative exponents

Another Way to Label a Log Scale

In Figures 4.18 and 4.19, the log scale has been labeled so that exponents are evenly spaced. Another way to label a log scale is with the values themselves instead of the exponents. This has been done in Figure 4.20.

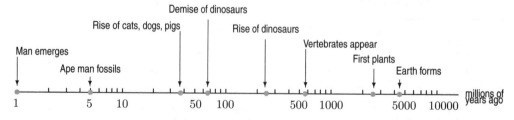

Figure 4.20: Axis labeled using the actual values, not with logs

Notice the characteristic way that the labels and tick marks "pile up" on each interval. The even spacing between exponents on log scales leads to uneven spacing in values. Although the values 10, 20, 30, 40, and 50 are evenly spaced, their corresponding exponents are not: $\log 10 = 1$, $\log 20 = 1.30$, $\log 30 = 1.48$, $\log 40 = 1.60$, and $\log 50 = 1.70$. Therefore, when we label an axis according to values on a scale that is spaced according to exponents, the labels get bunched up.

Log-Log Scales

Table 4.6 shows the average metabolic rate in kilocalories per day (kcal/day) for animals of different weights.[8] (A kilocalorie is the same as a standard nutritional calorie.) For instance, a 1-lb rat consumes about 35 kcal/day, whereas a 1750-lb horse consumes almost 9500 kcal/day.

Table 4.6   *The metabolic rate (in kcal/day) for animals of different weights*

Animal	Weight (lbs)	Rate (kcal/day)
Rat	1	35
Cat	8	166
Human	150	2000
Horse	1750	9470

It is not practical to plot these data on an ordinary set of axes. The values span too broad a range. However, we can plot the data using log scales for both the horizontal (weight) axis and the vertical (rate) axes. See Figure 4.21. Figure 4.22 shows a close-up view of the data point for cats to make it easier to see how the labels work. Once again, notice the characteristic piling up of labels and gridlines. This happens for the same reason that it happened in Figure 4.20.

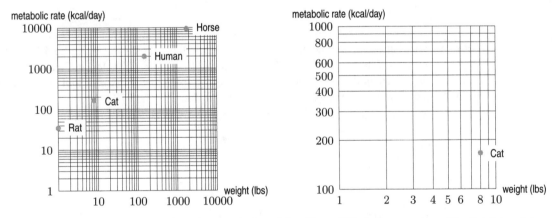

Figure 4.21: Metabolic rate (in kcal/hr) plotted against body weight   Figure 4.22: A close-up view of the Cat data point

Using Logs to Fit an Exponential Function to Data

In Section 1.6 we used linear regression to find the equation for a line of best fit for a set of data. What if the data do not lie close to a straight line, but instead approximate the graph of some other function? In this section we see how logarithms help us fit data with an exponential function of the form $Q = a \cdot b^t$.

[8]*The New York Times*, January 11, 1999.

Sales of Compact Discs

Table 4.7 shows the fall in the sales of vinyl long-playing records (LPs) and the rise of compact discs (CDs) during for the years 1982 through 1993.[9]

Table 4.7   *CD and LP sales*

t, years since 1982	c, CDs (millions)	l, LPs (millions)
0	0	244
1	0.8	210
2	5.8	205
3	23	167
4	53	125
5	102	107
6	150	72
7	207	35
8	287	12
9	333	4.8
10	408	2.3
11	495	1.2

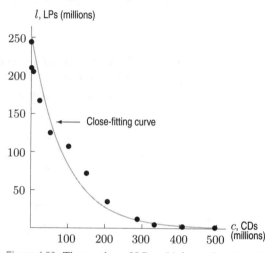

Figure 4.23: The number of LPs sold, l, as a function of number of CDs sold, c

From Table 4.7, we see that as CD sales rose dramatically during the 1980s and early 1990s, LP sales declined equally dramatically. Figure 4.23 shows the number of LPs sold in a given year as a function of the number of CDs sold that year.

Using a Log Scale to Linearize Data

In Section 4.4, we saw that a log scale allows us to compare values that vary over a wide range. Let's see what happens when we use a log scale to plot the data shown in Figure 4.23. Table 4.8 shows values $\log l$, where l is LP sales. These are plotted against c, CD sales, in Figure 4.24. Notice that plotting the data in this way tends to *linearize* the graph—that is, make it look more like a line. A line has been drawn in to emphasize the trend in the data.

Table 4.8   *Values of $y = \ln l$ and c.*

c, CDs	l, LPs	$y = \ln l$
0	244	5.50
0.8	210	5.35
5.8	205	5.32
23	167	5.12
53	125	4.83
102	107	4.67
150	72	4.28
207	35	3.56
287	12	2.48
333	4.8	1.57
408	2.3	0.83
495	1.2	0.18

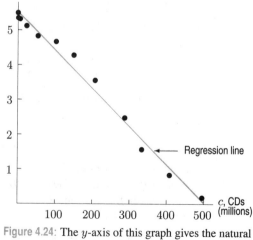

Figure 4.24: The y-axis of this graph gives the natural log of LP sales

[9]Data from Recording Industry Association of America, Inc., 1998

Finding a Formula for the Curve

We say that the data in the third column of Table 4.8 have been *transformed*. A calculator or computer gives a regression line for the transformed data:[10]

$$y = 5.52 - 0.011c.$$

Notice that this equation gives y in terms of c. To transform the equation back to our original variables, l and c, we substitute $\ln l$ for y, giving

$$\ln l = 5.52 - 0.011c.$$

We solve for l by raising e to both sides:

$$e^{\ln l} = e^{5.52 - 0.011c}$$
$$= (e^{5.52})(e^{-0.011c}) \qquad \text{Using an exponent rule.}$$

Since $e^{\ln l} = l$ and $e^{5.52} \approx 250$, we have

$$l = 250e^{-0.011c}.$$

This is the equation of the curve in Figure 4.23.

Fitting An Exponential Function To Data

In general, to fit an exponential formula, $N = ae^{kt}$, to a set of data of the form (t, N), we use three steps. First, we transform the data by taking the natural log of both sides and making the substitution $y = \ln N$. This leads to the equation

$$y = \ln N = \ln\left(ae^{kt}\right)$$
$$= \ln a + \ln e^{kt}$$
$$= \ln a + kt.$$

Setting $b = \ln a$ gives a linear equation with k as the slope and b as the y-intercept.

$$y = b + kt.$$

Secondly we can now use linear regression on the variables t and y. (Remember that $y = \ln N$.) Finally, as step three, we transform the linear regression equation back into our original variables by substituting $\ln N$ for y and solving for N.

Exercises and Problems for Section 4.4

Exercises

In Exercises 1–4, you wish to graph the quantities on a standard piece of paper. On which should you use a logarithmic scale? On which a linear scale? Why?

1. The wealth of 20 different people, one of whom is a multi-billionaire.

2. The number of diamonds owned by 20 people, one of whom is a multi-billionaire.

3. The number of meals per week eaten in restaurants for a random sample of 20 people worldwide.

4. The number of tuberculosis bacteria in 20 different people, some never exposed to the disease, some slightly exposed, some with mild cases, and some dying of it.

---

[10]The values obtained by a computer or another calculator may vary slightly from the ones given.

5. (a) Use a calculator to fill in the following tables (round to 4 decimal digits).

n	1	2	3	4	5	6	7	8	9
$\log n$									

n	10	20	30	40	50	60	70	80	90
$\log n$									

(b) Using the results of part (a), plot the integer points 2 through 9 and the multiples of 10 from 20 to 90 on the log scaled axis shown in Figure 4.25.

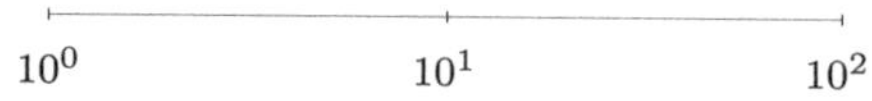

10^0 10^1 10^2

Figure 4.25

For the tables in Problem 6–8,

(a) Use linear regression to find a linear function $y = b + mx$ that fits the data. Record the correlation coefficient.

(b) Use linear regression on the values x and $\ln y$ to fit a function of the form $\ln y = b + mx$. Record the correlation coefficient. Convert to an exponential function $y = ae^{kx}$.

(c) Compare the correlation coefficients. Graph the data and the two functions to assess which function fits best.

6.

x	y
30	70
85	120
122	145
157	175
255	250
312	300

7.

x	y
8	23
17	150
23	496
26	860
32	2720
37	8051

8.

x	y
3.2	35
4.7	100
5.1	100
5.5	150
6.8	200
7.6	300

Problems

9. The signing of the Declaration of Independence is marked on the log scale in Figure 4.19 on page 178. To two decimal places, what is its position?

10. (a) Draw a line segment about 5 inches long. On it, choose an appropriate linear scale and mark points that represent the integral powers of two from zero to the sixth power. What is true about the location of the points as the exponents get larger?

(b) Draw a second line segment. Repeat the process in (a) but this time use a logarithmic scale so that the units are now powers of ten. What do you notice about the location of these points?

11. Table 4.9 shows the numbers of deaths in 2002 due to various causes in the US.[11]

(a) Explain why a log scale is necessary to plot the data from Table 4.9.

(b) Find the log of each value given.

(c) Plot the data using a log scale. Label each point with the related cause.

Table 4.9

Cause	Deaths
Scarlet fever	2
Whooping cough	18
Asthma	4261
HIV	14,011
Kidney Diseases	40,974
Accidents	106,742
Malignant neoplasms	550,271
Cardiovascular Disease	918,828
All causes	2,443,387

12. Table 4.10 shows the typical body masses in kilograms for various animals.[12]

(a) Find the log of the body mass of each animal to two decimal places.

(b) Plot the body masses for each animal in Table 4.10 on a linear scale using A to identify the Blue Whale, B to identify the African Elephant, and so on down to L to identify the Hummingbird.

---

[11] www.cdc.gov/nchs/data/nvsr/nvsr53/nvsr53_05.pdf, accessed December 22, 2005.

[12] R. McNiell Alexander, *Dynamics of Dinosaurs and Other Extinct Giants*. (New York: Columbia University Press, 1989) and H. Tennekes, *The Simple Science of Flight* (Cambridge: MIT Press, 1996).

(c) Plot and label the body masses for each animal in Table 4.10 on a logarithmic scale.

(d) Which scale, (b) or (c), is more useful?

Table 4.10

Animal	Body mass	Animal	Body mass
Blue Whale	91000	Lion	180
African Elephant	5450	Human	70
White Rhinoceros	3000	Albatross	11
Hippopotamus	2520	Hawk	1
Black Rhinoceros	1170	Robin	0.08
Horse	700	Hummingbird	0.003

13. Figure 4.26 shows the populations of eleven different places, with the scale markings representing the logarithm of the population. Give the approximate populations of each place.

Figure 4.26

14. Table 4.11 shows the dollar value of some items in 2004. Plot and label these values on a log scale.

Table 4.11

Item	Dollar value	Item	Dollar value
Pack of gum	0.50	New house	264,400
Movie ticket	9.00	Lottery winnings	100 million
New computer	1200	Bill Gates' worth	46.6 bn
Year at college	27,500	National debt	7,500 bn
Luxury car	60,400	US GDP	11,700 bn

15. Table 4.12 shows the sizes of various organisms. Plot and label these values on a log scale.

Table 4.12

Animal	Size (cm)	Animal	Size (cm)
Virus	0.0000005	Domestic cat	60
Bacterium	0.0002	Wolf (with tail)	200
Human cell	0.002	Thresher shark	600
Ant	0.8	Giant squid	2200
Hummingbird	12	Sequoia	7500

16. (a) Complete the Table 4.13 with values of $y = 3^x$.

(b) Complete Table 4.14 with values for $y = \log(3^x)$. What kind of function is this?

(c) Complete tables for $f(x) = 2 \cdot 5^x$ and $g(x) = \log(2 \cdot 5^x)$. What kinds of functions are these?

(d) What seems to be true about a function which is the logarithm of an exponential function? Is this true in general?

Table 4.13

x	0	1	2	3	4	5
$y = 3^x$						

Table 4.14

x	0	1	2	3	4	5
$y = \log(3^x)$						

17. Repeat part (b) and (c) of Problem 16 using the natural log function. Is your answer to part (d) the same?

18. Table 4.15 shows the value, y, of US imports from China with x in years since 1985.

(a) Find a formula for a linear function $y = b + mx$ that approximates the data.

(b) Find $\ln y$ for each y value, and use the x and $\ln y$ values to find a formula for a linear function $\ln y = b + mx$ that approximates the data.

(c) Use the equation in part (b) to find an exponential function of the form $y = ae^{kx}$ that fits the data.

Table 4.15 *Value of US imports from China in millions of dollars*

	1985	1986	1987	1988	1989	1990	1991
x	0	1	2	3	4	5	6
y	3862	4771	6293	8511	11,990	15,237	18,976

19. Table 4.16 shows newspapers' share of the expenditure of national advertisers. Using the method of Problem 18, fit an exponential function of the form $y = ae^{kx}$ to the data, where y is percent share and x is the number of years since 1950.

Table 4.16 *Newspapers' share of advertising*

	1950	1960	1970	1980	1990	1992
x	0	10	20	30	40	42
y	16.0	10.8	8.0	6.7	5.8	5.0

20. To study how recognition memory decreases with time, the following experiment was conducted. The subject read a list of 20 words slowly aloud, and later, at different time intervals, was shown a list of 40 words containing the 20 words that he or she had read. The percentage, P, of words recognized was recorded as a function of t, the time elapsed in minutes. Table 4.17 shows the averages for 5 different subjects.[13] This is modeled by $P = a \ln t + b$.

(a) Find $\ln t$ for each value of t, and then use regression on a calculator or computer to estimate a and b.

(b) Graph the data points and regression line on a coordinate system of P against $\ln t$.

(c) When does this model predict that the subjects will recognize no words? All words?

(d) Graph the data points and curve $P = a \ln t + b$ on a coordinate system with P against t, with $0 \le t \le 10{,}500$.

Table 4.17   *Percentage of words recognized*

t, min	5	15	30	60	120	240
$P\%$	73.0	61.7	58.3	55.7	50.3	46.7

t, min	480	720	1440	2880	5760	10,080
$P\%$	40.3	38.3	29.0	24.0	18.7	10.3

21. Table 4.18 gives the length ℓ (in cm) and weight w (in gm) of 16 different fish known as threadfin bream (*Nemipterus marginatus*) found in the South China Sea.[14]

(a) Let $W = \ln w$ and $L = \ln \ell$. For these sixteen data points, plot W on the vertical axis and L on the horizontal axis. Describe the resulting scatterplot.

(b) Fitting a line to the scatterplot you drew in part (a), find a possible formula for W in terms of L.

(c) Based on your formula for part (b), find a possible formula for w in terms of ℓ.

(d) Comment on your formula, keeping in mind what you know about units as well the typical relationship between weight, volume, and length.

Table 4.18   *Length and weight of fish*

Type	1	2	3	4	5	6	7	8
ℓ	8.1	9.1	10.2	11.9	12.2	13.8	14.8	15.7
w	6.3	9.6	11.6	18.5	26.2	36.1	40.1	47.3

Type	9	10	11	12	13	14	15	16
ℓ	16.6	17.7	18.7	19.0	20.6	21.9	22.9	23.5
w	65.6	69.4	76.4	82.5	106.6	119.8	169.2	173.3

22. A light, flashing regularly, consists of cycles, each cycle having a dark phase and a light phase. The frequency of this light is measured in cycles per second. As the frequency is increased, the eye initially perceives a series of flashes of light, then a coarse flicker, a fine flicker, and ultimately a steady light. The frequency at which the flickering disappears is called the fusion frequency.[15] Table 4.19 shows the results of an experiment[16] in which the fusion frequency F was measured as a function of the light intensity I. It is modeled by $F = a \ln I + b$.

(a) Find $\ln I$ for each value of I, and then use linear regression on a calculator or computer to estimate a and b in the equation $F = a \ln I + b$.

(b) Plot F against $\ln I$, showing the data points and the line.

(c) Plot F against I, showing the data points and the curve and give its equation.

(d) The units of I are arbitrary, that is, not given. If the units of I were changed, which of the constants a and b would be affected, and in what way?

Table 4.19   *Fusion frequency, F, as a function of the light intensity, I*

I	0.8	1.9	4.4	10.0	21.4	48.4	92.5	218.7	437.3	980.0
F	8.0	12.1	15.2	18.5	21.7	25.3	28.3	31.9	35.2	38.2

23. (a) Plot the data given by Table 4.20. What kind of function might fit this data well?

(b) Using the substitution $z = \ln x$, transform the data in Table 4.20, and compile your results into a new table. Plot the transformed data as $\ln x$ versus y.

(c) What kind of function gives a good fit to the plot you made in part (b)? Find a formula for y in terms of z that fits the data well.

(d) Using the formula from part (c), find a formula for y in terms of x that gives a good fit to the data in Table 4.20.

(e) What does your formula from part (d) tell you about x as a function of y (as opposed to y as a function of x)?

Table 4.20

x	0.21	0.55	1.31	3.22	5.15	12.48
y	-11	-2	6.5	16	20.5	29

---

[13]Adapted from D. Lewis, *Quantitative Methods in Psychology*. (New York: McGraw-Hill, 1960).

[14]Data taken from *Introduction to Tropical Fish Stock Assessment* by Per Sparre, Danish Institute for Fisheries Research, and Siebren C. Venema, FAO Fisheries Department, available at http://www.fao.org/docrep/W5449E/w5449e00.htm. This source cites the following original reference: Pauly, D., 1983. Some simple methods for the assessment of tropical fish stocks.

[15]R. S. Woodworth, *Experimental Psychology*. (New York: Holt and Company, 1948).

[16]D. Lewis, *Quantitative Methods in Psychology*. (New York: McGraw-Hill, 1960).

CHAPTER SUMMARY

- **Logarithms**
  Common log: $y = \log x$ means $10^y = x$.
  $\log 10 = 1, \log 1 = 0$.
  Natural log: $y = \ln x$ means $e^y = x$.
  $\ln e = 1, \ln 1 = 0$.

- **Properties of Logs**

$$\log(ab) = \log a + \log b.$$

$$\log(a/b) = \log a - \log b.$$

$$\log(b^t) = t \log b.$$

$$\log(10^x) = 10^{\log x} = x.$$

- **Converting between base b and base e**
  If $Q = ab^t$ and $Q = ae^{kt}$, then $k = \ln b$.

- **Solving Equations using Logs**
  Solve equations such as $ab^t = c$ and $ae^{kt} = c$ using logs.
  Not all exponential equations can be solved with logs, e.g. $2^t = 3 + t$.

- **Logarithmic Functions**
  Graph; domain; range; concavity; asymptotes.

- **Applications of Logarithms**
  Doubling time; half life;
  Chemical acidity; orders of magnitude; decibels.

- **Logarithmic Scales**
  Plotting data; log-log scales. Linearizing data and fitting curves to data using logs.

- **Limits and Limits from the Right and from the Left**

REVIEW EXERCISES AND PROBLEMS FOR CHAPTER FOUR

Exercises

In Exercises 1–4, convert to the form $Q = ae^{kt}$.

1. $Q = 12(0.9)^t$

2. $Q = 16(0.487)^t$

3. $Q = 14(0.862)^{1.4t}$

4. $Q = 721(0.98)^{0.7t}$

In Exercises 5–6, convert to the form $Q = ab^t$.

5. $Q = 7e^{-10t}$

6. $Q = 5e^t$

For Exercises 7–10, use logarithms to solve for t.

7. $3^t = 50$

8. $e^{0.15t} = 25$

9. $40e^{-0.2t} = 12$

10. $5 \cdot 2^t = 100$

In Exercises 11–12, give the starting value a, the growth factor b, the growth rate r, and the continuous growth rate k.

11. $Q = \dfrac{(1.13)^t}{20}$

12. $Q = \dfrac{200}{e^{0.177(t-2)}}$

13. The following populations, $P(t)$, are given in millions in year t. Describe the growth of each population in words. Give both the percent annual growth rate and the continuous growth rate per year.

(a) $P(t) = 51(1.03)^t$
(b) $P(t) = 15e^{0.03t}$
(c) $P(t) = 7.5(0.94)^t$
(d) $P(t) = 16e^{-0.051t}$
(e) $P(t) = 25(2)^{t/18}$
(f) $P(t) = 10(\frac{1}{2})^{t/25}$

14. A population, $P(t)$ (in millions) in year t, increases exponentially. Suppose $P(8) = 20$ and $P(15) = 28$.

(a) Find a formula for $P(t)$ without using e.
(b) If $P(t) = ae^{kt}$, find k.

Solve the equations in Exercises 15–26 exactly if possible.

15. $400(1.112)^t = 1328$

16. $0.007e^{-1.22t} = 0.002$

17. $55e^{0.571t} = 28e^{0.794t}$

18. $100^{2x+3} = \sqrt[3]{10,000}$

19. $5 \cdot 1.1^x = 55$

20. $7e^{2t} = 2e^{0.9t}$

21. $0.01^x = \dfrac{1}{\sqrt{10}}$

22. $16.3(1.072)^t = 18.5$

23. $13e^{0.081t} = 25e^{0.032t}$

24. $87e^{0.066t} = 3t + 7$

25. $\dfrac{\log x^2 + \log x^3}{\log(100x)} = 3$

26. $220e^{1.323t} = 500e^{1.118t}$

In Exercises 27–29, simplify fully.

27. $\log\left(100^{x+1}\right)$

28. $\ln\left(e \cdot e^{2+M}\right)$

29. $\ln(A + B) - \ln(A^{-1} + B^{-1})$

Problems

In Problems 30–33, find a formula for the exponential function.

30. $P = f(t)$ gives the size of a population that begins with 22,000 members and grows at a continuous annual rate of 1.76%.

31. The graph of g contains $(-30, 200)$ and $(20, 60)$.

32. $V = h(t)$ is the value after t years of $650 invested at 2.95% annual interest, compounded monthly.

33. $Q = p(t)$ describes a value that begins at 5000 and that doubles every 30 years.

34. **(a)** What is the domain and range of $f(x) = 10^x$? What is the asymptote of $f(x) = 10^x$?
   (b) What does your answer to part (a) tell you about the domain, range, and asymptotes of $g(x) = \log x$?

35. What is the domain of $y = \ln(x^2 - x - 6)$?

36. The balance B (in $) in an account after t years is given by $B = 5000(1.12)^t$.

   (a) What is the balance after 5 years? 10 years?
   (b) When is the balance $10,000? $20,000?

37. The populations (in thousands) of two cities are given by

$$P_1 = 51(1.031)^t \quad \text{and} \quad P_2 = 63(1.052)^t,$$

where t is the number of years since 1980. When does the population of P_1 equal that of P_2?

38. **(a)** Let $B = 5000(1.06)^t$ give the balance of a bank account after t years. If the formula for B is written $B = 5000e^{kt}$, estimate the value of k correct to four decimal places. What is the financial meaning of k?
   (b) The balance of a bank account after t years is given by the formula $B = 7500e^{0.072t}$. If the formula for B is written $B = 7500b^t$, find b exactly, and give the value of b correct to four decimal places. What is the financial meaning of b?

39. In 2005, the population of the country Erehwon was 50 million people and increasing by 2.9% every year. The population of the country Ecalpon, on other hand, was 45 million people and increasing by 3.2% every year.

   (a) For each country, write a formula expressing the population as a function of time t, where t is the number of years since 2005.
   (b) Find the value(s) of t, if any, when the two countries have the same population.
   (c) When is the population of Ecalpon double that of Erehwon?

40. The following is excerpted from an article that appeared in the January 8, 1990 *Boston Globe*.

> Men lose roughly 2 percent of their bone mass per year in the same type of loss that can severely affect women after menopause, a study indicates. "There is a problem with osteoporosis in men that hasn't been appreciated. It's a problem that needs to be recognized and addressed," said Dr. Eric Orwoll, who led the study by the Oregon Health Sciences University. The bone loss was detected at all ages and the 2 percent rate did not appear to vary, Orwoll said.

   (a) Assume that the average man starts losing bone mass at age 30. Let M_0 be the average man's bone mass at this age. Express the amount of remaining bone mass as a function of the man's age, a.
   (b) At what age will the average man have lost half his bone mass?

41. The number of bacteria present in a culture after t hours is given by the formula $N = 1000e^{0.69t}$.

   (a) How many bacteria will there be after $1/2$ hour?
   (b) How long before there are 1,000,000 bacteria?
   (c) What is the doubling time?

42. Oil leaks from a tank. At hour $t = 0$ there are 250 gallons of oil in the tank. Each hour after that, 4% of the oil leaks out.

   (a) What percent of the original 250 gallons has leaked out after 10 hours? Why is it less than $10 \cdot 4\% = 40\%$?
   (b) If $Q(t) = Q_0 e^{kt}$ is the quantity of oil remaining after t hours, find the value of k. What does k tell you about the leaking oil?

43. A population increases from 30,000 to 34,000 over a 5-year period at a constant annual percent growth rate.

   (a) By what percent did the population increase in total?
   (b) At what constant percent rate of growth did the population increase each year?
   (c) At what continuous annual growth rate did this population grow?

44. Radioactive carbon-14 decays according to the function $Q(t) = Q_0 e^{-0.000121t}$ where t is time in years, $Q(t)$ is the quantity remaining at time t, and Q_0 is the amount of present at time $t = 0$. Estimate the age of a skull if 23% of the original quantity of carbon-14 remains.

45. Suppose 2 mg of a drug is injected into a person's bloodstream. As the drug is metabolized, the quantity diminishes at the continuous rate of 4% per hour.

    (a) Find a formula for $Q(t)$, the quantity of the drug remaining in the body after t hours.

    (b) By what percent does the drug level decrease during any given hour?

    (c) The person must receive an additional 2 mg of the drug whenever its level has diminished to 0.25 mg. When must the person receive the second injection?

    (d) When must the person receive the third injection?

46. Suppose that $u = \log 2$ and $v = \log 5$.

    (a) Find possible formulas for the following expressions in terms of u and/or v. Your answers should not involve logs.

        (i) $\log(0.4)$ (ii) $\log 0.25$

        (iii) $\log 40$ (iv) $\log \sqrt{10}$

    (b) Justify the statement: $\log(7) \approx \frac{1}{2}(u + 2v)$.

47. Solve the following equations. Give approximate solutions if exact ones can't be found.

    (a) $e^{x+3} = 8$ **(b)** $4(1.12^x) = 5$

    (c) $e^{-0.13x} = 4$ **(d)** $\log(x - 5) = 2$

    (e) $2\ln(3x) + 5 = 8$ **(f)** $\ln x - \ln(x-1) = 1/2$

    (g) $e^x = 3x + 5$ **(h)** $3^x = x^3$

    (i) $\ln x = -x^2$

48. Solve for x exactly.

    (a) $\dfrac{3^x}{5^{x-1}} = 2^{x-1}$

    (b) $-3 + e^{x+1} = 2 + e^{x-2}$

    (c) $\ln(2x - 2) - \ln(x - 1) = \ln x$

    (d) $9^x - 7 \cdot 3^x = -6$

    (e) $\ln\left(\dfrac{e^{4x} + 3}{e}\right) = 1$

    (f) $\dfrac{\ln(8x) - 2\ln(2x)}{\ln x} = 1$

Problems 49–50 involve the Rule of 70, which gives quick estimates of the doubling time of an exponentially growing quantity. If $r\%$ is the annual growth rate of the quantity, then the Rule of 70 says

$$\text{Doubling time in years} \approx \frac{70}{r}.$$

49. Use the Rule of 70 by estimate how long it takes a $1000 investment to double if it grows at the following annual rates: 1%, 2%, 5%, 7%, 10%. Compare with the actual doubling times.

50. Using natural logs, solve for the doubling time for $Q = ae^{kt}$. Use your result to explain why the Rule of 70 works.

51. You want to borrow $25,000 to buy a Ford Explorer XL. The best available annual interest rate is 6.9%, compounded monthly. Determine how long it will take to pay off the loan if you can only afford monthly payments of $330. To do this, use the loan payment formula

$$P = \frac{Lr/12}{1 - (1 + (r/12))^{-m}},$$

where P is the monthly payment, L is the amount borrowed, r is the annual interest rate, and m is the number of months the loan is carried.

52. A rubber ball is dropped onto a hard surface from a height of 6 feet, and it bounces up and down. At each bounce it rises to 90% of the height from which it fell.

    (a) Find a formula for $h(n)$, the height reached by the ball on bounce n.

    (b) How high will the ball bounce on the 12th bounce?

    (c) How many bounces before the ball rises no higher than an inch?

53. A manager at Saks Fifth Avenue wants to estimate the number of customers to expect on the last shopping day before Christmas. She collects data from three previous years, and determines that the crowds follow the same general pattern. When the store opens at 10 am, 500 people enter, and the total number in the store doubles every 40 minutes. When the number of people in the store reaches 10,000, security guards need to be stationed at the entrances to control the crowds. At what time should the guards be commissioned?

54. The Richter scale is a measure of the ground motion that occurs during an earthquake. The intensity, R, of an earthquake as measured on the Richter scale is given by

$$R = \log\left(\frac{a}{T}\right) + B$$

where a is the amplitude (in microns) of vertical ground motion, T is the period (in seconds) of the seismic wave, and B is a constant. Let $B = 4.250$ and $T = 2.5$. Find a if

    (a) $R = 6.1$ **(b)** $R = 7.1$

    (c) Compare the values of R in parts (a) and (b). How do the corresponding values of a compare?

55. Since $e = 2.718\ldots$ we know that $2 < e < 3$, which means that $2^2 < e^2 < 3^2$. Without using a calculator, explain why

    (a) $1 < \ln 3 < 2$ **(b)** $1 < \ln 4 < 2$

CHECK YOUR UNDERSTANDING

Are the statements in Problems 1–29 true or false? Give an explanation for your answer.

1. If x is a positive number, $\log x$ is the exponent of 10 that gives x.

2. If $10^y = x$ then $\log x = y$.

3. The quantity 10^{-k} is a negative number when k is positive.

4. For any n, we have $\log(10^n) = n$.

5. If $n > 0$, then $10^{\log n} = n$.

6. If a and b are positive, $\log\left(\dfrac{a}{b}\right) = \dfrac{\log a}{\log b}$.

7. If a and b are positive, $\ln(a + b) = \ln a + \ln b$.

8. For any value a, $\log a = \ln a$.

9. For any value x, $\ln(e^{2x}) = 2x$.

10. The function $y = \log x$ has an asymptote at $y = 0$.

11. The graph of the function $y = \log x$ is concave down.

12. The reflected graph of $y = \log x$ across the line $y = x$ is the graph of $y = 10^x$.

13. If $y = \log \sqrt{x}$ then $y = \frac{1}{2}\log x$.

14. The function $y = \log(b^t)$ is always equal to $y = (\log b)^t$.

15. The values of $\ln e$ and $\log 10$ are both 1.

16. If $7.32 = e^t$ then $t = \dfrac{7.32}{e}$.

17. If $50(0.345)^t = 4$, then $t = \dfrac{\log(4/50)}{\log 0.345}$.

18. If $ab^t = n$, then $t = \dfrac{\log(n/a)}{\log b}$.

19. The doubling time of a quantity $Q = Q_0 e^{kt}$ is the time it takes for any t-value to double.

20. The half-life of a quantity is the time it takes for the quantity to be reduced by half.

21. If the half-life of a substance is 5 hours then there will be $\frac{1}{4}$ of the substance in 25 hours.

22. If $y = 6(3)^t$, then $y = 6e^{(\ln 3)t}$.

23. If a population doubles in size every 20 years, its annual continuous growth rate is 20%.

24. If $Q = Q_0 e^{kt}$, then $t = \dfrac{\ln(Q/Q_0)}{k}$.

25. Log scales provide a way to graph quantities that have vastly different magnitudes.

26. In a graph made using a log-log scale, consecutive powers of 10 are equally spaced on the horizontal axis and on the vertical axis.

27. One million and one billion differ by one order of magnitude.

28. After fitting a data set with both an exponential function, $y = Ae^{kx}$, and a power function, $y = Bx^n$, we must have $B = A$.

29. Given the points on a cubic curve, $(1, 1)$, $(2, 8)$, $(3, 27)$ and $(4, 64)$ it is not possible to fit an exponential function to this data.

TOOLS FOR CHAPTER 4: LOGARITHMS

We list the definitions and properties of the common and natural logarithms.

Properties of Logarithms If $M, N > 0$:

- Logarithm of a product: $\log MN = \log M + \log N$ $\ln MN = \ln M + \ln N$
- Logarithm of a quotient: $\log M/N = \log M - \log N$ $\ln M/N = \ln M - \ln N$
- Logarithm of a power: $\log M^P = P \log M$ $\ln M^P = P \ln M$
- Logarithm of 1: $\log 1 = 0$ $\ln 1 = 0$
- Logarithm of the base: $\log 10 = 1$ $\ln e = 1$

Be aware of the following two common errors,

$$\log(M + N) \neq (\log M)(\log N)$$

and

$$\log(M - N) \neq \frac{\log M}{\log N}.$$

Relationships Between Logarithms and Exponents

- $\log N = x$ if and only if $10^x = N$ $\ln N = x$ if and only if $e^x = N$
- $\log 10^x = x$ $\ln e^x = x$
- $10^{\log x} = x$, for $x > 0$ $e^{\ln x} = x$, for $x > 0$

Example 1   Evaluate without a calculator:

     (a) $\log 10{,}000$ (b) $\ln 1$

Solution   (a) Common logarithms are powers of 10. The power of 10 needed to get 10,000 is 4, so $\log 10{,}000 = 4$.

     (b) Natural logarithms are powers of e. The power of e needed to get 1 is zero, so $\ln 1 = 0$.

Example 2   Write the equation in exponential form

     (a) $\log x = -3$ (b) $\ln x = \sqrt{2}$

Solution   (a) By definition $\log x = -3$ means $10^{-3} = x$.

     (b) By definition $\ln x = \sqrt{2}$ means $e^{\sqrt{2}} = x$.

Example 3   Write the equation in logarithmic form

     (a) $10^x = 1000$ (b) $10^{-2} = 0.01$ (c) $e^{-1} = 0.368$

Solution   (a) By definition $10^x = 1000$ means $\log 1000 = x$.

     (b) By definition $10^{-2} = 0.01$ means $\log 0.01 = -2$.

     (c) By definition $e^{-1} = 0.368$ means $\ln 0.368 = -1$.

Example 4   Write the expression using sums and/or differences of logarithmic expressions which do not contain the logarithms of products, quotients or powers.

(a) $\log(10x)$

(b) $\ln\left(\dfrac{e^2}{\sqrt{x}}\right)$

Solution   (a)

$$\log(10x) = \log 10 + \log x \quad \text{Logarithm of a product}$$
$$= 1 + \log x \quad \text{Logarithm of the base.}$$

(b)

$$\ln\left(\frac{e^2}{\sqrt{x}}\right) = \ln e^2 - \ln\sqrt{x} \quad \text{Logarithm of a quotient}$$
$$= \ln e^2 - \ln x^{1/2}$$
$$= 2\ln e - \frac{1}{2}\ln x \quad \text{Logarithm of a power}$$
$$= 2 \cdot 1 - \frac{1}{2}\ln x \quad \text{Logarithm of the base}$$
$$= 2 - \frac{1}{2}\ln x.$$

Example 5   Write the expression as a single logarithm.

(a) $\ln x - 2\ln y$

(b) $3\left(\log x + \frac{4}{3}\log y\right)$

Solution   (a)

$$\ln x - 2\ln y = \ln x - \ln y^2 \quad \text{Logarithm of a power}$$
$$= \ln\left(\frac{x}{y^2}\right) \quad \text{Logarithm of a quotient.}$$

(b)

$$3\left(\log x + \frac{4}{3}\log y\right) = 3\log x + 4\log y$$
$$= \log x^3 + \log y^4 \quad \text{Logarithm of a power}$$
$$= \log(x^3 y^4) \quad \text{Logarithm of a product.}$$

Example 6   Express in terms of x without logarithms.

(a) $e^{3\ln x}$

(b) $\log 10^{2x}$

Solution   (a)

$$e^{3\ln x} = e^{\ln x^3} \quad \text{Logarithm of a power}$$
$$= x^3 \quad \text{Logarithm of the base.}$$

(b) $\log 10^{2x} = 2x \quad \text{Logarithm of the base.}$

Example 7   Solve the equation for x.

(a) $12e^x = 5$ (b) $2^{-3x} = 17$

Solution   (a)

$$12e^x = 5$$
$$e^x = \frac{5}{12} \quad \text{Dividing by 12}$$
$$\ln e^x = \ln\left(\frac{5}{12}\right) \quad \text{Taking ln of both sides}$$
$$x = \ln\left(\frac{5}{12}\right) \quad \text{Logarithm of the base.}$$

(b)

$$2^{-3x} = 17$$
$$\log 2^{-3x} = \log 17 \quad \text{Taking logs of both sides}$$
$$-3x \log 2 = \log 17 \quad \text{Logarithm of a power}$$
$$-3x = \frac{\log 17}{\log 2} \quad \text{Dividing by log 2}$$
$$x = -\frac{\log 17}{3 \log 2} \quad \text{Dividing by -3.}$$

Example 8   Solve the equation for x.

(a) $2(\log(2x + 50)) - 4 = 0$ (b) $\ln(x + 2) = 3$

Solution   (a)

$$2(\log(2x + 50)) - 4 = 0$$
$$2(\log(2x + 50)) = 4$$
$$\log(2x + 50) = 2$$
$$10^{\log(2x+50)} = 10^2 \quad \text{Converting to exponential form}$$
$$2x + 50 = 10^2$$
$$2x + 50 = 100$$
$$2x = 50$$
$$x = 25.$$

(b)

$$\ln(x + 2) = 3$$
$$e^{\ln(x+2)} = e^3 \quad \text{Raise } e \text{ to each side}$$
$$x + 2 = e^3$$
$$x = e^3 - 2.$$

Exercises to Tools for Chapter 4

For Exercises 1–10, evaluate without a calculator.

1. $\log(\log 10)$

2. $\ln(\ln e)$

3. $\log 0.0001$

4. $2 \ln e^4$

5. $\dfrac{\log 100^6}{\log 100^2}$

6. $\ln\left(\dfrac{1}{e^5}\right)$

7. $\dfrac{\log 1}{\log 10^5}$

8. $e^{\ln 3} - \ln e$

9. $\sqrt{\log 10{,}000}$

10. $10^{\log 7}$

For Exercises 11–16, rewrite the exponential equation in equivalent logarithmic form.

11. $10^5 = 100{,}000$

12. $10^{-4} = 0.0001$

13. $10^{0.477} = 3$

14. $e^2 = 7.389$

15. $e^{-2} = 0.135$

16. $e^{2x} = 7$

For Exercises 17–20, rewrite the logarithmic equation in equivalent exponential form.

17. $\log 0.01 = -2$

18. $\log(x + 3) = 2$

19. $\ln x = -1$

20. $\ln 4 = x^2$

For Exercises 21–31, if possible, write the expression using sums and/or differences of logarithmic expressions which do not contain the logarithms of products, quotients or powers.

21. $\log 2x$

22. $\ln(x(7 - x)^3)$

23. $\dfrac{\ln x}{2}$

24. $\log\left(\dfrac{x}{5}\right)$

25. $\log\left(\dfrac{x^2 + 1}{x^3}\right)$

26. $\ln\sqrt{\dfrac{x - 1}{x + 1}}$

27. $\log(x^2 + y^2)$

28. $\ln\left(\dfrac{xy^2}{z}\right)$

29. $\log(x^2 - y^2)$

30. $(\log x)(\log y)$

31. $\dfrac{\ln x^2}{\ln(x + 2)}$

For Exercises 32–40, rewrite the expression as a single logarithm.

32. $\log 12 + \log x$

33. $\ln x^3 + \ln x^2$

34. $\ln x^2 - \ln(x + 10)$

35. $\frac{1}{2}\log x + 4\log y$

36. $\log 3 + 2\log\sqrt{x}$

37. $\frac{1}{3}\log 8 - \frac{1}{2}\log 25$

38. $3\left(\log(x + 1) + \frac{2}{3}\log(x + 4)\right)$

39. $\ln x + \ln\left(\dfrac{y}{2}(x + 4)\right) + \ln z^{-1}$

40. $2\log(9 - x^2) - (\log(3 + x) + \log(3 - x))$

For Exercises 41–52, simplify the expression if possible.

41. $10^{-\log 5x}$

42. $e^{-3\ln t}$

43. $2\ln e^{\sqrt{x}}$

44. $\log(A^2 + B^2)$

45. $t\ln e^{t/2}$

46. $10^{2 + \log x}$

47. $\log 10x - \log x$

48. $2\ln x^{-2} + \ln x^4$

49. $\ln\sqrt{x^2 + 16}$

50. $\log 100^{2z}$

51. $\dfrac{\ln e}{\ln e^2}$

52. $\ln\dfrac{1}{e^x + 1}$

For Exercises 53–62, solve for x using logarithms.

53. $4^x = 9$

54. $12^x = 7$

55. $3 \cdot 5^x = 9$

56. $4 \cdot 13^{3x} = 17$

57. $e^x = 8$

58. $2e^x = 13$

59. $e^{-5x} = 9$

60. $e^{7x} = 5e^{3x}$

61. $12^{5x} = 3 \cdot 15^{2x}$

62. $19^{6x} = 77 \cdot 7^{4x}$

In Exercises 63–68, solve for x.

63. $\log(2x + 7) = 2$

64. $3\log(4x + 9) - 6 = 2$

65. $4\log(9x + 17) - 5 = 1$

66. $\log(2x) = \log(x + 10)$

67. $\ln(3x + 4) = 5$

68. $2\ln(6x - 1) + 5 = 7$

Chapter Five

TRANSFORMATIONS OF FUNCTIONS AND THEIR GRAPHS

We have introduced the families of linear, exponential, and logarithmic functions and we will study several other families in the later chapters. Before going on to the next family, we introduce some tools that are useful for analyzing every family of functions. These tools allow us to transform members of a family into one another by shifting, flipping, and stretching their graphs. In the process, we construct another family, the family of quadratic functions.

Throughout the chapter, we consider the relationship between changes made to the formula of a function and changes made to its graph.

The Tools Section on page 239 reviews completing the square.

5.1   VERTICAL AND HORIZONTAL SHIFTS

Suppose we shift the graph of some function vertically or horizontally, giving the graph of a new function. In this section we investigate the relationship between the formulas for the original function and the new function.

Vertical and Horizontal Shift: The Heating Schedule For an Office Building

We start with an example of a vertical shift in the context of the heating schedule for a building.

Example 1   To save money, an office building is kept warm only during business hours. Figure 5.1 shows the temperature, H, in °F, as a function of time, t, in hours after midnight. At midnight ($t = 0$), the building's temperature is 50°F. This temperature is maintained until 4 am. Then the building begins to warm up so that by 8 am the temperature is 70°F. At 4 pm the building begins to cool. By 8 pm, the temperature is again 50°F.

Suppose that the building's superintendent decides to keep the building 5°F warmer than before. Sketch a graph of the resulting function.

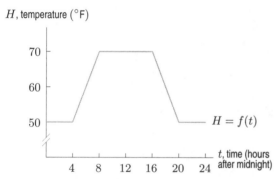

Figure 5.1: The heating schedule at an office building

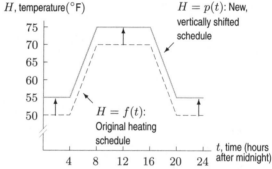

Figure 5.2: Graph of new heating schedule, $H = p(t)$, obtained by shifting original graph, $H = f(t)$, upward by 5 units

Solution   The graph of f, the heating schedule function of Figure 5.1, is shifted upward by 5 units. The new heating schedule, $H = p(t)$, is graphed in Figure 5.2. The building's overnight temperature is now 55°F instead of 50°F and its daytime temperature is 75°F instead of 70°F. The 5°F increase in temperature corresponds to the 5-unit vertical shift in the graph.

The next example involves shifting a graph horizontally.

Example 2   The superintendent then changes the original heating schedule to start two hours earlier. The building now begins to warm at 2 am instead of 4 am, reaches 70°F at 6 am instead of 8 am, begins cooling off at 2 pm instead of 4 pm, and returns to 50°F at 6 pm instead of 8 pm. How are these changes reflected in the graph of the heating schedule?

Solution   Figure 5.3 gives a graph of $H = q(t)$, the new heating schedule, which is obtained by shifting the graph of the original heating schedule, $H = f(t)$, two units to the left.

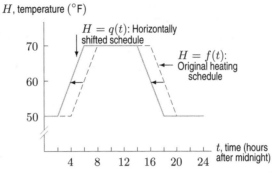

Figure 5.3: Graph of new heating schedule, $H = q(t)$, found by shifting, f, the original graph 2 units to the left

Notice that the upward shift in Example 1 results in a warmer temperature, whereas the leftward shift in Example 2 results in an earlier schedule.

Formulas for a Vertical or Horizontal Shift

How does a horizontal or vertical shift of a function's graph affect its formula?

Example 3   In Example 1, the graph of the original heating schedule, $H = f(t)$, was shifted upward by 5 units; the result was the warmer schedule $H = p(t)$. How are the formulas for $f(t)$ and $p(t)$ related?

Solution   The temperature under the new schedule, $p(t)$, is always 5°F warmer than the temperature under the old schedule, $f(t)$. Thus,

$$\begin{array}{c}\text{New temperature} \\ \text{at time } t\end{array} = \begin{array}{c}\text{Old temperature} \\ \text{at time } t\end{array} + 5.$$

Writing this algebraically:

$$\underbrace{p(t)}_{\substack{\text{New temperature} \\ \text{at time } t}} = \underbrace{f(t)}_{\substack{\text{Old temperature} \\ \text{at time } t}} + \ 5.$$

The relationship between the formulas for p and f is given by the equation $p(t) = f(t) + 5$.

We can get information from the relationship $p(t) = f(t) + 5$, although we do not have an explicit formula for f or p.

Suppose we need to know the temperature at 6 am under the schedule $p(t)$. The graph of $f(t)$ shows that under the old schedule $f(6) = 60$. Substituting $t = 6$ into the equation relating f and p gives $p(6)$:

$$p(6) = f(6) + 5 = 60 + 5 = 65.$$

Thus, at 6 am the temperature under the new schedule is 65°F.

Example 4   In Example 2 the heating schedule was changed to 2 hours earlier, shifting the graph horizontally 2 units to the left. Find a formula for q, this new schedule, in terms of f, the original schedule.

Solution   The old schedule always reaches a given temperature 2 hours after the new schedule. For example, at 4 am the temperature under the new schedule reaches $60°$. The temperature under the old schedule reaches $60°$ at 6 am, 2 hours later. The temperature reaches $65°$ at 5 am under the new schedule, but not until 7 am, under the old schedule. In general, we see that

$$\begin{array}{ccc} \text{Temperature under new schedule} & & \text{Temperature under old schedule} \\ \text{at time } t & = & \text{at time } (t+2), \text{ two hours later.} \end{array}$$

Algebraically, we have

$$q(t) = f(t+2).$$

This is a formula for q in terms of f.

Let's check the formula from Example 4 by using it to calculate $q(14)$, the temperature under the new schedule at 2 pm. The formula gives

$$q(14) = f(14+2) = f(16).$$

Figure 5.1 shows that $f(16) = 70$. Thus, $q(14) = 70$. This agrees with Figure 5.3.

Translations of a Function and Its Graph

In the heating schedule example, the function representing a warmer schedule,

$$p(t) = f(t) + 5,$$

has a graph which is a vertically shifted version of the graph of f. On the other hand, the earlier schedule is represented by

$$q(t) = f(t+2)$$

and its graph is a horizontally shifted version of the graph of f. Adding 5 to the temperature, or output value, $f(t)$, shifted its graph *up* five units. Adding 2 to the time, or input value, t, shifted its graph to the *left* two units. Generalizing these observations to any function g:

> If $y = g(x)$ is a function and k is a constant, then the graph of
> - $y = g(x) + k$ is the graph of $y = g(x)$ shifted vertically $|k|$ units. If k is positive, the shift is up; if k is negative, the shift is down.
> - $y = g(x + k)$ is the graph of $y = g(x)$ shifted horizontally $|k|$ units. If k is positive, the shift is to the left; if k is negative, the shift is to the right.

A vertical or horizontal shift of the graph of a function is called a *translation* because it does not change the shape of the graph, but simply translates it to another position in the plane. Shifts or translations are the simplest examples of *transformations* of a function. We will see others in later sections of Chapter 5.

Inside and Outside Changes

Since $y = g(x + k)$ involves a change to the input value, x, it is called an *inside change* to g. Similarly, since $y = g(x) + k$ involves a change to the output value, $g(x)$, it is called an *outside change*. In general, an inside change in a function results in a horizontal change in its graph, whereas an outside change results in a vertical change.

In this section, we consider changes to the input and output of a function. For the function

$$Q = f(t),$$

a change inside the function's parentheses can be called an "inside change" and a change outside the function's parentheses can be called an "outside change."

Example 5
If $n = f(A)$ gives the number of gallons of paint needed to cover a house of area A ft^2, explain the meaning of the expressions $f(A + 10)$ and $f(A) + 10$ in the context of painting.

Solution
These two expressions are similar in that they both involve adding 10. However, for $f(A + 10)$, the 10 is added on the inside, so 10 is added to the area, A. Thus,

$$n = f(\underbrace{A + 10}_{\text{Area}}) = \begin{array}{c} \text{Amount of paint needed} \\ \text{to cover an area of } (A + 10) \text{ ft}^2 \end{array} = \begin{array}{c} \text{Amount of paint needed to cover} \\ \text{an area 10 ft}^2 \text{ larger than } A. \end{array}$$

The expression $f(A) + 10$ represents an outside change. We are adding 10 to $f(A)$, which represents an amount of paint, not an area. We have

$$n = \underbrace{f(A)}_{\substack{\text{Amount} \\ \text{of paint}}} + 10 = \begin{array}{c} \text{Amount of paint needed} \\ \text{to cover region of area } A \end{array} + 10 \text{ gals} = \begin{array}{c} \text{10 gallons more paint than} \\ \text{amount needed to cover area } A. \end{array}$$

In $f(A + 10)$, we added 10 square feet on the inside of the function, which means that the area to be painted is now 10 ft^2 larger. In $f(A) + 10$, we added 10 gallons to the outside, which means that we have 10 more gallons of paint than we need.

Example 6
Let $s(t)$ be the average weight (in pounds) of a baby at age t months. The weight, V, of a particular baby named Jonah is related to the average weight function $s(t)$ by the equation

$$V = s(t) + 2.$$

Find Jonah's weight at ages $t = 3$ and $t = 6$ months. What can you say about Jonah's weight in general?

Solution
At $t = 3$ months, Jonah's weight is

$$V = s(3) + 2.$$

Since $s(3)$ is the average weight of a 3-month old boy, we see that at 3 months, Jonah weighs 2 pounds more than average. Similarly, at $t = 6$ months we have

$$V = s(6) + 2,$$

which means that, at 6 months, Jonah weighs 2 pounds more than average. In general, Jonah weighs 2 pounds more than average for babies of his age.

Example 7   The weight, W, of another baby named Ben is related to $s(t)$ by the equation

$$W = s(t + 4).$$

What can you say about Ben's weight at age $t = 3$ months? At $t = 6$ months? Assuming that babies increase in weight over the first year of life, decide if Ben is of average weight for his age, above average, or below average.

Solution   Since $W = s(t + 4)$, at age $t = 3$ months Ben's weight is given by

$$W = s(3 + 4) = s(7).$$

We defined $s(7)$ to be the average weight of a 7-month old baby. At age 3 months, Ben's weight is the same as the average weight of 7-month old babies. Since, on average, a baby's weight increases as the baby grows, this means that Ben is heavier than the average for a 3-month old. Similarly, at age $t = 6$, Ben's weight is given by

$$W = s(6 + 4) = s(10).$$

Thus, at 6 months, Ben's weight is the same as the average weight of 10-month old babies. In both cases, we see that Ben is above average in weight.

Notice that in Example 7, the equation

$$W = s(t + 4)$$

involves an inside change, or a change in months. This equation tells us that Ben weighs as much as babies who are 4 months older than he is. However in Example 6, the equation

$$V = s(t) + 2$$

involves an outside change, or a change in weight. This equation tells us that Jonah is 2 pounds heavier than the average weight of babies his age. Although both equations tell us that the babies are heavier than average for their age, they vary from the average in different ways.

Combining Horizontal and Vertical Shifts

We have seen what happens when we shift a function's graph either horizontally or vertically. What happens if we shift it both horizontally and vertically?

Example 8   Let r be the transformation of the heating schedule function, $H = f(t)$, defined by the equation

$$r(t) = f(t - 2) - 5.$$

(a) Sketch the graph of $H = r(t)$.
(b) Describe in words the heating schedule determined by r.

Solution
    (a) To graph r, we break this transformation into two steps. First, we sketch a graph of $H = f(t-2)$. This is an inside change to the function f and it results in the graph of f being shifted 2 units to the right. Next, we sketch a graph of $H = f(t-2) - 5$. This graph can be found by shifting our sketch of $H = f(t-2)$ down 5 units. The resulting graph is shown in Figure 5.4. The graph of r is the graph of f shifted 2 units to the right and 5 units down.

    (b) The function r represents a schedule that is both 2 hours later and 5 degrees cooler than the original schedule.

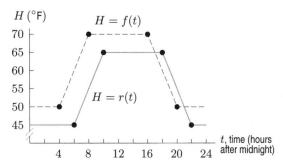

Figure 5.4: Graph of $r(t) = f(t-2) - 5$ is graph of $H = f(t)$ shifted right by 2 and down by 5

We can use transformations to understand an unfamiliar function by relating it to a function we already know.

Example 9   A graph of $f(x) = x^2$ is in Figure 5.5. Define g by shifting the graph of f to the right 2 units and down 1 unit; see Figure 5.6. Find a formula for g in terms of f. Find a formula for g in terms of x.

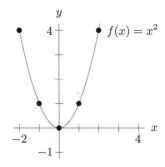

Figure 5.5: The graph of $f(x) = x^2$

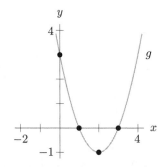

Figure 5.6: The graph of g, a transformation of f

Solution
    The graph of g is the graph of f shifted to the right 2 units and down 1 unit, so a formula for g is $g(x) = f(x-2) - 1$. Since $f(x) = x^2$, we have $f(x-2) = (x-2)^2$. Therefore,

$$g(x) = (x-2)^2 - 1.$$

It is a good idea to check by graphing $g(x) = (x-2)^2 - 1$ and comparing the graph with Figure 5.6.

Exercises and Problems for Section 5.1

Exercises

1. Using Table 5.1, complete the tables for g, h, k, m, where:

(a) $g(x) = f(x - 1)$ **(b)** $h(x) = f(x + 1)$
(c) $k(x) = f(x) + 3$ **(d)** $m(x) = f(x - 1) + 3$

Explain how the graph of each function relates to the graph of $f(x)$.

Table 5.1

x	-2	-1	0	1	2
$f(x)$	-3	0	2	1	-1

x	-1	0	1	2	3
$g(x)$					

x	-3	-2	-1	0	1
$h(x)$					

x	-2	-1	0	1	2
$k(x)$					

x	-1	0	1	2	3
$m(x)$					

In Exercises 2–5, graph the transformations of $f(x)$ in Figure 5.7.

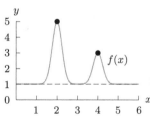

Figure 5.7

2. $y = f(x + 2)$ **3.** $y = f(x) + 2$

4. $y = f(x - 1) - 5$ **5.** $y = f(x + 6) - 4$

6. Let $f(x) = 4^x$, $g(x) = 4^x + 2$, and $h(x) = 4^x - 3$. What is the relationship between the graph of $f(x)$ and the graphs of $h(x)$ and $g(x)$?

7. Let $f(x) = \left(\frac{1}{3}\right)^x$, $g(x) = \left(\frac{1}{3}\right)^{x+4}$, and $h(x) = \left(\frac{1}{3}\right)^{x-2}$. How do the graphs of $g(x)$ and $h(x)$ compare to the graph of $f(x)$?

8. Match the graphs in (a)–(f) with the formulas in (i)–(vi).

(i) $y = |x|$ (ii) $y = |x| - 1.2$
(iii) $y = |x - 1.2|$ (iv) $y = |x| + 2.5$
(v) $y = |x + 3.4|$ (vi) $y = |x - 3| + 2.7$

(a) 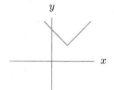 (b)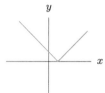

(c) 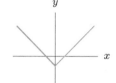 (d)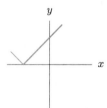

(e) 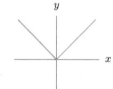 (f)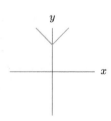

9. The graph of $f(x)$ contains the point $(3, -4)$. What point must be on the graph of

(a) $f(x) + 5$?   **(b)** $f(x + 5)$?
(c) $f(x - 3) - 2$?

10. The domain of the function $g(x)$ is $-2 < x < 7$. What is the domain of $g(x - 2)$?

11. The range of the function $R(s)$ is $100 \le R(s) \le 200$. What is the range of $R(s) - 150$?

Write a formula and graph the transformations of $m(n) = \frac{1}{2}n^2$ in Exercises 12–19.

12. $y = m(n) + 1$ **13.** $y = m(n + 1)$

14. $y = m(n) - 3.7$ **15.** $y = m(n - 3.7)$

16. $y = m(n) + \sqrt{13}$ **17.** $y = m(n + 2\sqrt{2})$

18. $y = m(n + 3) + 7$ **19.** $y = m(n - 17) - 159$

216

Write a formula and graph the transformations of $k(w) = 3^w$ in Exercises 20–25.

20. $y = k(w) - 3$ **21.** $y = k(w - 3)$

22. $y = k(w) + 1.8$ **23.** $y = k(w + \sqrt{5})$

24. $y = k(w + 2.1) - 1.3$ **25.** $y = k(w - 1.5) - 0.9$

Problems

26. (a) Using Table 5.2, evaluate

  (i) $f(x)$ for $x = 6$.

  (ii) $f(5) - 3$.

  (iii) $f(5 - 3)$.

  (iv) $g(x) + 6$ for $x = 2$.

  (v) $g(x + 6)$ for $x = 2$.

  (vi) $3g(x)$ for $x = 0$.

  (vii) $f(3x)$ for $x = 2$.

  (viii) $f(x) - f(2)$ for $x = 8$.

  (ix) $g(x + 1) - g(x)$ for $x = 1$.

(b) Solve

  (i) $g(x) = 6$.   (ii) $f(x) = 574$.

  (iii) $g(x) = 281$.

(c) The values in the table were obtained using the formulas $f(x) = x^3 + x^2 + x - 10$ and $g(x) = 7x^2 - 8x - 6$. Use the table to find two solutions to the equation $x^3 + x^2 + x - 10 = 7x^2 - 8x - 6$.

Table 5.2

x	0	1	2	3	4	5	6	7	8	9
$f(x)$	-10	-7	4	29	74	145	248	389	574	809
$g(x)$	-6	-7	6	33	74	129	198	281	378	489

27. The graph of $g(x)$ contains the point $(-2, 5)$. Write a formula for a translation of g whose graph contains the point

  (a) $(-2, 8)$ **(b)** $(0, 5)$

28. (a) Let $f(x) = \left(\dfrac{x}{2}\right)^3 + 2$. Calculate $f(-6)$.

  (b) Solve $f(x) = -6$.

  (c) Find points that correspond to parts (a) and (b) on the graph of $f(x)$ in Figure 5.8.

  (d) Calculate $f(4) - f(2)$. Draw a vertical line segment on the y-axis that illustrates this calculation.

  (e) If $a = -2$, compute $f(a + 4)$ and $f(a) + 4$.

  (f) In part (e), what x-value corresponds to $f(a + 4)$? To $f(a) + 4$?

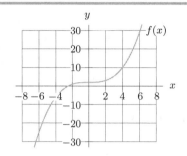

Figure 5.8

29. The function $P(t)$ gives the number of people in a certain population in year t. Interpret in terms of population:

  (a) $P(t) + 100$ **(b)** $P(t + 100)$

30. Describe a series of shifts which translates the graph of $y = (x + 3)^3 - 1$ onto the graph of $y = x^3$.

31. Graph $f(x) = \ln(|x - 3|)$ and $g(x) = \ln(|x|)$. Find the vertical asymptotes of both functions.

32. Graph $y = \log x$, $y = \log(10x)$, and $y = \log(100x)$. How do the graphs compare? Use a property of logs to show that the graphs are vertical shifts of one another.

Explain in words the effects of the transformations in Exercises 33–38 on the graph of $q(z)$. Assume a, b are positive constants.

33. $q(z) + 3$ **34.** $q(z) - a$

35. $q(z + 4)$ **36.** $q(z - a)$

37. $q(z + b) - a$ **38.** $q(z - 2b) + ab$

39. Suppose $S(d)$ gives the height of high tide in Seattle on a specific day, d, of the year. Use shifts of the function $S(d)$ to find formulas for each of the following functions:

  (a) $T(d)$, the height of high tide in Tacoma on day d, given that high tide in Tacoma is always one foot higher than high tide in Seattle.

  (b) $P(d)$, the height of high tide in Portland on day d, given that high tide in Portland is the same height as the previous day's high tide in Seattle.

40. Table 5.3 contains values of $f(x)$. Each function in parts (a)–(c) is a translation of $f(x)$. Find a possible formula for each of these functions in terms of f. For example, given the data in Table 5.4, you could say that $k(x) = f(x) + 1$.

Table 5.3

x	0	1	2	3	4	5	6	7
$f(x)$	0	0.5	2	4.5	8	12.5	18	24.5

Table 5.4

x	0	1	2	3	4	5	6	7
$k(x)$	1	1.5	3	5.5	9	13.5	19	25.5

(a)

x	0	1	2	3	4	5	6	7
$h(x)$	−2	−1.5	0	2.5	6	10.5	16	22.5

(b)

x	0	1	2	3	4	5	6	7
$g(x)$	0.5	2	4.5	8	12.5	18	24.5	32

(c)

x	0	1	2	3	4	5	6	7
$i(x)$	−1.5	0	2.5	6	10.5	16	22.5	30

41. For $t \geq 0$, let $H(t) = 68 + 93(0.91)^t$ give the temperature of a cup of coffee in degrees Fahrenheit t minutes after it is brought to class.

(a) Find formulas for $H(t + 15)$ and $H(t) + 15$.
(b) Graph $H(t)$, $H(t + 15)$, and $H(t) + 15$.
(c) Describe in practical terms a situation modeled by the function $H(t + 15)$. What about $H(t) + 15$?
(d) Which function, $H(t+15)$ or $H(t)+15$, approaches the same final temperature as the function $H(t)$? What is that temperature?

42. At a jazz club, the cost of an evening is based on a cover charge of $20 plus a beverage charge of $7 per drink.

(a) Find a formula for $t(x)$, the total cost for an evening in which x drinks are consumed.
(b) If the price of the cover charge is raised by $5, express the new total cost function, $n(x)$, as a transformation of $t(x)$.
(c) The management increases the cover charge to $30, leaves the price of a drink at $7, but includes the first two drinks for free. For $x \geq 2$, express $p(x)$, the new total cost, as a transformation of $t(x)$.

43. A hot brick is removed from a kiln and set on the floor to cool. Let t be time in minutes after the brick was removed. The difference, $D(t)$, between the brick's temperature, initially $350°F$, and room temperature, $70°F$, decays exponentially over time at a rate of 3% per minute. The brick's temperature, $H(t)$, is a transformation of $D(t)$. Find a formula for $H(t)$. Compare the graphs of $D(t)$ and $H(t)$, paying attention to the asymptotes.

44. Suppose $T(d)$ gives the average temperature in your hometown on the dth day of last year (where $d = 1$ is January 1st, and so on).

(a) Graph $T(d)$ for $1 \leq d \leq 365$.
(b) Give a possible value for each of the following: $T(6); T(100); T(215); T(371)$.
(c) What is the relationship between $T(d)$ and $T(d + 365)$? Explain.
(d) If you were to graph $w(d) = T(d + 365)$ on the same axes as $T(d)$, how would the two graphs compare?
(e) Do you think the function $T(d) + 365$ has any practical significance? Explain.

45. Let $f(x) = e^x$ and $g(x) = 5e^x$. If $g(x) = f(x - h)$, find h.

5.2   REFLECTIONS AND SYMMETRY

In Section 5.1 we saw that a horizontal shift of the graph of a function results from a change to the input of the function. (Specifically, adding or subtracting a constant inside the function's parentheses.) A vertical shift corresponds to an outside change.

In this section we consider the effect of reflecting a function's graph about the x or y-axis. A reflection about the x-axis corresponds to an outside change to the function's formula; a reflection about the y-axis and corresponds to an inside change.

A Formula for a Reflection

Figure 5.9 shows the graph of a function $y = f(x)$ and Table 5.5 gives a corresponding table of values. Note that we do not need an explicit formula for f.

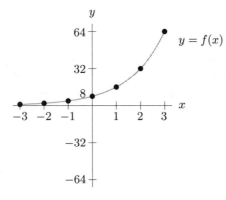

Figure 5.9: A graph of the function $y = f(x)$

Table 5.5   *Values of the function* $y = f(x)$

x	y
-3	1
-2	2
-1	4
0	8
1	16
2	32
3	64

Figure 5.10 shows a graph of a function $y = g(x)$, resulting from a vertical reflection of the graph of f about the x-axis. Figure 5.11 is a graph of a function $y = h(x)$, resulting from a horizontal reflection of the graph of f about the y-axis. Figure 5.12 is a graph of a function $y = k(x)$, resulting from a horizontal reflection of the graph of f about the y-axis followed by a vertical reflection about the x-axis.

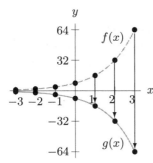

Figure 5.10: Graph reflected about x-axis

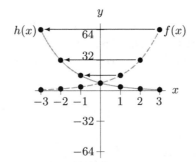

Figure 5.11: Graph reflected about y-axis

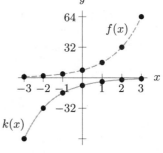

Figure 5.12: Graph reflected about y- and x-axes

Example 1   Find a formula in terms of f for   (a) $y = g(x)$ (b) $y = h(x)$ (c) $y = k(x)$

Solution   (a) The graph of $y = g(x)$ is obtained by reflecting the graph of f vertically about the x-axis. For example, the point $(3, 64)$ on the graph of f reflects to become the point $(3, -64)$ on the graph of g. The point $(2, 32)$ on the graph of f becomes $(2, -32)$ on the graph of g. See Table 5.6.

Table 5.6   *Values of the functions* $g(x)$ *and* $f(x)$ *graphed in Figure 5.10*

x	-3	-2	-1	0	1	2	3
$g(x)$	-1	-2	-4	-8	-16	-32	-64
$f(x)$	1	2	4	8	16	32	64

Notice that when a point is reflected vertically about the x-axis, the x-value stays fixed, while the y-value changes sign. That is, for a given x-value,

$$y\text{-value of } g \text{ is the negative of } y\text{-value of } f.$$

Algebraically, this means

$$g(x) = -f(x).$$

(b) The graph of $y = h(x)$ is obtained by reflecting the graph of $y = f(x)$ horizontally about the y-axis. In part (a), a vertical reflection corresponded to an outside change in the formula, specifically, multiplying by -1. Thus, you might guess that a horizontal reflection of the graph corresponds to an inside change in the formula. This is correct. To see why, consider Table 5.7.

Table 5.7   *Values of the functions $h(x)$ and $f(x)$ graphed in Figure 5.11*

x	-3	-2	-1	0	1	2	3
$h(x)$	64	32	16	8	4	2	1
$f(x)$	1	2	4	8	16	32	64

Notice that when a point is reflected horizontally about the y-axis, the y-value remains fixed, while the x-value changes sign. For example, since $f(-3) = 1$ and $h(3) = 1$, we have $h(3) = f(-3)$. Since $f(-1) = 4$ and $h(1) = 4$, we have $h(1) = f(-1)$. In general,

$$h(x) = f(-x).$$

(c) The graph of the function $y = k(x)$ results from a horizontal reflection of the graph of f about the y-axis, followed by a vertical reflection about the x-axis. Since a horizontal reflection corresponds to multiplying the inputs by -1 and a vertical reflection corresponds to multiplying the outputs by -1, we have

Vertical reflection across the x-axis
$$k(x) = -f(-x).$$
Horizontal reflection across the y-axis

Let's check a point. If $x = 1$, then the formula $k(x) = -f(-x)$ gives:

$$k(1) = -f(-1) = -4 \qquad \text{since } f(-1) = 4.$$

This result is consistent with the graph, since $(1, -4)$ is on the graph of $k(x)$.

For a function f:
- The graph of $y = -f(x)$ is a reflection of the graph of $y = f(x)$ about the x-axis.
- The graph of $y = f(-x)$ is a reflection of the graph of $y = f(x)$ about the y-axis.

Symmetry About the y-Axis

The graph of $p(x) = x^2$ in Figure 5.13 is *symmetric* about the y-axis. In other words, the part of the graph to the left of the y-axis is the mirror image of the part to the right of the y-axis. Reflecting the graph of $p(x)$ about the y-axis gives the graph of $p(x)$ again.

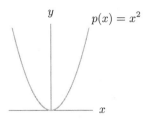

Figure 5.13: Reflecting the graph of $p(x) = x^2$ about the y-axis does not change its appearance

Symmetry about the y-axis is called *even symmetry*, because power functions with even exponents, such as $y = x^2$, $y = x^4$, $y = x^6$, ... have this property. Since $y = p(-x)$ is a reflection of the graph of p about the y-axis and $p(x)$ has even symmetry, we have

$$p(-x) = p(x).$$

To check this relationship, let $x = 2$. Then $p(2) = 2^2 = 4$, and $p(-2) = (-2)^2 = 4$, so $p(-2) = p(2)$. This means that the point $(2, 4)$ and its reflection about the y-axis, $(-2, 4)$, are both on the graph of $p(x)$.

Example 2   For the function $p(x) = x^2$, check algebraically that $p(-x) = p(x)$ for all x.

Solution   Substitute $-x$ into the formula for $p(x)$ giving

$$p(-x) = (-x)^2 = (-x) \cdot (-x)$$
$$= x^2$$
$$= p(x).$$

Thus, $p(-x) = p(x)$.

In general,

If f is a function, then f is called an **even function** if, for all values of x in the domain of f,

$$f(-x) = f(x).$$

The graph of f is symmetric about the y-axis.

Symmetry About the Origin

Figures 5.14 and 5.15 show the graph of $q(x) = x^3$. Reflecting the graph of q first about the y-axis and then about the x-axis (or vice-versa) gives the graph of q again. This kind of symmetry is called symmetry about the origin, or *odd symmetry*.

In Example 1, we saw that $y = -f(-x)$ is a reflection of the graph of $y = f(x)$ about both the y-axis and the x-axis. Since $q(x) = x^3$ is symmetric about the origin, q is the same function as this double reflection. That is,

$$q(x) = -q(-x) \quad \text{which means that} \quad q(-x) = -q(x).$$

To check this relationship, let $x = 2$. Then $q(2) = 2^3 = 8$, and $q(-2) = (-2)^3 = -8$, so $q(-2) = -q(2)$. This means the point $(2, 8)$ and its reflection about the origin, $(-2, -8)$, are both on the graph of q.

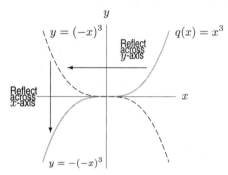

Figure 5.14: If the graph is reflected about the y-axis and then about the x-axis, it does not change

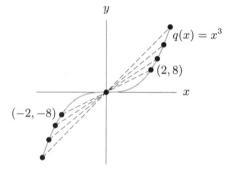

Figure 5.15: If every point on this graph is reflected about the origin, the graph is unchanged

Example 3   For the function $q(x) = x^3$, check algebraically that $q(-x) = -q(x)$ for all x.

Solution   We evaluate $q(-x)$ giving

$$q(-x) = (-x)^3 = (-x) \cdot (-x) \cdot (-x)$$
$$= -x^3$$
$$= -q(x).$$

Thus, $q(-x) = -q(x)$.

In general,

> If f is a function, then f is called an **odd function** if, for all values of x in the domain of f,
>
> $$f(-x) = -f(x).$$
>
> The graph of f is symmetric about the origin.

Example 4   Determine whether the following functions are symmetric about the y-axis, the origin, or neither.
(a) $f(x) = |x|$ (b) $g(x) = 1/x$ (c) $h(x) = -x^3 - 3x^2 + 2$

Solution   The graphs of the functions in Figures 5.16, 5.17, and 5.18 can be helpful in identifying symmetry.

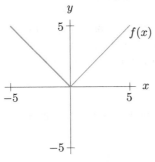

Figure 5.16: The graph of $f(x) = |x|$ appears to be symmetric about the y-axis

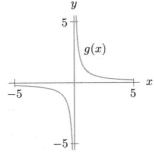

Figure 5.17: The graph of $g(x) = 1/x$ appears to be symmetric about the origin

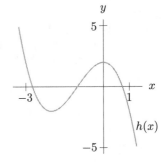

Figure 5.18: The graph of $h(x) = -x^3 - 3x^2 + 2$ is symmetric neither about the y-axis nor about the origin

From the graphs it appears that f is symmetric about the y-axis (even symmetry), g is symmetric about the origin (odd symmetry), and h has neither type of symmetry. However, how can we be sure that $f(x)$ and $g(x)$ are really symmetric? We check algebraically.

If $f(-x) = f(x)$, then f has even symmetry. We check by substituting $-x$ in for x:

$$f(-x) = |-x|$$
$$= |x|$$
$$= f(x).$$

Thus, f does have even symmetry.

If $g(-x) = -g(x)$, then g is symmetric about the origin. We check by substituting $-x$ for x:

$$g(-x) = \frac{1}{-x}$$
$$= -\frac{1}{x}$$
$$= -g(x).$$

Thus, g is symmetric about the origin.

The graph of h does not exhibit odd or even symmetry. To confirm, look at an example, say $x = 1$:

$$h(1) = -1^3 - 3 \cdot 1^2 + 2 = -2.$$

Now substitute $x = -1$, giving

$$h(-1) = -(-1)^3 - 3 \cdot (-1)^2 + 2 = 0.$$

Thus $h(1) \neq h(-1)$, so the function is not symmetric about the y-axis. Also, $h(-1) \neq -h(1)$, so the function is not symmetric about the origin.

Combining Shifts and Reflections

We can combine the horizontal and vertical shifts from Section 5.1 with the horizontal and vertical reflections of this section to make more complex transformations of functions

Example 5   A cold yam is placed in a hot oven. Newton's Law of Heating tells us that the difference between the oven's temperature and the yam's temperature decays exponentially with time. The yam's temperature is initially $0°F$, the oven's temperature is $300°F$, and the temperature difference decreases by 3% per minute. Find a formula for $Y(t)$, the yam's temperature at time t.

Solution   Let $D(t)$ be the difference between the oven's temperature and the yam's temperature, which is given by an exponential function $D(t) = ab^t$. The initial temperature difference is $300°F - 0°F = 300°F$, so $a = 300$. The temperature difference decreases by 3% per minute, so $b = 1 - 0.03 = 0.97$. Thus,

$$D(t) = 300(0.97)^t.$$

If the yam's temperature is represented by $Y(t)$, then the temperature difference is given by

$$D(t) = 300 - Y(t),$$

so, solving for $Y(t)$, we have

$$Y(t) = 300 - D(t),$$

giving

$$Y(t) = 300 - 300(0.97)^t.$$

Writing $Y(t)$ in the form

$$Y(t) = \underbrace{-D(t)}_{\text{Reflect}} + \underbrace{300}_{\text{Shift}}$$

shows that the graph of Y is obtained by reflecting the graph of D about the t-axis and then shifting it vertically up 300 units. Notice that the horizontal asymptote of D, which is on the t-axis, is also shifted upward, resulting in a horizontal asymptote at $300°F$ for Y.

Figures 5.19 and 5.20 give the graphs of D and Y. Figure 5.20 shows that the yam heats up rapidly at first and then its temperature levels off toward $300°F$, the oven temperature.

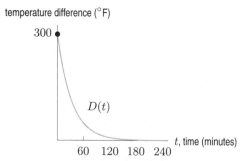

Figure 5.19: Graph of $D(t) = 300(0.97)^t$, the temperature difference between the yam and the oven

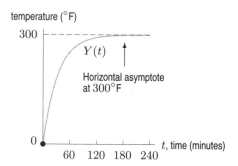

Figure 5.20: The transformation $Y(t) = -D(t) + 300$, where $D(t) = 300(0.97)^t$

Note that the temperature difference, D, is a decreasing function, so its average rate of change is negative. However, Y, the yam's temperature, is an increasing function, so its average rate of change is positive. Reflecting the graph of D about the t-axis to obtain the graph of Y changed the sign of the average rate of change.

Exercises and Problems for Section 5.2

Exercises

1. The graph of $y = f(x)$ contains the point $(2, -3)$. What point must lie on the reflected graph if the graph is reflected

  (a) About the y-axis?   **(b)** About the x-axis?

2. The graph of $P = g(t)$ contains the point $(-1, -5)$.

  (a) If the graph has even symmetry, which other point must lie on the graph?
  (b) What point must lie on the graph of $-g(t)$?

3. The graph of $H(x)$ is symmetric about the origin. If $H(-3) = 7$, what is $H(3)$?

4. The range of $Q(x)$ is $-2 \leq Q(x) \leq 12$. What is the range of $-Q(x)$?

5. If the graph of $y = e^x$ is reflected about the x-axis, what is the formula for the resulting graph? Check by graphing both functions together.

6. If the graph of $y = e^x$ is reflected about the y-axis, what is the formula for the resulting graph? Check by graphing both functions together.

7. Complete the following tables using $f(p) = p^2 + 2p - 3$, and $g(p) = f(-p)$, and $h(p) = -f(p)$. Graph the three functions. Explain how the graphs of g and h are related to the graph of f.

p	-3	-2	-1	0	1	2	3
$f(p)$							

p	-3	-2	-1	0	1	2	3
$g(p)$							

p	-3	-2	-1	0	1	2	3
$h(p)$							

8. Graph $y = f(x) = 4^x$ and $y = f(-x)$ on the same set of axes. How are these graphs related? Give an explicit formula for $y = f(-x)$.

9. Graph $y = g(x) = \left(\frac{1}{3}\right)^x$ and $y = -g(x)$ on the same set of axes. How are these graphs related? Give an explicit formula for $y = -g(x)$.

Give a formula and graph for each of the transformations of $m(n) = n^2 - 4n + 5$ in Exercises 10–13.

10. $y = m(-n)$

11. $y = -m(n)$

12. $y = -m(-n)$

13. $y = -m(-n) + 3$

Give a formula and graph for each of the transformations of $k(w) = 3^w$ in Exercises 14–19.

14. $y = k(-w)$

15. $y = -k(w)$

16. $y = -k(-w)$

17. $y = -k(w - 2)$

18. $y = k(-w) + 4$

19. $y = -k(-w) - 1$

In Exercises 20–23, show that the function is even, odd, or neither.

20. $f(x) = 7x^2 - 2x + 1$

21. $f(x) = 4x^7 - 3x^5$

22. $f(x) = 8x^6 + 12x^2$

23. $f(x) = x^5 + 3x^3 - 2$

Problems

24. (a) Graph the function obtained from $f(x) = x^3$ by first reflecting about the x-axis, then translating up two units. Write a formula for the resulting function.
  (b) Graph the function obtained from f by first translating up two units, then reflecting about the x-axis. Write a formula for the resulting function.
  (c) Are the functions in parts (a) and (b) the same?

25. (a) Graph the function obtained from $g(x) = 2^x$ by first reflecting about the y-axis, then translating down three units. Write a formula for the resulting function.

  (b) Graph the function obtained from g by first translating down three units, then reflecting about the y-axis. Write a formula for the resulting function.
  (c) Are the functions in parts (a) and (b) the same?

26. If the graph of a line $y = b + mx$ is reflected about the y-axis, what are the slope and intercepts of the resulting line?

27. Graph $y = \log(1/x)$ and $y = \log x$ on the same axes. How are the two graphs related? Use the properties of logarithms to explain the relationship algebraically.

28. The function $d(t)$ graphed in Figure 5.21 gives the winter temperature in °F at a high school, t hours after midnight.

(a) Describe in words the heating schedule for this building during the winter months.
(b) Graph $c(t) = 142 - d(t)$.
(c) Explain why c might describe the cooling schedule for summer months.

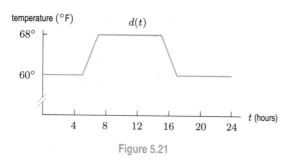

Figure 5.21

29. Using Figure 5.22, match the formulas (i)–(vi) with a graph from (a)–(f).

(i) $y = f(-x)$ (ii) $y = -f(x)$
(iii) $y = f(-x) + 3$ (iv) $y = -f(x - 1)$
(v) $y = -f(-x)$ (vi) $y = -2 - f(x)$

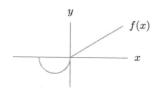

Figure 5.22

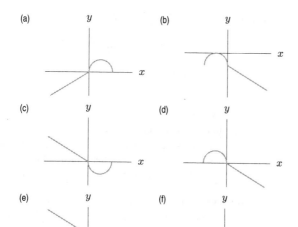

30. In Table 5.8, fill in as many y-values as you can if you know that f is

(a)   An even function   (b)   An odd function.

Table 5.8

x	−3	−2	−1	0	1	2	3
y	5		−4			−8	

31. Figure 5.23 shows the graph of a function f in the second quadrant. In each of the following cases, sketch $y = f(x)$, given that f is symmetric about

(a)   The y-axis.   (b)   The origin.   (c)   The line $y = x$.

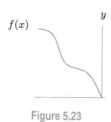

Figure 5.23

32. For each table, decide whether the function could be symmetric about the y-axis, about the origin, or neither.

(a)

x	−3	−2	−1	0	1	2	3
$f(x)$	6	1	−2	−3	−2	1	6

(b)

x	−3	−2	−1	0	1	2	3
$g(x)$	−8.1	−2.4	−0.3	0	0.3	2.4	8.1

(c)

x	−3	−2	−1	0	1	2	3
$f(x) + g(x)$	−2.1	−1.4	−2.3	−3	−1.7	3.4	14.1

(d)

x	−3	−2	−1	0	1	2	3
$f(x + 1)$	1	−2	−3	−2	1	6	13

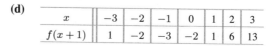

33. A function is called symmetric about the line $y = x$ if interchanging x and y gives the same graph. The simplest example is the function $y = x$. Graph another straight line that is symmetric about the line $y = x$ and give its equation.

34. Show that the graph of the function h is symmetric about the origin, given that

$$h(x) = \frac{1 + x^2}{x - x^3}.$$

35. Comment on the following justification that the function $f(x) = x^3 - x^2 + 1$ is an even function: Because $f(0) = 1 \neq -f(0)$, we know that $f(x)$ is not odd. If a function is not odd, it must be even.

36. Is it possible for an odd function whose domain is all real numbers to be strictly concave up?

37. If f is an odd function and defined at $x = 0$, what is the value of $f(0)$? Explain how you can use this result to show that $c(x) = x + 1$ and $d(x) = 2^x$ are not odd.

38. In the first quadrant an even function is increasing and concave down. What can you say about the function's behavior in the second quadrant?

39. Show that the power function $f(x) = x^{1/3}$ is odd. Give a counterexample to the statement that all power functions of the form $f(x) = x^p$ are odd.

40. Graph $s(x) = 2^x + \left(\frac{1}{2}\right)^x$, $c(x) = 2^x - \left(\frac{1}{2}\right)^x$, and $n(x) = 2^x - \left(\frac{1}{2}\right)^{x-1}$. State whether you think these functions are even, odd or neither. Show that your statements are true using algebra. That is, prove or disprove statements such as $s(-x) = s(x)$.

41. There are functions which are *neither* even nor odd. Is there a function that is *both* even and odd?

42. Some functions are symmetric about the y-axis. Is it possible for a function to be symmetric about the x-axis?

5.3 VERTICAL STRETCHES AND COMPRESSIONS

We have studied translations and reflections of graphs. In this section, we consider vertical stretches and compressions of graphs. As with a vertical translation, a vertical stretch or compression of a function is represented by an outside change to its formula.

Vertical Stretch: A Stereo Amplifier

A stereo amplifier takes a weak signal from a cassette-tape deck, compact disc player, or radio tuner, and transforms it into a stronger signal to power a set of speakers.

Figure 5.24 shows a graph of a typical radio signal (in volts) as a function of time, t, both before and after amplification. In this illustration, the amplifier has boosted the strength of the signal by a factor of 3. (The amount of amplification, or *gain*, of most stereos is considerably greater than this.)

Notice that the wave crests of the amplified signal are 3 times as high as those of the original signal; similarly, the amplified wave troughs are 3 times deeper than the original wave troughs. If f is the original signal function and V is the amplified signal function, then

$$\underbrace{\text{Amplified signal strength at time } t}_{V(t)} = 3 \cdot \underbrace{\text{Original signal strength at time } t}_{f(t)},$$

so we have

$$V(t) = 3 \cdot f(t).$$

This formula tells us that values of the amplified signal function are 3 times the values of the original signal. The graph of V is the graph of f stretched vertically by a factor of 3. As expected, a vertical stretch of the graph of $f(t)$ corresponds to an outside change in the formula.

Notice that the t-intercepts remain fixed under a vertical stretch, because the f-value of these points is 0, which is unchanged when multiplied by 3.

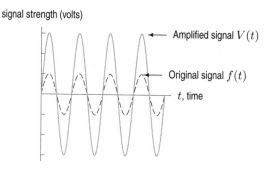

Figure 5.24: A stereo amplifier transforms a weak signal into a signal 3 times as strong

Negative Stretch Factor

What happens if we multiply a function by a negative stretch factor? Figure 5.25 gives a graph of a function $y = f(x)$, together with a graph of $y = -2 \cdot f(x)$. The stretch factor of f is $k = -2$. We think of $y = -2f(x)$ as a combination of two separate transformations of $y = f(x)$. First, the graph is stretched by a factor of 2, then it is reflected across the x-axis.

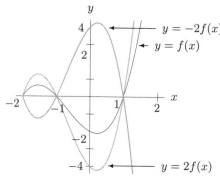

Figure 5.25: The graph of $y = -2f(x)$ is a vertically stretched version of the graph of $y = f(x)$ that has been reflected across the x-axis

Formula for Vertical Stretch or Compression

Generalizing the examples gives the following result:

> If f is a function and k is a constant, then the graph of $y = k \cdot f(x)$ is the graph of $y = f(x)$
> - Vertically stretched by a factor of k, if $k > 1$.
> - Vertically compressed by a factor of k, if $0 < k < 1$.
> - Vertically stretched or compressed by a factor $|k|$ and reflected across x-axis, if $k < 0$.

Example 1   A yam is placed in a 300°F oven. Suppose that Table 5.9 gives values of $H = r(t)$, the yam's temperature t minutes after being placed in the oven. Figure 5.26 shows these data points with a curve drawn in to emphasize the trend.

Table 5.9   *Temperature of a yam*

t, time (min)	$r(t)$, temperature (°F)
0	0
10	150
20	225
30	263
40	281
50	291
60	295

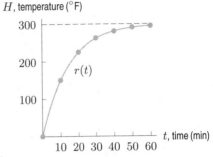

Figure 5.26: The temperature of a yam at time t

(a) Describe the function r in words. What do the data indicate about the yam's temperature?
(b) Make a table of values for $q(t) = 1.5r(t)$. Sketch a graph of this new function. Under what condition might q describe the yam's temperature?

Solution   (a) The function r is increasing and concave down. The yam starts out at 0°F and warms up quickly, reaching 150°F after 10 minutes. It continues to heat up, although more slowly, climbing by 75°F in the next 10 minutes and by 38°F in the 10 minutes after that. The temperature levels off around 300°F, the oven's temperature, represented by a horizontal asymptote.
(b) We calculate values of $q(t)$ from values of r. For example, Table 5.9 gives $r(0) = 0$ and $r(10) = 150$. Thus,

$$q(0) = 1.5r(0)$$
$$= 1.5 \cdot 0$$
$$= 0.$$

Similarly, $q(10) = 1.5(150) = 225$, and so on. The values for $q(t)$ are 1.5 times as large as the corresponding values for $r(t)$.

The data in Table 5.10 are plotted in Figure 5.27. The graph of q is a vertically stretched version of the graph of r, because the stretch factor of $k = 1.5$ is larger than 1. The horizontal asymptote of r was $H = 300$, so the horizontal asymptote of q is $H = 1.5 \cdot 300 = 450$. This suggests that the yam has been placed in a 450°F oven instead of a 300°F oven.

Table 5.10   *Values of $q(t) = 1.5r(t)$*

t, time (min)	$q(t)$, temperature (°F)
0	0
10	225
20	337.5
30	394.5
40	421.5
50	436.5
60	442.5

Figure 5.27: Graph of $q(t) = 1.5r(t)$

Stretch Factors and Average Rates of Change

Consider again the graph of the radio signal and its amplification in Figure 5.24. Notice that the amplified signal, V, is increasing on the same intervals as the original signal, f. Similarly, both functions decrease on the same intervals.

Stretching or compressing a function vertically does not change the intervals on which the function increases or decreases. However, the average rate of change of a function, visible in the steepness of the graph, is altered by a vertical stretch or compression.

Example 2   In Example 1, the function $H = r(t)$ gives the temperature (in °F) of a yam placed in a 300°F oven. The function $q(t) = 1.5r(t)$ gives the temperature of the yam placed in a 450°F oven.
(a) Calculate the average rate of change of r over 10-minute intervals. What does this tell you about the yam's temperature?
(b) Now calculate the average rate of change of q over 10-minute intervals. What does this tell you about the yam's temperature?

Solution   (a) On the first interval, from $t = 0$ to $t = 10$, we have

$$\begin{aligned} \text{Average rate of change} \\ \text{of temperature, } r \end{aligned} = \frac{\Delta H}{\Delta t} = \frac{r(10) - r(0)}{10 - 0}$$

$$= \frac{150 - 0}{10} \quad \text{(referring to Table 5.9)}$$

$$= 15°\text{F/min}.$$

Thus, during the first 10 minute interval, the yam's temperature increased at an average rate of 15°F per minute.

On the second time interval from $t = 10$ to $t = 20$,

$$\begin{aligned} \text{Average rate of change} \\ \text{of temperature} \end{aligned} = \frac{\Delta H}{\Delta t} = \frac{225 - 150}{10} = 7.5°\text{F/min},$$

and on the third interval from $t = 20$ to $t = 30$,

$$\begin{aligned} \text{Average rate of change} \\ \text{of temperature} \end{aligned} = \frac{\Delta H}{\Delta t} = \frac{263 - 225}{10} = 3.8°\text{F/min}.$$

See Table 5.11.

Table 5.11   *The average rate of change of yam's temperature, $r(t)$*

Time interval (min)	0 − 10	10 − 20	20 − 30	30 − 40	40 − 50	50 − 60
Average rate of change of r (°F/min)	15	7.5	3.8	1.8	1.0	0.4

(b) The data in Table 5.10 was used to calculate the average rate of change of $q(t) = 1.5r(t)$ in Table 5.12.

Table 5.12   *The average rate of change of yam's temperature, $q(t)$*

Time interval (min)	0 − 10	10 − 20	20 − 30	30 − 40	40 − 50	50 − 60
Average rate of change of q (°F/min)	22.5	11.25	5.7	2.7	1.5	0.6

Comparing the average rates of change on each 10-minute interval, we see that q's average rate of change is 1.5 times r's. Thus, q depicts a yam whose temperature increases more quickly than r does.

In the last example, multiplying a function by a stretch factor k has the effect of multiplying the function's average rate of change on each interval by the same factor. We check this statement algebraically for the function $g(x) = k \cdot f(x)$. On the interval from a to b,

$$\begin{array}{l} \text{Average rate of change} \\ \text{of } y = g(x) \end{array} = \frac{\Delta y}{\Delta x} = \frac{g(b) - g(a)}{b - a}.$$

But $g(b) = k \cdot f(b)$ and $g(a) = k \cdot f(a)$. Thus,

$$\begin{array}{l} \text{Average rate of change} \\ \text{of } y = g(x) \end{array} = \frac{\Delta y}{\Delta x} = \frac{k \cdot f(b) - k \cdot f(a)}{b - a}$$

$$= k \cdot \frac{f(b) - f(a)}{b - a} \quad \text{(factoring out } k\text{)}$$

$$= k \cdot \left(\begin{array}{c} \text{Average rate of change} \\ \text{of } f \end{array} \right).$$

In general, we have the following result:

If $g(x) = k \cdot f(x)$, then on any interval,

$$\text{Average rate of change of } g = k \cdot (\text{Average rate of change of } f).$$

Combining Transformations

Any transformations of functions can be combined.

Example 3   The function $y = f(x)$ is graphed in Figure 5.28. Graph the function $g(x) = -\frac{1}{2}f(x + 3) - 1$.

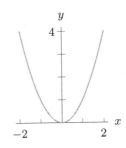

Figure 5.28: Graph of $y = f(x)$

Solution   To combine several transformations, always work from inside the parentheses outward as in Figure 5.29. The graphs corresponding to each step are shown in Figure 5.30. Note that we did not need a formula for f to graph g.

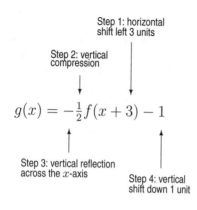

Step 1: horizontal
shift left 3 units

Step 2: vertical
compression

$$g(x) = -\tfrac{1}{2} f(x+3) - 1$$

Step 3: vertical reflection
across the x-axis

Step 4: vertical
shift down 1 unit

Figure 5.29

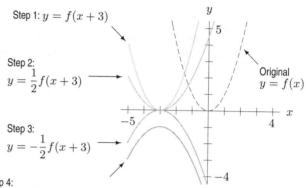

Step 1: $y = f(x+3)$

Step 2:
$y = \dfrac{1}{2} f(x+3)$

Step 3:
$y = -\dfrac{1}{2} f(x+3)$

Step 4:
$g(x) = -\dfrac{1}{2} f(x+3) - 1$

Original
$y = f(x)$

Figure 5.30: The graph of $y = f(x)$ transformed in four steps into $g(x) = -(1/2)f(x+3) - 1$

Exercises and Problems for Section 5.3

Exercises

1. Let $y = f(x)$. Write a formula for the transformation which both increases the y-value by a factor of 10 and shifts the graph to the right by 2 units.

2. The graph of the function $g(x)$ contains the point $(5, \tfrac{1}{3})$. What point must be on the graph of $y = 3g(x) + 1$?

3. The range of the function $C(x)$ is $-1 \le C(x) \le 1$. What is the range of $0.25C(x)$?

In Exercises 4–7, graph and label $f(x)$, $4f(x)$, $-\tfrac{1}{2}f(x)$, and $-5f(x)$ on the same axes.

4. $f(x) = \sqrt{x}$

5. $f(x) = -x^2 + 7x$

6. $f(x) = e^x$

7. $f(x) = \ln x$

8. Using Table 5.13, make tables for the following transformations of f on an appropriate domain.

(a) $\tfrac{1}{2}f(x)$ (b) $-2f(x+1)$ (c) $f(x) + 5$
(d) $f(x - 2)$ (e) $f(-x)$ (f) $-f(x)$

Table 5.13

x	-3	-2	-1	0	1	2	3
$f(x)$	2	3	7	-1	-3	4	8

9. Using Table 5.14, create a table of values for

(a) $f(-x)$ (b) $-f(x)$ (c) $3f(x)$

(d) Which of these tables from parts (a), (b), and (c) represents an even function?

Table 5.14

x	-4	-3	-2	-1	0	1	2	3	4
$f(x)$	13	6	1	-2	-3	-2	1	6	13

10. Figure 5.31 is a graph of $y = x^{3/2}$. Match the following functions with the graphs in Figure 5.32.

(a) $y = x^{3/2} - 1$ (b) $y = (x-1)^{3/2}$
(c) $y = 1 - x^{3/2}$ (d) $y = \tfrac{3}{2}x^{3/2}$

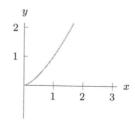

Figure 5.31

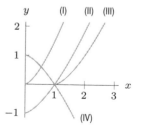

Figure 5.32

Without a calculator, graph the transformations in Exercises 11–16. Label at least three points.

11. $y = f(x + 3)$ if $f(x) = |x|$

12. $y = f(x) + 3$ if $f(x) = |x|$

13. $y = -g(x)$ if $g(x) = x^2$

14. $y = g(-x)$ if $g(x) = x^2$

15. $y = 3h(x)$ if $h(x) = 2^x$

16. $y = 0.5h(x)$ if $h(x) = 2^x$

17. Using Figure 5.33, match the functions (i)–(v) with a graph (a)–(i).

(i) $y = 2f(x)$ (ii) $y = \frac{1}{3}f(x)$

(iii) $y = -f(x) + 1$ (iv) $y = f(x + 2) + 1$

(v) $y = f(-x)$

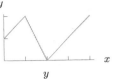
(a)

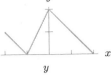
(b)

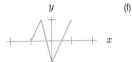
(c) (d)

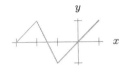
(e)

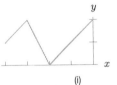
(f)

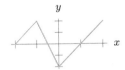
(g)

(h)

(i)

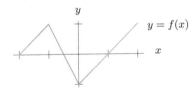

$y = f(x)$

Figure 5.33

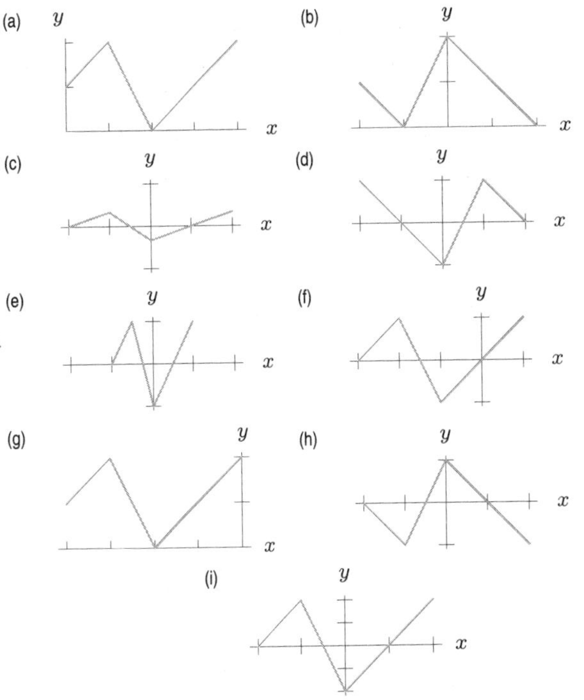

Problems

18. Describe the effect of the transformation $2f(x + 1) - 3$ on the graph of $y = f(x)$.

19. The function $s(t)$ gives the distance (miles) in terms of time (hours). If the average rate of change of $s(t)$ on $0 \leq t \leq 4$ is 70 mph, what is the average rate of change of $\frac{1}{2}s(t)$ on this interval?

In Problems 20–24, let $f(t) = 1/(1 + x^2)$. Graph the function given, labeling intercepts and asymptotes.

20. $y = f(t)$ **21.** $y = f(t - 3)$

22. $y = 0.5f(t)$ **23.** $y = -f(t)$

24. $y = f(t + 5) - 5$

25. The number of gallons of paint, $n = f(A)$, needed to cover a house is a function of the surface area, in ft². Match each story to one expression.

(a) I figured out how many gallons I needed and then bought two extra gallons just in case.

(b) I bought enough paint to cover my house twice.

(c) I bought enough paint to cover my house and my welcome sign, which measures 2 square feet.

(i) $2f(A)$ (ii) $f(A + 2)$ (iii) $f(A) + 2$

26. The US population in millions is $P(t)$ today and t is in years. Match each statement (I)–(IV) with one of the formulas (a)–(h).

I.   The population 10 years before today.

II. Today's population plus 10 million immigrants.

III. Ten percent of the population we have today.

IV. The population after 100,000 people have emigrated.

(a) $P(t) - 10$ (b) $P(t - 10)$ (c) $0.1P(t)$

(d) $P(t) + 10$ (e) $P(t + 10)$ (f) $P(t)/0.1$

(g) $P(t) + 0.1$ (h) $P(t) - 0.1$

27. Let $R = P(t)$ be the number of rabbits living in the national park in month t. (See Example 5 on page 5.) What do the following expressions represent?

(a) $P(t + 1)$ (b) $2P(t)$

28. Without a calculator, match each formula (a)–(e) with a graph in Figure 5.34. There may be no answer or several answers.

(a) $y = 3 \cdot 2^x$ **(b)** $y = 5^{-x}$ **(c)** $y = -5^x$
(d) $y = 2 - 2^{-x}$ **(e)** $y = 1 - \left(\frac{1}{2}\right)^x$

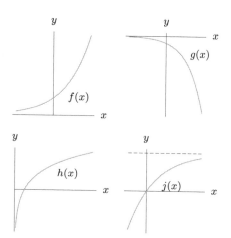

Figure 5.34

Graph the transformations of f in Problems 29–33 using Figure 5.35. Label the points corresponding to A and B.

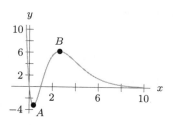

Figure 5.35

29. $y = f(x - 3)$ **30.** $y = f(x) - 3$

31. $y = f(-x)/3$ **32.** $y = -2f(x)$

33. $y = 5 - f(x + 5)$

34. Using Figure 5.36, find formulas, in terms of f, for the horizontal and vertical shifts of the graph of f in parts (a)–(c). What is the equation of each asymptote?

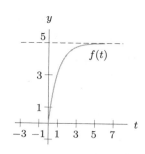

Figure 5.36

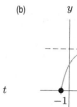

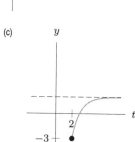

35. Using Figure 5.37, find formulas, in terms of f, for the transformations of f in parts (a)–(c).

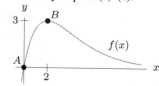

Figure 5.37

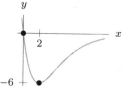

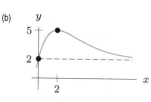

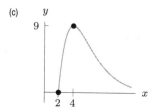

36. In Figure 5.38, the point b is labeled on the x-axis. On the y-axis, locate and label the output values:

(a) $f(b)$ **(b)** $-2f(b)$ **(c)** $-2f(-b)$

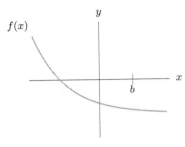

Figure 5.38

points on the graph of $y = f(x)$ stay fixed under these transformations? Compare the intervals on which all three functions are increasing and decreasing.

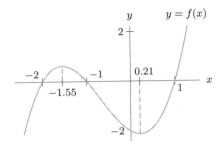

Figure 5.39

37. Figure 5.39 gives a graph of $y = f(x)$. Consider the transformations $y = \frac{1}{2}f(x)$ and $y = 2f(x)$. Which

38. Let $f(x) = e^x$ and $g(x) = 5e^{x-2}$. If $g(x) = kf(x)$, find k.

5.4 HORIZONTAL STRETCHES AND COMPRESSIONS

In Section 5.3, we observed that a vertical stretch of a function's graph corresponds to an outside change in its formula, specifically, multiplication by a stretch factor. Since horizontal changes generally correspond to inside changes, we expect that a horizontal stretch will correspond to a constant multiple of the inputs. This turns out to be the case.

Horizontal Stretch: A Lighthouse Beacon

The beacon in a lighthouse turns once per minute, and its beam sweeps across a beach house. Figure 5.40 gives a graph of $L(t)$, the intensity, or brightness, of the light striking the beach house as a function of time.

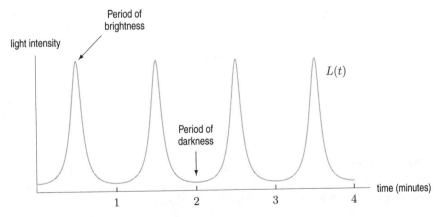

Figure 5.40: Light intensity or brightness, $L(t)$, as a function of time

Now suppose the lighthouse beacon turns twice as fast as before, so that its beam sweeps past the beach house twice instead of once each minute. The periods of brightness now occur twice

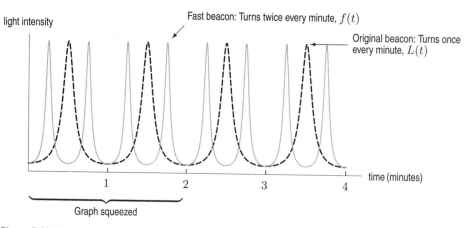

Figure 5.41: Comparing light intensity from the fast beacon, $f(t)$, to light intensity from the original beacon, $L(t)$

as often. See Figure 5.41. The graph of $f(t)$, the intensity of light from this faster beacon, is a horizontal squeezing or compression of the original graph of $L(t)$.

If the lighthouse beacon turns at half its original rate, so that its beam sweeps past the beach house once every two minutes instead of once every minute, the periods of brightness occur half as often as originally. Slowing the beacon's speed results in a horizontal stretch of the original graph, illustrated by the graph of $s(t)$, the light intensity of the slow beacon, in Figure 5.42.

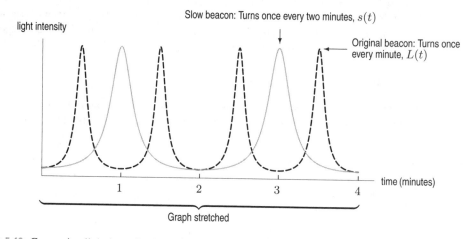

Figure 5.42: Comparing light intensity from the slow beacon, $s(t)$, to light intensity from the original beacon, $L(t)$

Formula for Horizontal Stretch or Compression

How are the formulas for the three light functions related? We expect that multiplying the function's input by a constant will horizontally stretch or compress its graph. The fast beacon corresponds to speeding up by a factor of 2, or multiplying the input times by 2. Thus

$$f(t) = L(2t).$$

Similarly for the slow beacon, the input times are multiplied by $1/2$, so

$$s(t) = L(\tfrac{1}{2}t).$$

Generalizing the lighthouse example gives the following result:

If f is a function and k a positive constant, then the graph of $y = f(kx)$ is the graph of f
- Horizontally compressed by a factor of $1/k$ if $k > 1$,
- Horizontally stretched by a factor of $1/k$ if $k < 1$.

If $k < 0$, then the graph of $y = f(kx)$ also involves a horizontal reflection about the y-axis.

Example 1   Values of the function $f(x)$ are in Table 5.15 and its graph is in Figure 5.43. Make a table and a graph of the function $g(x) = f(\frac{1}{2}x)$.

Table 5.15   *Values of $f(x)$*

x	$f(x)$
-3	0
-2	2
-1	0
0	-1
1	0
2	-1
3	1

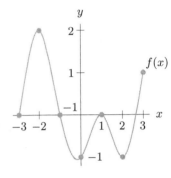

Figure 5.43

Solution   To make a table for $g(x) = f(\frac{1}{2}x)$, we substitute values for x. For example, if $x = 4$, then
$$g(4) = f(\tfrac{1}{2} \cdot 4) = f(2).$$
Table 5.15 shows that $f(2) = -1$, so
$$g(4) = f(2) = -1.$$
This result is recorded in Table 5.16. If $x = 6$, since Table 5.15 gives $f(3) = 1$, we have
$$g(6) = f(\tfrac{1}{2} \cdot 6) = f(3) = 1.$$
In Figure 5.44, we see that the graph of g is the graph of f stretched horizontally away from the y-axis. Substituting $x = 0$, gives
$$g(0) = f(\tfrac{1}{2} \cdot 0) = f(0) = -1,$$
so the y-intercept remains fixed (at -1) under a horizontal stretch.

Table 5.16   *Values of $g(x) = f(\frac{1}{2}x)$*

x	$g(x)$
-6	0
-4	2
-2	0
0	-1
2	0
4	-1
6	1

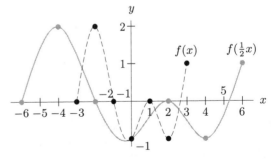

Figure 5.44: The graph of $g(x) = f(\frac{1}{2}x)$ is the graph of $y = f(x)$ stretched away from the y-axis by a factor of 2

Example 1 shows the effect of an inside multiple of $1/2$. The next example shows the effect on the graph of an inside multiple of 2.

Example 2   Let $f(x)$ be the function in Example 1. Make a table and a graph for the function $h(x) = f(2x)$.

Solution   We use Table 5.15 and the formula $h(x) = f(2x)$ to evaluate $h(x)$ at several values of x. For example, if $x = 1$, then

$$h(1) = f(2 \cdot 1) = f(2).$$

Table 5.15 shows that $f(2) = -1$, so $h(1) = -1$. These values are recorded in Table 5.17. Similarly, substituting $x = 1.5$, gives

$$h(1.5) = f(2 \cdot 1.5) = f(3) = 1.$$

Since $h(0) = f(2 \cdot 0) = f(0)$, the y-intercept remains fixed (at -1). In Figure 5.45 we see that the graph of h is the graph of f compressed by a factor of 2 horizontally toward the y-axis.

Table 5.17   *Values of $h(x) = f(2x)$*

x	$h(x)$
-1.5	0
-1.0	2
-0.5	0
0.0	-1
0.5	0
1.0	-1
1.5	1

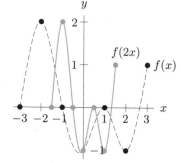

Figure 5.45: The graph of $h(x) = f(2x)$ is the graph of $y = f(x)$ compressed horizontally by a factor of 2

In Chapter 3, we used the function $P = 263e^{0.009t}$ to model the US population in millions. This function is a transformation of the exponential function $f(t) = e^t$, since we can write

$$P = 263e^{0.009t} = 263f(0.009t).$$

The US population is $f(t) = e^t$ stretched vertically by a factor of 263 and stretched horizontally by a factor of $1/0.009 \approx 111$.

Example 3   Match the functions $f(t) = e^t, g(t) = e^{0.5t}, h(t) = e^{0.8t}, j(t) = e^{2t}$ with the graphs in Figure 5.46.

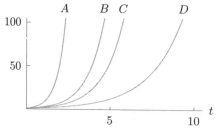

Figure 5.46

Solution   Since the function $j(t) = e^{2t}$ climbs fastest of the four and $g(t) = e^{0.5t}$ climbs slowest, graph A must be j and graph D must be g. Similarly, graph B is f and graph C is h.

Exercises and Problems for Section 5.4

Exercises

1. The point $(2, 3)$ lies on the graph of $g(x)$. What point must lie on the graph of $g(2x)$?

2. Describe the effect of the transformation $10f(\frac{1}{10}x)$ on the graph of $f(x)$.

3. Using Table 5.18, make a table of values for $f(\frac{1}{2}x)$ for an appropriate domain.

Table 5.18

x	-3	-2	-1	0	1	2	3
$f(x)$	2	3	7	-1	-3	4	8

4. Fill in all the blanks in Table 5.19 for which you have sufficient information.

Table 5.19

x	-3	-2	-1	0	1	2	3
$f(x)$	-4	-1	2	3	0	-3	-6
$f(\frac{1}{2}x)$							
$f(2x)$							

5. Graph $m(x) = e^x$, $n(x) = e^{2x}$, and $p(x) = 2e^x$ on the same axes and describe how the graphs of $n(x)$ and $p(x)$ compare with that of $m(x)$.

6. Graph $y = h(3x)$ if $h(x) = 2^x$.

In Exercises 7–9, graph and label $f(x)$, $f(\frac{1}{2}x)$, and $f(-3x)$ on the same axes between $x = -2$ and $x = 2$.

7. $f(x) = e^x + x^3 - 4x^2$

8. $f(x) = e^{x+7} + (x - 4)^3 - (x + 2)^2$

9. $f(x) = \ln(x^4 + 3x^2 + 4)$

10. Using Figure 5.47, match each function to a graph (if any) that represents it:

(i) $y = f(2x)$ (ii) $y = 2f(2x)$ (iii) $y = f(\frac{1}{2}x)$

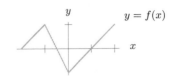

$y = f(x)$

Figure 5.47

(a)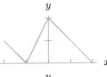

(b)

(c)

(d)

(e)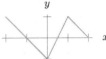

(f)

(g)

(h)

(i)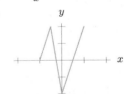

Problems

11. For the function $f(p)$ an input of 2 yields an output value of 4. What value of p would you use to have $f(3p) = 4$?

12. The domain of $l(x)$ is $-12 \leq x \leq 12$ and its range is $0 \leq l(x) \leq 3$. What are the domain and range of

   (a) $l(2x)$?   **(b)** $l(\frac{1}{2}x)$?

13. The point (a, b) lies on the graph of $y = f(x)$. If the graph is stretched away from the y-axis by a factor of d (where $d > 1$), and then translated upward by c units, what are the new coordinates for the point (a, b)?

In Problems 14–15, graph the transformation of f, the function in Figure 5.48.

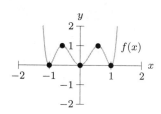

Figure 5.48

14. $y = -2f(x-1)$ **15.** $y = f(x/2) - 1$

16. Every day I take the same taxi over the same route from home to the train station. The trip is x miles, so the cost for the trip is $f(x)$. Match each story in (a)–(d) to a function in (i)–(iv) representing the amount paid to the driver.

    (a) I received a raise yesterday, so today I gave my driver a five dollar tip.

    (b) I had a new driver today and he got lost. He drove five extra miles and charged me for it.

    (c) I haven't paid my driver all week. Today is Friday and I'll pay what I owe for the week.

    (d) The meter in the taxi went crazy and showed five times the number of miles I actually traveled.

    (i) $5f(x)$ **(ii)** $f(x) + 5$

    (iii) $f(5x)$ **(iv)** $f(x+5)$

17. A company projects a total profit, $P(t)$ dollars, in year t. Explain the economic meaning of $r(t) = 0.5P(t)$ and $s(t) = P(0.5t)$.

18. Let $A = f(r)$ be the area of a circle of radius r.

    (a) Write a formula for $f(r)$.

    (b) Which expression represents the area of a circle whose radius is increased by 10%? Explain.

        (i) $0.10f(r)$ **(ii)** $f(r+0.10)$ **(iii)** $f(0.10r)$
        (iv) $f(1.1r)$ **(v)** $f(r)+0.10$

    (c) By what percent does the area increase if the radius is increased by 10%?

In Problems 19–20, state which graph represents

(a) $f(x)$ **(b)** $f(-2x)$ **(c)** $f(-\frac{1}{2}x)$ **(d)** $f(2x)$

19.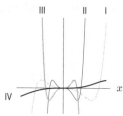

20.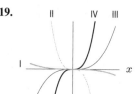

21. Find a formula for the function in Figure 5.50 as a transformation of the function f in Figure 5.49.

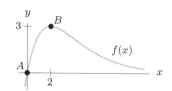

Figure 5.49

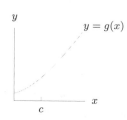

Figure 5.50

22. This problem investigates the effect of a horizontal stretch on the zeros of a function.

    (a) Graph $f(x) = 4 - x^2$. Mark the zeros of f on the graph.

    (b) Graph and find a formula for $g(x) = f(0.5x)$. What are the zeros of $g(x)$?

    (c) Graph and find a formula for $h(x) = f(2x)$. What are the zeros of $h(x)$?

    (d) Without graphing, what are the zeros of $f(10x)$?

23. In Figure 5.51, the point c is labeled on the x-axis. On the y-axis, locate and label output values:

    (a) $g(c)$ **(b)** $2g(c)$ **(c)** $g(2c)$

Figure 5.51

Table 5.20 gives values of $T = f(d)$, the average temperature (in °C) at a depth d meters in a borehole in Belleterre, Quebec. The functions in Problems 24–29 describe boreholes near Belleterre. Construct a table of values for each function and describe in words what it tells you about the borehole.[1]

24. $g(d) = f(d) - 3$

25. $h(d) = f(d + 5)$

26. $m(d) = f(d - 10)$

27. $n(d) = 1.5f(d)$

28. $p(d) = f(0.8d)$

29. $q(d) = 1.5f(d) + 2$

Table 5.20

d, depth (m)	25	50	75	100
T, temp (°C)	5.5	5.2	5.1	5.1
d, depth (m)	125	150	175	200
T, temp (°C)	5.3	5.5	5.75	6

5.5 THE FAMILY OF QUADRATIC FUNCTIONS

In Chapter 2, we looked at the example of a baseball which is popped up by a batter. The height of the ball above the ground was modeled by the quadratic function $y = f(t) = -16t^2 + 64t + 3$, where t is time in seconds after the ball leaves the bat, and y is in feet. The function is graphed in Figure 5.52.

The point on the graph with the largest y value appears to be $(2, 67)$. (We show this in Example 5 on page 229.) This means that the baseball reaches its maximum height of 67 feet 2 seconds after being hit. The maximum point $(2, 67)$ is called the *vertex*.

The graph of a quadratic function is called a *parabola*; its maximum (or minimum, if the parabola opens upward) is the vertex.

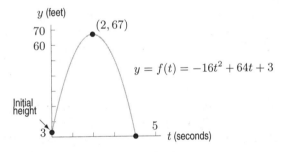

Figure 5.52: Height of baseball at time t

The Vertex of a Parabola

The graph of the function $y = x^2$ is a parabola with vertex at the origin. All other functions in the quadratic family turn out to be transformations of this function. Let's first graph a quadratic function of the form $y = a(x - h)^2 + k$ and locate its vertex.

Example 1   Let $f(x) = x^2$ and $g(x) = -2(x + 1)^2 + 3$.

(a) Express the function g in terms of the function f.

(b) Sketch a graph of f. Transform the graph of f into the graph of g.

(c) Multiply out and simplify the formula for g.

(d) Explain how the formula for g can be used to obtain the vertex of the graph of g.

---

[1] Hugo Beltrami of St. Francis Xavier University and David Chapman of the University of Utah posted this data at http://esrc.stfx.ca/borehole/node3.html, accessed December 20, 2005.

Solution   (a) Since $f(x+1) = (x+1)^2$, we have

$$g(x) = -2f(x+1) + 3.$$

(b) The graph of $f(x) = x^2$ is shown at the left in Figure 5.53. The graph of g is obtained from the graph of f in four steps, as shown in Figure 5.53.

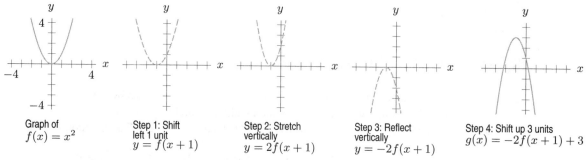

| Graph of $f(x) = x^2$ | Step 1: Shift left 1 unit $y = f(x+1)$ | Step 2: Stretch vertically $y = 2f(x+1)$ | Step 3: Reflect vertically $y = -2f(x+1)$ | Step 4: Shift up 3 units $g(x) = -2f(x+1) + 3$ |

Figure 5.53: The graph of $f(x) = x^2$, on the left, is transformed in four steps into the graph of $g(x) = -2(x+1)^2 + 3$, on the right

(c) Multiplying out gives $g(x) = -2(x^2 + 2x + 1) + 3 = -2x^2 - 4x + 1$

(d) The vertex of the graph of f is $(0,0)$. In Step 1 the vertex shifts 1 unit to the left (because of the $(x+1)$ in the formula), and in Step 4 the vertex shifts 3 units up (because of the $+3$ in the formula). Thus, the vertex of the graph of g is at $(-1, 3)$.

In general, the graph of $g(x) = a(x-h)^2 + k$ is obtained from the graph of $f(x) = x^2$ by shifting horizontally $|h|$ units, stretching vertically by a factor of a (and reflecting about the x-axis if $a < 0$), and shifting vertically $|k|$ units. In the process, the vertex is shifted from $(0, 0)$ to the point (h, k). The graph of the function is symmetrical about a vertical line through the vertex, called the *axis of symmetry*.

Formulas for Quadratic Functions

The function g in Example 1 can be written in two ways:

$$g(x) = -2(x+1)^2 + 3$$

and

$$g(x) = -2x^2 - 4x + 1.$$

The first version is helpful for understanding the graph of the quadratic function and finding its vertex. In general, we have the following:

> The **standard form** for a **quadratic function** is
>
> $$y = ax^2 + bx + c, \quad \text{where } a, \ b, \ c \text{ are constants, } a \neq 0.$$
>
> The **vertex form** is
>
> $$y = a(x - h)^2 + k, \quad \text{where } a, \ h, \ k \text{ are constants, } a \neq 0.$$
>
> The graph of a quadratic function is called a **parabola**. The parabola
> - Has vertex (h, k)
> - Has axis of symmetry $x = h$
> - Opens upward if $a > 0$ or downward if $a < 0$

Thus, any quadratic function can be expressed in both standard form and vertex form. To convert from vertex form to standard form, we multiply out the squared term. To convert from standard form to vertex form, we *complete the square*.

Example 2 Put these quadratic functions into vertex form by completing the square and then graph them.

(a) $s(x) = x^2 - 6x + 8$ (b) $t(x) = -4x^2 - 12x - 8$

Solution

(a) To complete the square,[2] find the square of half of the coefficient of the x-term, $(-6/2)^2 = 9$. Add and subtract this number after the x-term:

$$s(x) = \underbrace{x^2 - 6x + 9}_{\text{Perfect square}} -9 + 8,$$

so

$$s(x) = (x - 3)^2 - 1.$$

The vertex of s is $(3, -1)$ and the axis of symmetry is the vertical line $x = 3$. There is no vertical stretch since $a = 1$, and the parabola opens upward. See Figure 5.54.

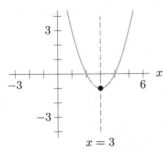

Figure 5.54: $s(x) = x^2 - 6x + 8$

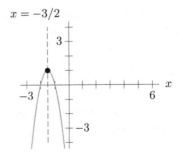

Figure 5.55: $t(x) = -4x^2 - 12x - 8$

---

[2]A more detailed explanation of this method is in the Tools section for this chapter.

(b) To complete the square, first factor out -4, the coefficient of x^2, giving

$$t(x) = -4(x^2 + 3x + 2).$$

Now add and subtract the square of half the coefficient of the x-term, $(3/2)^2 = 9/4$, inside the parentheses. This gives

$$t(x) = -4\left(\underbrace{x^2 + 3x + \frac{9}{4}}_{\text{Perfect square}} - \frac{9}{4} + 2\right)$$

$$t(x) = -4\left(\left(x + \frac{3}{2}\right)^2 - \frac{1}{4}\right)$$

$$t(x) = -4\left(x + \frac{3}{2}\right)^2 + 1.$$

The vertex of t is $(-3/2, 1)$, the axis of symmetry is $x = -3/2$, the vertical stretch factor is 4, and the parabola opens downward. See Figure 5.55.

Finding a Formula From a Graph

If we know the vertex of a quadratic function and one other point, we can use the vertex form to find its formula.

Example 3   Find the formula for the quadratic function graphed in Figure 5.56.

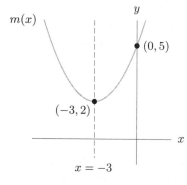

Figure 5.56

Solution   Since the vertex is given, we use the form $m(x) = a(x - h)^2 + k$ and find a, h, and k. The vertex is $(-3, 2)$, so $h = -3$ and $k = 2$. Thus,

$$m(x) = a(x - (-3))^2 + 2,$$

so

$$m(x) = a(x + 3)^2 + 2.$$

To find a, use the y-intercept $(0, 5)$. Substitute $x = 0$ and $y = m(0) = 5$ into the formula for $m(x)$ and solve for a:

$$5 = a(0 + 3)^2 + 2$$
$$3 = 9a$$
$$a = \frac{1}{3}.$$

Thus, the formula is

$$m(x) = \frac{1}{3}(x+3)^2 + 2.$$

If we want the formula in standard form, we multiply out:

$$m(x) = \frac{1}{3}x^2 + 2x + 5.$$

Example 4   Find the equation of the parabola in Figure 5.57 using the factored form.

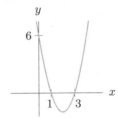

Figure 5.57

Solution   Since the parabola has x-intercepts at $x = 1$ and $x = 3$, its formula can be written as

$$y = a(x-1)(x-3).$$

Substituting $x = 0, y = 6$ gives

$$6 = a(3)$$
$$a = 2.$$

Thus, the equation is

$$y = 2(x-1)(x-3).$$

Applications of Quadratic Functions

In applications, it is often useful to find the maximum or minimum value of a quadratic function. First, we return to the baseball example which started this section.

Example 5   For t in seconds, the height of a baseball in feet is given by the formula

$$y = f(t) = -16t^2 + 64t + 3.$$

Using algebra, find the maximum height reached by the baseball and the time at which the ball reaches the ground.

Solution   To find the maximum height, complete the square to find the vertex:

$$\begin{aligned} y = f(t) &= -16(t^2 - 4t) + 3 \\ &= -16(t^2 - 4t + 4 - 4) + 3 \\ &= -16(t^2 - 4t + 4) - 16(-4) + 3 \\ &= -16(t-2)^2 + 16 \cdot 4 + 3 \\ &= -16(t-2)^2 + 67. \end{aligned}$$

Thus, the vertex is at the point $(2, 67)$. This means that the ball reaches it maximum height of 67 feet at $t = 2$ seconds.

The time at which the ball hits the ground is found by solving $f(t) = 0$. We have

$$-16(t-2)^2 + 67 = 0$$
$$(t-2)^2 = \frac{67}{16}$$
$$t - 2 = \pm\sqrt{\frac{67}{16}} \approx \pm 2.046.$$

The solutions are $t \approx -0.046$ and $t \approx 4.046$. Since the ball was thrown at $t = 0$, we want $t \geq 0$. Thus, the ball hits the ground approximately 4.046 seconds after being hit.

Example 6   A city decides to make a park by fencing off a section of riverfront property. Funds are allotted to provide 80 meters of fence. The area enclosed will be a rectangle, but only three sides will be enclosed by fence—the other side will be bound by the river. What is the maximum area that can be enclosed in this way?

Solution   Two sides are perpendicular to the bank of the river and have equal length, which we call h. The other side is parallel to the bank of the river. Call its length b. See Figure 5.58. Since the fence is 80 meters long,

$$2h + b = 80$$
$$b = 80 - 2h.$$

The area of the park, A, is the product of the lengths of two adjacent sides, so

$$A = bh = (80 - 2h)h$$
$$= -2h^2 + 80h.$$

The function $A = -2h^2 + 80h$ is quadratic. Since the coefficient of h^2 is negative, the parabola opens downward and we have a maximum at the vertex. The zeros of this quadratic function are $h = 0$ and $h = 40$, so the axis of symmetry, which is midway between the zeros, is $h = 20$. The vertex of a parabola occurs on its axis of symmetry. Thus, substituting $h = 20$ gives the maximum area:

$$A = (80 - 2 \cdot 20)20 = (80 - 40)20 = 40 \cdot 20 = 800 \text{ meter}^2.$$

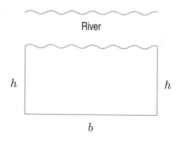

Figure 5.58

Exercises and Problems for Section 5.5

Exercises

For the quadratic functions in Exercises 1–2, state the coordinates of the vertex, the axis of symmetry, and whether the parabola opens upward or downward.

1. $f(x) = 3(x-1)^2 + 2$

2. $g(x) = -(x+3)^2 - 4$

3. Sketch the quadratic functions given in standard form. Identify the values of the parameters a, b, and c. Label the zeros, axis of symmetry, vertex, and y-intercept.

   (a) $g(x) = x^2 + 3$ (b) $f(x) = -2x^2 + 4x + 16$

4. Find the vertex and axis of symmetry of the graph of $v(t) = t^2 + 11t - 4$.

5. Find the vertex and axis of symmetry of the graph of $w(x) = -3x^2 - 30x + 31$.

6. Show that the function $y = -x^2 + 7x - 13$ has no real zeros.

7. Find the value of k so that the graph of $y = (x-3)^2 + k$ passes through the point $(6, 13)$.

8. The parabola $y = ax^2 + k$ has vertex $(0, -2)$ and passes through the point $(3, 4)$. Find its equation.

In Exercises 9–14, find a formula for the parabola.

9.
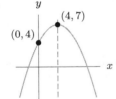

10.
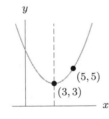

11.
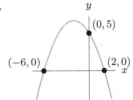

12.
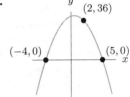

13.
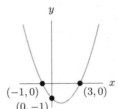

14.
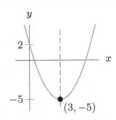

For Exercises 15–18, convert the quadratic functions to vertex form by completing the square. Identify the vertex and the axis of symmetry.

15. $f(x) = x^2 + 8x + 3$

16. $g(x) = -2x^2 + 12x + 4$

17. Using the vertex form, find a formula for the parabola with vertex $(2, 5)$ which passes through the point $(1, 2)$.

18. Using the factored form, find the formula for the parabola whose zeros are $x = -1$ and $x = 5$, and which passes through the point $(-2, 6)$.

Problems

In Problems 19–24, find a formula for the quadratic function whose graph has the given properties.

19. A vertex at $(4, 2)$ and a y-intercept of $y = 6$.

20. A vertex at $(4, 2)$ and a y-intercept of $y = -4$.

21. A vertex at $(4, 2)$ and zeros at $x = -3, 11$.

22. A y-intercept of $y = 7$ and x-intercepts at $x = 1, 4$.

23. A y-intercept of $y = 7$ and one zero at $x = -2$.

24. A vertex at $(-7, -3)$ and contains the point $(-3, -7)$.

25. Graph $y = x^2 - 10x + 25$ and $y = x^2$. Use a shift transformation to explain the relationship between the two graphs.

26. (a) Graph $h(x) = -2x^2 - 8x - 8$.
    (b) Compare the graphs of $h(x)$ and $f(x) = x^2$. How are these two graphs related? Be specific.

27. Let f be a quadratic function whose graph is a concave up parabola with a vertex at $(1, -1)$, and a zero at the origin.

    (a) Graph $y = f(x)$.
    (b) Determine a formula for $f(x)$.
    (c) Determine the range of f.
    (d) Find any other zeros.

28. Let $f(x) = x^2$ and let $g(x) = (x-3)^2 + 2$.

(a) Give the formula for g in terms of f, and describe the relationship between f and g in words.

(b) Is g a quadratic function? If so, find its standard form and the parameters a, b, and c.

(c) Graph g, labeling all important features.

29. If we know a quadratic function f has a zero at $x = -1$ and vertex at $(1, 4)$, do we have enough information to find a formula for this function? If your answer is yes, find it; if not, give your reasons.

30. Gwendolyn, a pleasant parabola, was taking a peaceful nap when her dream turned into a nightmare: she dreamt that a low-flying pterodactyl was swooping toward her. Startled, she flipped over the horizontal axis, darted up (vertically) by three units, and to the left (horizontally) by two units. Finally she woke up and realized that her equation was $y = (x-1)^2 + 3$. What was her equation before she had the bad dream?

31. A tomato is thrown vertically into the air at time $t = 0$. Its height, $d(t)$ (in feet), above the ground at time t (in seconds) is given by

$$d(t) = -16t^2 + 48t.$$

(a) Graph $d(t)$.

(b) Find t when $d(t) = 0$. What is happening to the tomato the first time $d(t) = 0$? The second time?

(c) When does the tomato reach its maximum height?

(d) What is the maximum height that the tomato reaches?

32. An espresso stand finds that its weekly profit is a function of the price, x, it charges per cup. If x is in dollars, the weekly profit is $P(x) = -2900x^2 + 7250x - 2900$ dollars.

(a) Approximate the maximum profit and the price per cup that produces that profit.

(b) Which function, $P(x-2)$ or $P(x)-2$, gives a function that has the same maximum profit? What price per cup produces that maximum profit?

(c) Which function, $P(x + 50)$ or $P(x) + 50$, gives a function where the price per cup that produces the maximum profit remains unchanged? What is the maximum profit?

33. If you have a string of length 50 cm, what are the dimensions of the rectangle of maximum area that you can enclose with your string? Explain your reasoning. What about a string of length k cm?

34. A football player kicks a ball at an angle of $37°$ above the ground with an initial speed of 20 meters/second. The height, h, as a function of the horizontal distance traveled, d, is given by:

$$h = 0.75d - 0.0192d^2.$$

(a) Graph the path the ball follows.

(b) When the ball hits the ground, how far is it from the spot where the football player kicked it?

(c) What is the maximum height the ball reaches during its flight?

(d) What is the horizontal distance the ball has traveled when it reaches its maximum height?[3]

35. A ballet dancer jumps in the air. The height, $h(t)$, in feet, of the dancer at time t, in seconds since the start of the jump, is given by[4]

$$h(t) = -16t^2 + 16Tt,$$

where T is the total time in seconds that the ballet dancer is in the air.

(a) Why does this model apply only for $0 \le t \le T$?

(b) When, in terms of T, does the maximum height of the jump occur?

(c) Show that the time, T, that the dancer is in the air is related to H, the maximum height of the jump, by the equation

$$H = 4T^2.$$

---

[3]Adapted from R. Halliday, D. Resnick, and K. Krane, *Physics*. (New York: Wiley, 1992), p.58.
[4]K. Laws, *The Physics of Dance*. (Schirmer, 1984).

CHAPTER SUMMARY

- **Vertical and Horizontal Shifts**
  Vertical: $y = g(x) + k$.
  Upward if $k > 0$; downward if $k < 0$.
  Horizontal: $y = g(x + k)$.
  Left if $k > 0$; right if $k < 0$.

- **Reflections**
  Across x-axis: $y = -f(x)$.
  Across y-axis: $y = f(-x)$.

- **Symmetry**
  About y-axis: $f(-x) = f(x)$; even function.
  About the origin: $f(-x) = -f(x)$; odd function.

- **Stretches and Compressions**
  Vertical: $y = kf(x)$. Stretch if $k > 0$; compress if $0 < k < 1$; reflect across x-axis if $k < 0$.
  Horizontal: $y = f(kx)$. Compress if $k > 0$; stretch if $0 < k < 1$; reflect across y-axis if $k < 0$.

- **Quadratic Functions**
  Standard form: $y = ax^2 + bx + c$.
  Vertex form: $y = a(x - h)^2 + k$.
  Opening upward if $a > 0$; downward if $a < 0$.
  Vertex (h, k), axis of symmetry $x = h$, maximum, minimum.
  Completing the square.

REVIEW EXERCISES AND PROBLEMS FOR CHAPTER FIVE

Exercises

1. Suppose $x = 2$. Determine the value of the input of the function f in each of the following expressions:

   (a) $f(2x)$ (b) $f(\frac{1}{2}x)$ (c) $f(x+3)$ (d) $f(-x)$

2. Determine the value of x in each of the following expressions which leads to an input of 2 to the function f:

   (a) $f(2x)$ (b) $f(\frac{1}{2}x)$ (c) $f(x+3)$ (d) $f(-x)$

3. The point $(2, 5)$ is on the graph of $y = f(x)$. Give the coordinates of one point on the graph of each of the following functions.

   (a) $y = f(x - 4)$ (b) $y = f(x) - 4$
   (c) $y = f(4x)$ (d) $y = 4f(x)$

4. The point $(-3, 4)$ is on the graph of $y = g(x)$. Give the coordinates of one point on the graph of each of the following functions.

   (a) $y = g(\frac{1}{3}x)$ (b) $y = \frac{1}{3}g(x)$
   (c) $y = g(-3x)$ (d) $y = -g(3x)$

Are the functions in Exercises 5–10 even, odd, or neither?

5. $a(x) = \dfrac{1}{x}$ 6. $m(x) = \dfrac{1}{x^2}$

7. $e(x) = x + 3$ 8. $p(x) = x^2 + 2x$

9. $b(x) = |x|$ 10. $q(x) = 2^{x+1}$

11. Let $f(x) = 1 - x$. Evaluate and simplify:

   (a) $f(2x)$ (b) $f(x + 1)$ (c) $f(1 - x)$
   (d) $f(x^2)$ (e) $f(1/x)$ (f) $f(\sqrt{x})$

12. Fill in all the blanks in Table 5.21 for which you have sufficient information.

Table 5.21

x	-3	-2	-1	0	1	2	3
$f(x)$	-4	-1	2	3	0	-3	-6
$f(-x)$							
$-f(x)$							
$f(x) - 2$							
$f(x - 2)$							
$f(x) + 2$							
$f(x + 2)$							
$2f(x)$							
$-f(x)/3$							

In Exercises 13–16, find a formula for the parabola.

13.
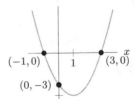

14.
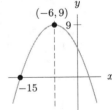

15.
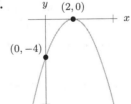

16.
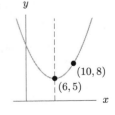

Problems

In Problems 17–18, use Figure 5.59 to sketch the function.

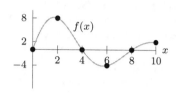

Figure 5.59

17. $y = f(x + 2) + 2$ **18.** $y = -2f(-x)$

In Problems 19–20, use Figure 5.59 to find a possible formula for the transformation of f shown.

19.

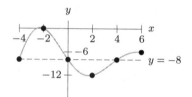

20.

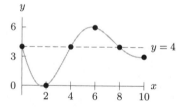

21. Let $D(p)$ be the number of iced cappuccinos sold each week by a coffeehouse when the price is p cents.

(a) What does the expression $D(225)$ represent?

(b) Do you think that $D(p)$ is an increasing function or a decreasing function? Why?

(c) What does the following equation tell you about p? $D(p) = 180$

(d) The coffeehouse sells n iced cappuccinos when they charge the average price in their area, t cents. Thus, $D(t) = n$. What is the meaning of the following expressions: $D(1.5t)$, $1.5D(t)$, $D(t+50)$, $D(t)+50$?

22. Suppose $w = j(x)$ is the average daily quantity of water (in gallons) required by an oak tree of height x feet.

(a) What does the expression $j(25)$ represent? What about $j^{-1}(25)$?

(b) What does the following equation tell you about v: $j(v) = 50$. Rewrite this statement in terms of j^{-1}.

(c) Oak trees are on average z feet high and a tree of average height requires p gallons of water. Represent this fact in terms of j and then in terms of j^{-1}.

(d) Using the definitions of z and p from part (c), what do the following expressions represent?

$$j(2z), \quad 2j(z), \quad j(z + 10), \quad j(z) + 10,$$

$$j^{-1}(2p), \quad j^{-1}(p + 10), \quad j^{-1}(p) + 10.$$

23. Without a calculator, match each of the functions (a)–(f) with one of the graphs (I) – (VI).

(a) $y = e^x$ (b) $y = e^{5x}$ (c) $y = 5e^x$
(d) $y = e^{x+5}$ (e) $y = e^{-x}$ (f) $y = e^x + 5$

(I)
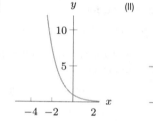

(II)
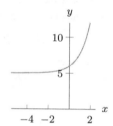

(III)
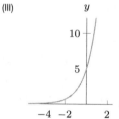

(IV)
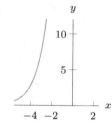

(V)
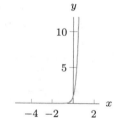

(VI)
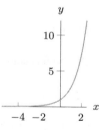

24. The graph in Figure 5.60 gives the number of hours of daylight in Charlotte, North Carolina on day d of the year, where $d = 0$ is January 1. Graph the number of hours of daylight in Buenos Aires, Argentina, which is as far south of the equator as Charlotte is north. [Hint: When it is summer in the Northern Hemisphere, it is winter in the Southern Hemisphere.]

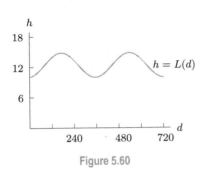

Figure 5.60

25. During a hurricane, a brick breaks loose from the top of a chimney, 38 feet above the ground. As the brick falls, its distance from the ground after t seconds is given by:

$$d(t) = -16t^2 + 38.$$

(a) Find formulas for $d(t) - 15$ and $d(t - 1.5)$.

(b) On the same axes, graph $d(t)$, $d(t) - 15$, $d(t - 1.5)$.

(c) Suppose $d(t)$ represents the height of a brick which began to fall at noon. What might $d(t) - 15$ represent? $d(t - 1.5)$?

(d) Using algebra, determine when the brick hits the ground:

    (i) If $d(t)$ represents the distance of the brick from the ground,

    (ii) If $d(t) - 15$ represents the distance of the brick from the ground.

(e) Use one of your answers in part (d) to determine when the brick hits the ground if $d(t - 1.5)$ represents its distance above the ground at time t.

The functions graphed in Problems 26–27 are transformations of some basic function. Give a possible formula for each one.

26.

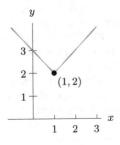

27.

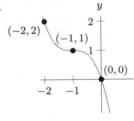

In Problems 28–29, use Figure 5.61 to find a formula for the transformations of $h(x)$.

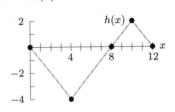

Figure 5.61

28.

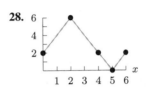

29.

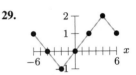

Problems 30–34 use Table 5.22 which gives the total cost, $C = f(n)$, for a carpenter to build n wooden chairs.

Table 5.22

n	0	10	20	30	40	50
$f(n)$	5000	6000	6800	7450	8000	8500

30. Evaluate the following expressions. Explain in everyday terms what they mean.

(a) $f(10)$ (b) $f(x)$ if $x = 30$

(c) z if $f(z) = 8000$ (d) $f(0)$

31. Find approximate values for p and q if $f(p) = 6400$ and $q = f(26)$.

32. Let $d_1 = f(30) - f(20)$, $d_2 = f(40) - f(30)$, and $d_3 = f(50) - f(40)$.

(a) Evaluate d_1, d_2 and d_3.

(b) What do these numbers tell you about the carpenter's cost of building chairs?

33. Graph $f(n)$. Label the quantities you found in Problems 30–32 on your graph.

34. The carpenter currently builds k chairs per week.

(a) What do the following expressions represent?

    (i) $f(k + 10)$ (ii) $f(k) + 10$

    (iii) $f(2k)$ (iv) $2f(k)$

(b) If the carpenter sells his chairs at 80% above cost, plus an additional 5% sales tax, write an expression for his gross income (including sales tax) each week.

35. In Figure 5.62, the value of d is labeled on the x-axis. Locate the following quantities on the y-axis:

   (a) $g(d)$ **(b)** $g(-d)$ **(c)** $-g(-d)$

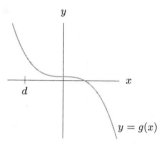

Figure 5.62

36. In Figure 5.63, the values c and d are labeled on the x-axis. On the y-axis, locate the following quantities:

   (a) $h(c)$ **(b)** $h(d)$
   (c) $h(c+d)$ **(d)** $h(c)+h(d)$

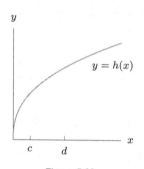

Figure 5.63

In Problems 37–39, use Figure 5.64 to find a formula for the graphs in terms of h.

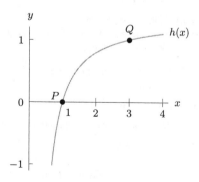

Figure 5.64

37.

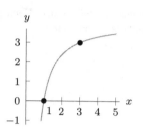

38.

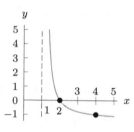

39.

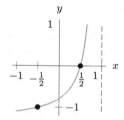

40. Let $T(d)$ be the low temperature in degrees Fahrenheit on the dth day of last year (where $d = 1$ is January 1st, and so on).

   (a) Sketch a possible graph of T for your home town for $1 \leq d \leq 365$.

   (b) Suppose n is a new function that reports the low temperature on day, d, in terms of degrees above (or below) freezing. (For example, if the low temperature on the 100th day of the year is 42°F, then $n(100) = 42 - 32 = 10$.) Write an expression for $n(d)$ as a shift of T. Graph n. How does the graph of n relate to the graph of T?

   (c) This year, something different has happened. The temperatures for each day are exactly the same as they were last year, except each temperature occurs a week earlier than it did last year. Suppose $p(d)$ gives the low temperature on the dth day of this year. Write an expression for $p(d)$ in terms of $T(d)$. Graph p. How do the graphs of p and T relate?

41. When slam-dunking, a basketball player seems to hang in the air at the height of his jump. The height $h(t)$, in feet above the ground, of a basketball player at time t, in seconds since the start of a jump, is given by

$$h(t) = -16t^2 + 16Tt,$$

where T is the total time in seconds that it takes to complete the jump. For a jump that takes 1 second to complete, how much of this time does the basketball player spend at the top 25% of the trajectory? [Hint: Find the maximum height reached. Then find the times at which the height is 75% of this maximum.]

42. A cube-shaped box has an edge of length x cm.

(a) Write a formula for the function $L(x)$ that gives the length of tape used to run a layer of tape around all the edges.

(b) Explain what would happen if your roll of tape contained $L(x) - 6$ cm of tape. What about $L(x - 6)$ cm of tape?

(c) If the tape must be wrapped beyond each corner for a distance of 1 cm, express the length of tape used in terms of a shift of the function L.

(d) Write a formula in terms of x for the function S that gives the surface area of the box.

(e) Write a formula in terms of x for the function V that gives the volume of the box.

Because the box is fragile, it is packed inside a larger box with room for packing material around it. There must be 5 cm of clearance between the smaller and larger boxes on every side.

(f) Express the surface area of the larger box as a shift of the function S.

(g) Express the volume of the larger box as a shift of V.

(h) The larger box has its edges taped. Express the length of tape used as a shift of the function L.

(i) The outside box needs to be double taped to reinforce it for shipping (every edge receives two layers of tape). Express the length of tape that needs to be used in terms of $L(x)$.

(j) The edge length of the outside box must be 20% longer than the edge length of the original box. Which expression gives the length of tape necessary to tape the edges, $1.2L(x)$ or $L(1.2x)$? Explain.

CHECK YOUR UNDERSTANDING

Are the statements in Problems 1–29 true or false? Give an explanation for your answer.

1. If $g(x) = f(x) + 3$ then the graph of $g(x)$ is a vertical shift of the graph of f.

2. If $g(t) = f(t - 2)$ then the graph of $g(t)$ can be obtained by shifting the graph of f two units to the left.

3. If $g(x) = f(x) + k$ and k is negative, the graph of $g(x)$ is the same as the graph of f, but shifted down.

4. Vertical and horizontal shifts are called translations.

5. The reflection of $y = x^2$ across the x-axis is $y = -x^2$.

6. If $f(x)$ is an odd function, then $f(x) = f(-x)$.

7. The graphs of odd functions are symmetric about the y-axis.

8. The graph of $y = -f(x)$ is the reflection of the graph of $y = f(x)$ across the x-axis.

9. The graph of $y = f(-x)$ is the reflection of the graph of $y = f(x)$ across the y-axis.

10. If the graph of a function f is symmetric about the y-axis then $f(x) = f(-x)$.

11. Figure 5.65 suggests that $g(x) = f(x + 2) + 1$.

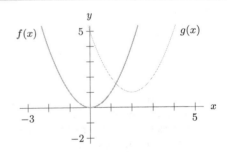

Figure 5.65

12. If $g(x) = x^2 + 4$ then $g(x - 2) = x^2$.

13. For any function f, we have $f(x + k) = f(x) + k$.

14. Figure 5.66 could be the graph of $f(x) = |x - 1| - 2$.

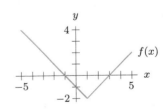

Figure 5.66

15. Let $f(x) = 3^x$. If the graph of $f(x)$ is reflected across the x-axis and then shifted up four units, the new graph has the equation $y = -3^x + 4$.

16. If $q(p) = p^2 + 2p + 4$ then $-q(-p) = p^2 - 2p + 4$.

17. Multiplying a function by a constant k, with $k > 1$, vertically stretches its graph.

18. If $g(x) = kf(x)$, then on any interval the average rate of change of g is k times the average rate of change of f.

19. Figure 5.67 suggests that $g(x) = -2f(x+1) + 3$.

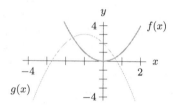

Figure 5.67

20. Using Table 5.23, we can conclude that if $g(x) = -\frac{1}{2}f(x+1) - 3$, then $g(-2) = -10$.

Table 5.23

x	-3	-2	-1	0	1	2	3
$f(x)$	10	6	4	1	-2	-4	-10

21. Shifting the graph of a function up by one unit and then compressing it vertically by a factor of $\frac{1}{2}$ produces the same result as first compressing the graph by a factor of $\frac{1}{2}$ and then shifting it up by one unit.

22. Figure 5.68 suggests that $g(x) = 3f(\frac{1}{2}x)$.

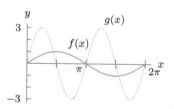

Figure 5.68

23. For the function given in Table 5.24, for $x = -2$, we have $3f(2x) + 1 = -2f(\frac{1}{2}x)$.

Table 5.24

x	-4	-3	-2	-1	0	1	2
$f(x)$	1	4	0	-2	0	0	-2

24. The graph of every quadratic equation is a parabola.

25. The maximum or minimum point of a parabola is called its vertex.

26. If a parabola is concave up its vertex is a maximum point.

27. If the equation of a parabola is written as $y = a(x - h)^2 + k$, then the vertex is located at the point $(-h, k)$.

28. If the equation of a parabola is written as $y = a(x - h)^2 + k$, then the axis of symmetry is found at $x = h$.

29. If the equation of a parabola is $y = ax^2 + bx + c$ and $a < 0$, then the parabola opens downward.

TOOLS FOR CHAPTER 5: COMPLETING THE SQUARE

Completing the Square

Another example of changing the form of an expression is the conversion of $ax^2 + bx + c$ into the form $a(x - h)^2 + k$. We make this conversion by *completing the square*, a method for producing a perfect square within a quadratic expression. A perfect square is an expression of the form:

$$(x + n)^2 = x^2 + 2nx + n^2$$

for some number n. In order to complete the square in a given expression, we must find that number n, which is half the coefficient of x. Before giving a general procedure, let's work through an example.

Example 1   Complete the square to rewrite $x^2 - 10x + 4$ in the form $a(x - h)^2 + k$.

Solution

Step 1: We divide the coefficient of x by 2, giving $\frac{1}{2}(-10) = -5$.
Step 2: We squaring the result of step 1, giving $(-5)^2 = 25$.
Step 3: Now add and subtract the 25 after the x-term:

$$x^2 - 10x + 4 = x^2 - 10x + (25 - 25) + 4$$
$$= \underbrace{(x^2 - 10x + 25)}_{\text{Perfect square}} - 25 + 4.$$

Step 4: Notice that we have created a perfect square, $x^2 - 10x + 25$. The next step is to factor the perfect square and combine the constant terms, $-25 + 4$, giving the final result:

$$x^2 - 10x + 4 = (x - 5)^2 - 21.$$

Thus, $a = +1$, $h = +5$, and $k = -21$.

The procedure we followed can be summarized as follows:

To complete the square in the expression $x^2 + bx + c$, divide the coefficient of x by 2, giving $b/2$. Then add and subtract $(b/2)^2 = b^2/4$ and factor the perfect square:

$$x^2 + bx + c = \left(x + \frac{b}{2}\right)^2 - \frac{b^2}{4} + c.$$

To complete the square in the expression $ax^2 + bx + c$, factor out a first.

The next example has a coefficient a with $a \neq 1$. After factoring out the coefficient, we follow the same steps as in Example 1.

Example 2   Complete the square in the formula $h(x) = 5x^2 + 30x - 10$.

Solution   We first factor out 5:
$$h(x) = 5(x^2 + 6x - 2).$$

Now we complete the square in the expression $x^2 + 6x - 2$.
Step 1: Divide the coefficient of x by 2, giving 3.
Step 2: Square the result: $3^2 = 9$.
Step 3: Add the result after the x term, then subtract it:
$$h(x) = 5(\underbrace{x^2 + 6x + 9}_{\text{Perfect square}} - 9 - 2).$$

Step 4: Factor the perfect square and simplify the rest:
$$h(x) = 5\left((x+3)^2 - 11\right).$$

Now that we have completed the square, we can multiply by the 5:
$$h(x) = 5(x+3)^2 - 55.$$

Deriving The Quadratic Formula

We derive a general formula for the zeros of $q(x) = ax^2 + bx + c$, with $a \neq 0$, by completing the square. To find the zeros, set $q(x) = 0$:
$$ax^2 + bx + c = 0.$$

Before we complete the square, we factor out the coefficient of x^2:
$$a\left(x^2 + \frac{b}{a}x + \frac{c}{a}\right) = 0.$$

Since $a \neq 0$, we can divide both sides by a:
$$x^2 + \frac{b}{a}x + \frac{c}{a} = 0.$$

To complete the square, we add and then subtract $((b/a)/2)^2 = b^2/(4a^2)$:
$$\underbrace{x^2 + \frac{b}{a}x + \frac{b^2}{4a^2}}_{\text{Perfect square}} - \frac{b^2}{4a^2} + \frac{c}{a} = 0.$$

We factor the perfect square and simplify the constant term, giving:
$$\left(x + \frac{b}{2a}\right)^2 - \left(\frac{b^2 - 4ac}{4a^2}\right) = 0 \qquad \text{since } \tfrac{-b^2}{4a^2} + \tfrac{c}{a} = \tfrac{-b^2}{4a^2} + \tfrac{4ac}{4a^2} = -\left(\tfrac{b^2-4ac}{4a^2}\right)$$

$$\left(x + \frac{b}{2a}\right)^2 = \frac{b^2 - 4ac}{4a^2} \qquad \text{adding } \frac{b^2 - 4ac}{4a^2} \text{ to both sides}$$

$$x + \frac{b}{2a} = \pm\sqrt{\frac{b^2 - 4ac}{4a^2}} = \frac{\pm\sqrt{b^2 - 4ac}}{2a} \qquad \text{taking the square root}$$

$$x = \frac{-b}{2a} \pm \frac{\sqrt{b^2 - 4ac}}{2a} \qquad \text{subtracting } b/2a$$

$$x = \frac{-b \pm \sqrt{b^2 - 4ac}}{2a}.$$

Exercises to Tools for Chapter 5

For Exercises 1–12, complete the square for each expression.

1. $x^2 + 8x$

2. $y^2 - 12y$

3. $w^2 + 7w$

4. $2r^2 + 20r$

5. $s^2 + 6s - 8$

6. $3t^2 + 24t - 13$

7. $a^2 - 2a - 4$

8. $n^2 + 4n - 5$

9. $c^2 + 3c - 7$

10. $3r^2 + 9r - 4$

11. $4s^2 + s + 2$

12. $12g^2 + 8g + 5$

In Exercises 13–16, rewrite in the form $a(x - h)^2 + k$.

13. $x^2 - 2x - 3$

14. $10 - 6x + x^2$

15. $-x^2 + 6x - 2$

16. $3x^2 - 12x + 13$

In Exercises 17–26, complete the square to find the vertex of the parabola.

17. $y = x^2 + 6x + 3$

18. $y = x^2 - x + 4$

19. $y = -x^2 - 8x + 2$

20. $y = x^2 - 3x - 3$

21. $y = -x^2 + x - 6$

22. $y = 3x^2 + 12x$

23. $y = -4x^2 + 8x - 6$

24. $y = 5x^2 - 5x + 7$

25. $y = 2x^2 - 7x + 3$

26. $y = -3x^2 - x - 2$

In Exercises 27–36, solve by completing the square.

27. $r^2 - 6r + 8 = 0$

28. $g^2 = 2g + 24$

29. $p^2 - 2p = 6$

30. $n^2 = 3n + 18$

31. $d^2 - d = 2$

32. $2r^2 + 4r - 5 = 0$

33. $2s^2 = 1 - 10s$

34. $5q^2 - 8 = 2q$

35. $7r^2 - 3r - 6 = 0$

36. $5p^2 + 9p = 1$

In Exercises 37–42, solve by using the quadratic formula.

37. $n^2 - 4n - 12 = 0$

38. $2y^2 + 5y = -2$

39. $6k^2 + 11k = -3$

40. $w^2 + w = 4$

41. $z^2 + 4z = 6$

42. $2q^2 + 6q - 3 = 0$

In Exercises 43–56, solve using factoring, completing the square, or the quadratic formula.

43. $r^2 - 2r = 8$

44. $-3t^2 + 4t + 9 = 0$

45. $n^2 + 4n - 3 = 2$

46. $s^2 + 3s = 1$

47. $z^3 + 2z^2 = 3z + 6$

48. $2q^2 + 4q - 5 = 8$

49. $25u^2 + 4 = 30u$

50. $v^2 - 4v - 9 = 0$

51. $3y^2 = 6y + 18$

52. $2p^2 + 23 = 14p$

53. $2w^3 + 24 = 6w^2 + 8w$

54. $4x^2 + 16x - 5 = 0$

55. $49m^2 + 70m + 22 = 0$

56. $8x^2 - 1 = 2x$

Chapter Eight

COMPOSITIONS, INVERSES, AND COMBINATIONS OF FUNCTIONS

In Chapter 5, we studied transformations of functions. The composite functions in this chapter are generalizations of these transformations. In Chapter 2, we introduced the inverse function and its notation, f^{-1}. In Chapter 3, we defined the inverse of the exponential function (that is, the logarithm) and in Chapter 6, we defined the inverses of the trigonometric functions. In this chapter, we consider inverse functions in more detail.

8.1 COMPOSITION OF FUNCTIONS

The Effect of a Drug on Heart Rates

A therapeutic drug has the side effect of raising a patient's heart rate. Table 8.1 gives the relationship between Q, the amount of drug in the patient's body (in milligrams), and r, the patient's heart rate (in beats per minute). We see that the higher the drug level, the faster the heart rate.

Table 8.1 *Heart rate, $r = f(Q)$, as a function of drug level, Q*

Q, drug level (mg)	0	50	100	150	200	250
r, heart rate (beats per minute)	60	70	80	90	100	110

A patient is given a 250 mg injection of the drug. Over time, the level of drug in the patient's bloodstream falls. Table 8.2 gives the drug level, Q, as a function of time, t.

Table 8.2 *Drug level, $Q = g(t)$, as a function of time, t, since the medication was given*

t, time (hours)	0	1	2	3	4	5	6	7	8
Q, drug level (mg)	250	200	160	128	102	82	66	52	42

Since heart rate depends on the drug level and drug level depends on time, the heart rate also depends on time. Tables 8.1 and 8.2 can be combined to give the patient's heart rate, r, as a function of t. For example, according to Table 8.2, at time $t = 0$ the drug level is 250 mg. According to Table 8.1, at this drug level, the patient's heart rate is 110 beats per minute. So $r = 110$ when $t = 0$. The results of similar calculations have been compiled in Table 8.3. Note that many of the entries, such as $r = 92$ when $t = 2$, are estimates.

Table 8.3 *Heart rate, $r = h(t)$, as a function of time, t*

t, time (hours)	0	1	2	3	4	5	6	7	8
r, heart rate (beats per minute)	110	100	92	86	80	76	73	70	68

Now, since

$$r = f(Q) \quad \text{or} \quad \underbrace{\text{Heart rate}}_{r} = f(\underbrace{\text{drug level}}_{Q}),$$

and

$$Q = g(t) \quad \text{or} \quad \underbrace{\text{Drug level}}_{Q} = g(\underbrace{\text{time}}_{t}),$$

we can substitute $Q = g(t)$ into $r = f(Q)$, giving

$$r = f(\underbrace{Q}_{g(t)}) = f(g(t)).$$

The function h in Table 8.3 is said to be the *composition* of the function f and g, written

$$h(t) = f(g(t)).$$

This formula represents the process that we used to find the values of $r = h(t)$ in Table 8.3.

Example 1 Use Tables 8.1 and 8.2 to estimate the values of: (a) $h(0)$ (b) $h(4)$

Solution   (a) If $t = 0$, then

$$r = h(0) = f(g(0)).$$

Table 8.2 shows that $g(0) = 250$, so

$$r = h(0) = f(\underbrace{250}_{g(0)}).$$

We see from Table 8.1 that $f(250) = 110$. Thus,

$$r = h(0) = \underbrace{110}_{f(250)}.$$

As before, this tells us that the patient's heart rate at time $t = 0$ is 110 beats per minute.

(b) If $t = 4$, then

$$h(4) = f(g(4)).$$

Working from the inner set of parentheses outward, we start by evaluating $g(4)$. Table 8.2 shows that $g(4) = 102$. Thus,

$$h(4) = f(\underbrace{102}_{g(4)}).$$

Table 8.1 does not have a value for $f(102)$. But since $f(100) = 80$ and $f(150) = 90$, we estimate that $f(102)$ is close to 80. Thus, we let

$$h(4) \approx \underbrace{80}_{f(102)}.$$

This indicates that four hours after the injection, the patient's heart rate is approximately 80 beats per minute.

> The function $f(g(t))$ is said to be a **composition** of f with g. The function $f(g(t))$ is defined by using the output of the function g as the input to f.

The composite function $f(g(t))$ is only defined for values in the domain of g whose $g(t)$ values are in the domain of f.

Formulas for Composite Functions

A possible formula for $r = f(Q)$, the heart rate as a function of drug level is

$$r = f(Q) = 60 + 0.2Q.$$

A possible formula for $Q = g(t)$, the drug level as a function of time is

$$Q = g(t) = 250(0.8)^t.$$

To find a formula for $r = h(t) = f(g(t))$, the heart rate as a function of time, we use the function $g(t)$ as the input to f. Thus,

$$r = f(\underbrace{\text{input}}_{g(t)}) = 60 + 0.2(\underbrace{\text{input}}_{g(t)}),$$

so

$$r = f(g(t)) = 60 + 0.2g(t).$$

Now, substitute the formula for $g(t)$. This gives

$$r = h(t) = f(g(t)) = 60 + 0.2 \cdot \underbrace{250(0.8)^t}_{g(t)}$$

so

$$r = h(t) = 60 + 50(0.8)^t.$$

We can check the formula against Table 8.3. For example, if $t = 4$

$$h(4) = 60 + 50(0.8)^4 = 80.48.$$

This result is in agreement with the value $h(4) \approx 80$ that we estimated in Table 8.3.

Example 2   Let $p(x) = 2x + 1$ and $q(x) = x^2 - 3$. Suppose $u(x) = p(q(x))$ and $v(x) = q(p(x))$.
(a) Calculate $u(3)$ and $v(3)$.
(b) Find formulas for $u(x)$ and $v(x)$.

Solution   (a) We want

$$u(3) = p(q(3)).$$

We start by evaluating $q(3)$. The formula for q gives $q(3) = 3^2 - 3 = 6$, so

$$u(3) = p(6).$$

The formula for p gives $p(6) = 2 \cdot 6 + 1 = 13$, so

$$u(3) = 13.$$

To calculate $v(3)$, we have

$$
\begin{aligned}
v(3) &= q(p(3)) \\
&= q(7) && \text{Because } p(3) = 2 \cdot 3 + 1 = 7 \\
&= 46 && \text{Because } q(7) = 7^2 - 3
\end{aligned}
$$

Notice that, $v(3) \neq u(3)$. The functions $v(x) = q(p(x))$ and $u(x) = p(q(x))$ are different.
(b) In the formula for u,

$$u(x) = p(\underbrace{q(x)}_{\text{Input for } p})$$

$$
\begin{aligned}
&= 2q(x) + 1 && \text{Because } p(\text{Input}) = 2 \cdot \text{Input} + 1 \\
&= 2(x^2 - 3) + 1 && \text{Substituting } q(x) = x^2 - 3 \\
&= 2x^2 - 5.
\end{aligned}
$$

Check this formula by evaluating $u(3)$, which we know to be 13:

$$u(3) = 2 \cdot 3^2 - 5 = 13.$$

In the formula for v,

$$v(x) = q(\underbrace{p(x)}_{\text{Input for } q})$$

$$
\begin{aligned}
&= q(2x + 1) && \text{Because } p(x) = 2x + 1 \\
&= (2x + 1)^2 - 3 && \text{Because } q(\text{Input}) = \text{Input}^2 - 3 \\
&= 4x^2 + 4x - 2.
\end{aligned}
$$

Check this formula by evaluating $v(3)$, which we know to be 46:

$$v(3) = 4 \cdot 3^2 + 4 \cdot 3 - 2 = 46.$$

So far we have considered examples of two functions composed together, but there is no limit on the number of functions that can be composed. Functions can even be composed with themselves.

Example 3   Let $p(x) = \sin x + 1$ and $q(x) = x^2 - 3$. Find a formula in terms of x for $w(x) = p(p(q(x)))$.

Solution   We work from inside the parentheses outward. First we find $p(q(x))$, and then input the result to p.

$$w(x) = p(p(q(x)))$$
$$= p(p(x^2 - 3))$$
$$= p(\underbrace{\sin(x^2 - 3) + 1}_{\text{Input for } p})$$
$$= \sin(\sin(x^2 - 3) + 1) + 1. \qquad \text{Because } p(\text{Input}) = \sin(\text{Input}) + 1$$

Composition of Functions Defined by Graphs

So far we have composed functions defined by tables and formulas. In the next example, we compose functions defined by graphs.

Example 4   Let u and v be two functions defined by the graphs in Figure 8.1. Evaluate:

(a) $v(u(-1))$ (b) $u(v(5))$ (c) $v(u(0)) + u(v(4))$

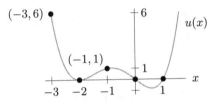
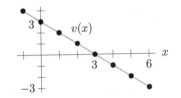

Figure 8.1: Evaluate the composition of functions u and v defined by their graphs

Solution   (a) To evaluate $v(u(-1))$, start with $u(-1)$. From Figure 8.1, we see that $u(-1) = 1$. Thus,
$$v(u(-1)) = v(1).$$

From the graph we see that $v(1) = 2$, so
$$v(u(-1)) = 2.$$

(b) Since $v(5) = -2$, we have $u(v(5)) = u(-2) = 0$.

(c) Since $u(0) = 0$, we have $v(u(0)) = v(0) = 3$.
Since $v(4) = -1$, we have $u(v(4)) = u(-1) = 1$.
Thus $v(u(0)) + u(v(4)) = 3 + 1 = 4$.

Decomposition of Functions

Sometimes we reason backward to find the functions which went into a composition. This process is called *decomposition*.

Example 5   Let $h(x) = f(g(x)) = e^{x^2+1}$. Find possible formulas for $f(x)$ and $g(x)$.

Solution   In the formula $h(x) = e^{x^2+1}$, the expression $x^2 + 1$ is in the exponent. Thus, we can take the inside function to be $g(x) = x^2 + 1$. This means that we can write
$$h(x) = e^{\underbrace{x^2 + 1}_{g(x)}} = e^{g(x)}.$$

Then the outside function is $f(x) = e^x$. We check that composing f and g gives h:

$$f(g(x)) = f(x^2 + 1) = e^{x^2+1} = h(x).$$

There are many possible solutions to Example 5. For example, we might choose $f(x) = e^{x+1}$ and $g(x) = x^2$. Then

$$f(g(x)) = e^{g(x)+1} = e^{x^2+1} = h(x).$$

Alternatively, we might choose $f(x) = e^{x^2+1}$ and $g(x) = x$. Although this satisfies the condition that $h(x) = f(g(x))$, it is not very useful, because f is the same as h. This kind of decomposition is referred to as *trivial*. Another example of a trivial decomposition of $h(x)$ is $f(x) = x$ and $g(x) = e^{x^2+1}$.

Example 6   The vertex formula for the family of quadratic functions is

$$p(x) = a(x - h)^2 + k.$$

Decompose the formula into three simple functions. That is, find formulas for u, v, and w where

$$p(x) = u(v(w(x))),$$

Solution   We work from inside the parentheses outward. In the formula $p(x) = a(x - h)^2 + k$, we have the expression $x - h$ inside the parentheses. In the formula $p(x) = u(v(w(x)))$, the innermost function is $w(x)$. Thus, we let

$$w(x) = x - h.$$

In the formula $p(x) = a(x - h)^2 + k$, the first operation done to $x - h$ is squaring. Thus, we let

$$v(\text{Input}) = \text{Input}^2$$
$$v(x) = x^2.$$

So we have

$$v(w(x)) = v(x - h) = (x - h)^2.$$

Finally, to obtain $p(x) = a(x - h)^2 + k$, we multiply $(x - h)^2$ by a and add k. Thus, we let

$$u(\text{Input}) = a \cdot \text{Input} + k$$
$$u(x) = ax + k.$$

To check, we compute

$$
\begin{aligned}
u(v(w(x))) &= u(v(x - h)) && \text{Since } w(x) = x - h \\
&= u(\underbrace{(x - h)^2}_{\text{Input for } u}) && \text{Since } v(x - h) = (x - h)^2 \\
&= a(x - h)^2 + k && \text{Since } u((x - h)^2) = a \cdot (x - h)^2 + k.
\end{aligned}
$$

Exercises and Problems for Section 8.1

Exercises

1. Use Table 8.4 to construct a table of values for $r(x) = p(q(x))$.

Table 8.4

x	0	1	2	3	4	5
$p(x)$	1	0	5	2	3	4
$q(x)$	5	2	3	1	4	8

2. Let p and q be the functions in Exercise 1. Construct a table of values for $s(x) = q(p(x))$.

3. Using Tables 8.5 and 8.6, complete Table 8.7:

Table 8.5

x	$f(x)$
0	0
$\pi/6$	1/2
$\pi/4$	$\sqrt{2}/2$
$\pi/3$	$\sqrt{3}/2$
$\pi/2$	1

Table 8.6

y	$g(y)$
0	$\pi/2$
1/4	π
$\sqrt{2}/4$	0
1/2	$\pi/3$
$\sqrt{2}/2$	$\pi/4$
3/4	0
$\sqrt{3}/2$	$\pi/6$
1	0

Table 8.7

x	$g(f(x))$
0	
$\pi/6$	
$\pi/4$	
$\pi/3$	
$\pi/2$	

4. Let $f(x) = \sin 4x$ and $g(x) = \sqrt{x}$. Find formulas for $f(g(x))$ and $g(f(x))$.

5. Let $h(x) = 2^x$ and $k(x) = x^2$. Find formulas for $h(k(x))$ and $k(h(x))$.

6. Let $m(x) = 3 + x^2$ and $n(x) = \tan x$. Find formulas for $m(n(x))$ and $n(m(x))$.

Find formulas for the functions in Exercises 7–12 and simplify. Let $f(x) = x^2 + 1$, $g(x) = \dfrac{1}{x-3}$, and $h(x) = \sqrt{x}$.

7. $f(g(x))$　　　**8.** $g(f(x))$　　　**9.** $f(h(x))$

10. $h(f(x))$　　　**11.** $g(g(x))$　　　**12.** $g(f(h(x)))$

In Exercises 13–17, identify the function $f(x)$.

13. $h(x) = e^{f(x)} = e^{\sin x}$

14. $j(x) = \sqrt{f(x)} = \sqrt{\ln(x^2 + 4)}$

15. $k(x) = \sin(f(x)) = \sin(x^3 + 3x + 1)$

16. $l(x) = (f(x))^2 = \cos^2 2x$

17. $m(x) = \ln f(x) = \ln(5 + 1/x)$

Problems

In Problems 18–21, give a practical interpretation in words of the function.

18. $f(h(t))$, where $A = f(r)$ is the area of a circle of radius r and $r = h(t)$ is the radius of the circle at time t.

19. $k(g(t))$, where $L = k(H)$ is the length of a steel bar at temperature H and $H = g(t)$ is temperature at time t.

20. $R(Y(q))$, where R gives a farmer's revenue as a function of corn yield per acre, and Y gives the corn yield as a function of the quantity, q, of fertilizer.

21. $t(f(H))$, where $t(v)$ is the time of a trip at velocity v, and $v = f(H)$ is velocity at temperature H.

22. Complete Table 8.8 if $r(t) = q(p(t))$.

Table 8.8

t	$p(t)$	$q(t)$	$r(t)$
0	4	??	??
1	??	2	1
2	??	??	0
3	2	0	4
4	1	5	??
5	0	1	3

23. Complete Table 8.9 given that $h(x) = f(g(x))$.

Table 8.9

x	$f(x)$	$g(x)$	$h(x)$
0	1	2	5
1	9	0	
2		1	

24. Using Figure 8.2, estimate the following:

(a) $f(g(2))$ **(b)** $g(f(2))$ **(c)** $f(f(3))$ **(d)** $g(g(3))$

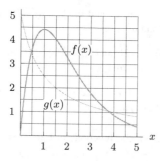

Figure 8.2

25. Use Figure 8.3 to calculate the following:

(a) $f(f(1))$ **(b)** $g(g(1))$
(c) $f(g(2))$ **(d)** $g(f(2))$

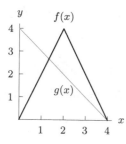

Figure 8.3

26. Use Figure 8.3 to find all solutions to the equations:

(a) $f(g(x)) = 0$ **(b)** $g(f(x)) = 0$

In Problems 27–30, use the information from Figures 8.4, and 8.5 to graph the functions.

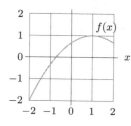

Figure 8.4

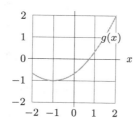

Figure 8.5

27. $f(g(x))$ **28.** $g(f(x))$ **29.** $f(f(x))$ **30.** $g(g(x))$

31. Complete Table 8.10, Table 8.11, and Table 8.12 given that $h(x) = g(f(x))$. Assume that different values of x lead to different values of $f(x)$.

Table 8.10

x	$f(x)$
-2	4
-1	
0	
1	5
2	1

Table 8.11

x	$g(x)$
1	
2	1
3	2
4	0
5	-1

Table 8.12

x	$h(x)$
-2	
-1	1
0	2
1	
2	-2

32. (a) Use Table 8.13 and Figure 8.6 to calculate:

(i) $f(g(4))$ (ii) $g(f(4))$
(iii) $f(f(0))$ (iv) $g(g(0))$

(b) Solve $g(g(x)) = 1$ for x.

Table 8.13

x	0	1	2	3	4	5
$f(x)$	2	5	3	4	1	0

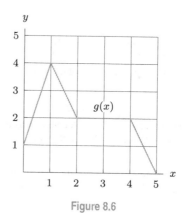

Figure 8.6

33. Let $f(x)$ and $g(x)$ be the functions in Figure 8.3.

(a) Graph the functions $f(g(x))$ and $g(f(x))$.
(b) On what interval(s) is $f(g(x))$ increasing?
(c) On what interval(s) is $g(f(x))$ increasing?

34. Find $f(f(1))$ for

$$f(x) = \begin{cases} 2 & \text{if } x \leq 0 \\ 3x + 1 & \text{if } 0 < x < 2 \\ x^2 - 3 & \text{if } x \geq 2 \end{cases}$$

35. Using your knowledge of the absolute value function, explain in a few sentences the relationship between the graph of $y = |\sin x|$ and the graph of $y = \sin x$.

36. Graph the following functions for $-2\pi \leq x \leq 2\pi$.

   (a) $f(x) = \sin x$ **(b)** $g(x) = |\sin x|$

   (c) $h(x) = \sin |x|$ **(d)** $i(x) = |\sin |x||$

   (e) Do any two of these functions have identical graphs? If so, explain why this makes sense.

37. Let $p(t) = 10(0.01)^t$ and $q(t) = \log t^2$. Solve the equation $q(p(t)) = 0$ for t.

38. Let $f(t) = \sin t$ and $g(t) = 3t - \pi/4$. Solve the equation $f(g(t)) = 1$ for t in the interval $0 \leq t \leq 2\pi/3$.

In Problems 39–42, find a simplified formula for the difference quotient

$$\frac{f(x+h) - f(x)}{h}.$$

39. $f(x) = x^2 + x$ **40.** $f(x) = \sqrt{x}$

41. $f(x) = \dfrac{1}{x}$ **42.** $f(x) = 2^x$

In Problems 43–45, let $x > 0$ and $k(x) = e^x$. Find a possible formula for $f(x)$.

43. $k(f(x)) = e^{2x}$ **44.** $f(k(x)) = e^{2x}$

45. $k(f(x)) = x$

Decompose the functions in Problems 46–51 into $u(v(x))$ for given u or v.

46. $y = \dfrac{1 + x^2}{2 + x^2}$ given that

   (a) $v(x) = x^2$ **(b)** $v(x) = x^2 + 1$

47. $y = e^{-\sqrt{x}}$ given that

   (a) $u(x) = e^x$ **(b)** $v(x) = \sqrt{x}$

48. $y = \sqrt{1 - x^3}$ given that

   (a) $u(x) = \sqrt{1 + x^3}$ **(b)** $v(x) = x^3$

49. $y = 2^{x+1}$ given that

   (a) $u(x) = 2x$ **(b)** $v(x) = -x$

50. $y = \sin^2 x$ given that

   (a) $u(x) = x^2$ **(b)** $v(x) = x^2$

51. $y = e^{2\cos x}$ given that

   (a) $u(x) = e^x$ **(b)** $v(x) = \cos x$

Decompose the functions in Problems 52–59 into two new functions, u and v, where v is the inside function, $u(x) \neq x$, and $v(x) \neq x$.

52. $f(x) = \sqrt{3 - 5x}$ **53.** $g(x) = \sin(x^2)$

54. $h(x) = \sin^2 x$ **55.** $k(x) = e^{\sin x} + \sin x$

56. $F(x) = (2x + 5)^3$ **57.** $G(x) = \dfrac{2}{1 + \sqrt{x}}$

58. $H(x) = 3^{2x-1}$ **59.** $J(x) = 8 - 2|x|$

60. You have two money machines, both of which increase any money inserted into them. The first machine doubles your money. The second adds five dollars. The money that comes out is described by $d(x) = 2x$, in the first case, and $a(x) = x + 5$, in the second, where x is the number of dollars inserted. The machines can be hooked up so that the money coming out of one machine goes into the other. Find formulas for each of the two possible composition machines. Is one machine more profitable than the other?

61. Currency traders often move investments from one country to another in order to make a profit. Table 8.14 gives exchange rates for US dollars, Japanese yen, and the European Union's euro.[1] In January, 2006, for example, 1 US dollar purchases 114.64 Japanese yen or 0.829 European euro. Similarly, 1 European euro purchases 138.29 Japanese yen or 1.2063 US dollars. Suppose

$$f(x) = \text{Number of yen one can buy with } x \text{ dollars}$$
$$g(x) = \text{Number of euros one can buy with } x \text{ dollars}$$
$$h(x) = \text{Number of euros one can buy with } x \text{ yen}$$

   (a) Find formulas for f, g, and h.

   (b) Evaluate and interpret in terms of currency: $h(f(1000))$.

Table 8.14   *Exchange rate for US dollars, Japanese yen and euros, January 10, 2006*

Amount invested	Dollars purchased	Yen purchased	Euros purchased
1 dollar	1.0000	114.64	0.829
1 yen	0.00872	1.0000	0.00723
1 euro	1.2063	138.29	1.0000

---

[1]www.x-rates.com, January 10, 2006. Currency exchange rates fluctuate constantly.

8.2   INVERSE FUNCTIONS

Inverse functions were introduced in Section 2.4. In Section 4.1, we defined the logarithm as the inverse function of the exponential function. In Section 6.7, we defined the arccosine as the inverse of cosine. We now study inverse functions in general.

Definition of Inverse Function

Recall that the statement $f^{-1}(50) = 20$ means that $f(20) = 50$. In fact, the values of f^{-1} are determined in just this way. In general,

> Suppose $Q = f(t)$ is a function with the property that each value of Q determines exactly one value of t. Then f has an **inverse function**, f^{-1} and
>
> $$f^{-1}(Q) = t \quad \text{if and only if} \quad Q = f(t).$$
>
> If a function has an inverse, it is said to be **invertible**.

The definitions of the logarithm and of the inverse cosine have the same form as the definition of f^{-1}. Since $y = \log x$ is the inverse function of $y = 10^x$, we have

$$x = \log y \quad \text{if and only if} \quad y = 10^x,$$

and since $y = \cos^{-1} t$ is the inverse function of $y = \cos t$,

$$t = \cos^{-1} y \quad \text{if and only if} \quad y = \cos t.$$

Example 1   Solve the equation $\sin x = 0.8$ using an inverse function.

Solution   The solution is $x = \sin^{-1}(0.8)$. A calculator (set in radians) gives $x = \sin^{-1}(0.8) \approx 0.927$.

Example 2   Suppose that g is an invertible function, with $g(10) = -26$ and $g^{-1}(0) = 7$. What other values of g and g^{-1} do you know?

Solution   Because $g(10) = -26$, we know that $g^{-1}(-26) = 10$; because $g^{-1}(0) = 7$, we know that $g(7) = 0$.

Example 3   A population is given by the formula $P = f(t) = 20 + 0.4t$ where P is the number of people (in thousands) and t is the number of years since 1980. Evaluate the following quantities. Explain in words what each tells you about the population.

(a) $f(25)$ (b) $f^{-1}(25)$
(c) Show how to estimate $f^{-1}(25)$ from a graph of f.

Solution   (a) Substituting $t = 25$, we have

$$f(25) = 20 + 0.4 \cdot 25 = 30.$$

Thus, in 2005 (year $t = 25$), we have $P = 30$, so the population was 30,000 people.

(b) We have $t = f^{-1}(P)$. Thus, in $f^{-1}(25)$, the 25 is a population. So $f^{-1}(25)$ is the year in which the population reaches 25 thousand. We find t by solving the equation

$$20 + 0.4t = 25$$

$$0.4t = 5$$

$$t = 12.5.$$

Therefore, $f^{-1}(25) = 12.5$, which means that the population reached 25,000 people 12.5 years after 1980, or midway into 1992.

(c) We can estimate $f^{-1}(25)$ by reading the graph of $P = f(t)$ backward as shown in Figure 8.7.

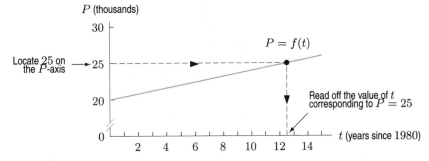

Figure 8.7: Using a graph of the function $P = f(t)$ to read off values of the inverse function $f^{-1}(P)$

Finding a Formula for an Inverse Function

It is sometimes possible to find a formula for an inverse function, f^{-1} from a formula for f. If the function $P = f(t)$ gives the population (in thousands) of a town in year t, then $f^{-1}(P)$ is the year in which the population reaches the value P. In Example 3 we found $f^{-1}(P)$ for $P = 25$. We now perform the same calculations for a general P. Since

$$P = 20 + 0.4t,$$

solving for t gives

$$0.4t = P - 20$$
$$t = \frac{P - 20}{0.4},$$

so

$$f^{-1}(P) = 2.5P - 50.$$

The values in Table 8.15 were calculated using the formula $P = f(t) = 20 + 0.4t$; the values in Table 8.16 were calculated using the formula for $t = f^{-1}(P) = 2.5P - 50$. The table for f^{-1} can be obtained from the table for f by interchanging its columns, because the inverse function reverses the roles of inputs and outputs.

Table 8.15

t	$P = f(t)$
0	20
5	22
10	24
15	26
20	28

Table 8.16

P	$t = f^{-1}(P)$
20	0
22	5
24	10
26	15
28	20

Example 4   Suppose you deposit \$500 into a savings account that pays 4% interest compounded annually. The balance, in dollars, in the account after t years is given by $B = f(t) = 500(1.04)^t$.

(a) Find a formula for $t = f^{-1}(B)$.

(b) What does the inverse function represent in terms of the account?

Solution   (a) To find a formula for f^{-1}, we solve for t in terms of B:

$$B = 500(1.04)^t$$

$$\frac{B}{500} = (1.04)^t$$

$$\log\left(\frac{B}{500}\right) = t \log 1.04 \qquad \text{Taking logs of both sides}$$

$$t = \frac{\log(B/500)}{\log 1.04}.$$

Thus, a formula for the inverse function is

$$t = f^{-1}(B) = \frac{\log(B/500)}{\log 1.04}.$$

(b) The function $t = f^{-1}(B)$ gives the number of years for the balance to grow to \$$B$.

In the previous example the variables of the function $B = f(t)$ had contextual meaning, so the inverse function was written as $t = f^{-1}(B)$. In abstract mathematical examples, a function $y = f(x)$ will often have its inverse function written with x as the independent variable. This situation is shown in the next example.

Example 5   Find the inverse of the function

$$f(x) = \frac{3x}{2x+1}.$$

Solution   First, we solve the equation $y = f(x)$ for x:

$$y = \frac{3x}{2x+1}$$

$$2xy + y = 3x$$

$$2xy - 3x = -y$$

$$x(2y - 3) = -y$$

$$x = \frac{-y}{2y - 3} = \frac{y}{3 - 2y}.$$

As before, we write $x = f^{-1}(y) = \frac{y}{3 - 2y}$.

Since y is now the independent variable, by convention we rewrite the inverse function with x as the independent variable. We have

$$f^{-1}(x) = \frac{x}{3 - 2x}.$$

Noninvertible Functions: Horizontal Line Test

Not every function has an inverse function. A function $Q = f(t)$ has no inverse if it returns the same Q-value for two different t-values. When that happens, the value of t cannot be uniquely determined from the value of Q.

For example, if $q(x) = x^2$ then $q(-3) = 9$ and $q(+3) = 9$. This means that we cannot say what the value $q^{-1}(9)$ would be. (Is it $+3$ or -3?). Thus, q is not invertible. In Figure 8.8, notice that the horizontal line $y = 9$ intersects the graph of $q(x) = x^2$ at two different points: $(-3, 9)$ and $(3, 9)$. This corresponds to the fact that the function q returns $y = 9$ for two different x-values, $x = +3$ and $x = -3$.

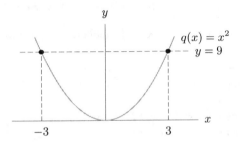

Figure 8.8: The graph of $q(x) = x^2$ fails the horizontal line test

We have the following general result:

The Horizontal Line Test   If there is a horizontal line which intersects a function's graph in more than one point, then the function does not have an inverse. If every horizontal line intersects a function's graph at most once, then the function has an inverse.

Evaluating an Inverse Function Graphically

Finding a formula for an inverse function can be difficult. However, this does not mean that the inverse function does not exist. Even without a formula, it may be possible to find values of the inverse function.

Example 6   Let $u(x) = x^3 + x + 1$. Explain why a graph suggests the function u is invertible. Assuming u has an inverse, estimate $u^{-1}(4)$.

Solution   To show that u is invertible, we could try to find a formula for u^{-1}. To do this, we would solve the equation $y = x^3 + x + 1$ for x. Unfortunately, this is difficult. However, the graph in Figure 8.9 suggests that u passes the horizontal line test and therefore that u is invertible. To estimate $u^{-1}(4)$, we find an x-value such that

$$x^3 + x + 1 = 4.$$

In Figure 8.9, the graph of $y = u(x)$ and the horizontal line $y = 4$ intersect at the point $x \approx 1.213$. Thus, tracing along the graph, we estimate $u^{-1}(4) \approx 1.213$.

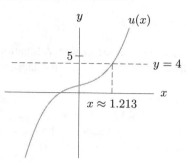

Figure 8.9: The graph of $u(x)$ passes the horizontal line test.
Since $u(1.213) \approx 4$, we have $u^{-1}(4) \approx 1.213$

In Example 6, even without a formula for u^{-1}, we can approximate $u^{-1}(a)$ for any value of a.

Example 7   Let $P(x) = 2^x$.

(a) Show that P is invertible.
(b) Find a formula for $P^{-1}(x)$.
(c) Sketch the graphs of P and P^{-1} on the same axes.
(d) What are the domain and range of P and P^{-1}?

Solution   (a) Since P is an exponential function with base 2, it is always increasing, and therefore passes the horizontal line test. (See the graph of P in Figure 8.10.) Thus, P has an inverse function.

(b) To find a formula for $P^{-1}(x)$, we solve for x in the equation

$$2^x = y.$$

We can take the log of both sides to get

$$\log 2^x = \log y$$
$$x \log 2 = \log y$$
$$x = P^{-1}(y) = \frac{\log y}{\log 2}.$$

Thus, we have a formula for P^{-1} with y as the input. To graph P and P^{-1} on the same axes, we write P^{-1} as a function of x:

$$P^{-1}(x) = \frac{\log x}{\log 2} = \frac{1}{\log 2} \cdot \log x = 3.322 \log x.$$

(c) Table 8.17 gives values of $P(x)$ for $x = -3, -2, \ldots, 3$. Interchanging the columns of Table 8.17 gives Table 8.18 for $P^{-1}(x)$. We use these tables to sketch Figure 8.10.

Table 8.17   *Values of* $P(x) = 2^x$

x	$P(x) = 2^x$
-3	0.125
-2	0.25
-1	0.5
0	1
1	2
2	4
3	8

Table 8.18   *Values of* $P^{-1}(x)$

x	$P^{-1}(x)$
0.125	-3
0.25	-2
0.5	-1
1	0
2	1
4	2
8	3

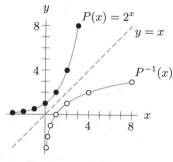

Figure 8.10: The graphs of $P(x) = 2^x$ and its inverse are symmetrical across the line $y = x$

(d) The domain of P, an exponential function, is all real numbers, and its range is all positive numbers. The domain of P^{-1}, a logarithmic function, is all positive numbers and its range is all real numbers.

The Graph, Domain, and Range of an Inverse Function

In Figure 8.10, we see that the graph of P^{-1} is the mirror-image of the graph of P across the line $y = x$. In general, this is true if the x- and y-axes have the same scale. To understand why this occurs, consider how a function is related to its inverse.

If f is an invertible function with, for example, $f(2) = 5$, then $f^{-1}(5) = 2$. Thus, the point $(2, 5)$ is on the graph of f and the point $(5, 2)$ is on the graph of f^{-1}. Generalizing, if (a, b) is any point on the graph of f, then (b, a) is a point on the graph of f^{-1}. Figure 8.11 shows how reflecting the point (a, b) across the line $y = x$ gives the point (b, a). Consequently, the graph of f^{-1} is the reflection of the graph of f across the line $y = x$.

Notice that outputs from a function are inputs to its inverse function. Similarly, outputs from the inverse function are inputs to the original function. This is expressed in the statement $f^{-1}(b) = a$ if and only if $f(a) = b$, and also in the fact that we can obtain a table for f^{-1} by interchanging the columns of a table for f. Consequently, the domain and range for f^{-1} are obtained by interchanging the domain and range of f. In other words,

$$\text{Domain of } f^{-1} = \text{Range of } f \qquad \text{and} \qquad \text{Range of } f^{-1} = \text{Domain of } f.$$

In Example 7, the function P has all real numbers as its domain and all positive numbers as its range; the function P^{-1} has all positive numbers as its domain and all real numbers as its range.

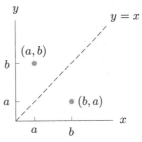

Figure 8.11: The reflection of the point (a, b) across the line $y = x$ is the point (b, a)

A Property of Inverse Functions

The fact that Tables 8.17 and 8.18 contain the same values, but with the columns switched, reflects the special relationship between the values of $P(x)$ and $P^{-1}(x)$. For the population function in Example 7

$$P^{-1}(2) = 1 \quad \text{and} \quad P(1) = 2 \quad \text{so} \quad P^{-1}(P(1)) = 1,$$

and

$$P^{-1}(0.25) = -2 \quad \text{and} \quad P(-2) = 0.25 \quad \text{so} \quad P^{-1}(P(-2)) = -2.$$

This result holds for any input x, so in general,

$$P^{-1}(P(x)) = x.$$

In addition, $P(P^{-1}(2)) = 2$ and $P(P^{-1}(0.25)) = 0.25$, and for any x

$$P(P^{-1}(x)) = x.$$

Similar reasoning holds for any other invertible function, suggesting the general result:

> If $y = f(x)$ is an invertible function and $y = f^{-1}(x)$ is its inverse, then
> - $f^{-1}(f(x)) = x$ for all values of x for which $f(x)$ is defined,
> - $f(f^{-1}(x)) = x$ for all values of x for which $f^{-1}(x)$ is defined.

This property tell us that composing a function and its inverse function returns the original value as the end result. We can use this property to decide whether two functions are inverses.

Example 8   (a) Check that $f(x) = \dfrac{x}{2x + 1}$ and $f^{-1}(x) = \dfrac{x}{1 - 2x}$ are inverse functions of each other.
(b) Graph f and f^{-1} on axes with the same scale. What are the domains and ranges of f and f^{-1}?

Solution   (a) To check that these functions are inverses, we compose

$$f^{-1}(f(x)) = \frac{f(x)}{1 - 2f(x)} = \frac{\dfrac{x}{2x + 1}}{1 - 2\left(\dfrac{x}{2x + 1}\right)}$$

$$= \frac{\dfrac{x}{2x + 1}}{\dfrac{2x + 1}{2x + 1} - \dfrac{2x}{2x + 1}}$$

$$= \frac{\dfrac{x}{2x + 1}}{\dfrac{1}{2x + 1}}$$

$$= x.$$

Similarly, you can check that $f(f^{-1}(x)) = x$.
(b) The graphs of f and f^{-1} in Figure 8.12 are symmetric about the line $y = x$.

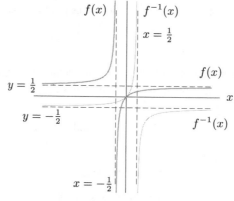

Figure 8.12: The graph of $f(x) = x/(2x + 1)$ and the inverse $f^{-1}(x) = x/(1 - 2x)$

The function $f(x) = x/(2x + 1)$ is undefined at $x = -1/2$, so its domain consists of all real numbers except $-1/2$. Figure 8.12 suggests that f has a horizontal asymptote at $y = 1/2$ which it does not cross and that its range is all real numbers except $1/2$.

Because the inverse function $f^{-1}(x) = x/(1 - 2x)$ is undefined at $x = 1/2$, its domain is all real numbers except $1/2$. Note that this is the same as the range of f. The graph of f^{-1} appears to have a horizontal asymptote which it does not cross at $y = -1/2$ suggesting that its range is all real numbers except $-1/2$. Note that this is the same as the domain of f.

The ranges of the functions f and f^{-1} can be confirmed algebraically.

Restricting the Domain

A function that fails the horizontal line test is not invertible. For this reason, the function $f(x) = x^2$ does not have an inverse function. However, by considering only part of the graph of f, we can eliminate the duplication of y-values. Suppose we consider the half of the parabola with $x \geq 0$. See Figure 8.13. This part of the graph does pass the horizontal line test because there is only one (positive) x-value for each y-value in the range of f.

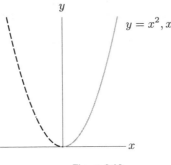

Figure 8.13

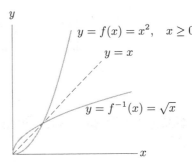

Figure 8.14

We can find an inverse for $f(x) = x^2$ on its restricted domain,[2] $x \geq 0$. Using the fact that $x \geq 0$ and solving $y = x^2$ for x gives

$$x = \sqrt{y}.$$

Thus a formula for the inverse function is

$$x = f^{-1}(y) = \sqrt{y}.$$

Rewriting the formula for f^{-1} with x as the input, we have

$$f^{-1}(x) = \sqrt{x}.$$

The graphs of f and f^{-1} are shown in Figure 8.14. Note that the domain of f is the the range of f^{-1}, and the domain of f^{-1} $(x \geq 0)$ is the range of f.

In Section 6.7 we restricted the domains of the sine, cosine, and tangent functions in order to define their inverse functions:

$$y = \sin^{-1} x \quad \text{if and only if} \quad x = \sin y \quad \text{and} \quad -\frac{\pi}{2} \leq y \leq \frac{\pi}{2}$$

$$y = \cos^{-1} x \quad \text{if and only if} \quad x = \cos y \quad \text{and} \quad 0 \leq y \leq \pi$$

$$y = \tan^{-1} x \quad \text{if and only if} \quad x = \tan y \quad \text{and} \quad -\frac{\pi}{2} < y < \frac{\pi}{2}.$$

---

[2]Technically, changing the domain results in a new function, but we will continue to call it $f(x)$.

The graphs of each of the inverse trigonometric functions are shown in Figures 8.15-8.17. Note the symmetry about the line $y = x$ for each trigonometric function and its inverse.

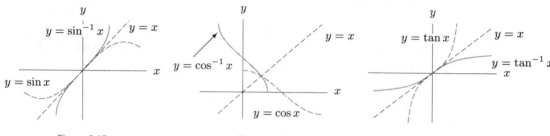

Figure 8.15   Figure 8.16   Figure 8.17

In each case, the restricted domain of the function is the range of the inverse function. In addition, the domain of the inverse is the range of the original function. For example

$$y = \sin x \qquad \text{has restricted domain } -\frac{\pi}{2} \leq x \leq \frac{\pi}{2} \qquad \text{and} \qquad \text{range} \quad -1 \leq y \leq 1$$
$$y = \sin^{-1} x \qquad \text{has domain} \qquad -1 \leq x \leq 1 \qquad \text{and} \qquad \text{range} \quad -\frac{\pi}{2} \leq y \leq \frac{\pi}{2}.$$

Exercises and Problems for Section 8.2

Exercises

In Exercises 1–6, use a graph to decide whether or not the function is invertible.

1. $y = x^6 + 2x^2 - 10$ **2.** $y = x^4 - 6x + 12$

3. $y = e^{x^2}$ **4.** $y = \cos(x^3)$

5. $y = |x|$ **6.** $y = x + \ln x$

In Exercises 7–14, check that the functions are inverses.

7. $f(x) = \dfrac{x}{4} - \dfrac{3}{2}$ and $g(t) = 4\left(t + \dfrac{3}{2}\right)$

8. $f(x) = 1 + 7x^3$ and $f^{-1}(x) = \sqrt[3]{\dfrac{x-1}{7}}$

9. $g(x) = 1 - \dfrac{1}{x-1}$ and $g^{-1}(x) = 1 + \dfrac{1}{1-x}$

10. $h(x) = \sqrt{2x}$ and $k(t) = \dfrac{t^2}{2}$, for $x, t \geq 0$

11. $f(x) = e^{x+1}$ and $f^{-1}(x) = \ln x - 1$

12. $f(x) = e^{2x}$ and $f^{-1}(x) = \dfrac{\ln x}{2}$

13. $f(x) = e^{x/2}$ and $f^{-1}(x) = 2 \ln x$

14. $f(x) = \ln(x/2)$ and $f^{-1}(x) = 2e^x$

Find the inverses of the functions in Exercises 15–27.

15. $h(x) = 12x^3$ **16.** $h(x) = \dfrac{x}{2x+1}$

17. $k(x) = 3 \cdot e^{2x}$ **18.** $g(x) = e^{3x+1}$

19. $n(x) = \log(x - 3)$ **20.** $h(x) = \ln(1 - 2x)$

21. $h(x) = \dfrac{\sqrt{x}}{\sqrt{x}+1}$ **22.** $g(x) = \dfrac{x-2}{2x+3}$

23. $f(x) = \sqrt{\dfrac{4-7x}{4-x}}$ **24.** $f(x) = \dfrac{\sqrt{x}+3}{11-\sqrt{x}}$

25. $f(x) = \ln\left(1 + \dfrac{1}{x}\right)$ **26.** $s(x) = \dfrac{3}{2 + \log x}$

27. $q(x) = \ln(x + 3) - \ln(x - 5)$

Problems

28. Let $f(x) = e^x$ and $g(x) = \ln x$.

    (a) Find $f(g(x))$ and $g(f(x))$. What can you conclude about the relationship between these two functions?

    (b) Graph $f(x)$ and $g(x)$ together on axes with the same scales. What is the line of symmetry of the graph?

29. Let $p(t) = 10^t$ and $q(t) = \log t$.

    (a) Find $p(q(t))$ and $q(p(t))$. What can you conclude about the relationship between these two functions?

    (b) Graph $p(t)$ and $q(t)$ together on ty-axes with the same scales. What is the line of symmetry of the graph?

30. Let $C = f(q) = 200 + 0.1q$ give the cost in dollars to manufacture q kg of a chemical. Find and interpret $f^{-1}(C)$.

31. Let $P = f(t) = 10e^{0.02t}$ give the population in millions at time t in years. Find and interpret $f^{-1}(P)$.

32. If $t = g(v)$ represents the time in hours it takes to drive to the next town at velocity v mph, what does $g^{-1}(t)$ represent? What are its units?

33. The noise level, N, of a sound in decibels is given by

$$N = f(I) = 10 \log \left(\frac{I}{I_0} \right),$$

where I is the intensity of the sound and I_0 is a constant. Find and interpret $f^{-1}(N)$.

Solve the equations in Problems 34–39 exactly. Use an inverse function when appropriate.

34. $7 \sin(3x) = 2$

35. $2^{x+5} = 3$

36. $x^{1.05} = 1.09$

37. $\ln(x + 3) = 1.8$

38. $\dfrac{2x + 3}{x + 3} = 8$

39. $\sqrt{x + \sqrt{x}} = 3$

40. Values of f and g are in Table 8.19. Based on this table:

    (a) Is $f(x)$ invertible? If not, explain why; if so, construct a table of values of $f^{-1}(x)$ for all values of x for which $f^{-1}(x)$ is defined.

    (b) Answer the same question as in part (a) for $g(x)$.

    (c) Make a table of values for $h(x) = f(g(x))$, with $x = -3, -2, -1, 0, 1, 2, 3$.

    (d) Explain why you cannot define a function $j(x)$ by the formula $j(x) = g(f(x))$.

Table 8.19

x	-3	-2	-1	0	1	2	3
$f(x)$	9	7	6	-4	-5	-8	-9
$g(x)$	3	1	3	2	-3	-1	3

41. Figure 8.18 defines the function f. Rank the following quantities in order from least to greatest: $0, f(0), f^{-1}(0), 3, f(3), f^{-1}(3)$.

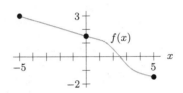

Figure 8.18

42. Let $f(x) = e^x$. Solve each of the following equations exactly for x.

    (a) $(f(x))^{-1} = 2$ **(b)** $f^{-1}(x) = 2$

    (c) $f(x^{-1}) = 2$

43. Simplify the expression $\cos^2(\arcsin t)$, using the property that inverses "undo" each other.

44. Let $Q = f(t) = 20(0.96)^{t/3}$ be the number of grams of a radioactive substance remaining after t years.

    (a) Describe the behavior of the radioactive substance as a function of time.

    (b) Evaluate $f(8)$. Explain the meaning of this quantity in practical terms.

    (c) Find a formula for $f^{-1}(Q)$ in terms of Q.

    (d) Evaluate $f^{-1}(8)$. Explain the meaning of this quantity in practical terms.

45. **(a)** What is the formula for the area of a circle in terms of its radius?

    (b) Graph this function for the domain all real numbers.

    (c) What domain actually applies in this situation? On separate axes, graph the function for this domain.

    (d) Find the inverse of the function in part (c).

    (e) Graph the inverse function on the domain you gave in part (c) on the same axes used in part (c).

    (f) If area is a function of the radius, is radius a function of area? Explain carefully.

46. A company believes there is a linear relationship between the consumer demand for its products and the price charged. When the price was \$3 per unit, the quantity demanded was 500 units per week. When the unit price was raised to \$4, the quantity demanded dropped to 300 units per week. Let $D(p)$ be the quantity per week demanded by consumers at a unit price of \$$p$.

 (a) Estimate and interpret $D(5)$.
 (b) Find a formula for $D(p)$ in terms of p.
 (c) Calculate and interpret $D^{-1}(5)$.
 (d) Give an interpretation of the slope of $D(p)$ in terms of demand.
 (e) Currently, the company can produce 400 units every week. What should the price of the product be if the company wants to sell all 400 units?
 (f) If the company produced 500 units per week instead of 400 units per week, would its weekly revenues increase, and if so, by how much?

47. Table 8.20 gives the number of cows in a herd.

 (a) Find an exponential function that approximates the data.
 (b) Find the inverse function of the function in part (a).
 (c) When do you predict that the herd will contain 400 cows?

Table 8.20

t (years)	0	1	2
$P(t)$ (cows)	150	165	182

48. Suppose $P = f(t)$ is the population (in thousands) in year t, and that $f(7) = 13$ and $f(12) = 20$,

 (a) Find a formula for $f(t)$ assuming f is exponential.
 (b) Find a formula for $f^{-1}(P)$.
 (c) Evaluate $f(25)$ and $f^{-1}(25)$. Explain what these expressions mean in terms of population.

49. A gymnast at Ringling Brothers, Barnum, & Bailey Circus is fired straight up in the air from a cannon. While she is in the air, a trampoline is moved into the spot where the cannon was. Figure 8.19 is a graph of the gymnast's height, h, as a function of time, t.

 (a) Approximately what is her maximum height?
 (b) Approximately when does she land on the trampoline?
 (c) Restrict the domain of $h(t)$ so that $h(t)$ has an inverse. That is, pick a piece of the graph on which $h(t)$ does have an inverse. Graph this new restricted function.
 (d) Change the story to go with your graph in part (c).

 (e) Graph the inverse of the function in part (c). Explain in your story why it makes sense that the inverse is a function.

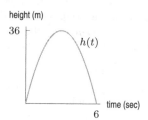

Figure 8.19

50. A 100 ml solution contains 99% alcohol and 1% water. Let $y = C(x)$ be the concentration of alcohol in the solution after x ml of alcohol are removed, so

$$C(x) = \frac{\text{Amount of alcohol}}{\text{Amount of solution}}.$$

 (a) What is $C(0)$?
 (b) Find a formula in terms of x for $C(x)$.
 (c) Find a formula in terms of y for $C^{-1}(y)$.
 (d) Explain the physical significance of $C^{-1}(y)$.

51. (a) How much alcohol do you think should be removed from the 99% solution in Problem 50 in order to obtain a 98% solution? (Make a guess.)
 (b) Express the exact answer to part (a) using the function C^{-1} you found in Problem 62.
 (c) Determine the exact answer to part (a). Are you surprised by your result?

The predicted pulse in beats per minute (bpm) of a healthy person fifteen minutes after consuming q milligrams of caffeine is given by $r = f(q)$. The amount of caffeine in a serving of coffee is q_c, and $r_c = f(q_c)$. Assume that f is an increasing function for non-toxic levels of caffeine. What do the statements in Problems 52–57 tell you about caffeine and a person's pulse?

52. $f(2q_c)$

53. $f^{-1}(r_c + 20)$

54. $2f^{-1}(r_c) + 20$

55. $f(q_c) - f(0)$

56. $f^{-1}(r_c + 20) - q_c$

57. $f^{-1}(1.1f(q_c))$

58. Suppose that f, g, and h are invertible and that

$$f(x) = g(h(x)).$$

Find a formula for $f^{-1}(x)$ in terms of g^{-1} and h^{-1}.

59. The von Bertalanffy growth model predicts the mean length L of fish of age t (in years):[3]

$$L = f(t) = L_\infty \left(1 - e^{-k(t+t_0)} \right), \text{ for constant } L_\infty, k, t_0.$$

Find a formula for f^{-1}. Describe in words what f^{-1} tells you about fish. What is the domain of f^{-1}?

8.3 COMBINATIONS OF FUNCTIONS

Like numbers, functions can be combined using addition, subtraction, multiplication, and division.

The Difference of Two Functions Defined by Formulas: A Measure of Prosperity

We can define new functions as the sum or difference of two functions. In Chapter 3, we discussed Thomas Malthus, who predicted widespread food shortages because he believed that human populations increase exponentially, whereas the food supply increases linearly. We considered a country with population $P(t)$ million in year t. The population is initially 2 million and grows at the rate of 4% per year, so

$$P(t) = 2(1.04)^t.$$

Let $N(t)$ be the number of people (in millions) that the country can feed in year t. The annual food supply is initially adequate for 4 million people and it increases by enough for an additional 0.5 million people every year. Thus

$$N(t) = 4 + 0.5t.$$

This country first experiences shortages in about 78 years. (See Figure 8.20.) When is it most prosperous?

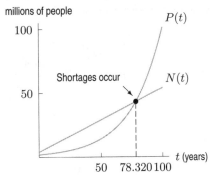

Figure 8.20: Predicted population, $P(t)$, and number of people who can be fed, $N(t)$, over a 100-year period

The answer depends on how we decide to measure prosperity. We could measure prosperity in one of the following ways:
- By the food surplus—that is, the amount of food the country has over and above its needs. This surplus food could be warehoused or exported in trade.
- By the per capita food supply—that is, how much food there is per person. (The term *per capita* means per person, or literally, "per head.") This indicates the portion of the country's wealth each person might enjoy.

[3] *Introduction to Tropical Fish Stock Assessment* by Per Sparre, Danish Institute for Fisheries Research, and Siebren C. Venema, FAO Fisheries Department, available at http://www.fao.org/docrep/W5449E/w5449e00.htm.

First, we choose to measure prosperity in terms of food surplus, $S(t)$, in year t, where

$$S(t) = \underbrace{\text{Number of people that can be fed}}_{N(t)} - \underbrace{\text{Number of people living in the country}}_{P(t)}$$

so

$$S(t) = N(t) - P(t).$$

For example, to determine the surplus in year $t = 25$, we evaluate

$$S(25) = N(25) - P(25).$$

Since $N(25) = 4 + 0.5(25) = 16.5$ and $P(25) = 2(1.04)^{25} \approx 5.332$, we have

$$S(25) \approx 16.5 - 5.332 = 11.168.$$

Thus, in year 25 the food surplus could feed 11.168 million additional people.

We use the formulas for N and P to find a formula for S:

$$S(t) = \underbrace{N(t)}_{4+0.5t} - \underbrace{P(t)}_{2(1.04)^t},$$

so

$$S(t) = 4 + 0.5t - 2(1.04)^t.$$

A graph of S is shown in Figure 8.21. The maximum surplus occurs sometime during the 48th year. In that year, there is surplus food sufficient for an additional 14.865 million people.

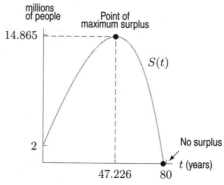

Figure 8.21: Surplus graphed using the formula
$S(t) = 4 + 0.5t - 2(1.04)^t$

The Sum and Difference of Two Functions Defined by Graphs

How does the graph of the surplus function S, shown in Figure 8.21, relate to the graphs of N and P in Figure 8.20? Since

$$S(t) = N(t) - P(t),$$

the value of $S(t)$ is represented graphically as the vertical distance between the graphs of $N(t)$ and $P(t)$. See Figure 8.22. Figure 8.23 shows the surplus plotted against time.

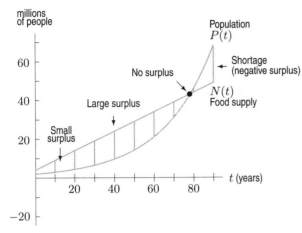

Figure 8.22: Surplus, $S(t) = N(t) - P(t)$, as vertical distance between $N(t)$ and $P(t)$ graphs

Figure 8.23: Surplus as a function of time

From year $t = 0$ to $t \approx 78.320$, the food supply is more than the population needs. Therefore the surplus, $S(t)$, is positive on this time interval. At time $t = 78.320$, the food supply is exactly sufficient for the population, so $S(t) = 0$, resulting in the horizontal intercept $t = 78.320$ on the graph of $S(t)$ in Figure 8.23. For times $t > 78.320$, the food supply is less than the population needs. Therefore the surplus is negative, representing a food shortage.

In the next example we consider a sum of two functions.

Example 1   Let $f(x) = x$ and $g(x) = \dfrac{1}{x}$. By adding vertical distances on the graphs of f and g, sketch

$$h(x) = f(x) + g(x) \quad \text{for } x > 0.$$

Solution   The graphs of f and g are shown in Figure 8.24. For each value of x, we add the vertical distances that represent $f(x)$ and $g(x)$ to get a point on the graph of $h(x)$. Compare the graph of $h(x)$ to the values shown in Table 8.21.

Table 8.21   *Adding function values*

x	$\frac{1}{4}$	$\frac{1}{2}$	1	2	4
$f(x) = x$	$\frac{1}{4}$	$\frac{1}{2}$	1	2	4
$g(x) = 1/x$	4	2	1	$\frac{1}{2}$	$\frac{1}{4}$
$h(x) = f(x) + g(x)$	$4\frac{1}{4}$	$2\frac{1}{2}$	2	$2\frac{1}{2}$	$4\frac{1}{4}$

Note that as x increases, $g(x)$ decreases toward zero, so the values of $h(x)$ get closer to the values of $f(x)$. On the other hand, as x approaches zero, $h(x)$ gets closer to $g(x)$.

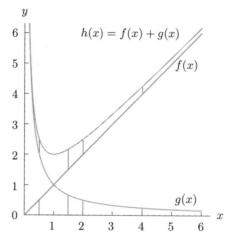

Figure 8.24: Graph of $h(x) = f(x) + g(x)$ constructed by adding vertical distances under f and g

Factoring a Function's Formula into a Product

It is often useful to be able to express a given function as a product of functions.

Example 2   Find exactly all the zeros of the function
$$p(x) = 2^x \cdot 6x^2 - 2^x \cdot x - 2^{x+1}.$$

Solution   We could approximate the zeros by finding the points where the graph of the function p crosses the x-axis. Unfortunately, these solutions are not exact. Alternatively, we can express p as a product. Using the fact that
$$2^{x+1} = 2^x \cdot 2^1 = 2 \cdot 2^x,$$
we rewrite the formula for p as
$$\begin{aligned}
p(x) &= 2^x \cdot 6x^2 - 2^x x - 2 \cdot 2^x \\
&= 2^x(6x^2 - x - 2) && \text{Factoring out } 2^x \\
&= 2^x(2x + 1)(3x - 2) && \text{Factoring the quadratic.}
\end{aligned}$$

Thus p is the product of the exponential function 2^x and two linear functions. Since p is a product, it equals zero if one or more of its factors equals zero. But 2^x is never equal to 0, so $p(x)$ equals zero if and only if one of the linear factors is zero:
$$\begin{aligned}
(2x + 1) = 0 \qquad & \text{or } (3x - 2) = 0 \\
x = -\frac{1}{2} \qquad\qquad & \qquad x = \frac{2}{3}.
\end{aligned}$$

The Quotient of Functions Defined by Formulas and Graphs: Prosperity

Now let's think about our second proposed measure of prosperity, the per capita food supply, $R(t)$. With this definition of prosperity
$$R(t) = \frac{\text{Number of people that can be fed}}{\text{Number of people living in the country}} = \frac{N(t)}{P(t)}.$$

For example,
$$R(25) = \frac{N(25)}{P(25)} = \frac{16.5}{5.332} \approx 3.1.$$

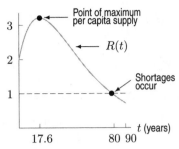

Figure 8.25: Per capita food supply,
$R(t) = \frac{N(t)}{P(t)}$

This means that in year 25, everybody in the country could, on average, have more than three times as much food as he or she needs. The formula for $R(t)$ is

$$R(t) = \frac{N(t)}{P(t)} = \frac{4 + 0.5t}{2(1.04)^t}.$$

From the graph of R in Figure 8.25, we see that the maximum per capita food supply occurs during the 18th year. Notice this maximum prosperity prediction is different from the one made using the surplus function $S(t)$.

However, both prosperity models predict that shortages begin after time $t = 78.320$. This is not a coincidence. The food surplus model predicts shortages when $S(t) = N(t) - P(t) < 0$, or $N(t) < P(t)$. The per capita food supply model predicts shortages when $R(t) < 1$, meaning that the amount of food available per person is less than the amount necessary to feed 1 person. Since $R(t) = \frac{N(t)}{P(t)} < 1$ is true only when $N(t) < P(t)$, the same condition leads to shortages.

The Quotient of Functions Defined by Tables: Per Capita Crime Rate

Table 8.22 gives the number of violent crimes committed in two cities between 2000 and 2005. It appears that crime in both cities is on the rise and that there is less crime in City B than in City A.

Table 8.22   *Number of violent crimes committed each year in two cities*

Year	2000	2001	2002	2003	2004	2005
t, years since 2000	0	1	2	3	4	5
Crimes in City A	793	795	807	818	825	831
Crimes in City B	448	500	525	566	593	652

Table 8.23 gives the population for these two cities from 2000 to 2005. The population of City A is larger than that of City B and both cities are growing.

Table 8.23   *Population of the two cities*

Year	2000	2001	2002	2003	2004	2005
t, years since 2000	0	1	2	3	4	5
Population of City A	61,000	62,100	63,220	64,350	65,510	66,690
Population of City B	28,000	28,588	29,188	29,801	30,427	31,066

Can we attribute the growth in crime in both cities to the population growth? Can we attribute the larger number of crimes in City A to its larger population? To answer these questions, we consider the per capita crime rate in each city.

Let's define $N_A(t)$ to be the number of crimes in City A during year t (where $t = 0$ means 2000). Similarly, let's define $P_A(t)$ to be the population of City A in year t. Then the per capita crime rate in City A, $r_A(t)$, is given by

$$r_A(t) = \frac{\text{Number of crimes in year } t}{\text{Number of people in year } t} = \frac{N_A(t)}{P_A(t)}.$$

We have defined a new function, $r_A(t)$, as the quotient of $N_A(t)$ and $P_A(t)$. For example, the data in Tables 8.22 and 8.23 shows that the per capita crime rate for City A in year $t = 0$ is

$$r_A(0) = \frac{N_A(0)}{P_A(0)} = \frac{793}{61,000} = 0.0130 \text{ crimes per person.}$$

Similarly, the per capita crime rate for the year $t = 1$ is

$$r_A(1) = \frac{N_A(1)}{P_A(1)} = \frac{795}{62,100} = 0.0128 \text{ crimes per person.}$$

Thus, the per capita crime rate in City A actually decreased from 0.0130 crimes per person in 2000 to 0.0128 crimes per person in 2001.

Example 3   (a) Make a table of values for $r_A(t)$ and $r_B(t)$, the per capita crime rates of Cities A and B.
(b) Use the table to decide which city is more dangerous.

Solution   (a) Table 8.24 gives values of $r_A(t)$ for $t = 0, 1, \ldots, 5$. The per capita crime rate in City A declined between 2000 and 2005 despite the fact that the total number of crimes rose during this period. Table 8.24 also gives values of $r_B(t)$, the per capita crime rate of City B, defined by

$$r_B(t) = \frac{N_B(t)}{P_B(t)},$$

where $N_B(t)$ is the number of crimes in City B in year t and $P_B(t)$ is the population of City B in year t. For example, the per capita crime rate in City B in year $t = 0$ is

$$r_B(0) = \frac{N_B(0)}{P_B(0)} = \frac{448}{28,000} = 0.016 \text{ crimes per person.}$$

Table 8.24   *Values of $r_A(t)$ and $r_B(t)$, the per capita violent crime rates of Cities A and B*

Year	2000	2001	2002	2003	2004	2005
t, years since 2000	0	1	2	3	4	5
$r_A(t) = N_A(t)/P_A(t)$	0.0130	0.0128	0.01276	0.01271	0.01259	0.01246
$r_B(t) = N_B(t)/P_B(t)$	0.01600	0.01749	0.01799	0.01899	0.01949	0.02099

(b) From Table 8.24, we see that between 2000 and 2005, City A has a lower per capita crime rate than City B. The crime rate of City A is decreasing, whereas the crime rate of City B is increasing. Thus, even though Table 8.22 indicates that there are more crimes committed in City A, Table 8.24 tells us that City B is, in some sense, more dangerous. Table 8.24 also tells us that, even though the number of crimes is rising in both cities, City A is getting safer, while City B is getting more dangerous.

Exercises and Problems for Section 8.3

In Exercises 1–6, find the following functions.

(a) $f(x) + g(x)$ (b) $f(x) - g(x)$
(c) $f(x)g(x)$ (d) $f(x)/g(x)$

1. $f(x) = x + 1 \quad g(x) = 3x^2$

2. $f(x) = x^2 + 4 \quad g(x) = x + 2$

3. $f(x) = x + 5 \quad g(x) = x - 5$

4. $f(x) = x^2 + 4 \quad g(x) = x^2 + 2$

5. $f(x) = x^3 \quad g(x) = x^2$

6. $f(x) = \sqrt{x} \quad g(x) = x^2 + 2$

In Exercises 7–12, find a simplified formula for the function. Let $m(x) = 3x^2 - x$, $n(x) = 2x$, and $o(x) = \sqrt{x + 2}$.

7. $f(x) = m(x) + n(x)$ **8.** $g(x) = (o(x))^2$

9. $h(x) = n(x)o(x)$ **10.** $i(x) = m(o(x))n(x)$

11. $j(x) = (m(x))/n(x)$

12. $k(x) = m(x) - n(x) - o(x)$

In Exercises 13–16, let $u(x) = e^x$ and $v(x) = 2x + 1$. Find a simplified formula for the function.

13. $f(x) = u(x)v(x)$ **14.** $g(x) = u(x)^2 + v(x)^2$

15. $h(x) = (v(u(x)))^2$ **16.** $k(x) = v(u(x)^2)$

Find formulas for the functions in Exercises 17–22. Let $f(x) = \sin x$ and $g(x) = x^2$.

17. $f(x) + g(x)$ **18.** $g(x)f(x)$

19. $f(x)/g(x)$ **20.** $f(g(x))$

21. $g(f(x))$ **22.** $1 - (f(x))^2$

23. **(a)** On the same set of axes, graph $f(x) = (x - 4)^2 - 2$ and $g(x) = -(x - 2)^2 + 8$.
     (b) Make a table of values for f and g for $x = 0, 1, 2, ..., 6$.
     (c) Make a table of values for $y = f(x) - g(x)$ for $x = 0, 1, 2, ..., 6$.
     (d) On your graph, sketch the vertical line segment of length $f(x) - g(x)$ for each integer value of x from 0 to 6. Check that the segment lengths agree with the values from part (c).
     (e) Plot the values from your table for the function $y = f(x) - g(x)$ on your graph.
     (f) Simplify the formulas for $f(x)$ and $g(x)$ in part (a). Find a formula for $y = f(x) - g(x)$.
     (g) Use part (f) to graph $y = f(x) - g(x)$ on the same axes as f and g. Does the graph pass through the points you plotted in part (e)?

24. Figure 8.26 shows a weight attached to the end of a spring which is hanging from the ceiling. The weight is pulled down from the ceiling and then released. The weight oscillates up and down, but over time, friction decreases the magnitude of the vertical oscillations. Which of the following functions could describe the distance of the weight from the ceiling, d, as a function of time, t?

(i) $d = 2 + \cos t$ (ii) $d = 2 + e^{-t} \cos t$
(iii) $d = 2 + \cos(e^t)$ (iv) $d = 2 + e^{\cos t}$

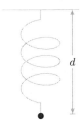

Figure 8.26

25. Table 8.25 gives the upper household income limits for the tenth and ninety-fifth percentiles t years after 1993.[4] For instance, $P_{10}(5) = 9{,}700$ tells us that in 1998 the maximum income for a household in the poorest 10% of all households was $9,700. Let $f(t) = P_{95}(t) - P_{10}(t)$ and $g(t) = P_{95}(t)/P_{10}(t)$.

     (a) Make tables of values for f and g.

---

[4]US Census Bureau, *The Changing Shape of the Nation's Income Distribution*, accessed December 29, 2005, at www.census.gov/prod/2000pubs/p60-204.pdf.

(b) Describe in words what f and g tell you about household income.

Table 8.25

Table 8.25

t (yrs)	0	1	2
$P_{10}(t)$ ($)	8670	8830	9279
$P_{95}(t)$ ($)	118,036	120,788	120,860
t (yrs)	3	4	5
$P_{10}(t)$ ($)	9256	9359	9700
$P_{95}(t)$ ($)	124,187	128,521	132,199

26. Use Table 8.26 to make tables of values for $x = -1, 0,$ $1, 2, 3, 4$ for the following functions.

(a) $h(x) = f(x) + g(x)$ **(b)** $j(x) = 2f(x)$
(c) $k(x) = (g(x))^2$ **(d)** $m(x) = g(x)/f(x)$

Table 8.26

x	−1	0	1	2	3	4
$f(x)$	−4	−1	2	5	8	11
$g(x)$	4	1	0	1	4	9

27. Use Figure 8.27 to graph the following functions.

(a) $y = g(x) - 3$ **(b)** $y = g(x) + x$

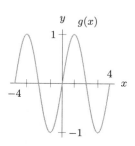

Figure 8.27

28. Graph $h(x) = f(x) + g(x)$ using Figure 8.28.

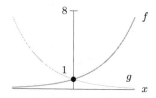

Figure 8.28

29. Use Figure 8.29 to graph $h(x) = g(x) - f(x)$. On the graph of $h(x)$, label the points whose x-coordinates are $x = a$, $x = b$, and $x = c$. Label the y-intercept.

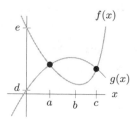

Figure 8.29

30. (a) Find possible formulas for the functions in Figure 8.30.
(b) Let $h(x) = f(x) \cdot g(x)$. Graph $f(x)$, $g(x)$ and $h(x)$ on the same set of axes.

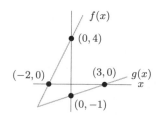

Figure 8.30

31. Use Figure 8.31 to graph $c(x) = a(x) \cdot b(x)$. [Hint: There is not enough information to determine formulas for a and b but you can use the method of Problem 30.]

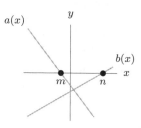

Figure 8.31

32. Sketch two linear functions whose product is the function f graphed in Figure 8.32(a). Explain why this is not possible for the function q graphed in Figure 8.32(b).

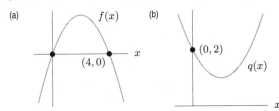

Figure 8.32

33. Let $f(x) = x + 1$ and $g(x) = x^2 - 1$. In parts (a)–(e), write a formula in terms of $f(x)$ and $g(x)$ for the function. Then evaluate the formula for $x = 3$. Write a formula in terms of x for each function. Check your formulas for $x = 3$.

(a) $h(x)$ is the sum of $f(x)$ and $g(x)$.
(b) $j(x)$ is the difference between $g(x)$ and twice $f(x)$.
(c) $k(x)$ is the product of $f(x)$ and $g(x)$.
(d) $m(x)$ is the ratio of $g(x)$ to $f(x)$.
(e) $n(x)$ is defined by $n(x) = (f(x))^2 - g(x)$.

34. An average of 50,000 people visit Riverside Park each day in the summer. The park charges $15.00 for admission. Consultants predict that for each $1.00 increase in the entrance price, the park would lose an average of 2500 customers per day. Express the daily revenue from ticket sales as a function of the number of $1.00 price increases. What ticket price maximizes the revenue from ticket sales?

35. In Figure 8.33, the line l_2 is fixed and the point P moves along l_2. Define $f(\theta)$ as the y-coordinate of P.

(a) Find a formula for $f(\theta)$ if $0 < \theta < \pi/2$. [Hint: Use the equation for l_2.]
(b) Graph $y = f(\theta)$ on the interval $-\pi \leq \theta \leq \pi$.
(c) How does the y-coordinate of P change as θ changes? Is $y = f(\theta)$ periodic?

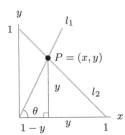

Figure 8.33

36. Describe the similarities and differences between the graphs of $y = \sin(1/x)$ and $y = 1/\sin x$.

37. Let $f(x) = kx^2 + B$ and $g(x) = C^{2x}$ and

$$h(x) = kx^2 C^{2x} + BC^{2x} + C^{2x}.$$

Suppose $f(3) = 7$ and $g(3) = 5$. Evaluate $h(3)$.

38. Is the following statement true or false? If $f(x) \cdot g(x)$ is an odd function, then both $f(x)$ and $g(x)$ are odd functions. Explain your answer.

39. (a) Is the sum of two even functions even, odd, or neither? Justify your answer.
(b) Is the sum of two odd functions even, odd, or neither? Justify your answer.
(c) Is the sum of an even and an odd function even, odd, or neither? Justify your answer.

40. Let $f(t)$ be the number of men and $g(t)$ be the number of women in Canada in year t. Let $h(t)$ be the average income, in Canadian dollars, of women in Canada in year t.

(a) Find the function $p(t)$ which gives the number of people in Canada in year t.
(b) Find the total amount of money $m(t)$ earned by Canadian women in year t.

41. At the Mauna Loa Observatory, measurements of CO_2 levels (ppm) in the atmosphere reveal a slow exponential increase due to deforestation and burning of fossil fuels, and a periodic seasonal variation.

(a) In 1960, the average CO_2 level was 316.75 parts per million and was rising by 0.4% per year. Write the average annual CO_2 level as an exponential function of time, t, in years since 1960.
(b) Each year, the CO_2 level oscillates once between 3.25 ppm above and 3.25 ppm below the average level. Write a sinusoidal function for the seasonal variation in CO_2 levels in terms of time, t.
(c) Graph the sum of your functions in parts (a) and (b).

42. In 1961 and 1962, large amounts of the radioactive isotope carbon-14 were produced by tests of nuclear bombs.[5] If t is years since 1963, the amount of carbon-14, as a percent in excess of the normal level, is given by

$$C(t) = 108(e^{-0.1t} - e^{-0.7t}).$$

(a) Graph the function.
(b) Approximately when was the level of carbon-14 the highest?
(c) What happens to the level of carbon-14 in the long-run?

43. Table 8.27 gives data on strawberry production from 2000 through 2004,[6] where t is in years since 2000. Let

---

[5] Adapted from Bolton, *Patterns in Physics*.
[6] www.usda.gov/nass/pubs/agstats.htm, accessed January 15, 2006.

$f_{CA}(t)$, $f_{FL}(t)$, and $f_{US}(t)$ be the harvested area in year t for strawberries grown in California, Florida, and the US overall, respectively. Likewise, let $g_{CA}(t)$, $g_{FL}(t)$, and $g_{US}(t)$ give the yield in thousands of pounds per acre for these three regions.

(a) Let $h_{CA}(t) = f_{CA}(t) \cdot g_{CA}(t)$. Create a table of values for $h_{CA}(t)$ for $0 \leq t \leq 4$. Describe in words what $h_{CA}(t)$ tells you about strawberry production.

(b) Let $p(t)$ be the fraction of all US strawberries (by weight) grown in Florida and California in year t. Find a formula for $p(t)$ in terms of f_{CA}, f_{FL}, f_{US}. Use Table 8.27 to make a table of values for $p(t)$.

Table 8.27

	Harvested area (acres)			Yield (1000 lbs per acre)		
t	CA	FL	US total	CA	FL	US total
0	27,600	6,300	47,650	59.0	35.0	42.0
1	26,400	6,500	46,100	52.5	26.0	37.8
2	28,500	6,900	47,900	56.5	25.5	39.4
3	29,600	7,100	48,700	62.0	22.0	42.8
3	33,200	7,100	51,600	59.0	23.0	42.9

CHAPTER SUMMARY

- **Composition of Functions**
  Notation: $h(t) = f(g(t))$.
  Domain and range; Decomposition.

- **Inverse Functions**
  Definition: $f^{-1}(Q) = t$ if and only if $Q = f(t)$.

- Invertibility; horizontal line test.
  Domain and range of an inverse function.
  Restricting domain of a function to construct an inverse.

- **Combinations of Functions**
  Sums, differences, products, quotients.

REVIEW EXERCISES AND PROBLEMS FOR CHAPTER EIGHT

Exercises

In Exercises 1–6, let $f(x) = 3x^2$, $g(x) = 9x - 2$, $m(x) = 4x$, and $r(x) = \sqrt{3x}$. Find and simplify the composite function.

1. $r(g(x))$

2. $f(r(x))$

3. $r(f(x))$

4. $g(f(x))$

5. $g(m(f(x)))$

6. $f(m(g(x)))$

In Exercises 7–8, find and simplify for $f(x) = 2^x$ and $g(x) = \dfrac{x}{x+1}$.

7. $f(g(x))$

8. $g(f(x))$

In Exercises 9–14, find simplified formulas if $f(x) = e^x$, $g(x) = 2x - 1$, and $h(x) = \sqrt{x}$.

9. $g(f(x))$ **10.** $g(x)f(x)$ **11.** $g(g(x))$

12. $f(g(h(x)))$ **13.** $f(g(x))h(x)$ **14.** $(f(h(x)))^2$

15. Find formulas for the following functions, given that
$$f(x) = x^2 + x, \qquad g(x) = 2x - 3. \qquad h(x) = \frac{x}{1-x}.$$

(a) $f(2x)$ (b) $g(x^2)$ (c) $h(1-x)$
(d) $(f(x))^2$ (e) $g^{-1}(x)$ (f) $(h(x))^{-1}$
(g) $f(x) \cdot g(x)$ (h) $h(f(x))$

In Exercises 16–18, find simplified formulas if $u(x) = \dfrac{1}{1+x^2}$, $v(x) = e^x$, and $w(x) = \ln x$.

16. $v(x)/u(x)$

17. $u(v(x)) \cdot w(v(x))$

18. $\dfrac{w(2+h) - w(2)}{h}$

In Exercises 19–22 find simplified formulas if $f(x) = x^{3/2}$, $g(x) = \dfrac{(3x-1)^2}{4}$, and $h(x) = \tan 2x$.

19. $f(x)h(x)$

20. $\dfrac{h(x)}{f(g(x))}$

21. $h(g(x)) - f(9x)$

22. $h(x/2)\cos x$

In Exercises 23–30, find a formula for the inverse function. Assume these functions are defined on domains on which they are invertible.

23. $f(x) = 3x - 7$

24. $j(x) = \sqrt{1 + \sqrt{x}}$

25. $h(x) = \dfrac{2x + 1}{3x - 2}$

26. $k(x) = \dfrac{3 - \sqrt{x}}{\sqrt{x} + 2}$

27. $g(x) = \dfrac{\ln x - 5}{2\ln x + 7}$

28. $h(x) = \log\left(\dfrac{x + 5}{x - 4}\right)$

29. $f(x) = \cos\sqrt{x}$

30. $g(x) = 2^{\sin x}$

Problems

31. Complete Table 8.28 given that $w(t) = v(u(t))$.

Table 8.28

t	u	v	w
0	2	3	—
1	—	—	2
2	1	1	4
3	—	2	0
4	0	0	—

32. Let $f(x) = \dfrac{1}{x + 1}$. Find and simplify $f\left(\dfrac{1}{x}\right) + \dfrac{1}{f(x)}$.

In Problems 33–36, suppose that $f(x) = g(h(x))$. Find possible formulas for $g(x)$ and $h(x)$ (There may be more than one possible answer. Assume $g(x) \neq x$ and $h(x) \neq x$.)

33. $f(x) = (x + 3)^2$

34. $f(x) = \sqrt{1 + \sqrt{x}}$

35. $f(x) = 9x^2 + 3x$

36. $f(x) = \dfrac{1}{x^2 + 8x + 16}$

Evaluate the expressions in Problems 37–38 using Figures 8.34 and 8.35, giving estimates if necessary.

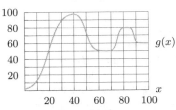

Figure 8.34

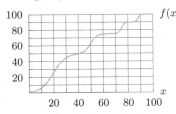

Figure 8.35

37. $f(g(65))$

38. $v(50)$ where $v(x) = g(x)f(x)$

Using Figures 8.36 and 8.37, graph the functions in Problems 39–42.

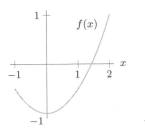

Figure 8.36

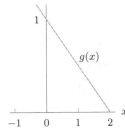

Figure 8.37

39. $f(x) - g(x)$

40. $f(g(x))$

41. $g(f(x))$

42. $g(f(x - 2))$

43. Using Figure 8.38, match the functions (a)–(g) and graphs (I)–(IV). There may be some functions whose graphs are not shown.

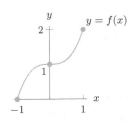

Figure 8.38

(a) $y = -f(x)$ **(b)** $y = f(-x)$
(c) $y = f(-x) - 2$ **(d)** $y = f^{-1}(x)$
(e) $y = -f^{-1}(x)$ **(f)** $y = f(x+1)$
(g) $y = -(f(x) - 2)$

(I) 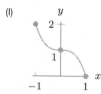   (II)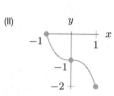

(III) 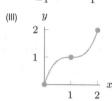   (IV)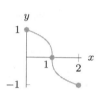

44. Use Figure 8.39.

(a) Evaluate $f(g(a))$.
(b) Evaluate $g(f(c))$.
(c) Evaluate $f^{-1}(b) - g^{-1}(b)$.
(d) For what positive value(s) of x is $f(x) \le g(x)$?

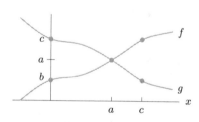

Figure 8.39

45. Let $f(x) = 12 - 4x$, $g(x) = 1/x$, and $h(x) = \sqrt{x - 4}$. Find the domain of the functions:

(a) $g(f(x))$ (b) $h(f(x))$

For Problems 46–50, let

$$p(x) = 2x - 3 \qquad q(x) = \sqrt{x} - 3$$
$$r(x) = \frac{2x - 1}{2x + 1} \qquad s(x) = (x - 1)^2$$

46. Find and simplify $p(q(x))$.

47. Find and simplify $r^{-1}(x)$.

48. Solve for x exactly: $p(x) = r(x)$.

49. Find $u(x)$ given that $q(x) = p(u(x))$.

50. Graph and label $p(s(x))$.

51. A research facility on the Isle of Shoals has 800 gallons of fresh water for a two-month period.

(a) There are 7 members of the research team and each is allotted 2 gallons of water per day for cooking and drinking. Find a formula for $f(t)$, the amount of fresh water left on the island after t days has elapsed.
(b) Evaluate and interpret the following expressions

(i) $f(0)$ (ii) $f^{-1}(0)$
(iii) t if $f(t) = \dfrac{1}{2}f(0)$ (iv) $800 - f(t)$

52. The rating, r, of an earthquake of intensity I is given by $r = f(I) = \log(I/I_0)$, where I_0 is a constant. Find and interpret $f^{-1}(r)$.

53. There is a linear relationship between the number of units, $N(x)$, of a product that a company sells and the amount of money, x, spent on advertising. If the company spends \$25,000 on advertising, it sells 400 units, and for each additional \$5,000 spent, it sells 20 units more.

(a) Calculate and interpret $N(20,000)$.
(b) Find a formula for $N(x)$ in terms of x.
(c) Give interpretations of the slope and the x- and y-intercepts of $N(x)$ if possible.
(d) Calculate and interpret $N^{-1}(500)$.
(e) An internal audit reveals that the profit made by the company on the sale of 10 units of its product, before advertising costs have been accounted for, is \$2,000. What are the implications regarding the company's advertising campaign? Discuss.

54. A hot brick is removed from a kiln at $200°C$ above room temperature. Over time, the brick cools off. After 2 hours have elapsed, the brick is $20°C$ above room temperature. Let t be the time in hours since the brick was removed from the kiln. Let $y = H(t)$ be the difference between the brick's and the room's temperature at time t. Assume that $H(t)$ is an exponential function.

(a) Find a formula for $H(t)$.
(b) How many degrees does the brick's temperature drop during the first quarter hour? During the next quarter hour?
(c) Find and interpret $H^{-1}(y)$.
(d) How much time elapses before the brick's temperature is $5°C$ above room temperature?
(e) Interpret the physical meaning of the horizontal asymptote of $H(t)$.

In Problems 55–61, you hire either Ace Construction or Space Contractors to build office space. Let $f(x)$ be the average total cost in dollars of building x square feet of office space, as estimated by Ace. Let $h(x)$ be the total number of square feet of office space you can build with x dollars, as estimated by Space.

55. Describe in words what the following statement tells you:
$$f(2000) = 200,000$$

56. Let $g(x) = f(x)/x$. Using the information from Problem 55, evaluate $g(2000)$, and describe in words what $g(2000)$ represents. [Hint: Think about the units.]

57. Ace tells you that, due to the economies of scale, "Building twice as much office space always costs less than twice as much." Express this statement symbolically, in terms of f and x. [Hint: If you are building x square feet, how do you represent the cost? How would you represent twice the cost? How do you represent the cost of building twice as many square feet?]

58. Suppose that $q > p$ and $p > 1$. Assuming that the contractor's statement in Problem 57 is correct, rank the following in increasing order, using inequality signs: $f(p)$, $g(p)$, $f(q)$, $g(q)$.

59. What does the statement $h(200,000) = 1500$ tell you?

60. Let $j(x)$ be the average cost in dollars per square foot of office space as estimated by Space Contractors. Give a formula for $j(x)$. (Your formula will have $h(x)$ in it.)

61. Research reveals that $h(f(x)) < x$ for every value of x you check. Explain the implications of this statement. [Hint: Which company seems more economical?]

In Problems 62–65, let $f(x)$ be an increasing function and let $g(x)$ be a decreasing function. Are the following functions increasing, decreasing, or is it impossible to tell? Explain.

62. $f(f(x))$

63. $g(f(x))$

64. $f(x) + g(x)$

65. $f(x) - g(x)$

66. For a positive integer x, let $f(x)$ be the remainder obtained by dividing x by 3. For example, $f(6) = 0$, because 6 divided by 3 equals 2 with a remainder of 0. Likewise, $f(7) = 1$, because 7 divided by 3 equals 2 with a remainder of 1.

    (a) Evaluate $f(8)$, $f(17)$, $f(29)$, $f(99)$.
    (b) Find a formula for $f(3x)$.
    (c) Is $f(x)$ invertible?
    (d) Find a formula in terms of $f(x)$ for $f(f(x))$.
    (e) Does $f(x + y)$ necessarily equal $f(x) + f(y)$?

CHECK YOUR UNDERSTANDING

Let $f(x) = \dfrac{1}{x}$, $g(x) = \sqrt{x}$, and $h(x) = x - 5$. Are the statements in Problems 1–10 true or false? Give an explanation for your answer.

1. $f(4) + g(4) = (f + g)(8)$.

2. $\dfrac{h(x)}{f(x)} = \dfrac{x - 5}{x}$.

3. $f(4) + g(4) = 2\frac{1}{4}$.

4. $f(g(x))$ is defined for all x.

5. $g(f(x)) = \sqrt{\dfrac{1}{x}}$.

6. $f(x)g(x) = f(g(x))$.

7. $2f(2) = g(1)$.

8. $f(1)g(1)h(1) = -4$.

9. $\dfrac{f(3) + g(3)}{h(3)} = \dfrac{\frac{1}{3} + \sqrt{3}}{-2}$.

10. $4h(2) = h(8)$.

Are the statements in Problems 11–37 true or false? Give an explanation for your answer.

11. If $f(x) = x^2$ and $g(x) = \sqrt{x + 3}$. Then $f(g(x))$ is defined for all x.

12. If $f(x) = x^2$ and $g(x) = \sqrt{x + 3}$. Then $f(g(6)) = 9$.

13. In general $f(g(x)) = g(f(x))$.

14. The formula for the area of a circle is $A = \pi r^2$ and the formula for the circumference of a circle is $C = 2\pi r$. Then the area of a circle as a function of the circumference is $A = \dfrac{C^2}{2\pi}$.

15. If $f(x) = x^2 + 2$ then $f(f(1)) = 11$.

16. If $h(x) = f(g(x))$, $h(2) = 1\frac{1}{4}$ and $g(2) = \frac{1}{2}$ then $f(x)$ might be equal to $x^2 + 1$.

17. If $f(x) = \dfrac{1}{x}$ then $f(x + h) = \dfrac{1}{x} + \dfrac{1}{h}$.

18. If $f(x) = x^2 + x$, then $\dfrac{f(x + h) - f(x)}{h} = 2x + h$.

19. If $f(x) = x^2$ and $g(x) = \sin x$ then $f(g(x)) = x^2 \sin x$.

20. If $f(x)$ and $g(x)$ are linear, then $f(g(x))$ is linear.

21. If $f(x)$ and $g(x)$ are quadratic, then $f(g(x))$ is quadratic.

22. There is more than one way to write $h(x) = 3(x^2 + 1)^3$ as a composition $h(x) = f(g(x))$.

23. The composition $f(g(x))$ is never the same as the composite $g(f(x))$.

24. If f and g are both increasing, then $h(x) = f(g(x))$ is also increasing.

25. The functions f and g given in Tables 8.29 and 8.30 satisfy $g(f(2)) = f(g(3))$.

Table 8.29

t	1	2	3	4
$f(t)$	3	1	2	4

Table 8.30

x	1	2	3	4
$g(x)$	3	4	1	2

26. If f is increasing and invertible, then f^{-1} is decreasing.

27. If there is a vertical line that intersects a graph in more than one point, then the graph does not represent a function.

28. Every function has an inverse.

29. If $g(3) = g(5)$, then g is not invertible.

30. If no horizontal line intersects the graph of a function in more than one point, then the function has an inverse.

31. Most quadratic functions have an inverse.

32. All linear functions of the form $f(x) = mx + b, m \neq 0$ have inverses.

33. The following table describes y as a function of x.

Table 8.31

x	1	2	3	4	5	6
y	3	4	7	8	5	3

34. The table in Problem 33 describes a function from x to y that is invertible.

35. The graph in Figure 8.40 is the graph of a function.

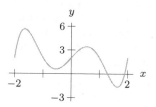

Figure 8.40

36. The function graphed in Figure 8.40 is invertible.

37. For an invertible function g, it is always true that $g^{-1}(g(x)) = x$.

Chapter Nine

POLYNOMIAL AND RATIONAL FUNCTIONS

This chapter begins with power functions. Sums and differences of power functions lead to the family of polynomial functions. Ratios of polynomials lead to the family of rational functions.

The chapter ends by comparing power, exponential, and logarithmic functions and by fitting functions to data.

The Tools Section on page 441 reviews algebraic fractions.

9.1 POWER FUNCTIONS

Proportionality and Power Functions

The following two examples introduce proportionality and power functions.

Example 1   The area, A, of a circle is proportional to the square of its radius, r:

$$A = \pi r^2.$$

Example 2   The weight, w, of an object is inversely proportional to the square of the object's distance, d, from the earth's center:[1]

$$w = \frac{k}{d^2} = kd^{-2}.$$

For an object with weight 44 pounds on the surface of the earth, which is about 3959 miles from the earth's center, we get the data listed in Table 9.1 and graphed in Figure 9.1.

Table 9.1   *Weight of an object, w, inversely proportional to the square of the objects's distance, d, from the earth's center*

d, miles	$w = f(d)$, lbs
4000	43.3
5000	27.8
6000	19.2
7000	14.1
8000	10.8

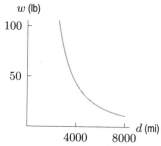

Figure 9.1: Weight, w, inversely proportional to the square of the object's distance, d, from the earth's center

A quantity y is **(directly) proportional to a power** of x if

$$y = kx^n, \qquad k \text{ and } n \text{ are constants.}$$

A quantity y is **inversely proportional** to x^n if

$$y = \frac{k}{x^n}, \qquad k \text{ and } n \text{ are constants, with } n > 0.$$

---

[1]There is a distinction between mass and weight. For example, an astronaut in orbit may be weightless, but he still has mass.

The functions in Examples 1 and 2 are power functions. Generalizing, we define:

> **A power function** is a function of the form
>
> $$f(x) = kx^p, \qquad \text{where } k \text{ and } p \text{ are constants.}$$

Example 3 Which of the following functions are power functions? For each power function, state the value of the constants k and p in the formula $y = kx^p$.

(a) $f(x) = 13\sqrt[3]{x}$ (b) $g(x) = 2(x+5)^3$ (c) $u(x) = \sqrt{\dfrac{25}{x^3}}$ (d) $v(x) = 6 \cdot 3^x$

Solution The functions f and u are power functions; the functions g and v are not.

(a) The function $f(x) = 13\sqrt[3]{x}$ is a power function because we can write its formula as

$$f(x) = 13x^{1/3}.$$

Here, $k = 13$ and $p = 1/3$.

(b) Although the value of $g(x) = 2(x+5)^3$ is proportional to the cube of $x+5$, it is *not* proportional to a power of x. We cannot write $g(x)$ in the form $g(x) = kx^p$; thus, g is not a power function.

(c) We can rewrite the formula for $u(x) = \sqrt{25/x^3}$ as

$$u(x) = \frac{\sqrt{25}}{\sqrt{x^3}} = \frac{5}{(x^3)^{1/2}} = \frac{5}{x^{3/2}} = 5x^{-3/2}.$$

Thus, u is a power function. Here, $k = 5$ and $p = -3/2$.

(d) Although the value of $v(x) = 6 \cdot 3^x$ is proportional to a power of 3, the power is not a constant—it is the variable x. In fact, $v(x) = 6 \cdot 3^x$ is an exponential function, not a power function. Notice that $y = 6 \cdot x^3$ is a power function. However, $6 \cdot x^3$ and $6 \cdot 3^x$ are quite different.

The Effect of the Power p

We now study functions whose constant of proportionality is $k = 1$ so that we can focus on the effect of the power p.

Graphs of the Special Cases $y = x^0$ and $y = x^1$

The power functions corresponding to $p = 0$ and $p = 1$ are both linear. The graph of $y = x^0 = 1$ is a horizontal line through the point $(1, 1)$. The graph of $y = x^1 = x$ is a line through the origin with slope $+1$.

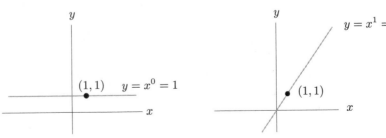

Figure 9.2: Graph of $y = x^0 = 1$ Figure 9.3: Graph of $y = x^1 = x$

Positive Integer Powers: $y = x^3,\ x^5,\ x^7\ldots$, and $y = x^2,\ x^4, x^6\ldots$

The graphs of all power functions with p a positive even integer have the same characteristic $\bigcup$-shape and are symmetric about the y-axis. For instance, the graphs of $y = x^2$ and $y = x^4$ in Figure 9.4 are similar in shape, although the graph of $y = x^4$ is flatter near the origin and steeper away from the origin than the graph of $y = x^2$.

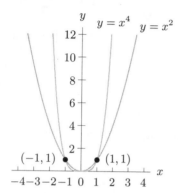

Figure 9.4: Graphs of positive even powers of x are $\bigcup$-shaped

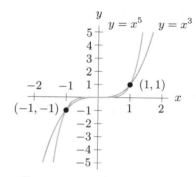

Figure 9.5: Graphs of positive odd powers of x are "chair"-shaped

The graphs of power functions with p a positive odd integer resemble the side view of a chair and are symmetric about the origin. Figure 9.5 shows the graphs of $y = x^3$ and $y = x^5$. The graph of $y = x^5$ is flatter near the origin and steeper far from the origin than the graph of $y = x^3$.

Negative Integer Powers: $y = x^{-1}, x^{-3}, x^{-5}, \ldots$ and $y = x^{-2}, x^{-4}, x^{-6}, \ldots$

For negative powers, if we rewrite

$$y = x^{-1} = \frac{1}{x}$$

and

$$y = x^{-2} = \frac{1}{x^2},$$

then it is clear that as $x > 0$ increases, the denominators increase and the functions decrease. The graphs of power functions with odd negative powers, $y = x^{-3}, x^{-5}, \ldots$ resemble the graph of $y = x^{-1} = 1/x$. The graphs of even integer powers, $y = x^{-4}, x^{-6}, \ldots$ are similar in shape to the graph of $y = x^{-2} = 1/x^2$. See Figures 9.6 and 9.7.

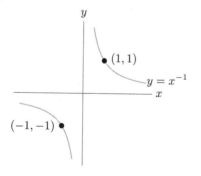

Figure 9.6: Graph of $y = x^{-1} = 1/x$

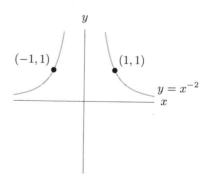

Figure 9.7: Graph of $y = x^{-2} = 1/x^2$

We see in Figures 9.6 and 9.7 that $y = 0$ is a horizontal asymptote and $x = 0$ is a vertical asymptote for the graphs of $y = 1/x$ and $y = 1/x^2$.

Numerically, the values of $1/x$ and $1/x^2$ can be made as close to zero as we like by choosing a sufficiently large x. See Table 9.2. Graphically, this means that the curves $y = 1/x$ and $y = 1/x^2$ get closer and closer to the x-axis for large values of x. We write $y \to 0$ as $x \to \infty$. Using limit notation, we see

$$\lim_{x \to \infty} \left(\frac{1}{x}\right) = 0 \quad \text{and} \quad \lim_{x \to \infty} \left(\frac{1}{x^2}\right) = 0$$

Table 9.2   *Values of x^{-1} and x^{-2} approach zero as x grows large*

x	0	10	20	30	40	50
$y = 1/x$	Undefined	0.1	0.05	0.033	0.025	0.02
$y = 1/x^2$	Undefined	0.01	0.0025	0.0011	0.0006	0.0004

On the other hand, as x gets close to zero, the values of $1/x$ and $1/x^2$ get very large. See Table 9.3. Graphically, this means that the curves $y = 1/x$ and $y = 1/x^2$ get very close to the y-axis as x gets close to zero. From Figure 9.6, we see that[2]

$$\lim_{x \to 0^+} \left(\frac{1}{x}\right) = \infty \quad \text{and} \quad \lim_{x \to 0^-} \left(\frac{1}{x}\right) = -\infty$$

From Figure 9.7, we see that

$$\lim_{x \to 0} \left(\frac{1}{x^2}\right) = \infty.$$

Table 9.3   *Values of x^{-1} and x^{-2} grow large as x approaches zero from the positive side*

x	0.1	0.05	0.01	0.001	0.0001	0
$y = 1/x$	10	20	100	1000	10,000	Undefined
$y = 1/x^2$	100	400	10,000	1,000,000	100,000,000	Undefined

Graphs of Positive Fractional Powers: $y = x^{1/2}, x^{1/3}, x^{1/4}, \ldots$

Figure 9.8 shows the graphs of $y = x^{1/2}$ and $y = x^{1/4}$. These graphs have the same shape, although $y = x^{1/4}$ is steeper near the origin and flatter away from the origin than $y = x^{1/2}$. The same can be said about the graphs of $y = x^{1/3}$ and $y = x^{1/5}$ in Figure 9.9. In general, if n is a positive integer, then the graph of $y = x^{1/n}$ resembles the graph of $y = x^{1/2}$ if n is even; if n is odd, the graph resembles the graph of $y = x^{1/3}$.

Notice that the graphs of $y = x^{1/2}$ and $y = x^{1/3}$ bend in a direction opposite to that of the graphs of $y = x^2$ and x^3. For example, the graph of $y = x^2$ is concave up, but the graph of $y = x^{1/2}$ is concave down. However, all these functions become infinitely large as x increases.

---

[2] Some authors say that these limits do not exist.

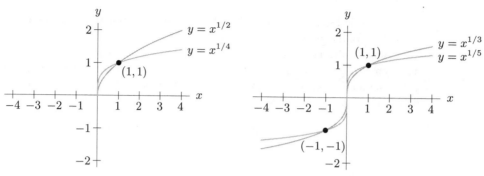

Figure 9.8: The graphs of $y = x^{1/2}$ and $y = x^{1/4}$ Figure 9.9: The graphs of $y = x^{1/3}$ and $y = x^{1/5}$

Example 4   The radius of a sphere is directly proportional to the cube root of its volume. If a sphere of radius 18.2 cm has a volume of 25,252.4 cm³, what is the radius of a sphere whose volume is 30,000 cm³?

Solution   Since the radius of the sphere is proportional to the cube root of its volume, we know that

$$r = kV^{1/3}, \qquad \text{for } k \text{ constant.}$$

We also know that $r = 18.2$ cm when $V = 25{,}252.4$ cm³, therefore

$$18.2 = k(25{,}252.4)^{1/3}$$

giving

$$k = \frac{18.2}{(25{,}252.4)^{1/3}} \approx 0.620.$$

Thus, when $V = 30{,}000$, we get $r = 0.620(30{,}000)^{1/3} \approx 19.3$, so the radius of the sphere is approximately 19.3 cm.

Finding the Formula for a Power Function

As is the case for linear and exponential functions, the formula of a power function can be found from two points on its graph.

Example 5   Water is leaking out of a container with a hole in the bottom. Torricelli's Law states that at any instant, the velocity v with which water escapes from the container is a power function of d, the depth of the water at that moment. When $d = 1$ foot, then $v = 8$ ft/sec; when $d = 1/4$ foot, then $v = 4$ ft/sec. Express v as a function of d.

Solution   Torricelli's Law tells us that $v = kd^p$, where k and p are constants. The fact that $v = 8$ when $d = 1$, gives $8 = k(1)^p$, so $k = 8$, and therefore $v = 8d^p$. Also $v = 4$ when $d = 1/4$, so

$$4 = 8 \left(\frac{1}{4} \right)^p.$$

Rewriting $(1/4)^p = 1/4^p$, we can solve for 4^p:

$$4 = 8 \cdot \frac{1}{4^p}$$

$$4^p = \frac{8}{4} = 2.$$

Since $4^{1/2} = 2$, we must have $p = 1/2$. Therefore we have $v = 8d^{1/2}$. *Note*: Torricelli's Law is often written in the form $v = \sqrt{2gd}$, where $g = 32$ ft/sec² is the acceleration due to gravity.

Exercises and Problems for Section 9.1

Exercises

Are the functions in Exercises 1–6 power functions? If so, write the function in the form $f(x) = kx^p$.

1. $g(x) = \dfrac{(-x^3)^3}{6}$

2. $R(t) = \dfrac{4}{\sqrt{16t}}$

3. $Q(t) = \left(\dfrac{1}{2\sqrt{t}}\right)^3$

4. $K(w) = \dfrac{w^4}{4\sqrt{w^3}}$

5. $T(s) = (6s^{-2})(es^{-3})$

6. $h(x) = 22(7^x)^2$

Do the power functions in Exercises 7–10 appear to have odd, even, or fractional powers?

7.

8.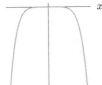

9.

10.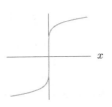

In Exercises 11–13, find a power function through the two points.

11. $(7,8)$ $(1,0.7)$ **12.** $(1,5)$ $(3,27)$ **13.** $(6,17)$ $(1,2)$

14. Find a possible formula for the power function $f(t)$ given that $f(3) = 5$ and $f(5) = 3$.

15. Suppose y is directly proportional to x. If $y = 6$ when $x = 4$, find the constant of proportionality and write the formula for y as a function of x. Use your formula to find x when $y = 8$.

16. Suppose y is inversely proportional to x. If $y = 6$ when $x = 4$, find the constant of proportionality and write the formula for y as a function of x. Use your formula to find x when $y = 8$.

17. Suppose c is directly proportional to the square of d. If $c = 45$ when $d = 3$, find the constant of proportionality and write the formula for c as a function of d. Use your formula to find c when $d = 5$.

18. Suppose c is inversely proportional to the square of d. If $c = 45$ when $d = 3$, find the constant of proportionality and write the formula for c as a function of d. Use your formula to find c when $d = 5$.

In Exercises 19–22, find possible formulas for the power functions.

19.

x	0	1	2	3
$j(x)$	0	2	16	54

20.

x	2	3	4	5
$f(x)$	12	27	48	75

21.

x	-6	-2	3	4
$g(x)$	36	4/3	$-9/2$	$-32/3$

22.

x	-2	$-1/2$	1/4	4
$h(x)$	$-1/2$	-8	-32	$-1/8$

23. Find **(a)** $\displaystyle\lim_{x \to \infty} x^{-4}$ **(b)** $\displaystyle\lim_{x \to -\infty} 2x^{-1}$

24. Find **(a)** $\displaystyle\lim_{t \to \infty} (t^{-3} + 2)$ **(b)** $\displaystyle\lim_{y \to -\infty} (5 - 7y^{-2})$

Problems

25. Compare the graphs of $y = x^{-2}$, $y = x^{-4}$, and $y = x^{-6}$. Describe the similarities and differences.

26. Describe the behavior of $y = x^{-10}$ and $y = -x^{10}$ as
(a) $x \to 0$ **(b)** $x \to \infty$ **(c)** $x \to -\infty$

27. Describe the behavior of $y = x^{-3}$ and $y = x^{1/3}$ as
(a) $x \to 0$ from the right   **(b)** $x \to \infty$

28. If $f(x) = kx^p$, p an integer, show that f is an even function if p is even, and an odd function if p is odd.

29. (a) Figure 9.10 shows $g(x)$, a mystery power function. If you learn that the point $(-1, 3)$ lies on its graph, do you have enough information to write a formula for $g(x)$?

(b) If you are told that the point $(1, -3)$ also lies on the graph, what new deductions can you make?

(c) If the point $(2, -96)$ lies on the graph g, in addition to the points already given, state three other points which also lie on it.

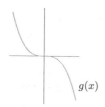

Figure 9.10

30. Figure 9.11 shows the power function $y = c(t)$. Is $c(t) = 1/t$ the only possible formula for c? Could there be others?

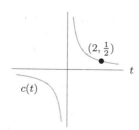

Figure 9.11

31. (a) One of the graphs in Figure 9.12 is $y = x^n$ and the other is $y = x^{1/n}$, where n is a positive integer. Which is which? How do you know?

(b) What are the coordinates of point A?

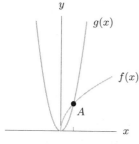

Figure 9.12

32. The circulation time of a mammal—that is, the average time it takes for all the blood in the body to circulate once and return to the heart—is governed by the equation

$$t = 17.4m^{1/4},$$

where m is the body mass of the mammal in kilograms, and t is the circulation time in seconds.[3]

(a) Complete Table 9.4 which shows typical body masses in kilograms for various mammals.[4]

(b) If the circulation time of one mammal is twice that of another, what is the relationship between their body masses?

Table 9.4

Animal	Body mass (kg)	Circulation time (sec)
Blue whale	91000	
African elephant	5450	
White rhinoceros	3000	
Hippopotamus	2520	
Black rhinoceros	1170	
Horse	700	
Lion	180	
Human	70	

33. Three ounces of broiled ground beef contains 245 calories.[5] Is the number of calories directly or inversely proportional to the number of ounces? Explain your reasoning and write a formula for the proportion. How many calories are there in 4 ounces of broiled hamburger?

34. A 30-second commercial during Super Bowl XL in 2006 cost advertisers $2.5 million. For the first Super Bowl in 1967, an advertiser could have purchased approximately 28.699 minutes of advertising time for the same amount of money.[6]

(a) Assuming that cost is proportional to time, find the cost of advertising, in dollars/second, during the 1967 and 2006 Super Bowls.

(b) How many times more expensive was Super Bowl advertising in 2006 than in 1967?

35. A group of friends rent a house at the beach for spring break. If nine of them share the house, it costs $150 each. Is the cost to each person directly or inversely proportional to the number of people sharing the house? Explain your reasoning and write a formula for the proportion. How many people are needed to share the house if each student wants to pay a maximum of $100 each?

[3] K. Schmidt-Nielsen, *Scaling, Why is Animal Size so Important?* (Cambridge: CUP, 1984).
[4] R. McNeill Alexander, *Dynamics of Dinosaurs and Other Extinct Giants.* (New York: Columbia University Press, 1989).
[5] The World Almanac Book of Facts, 1999 p. 718
[6] money.cnn.com/2006/01/03/news/companies/superbowlads, accessed January 15, 2006.

36. Driving at 55 mph, it takes approximately 3.5 hours to drive from Long Island to Albany, NY. Is the time the drive takes directly or inversely proportional to the speed? Explain your reasoning and write a formula for the proportion. To get to Albany in 3 hours, how fast would you have to drive?

37. On a map, 1/2 inch represents 5 miles. Is the map distance between two locations directly or inversely proportional to the actual distance which separates the two locations? Explain your reasoning and write a formula for the proportion. How far apart are two towns if the distance between these two towns on the map is 3.25 inches?

38. A volcano erupts in a powerful explosion. The sound from the explosion is heard in all directions for many hundreds of kilometers. The speed of sound is about 340 meters per second.

(a) Fill in Table 9.5 showing the distance, d, that the sound of the explosion has traveled at time t. Write a formula for d as a function t.

(b) How long after the explosion will a person living 200 km away hear the explosion?

(c) Fill Table 9.5 showing the land area, A, over which the explosion can be heard as a function of time. Write a formula for A as a function of t.

(d) The average population density around the volcano is 31 people per square kilometer. Write a formula for P as function of t, where P is the number of people who have heard the explosion at time t.

(e) Graph the function $P = f(t)$. How long will it take until 1 million people have heard the explosion?

Table 9.5

Time, t	5 sec	10 sec	1 min	5 min
Distance, d (km)				
Area, A (km^2)				

39. The thrust, T, delivered by a ship's propeller is proportional[7] to the square of the propeller rotation speed, R, times the fourth power of the propeller diameter, D.

(a) Write a formula for T in terms of R and D.

(b) What happens to the thrust if the propeller speed is doubled?

(c) What happens to the thrust if the propeller diameter is doubled?

(d) If the propeller diameter is increased by 50%, by how much can the propeller speed be reduced to deliver the same thrust?

40. Two oil tankers crash in the Pacific ocean. The spreading oil slick has a circular shape, and the radius of the circle is increasing at 200 meters per hour.

(a) Express the radius of the spill, r, as a power function of time, t, in hours since the crash.

(b) Express the area of the spill, A, as a power function of time, t.

(c) Clean-up efforts begin 7 hours after the spill. How large an area is covered by oil at that time?

41. When an aircraft flies horizontally, its *stall velocity* (the minimum speed required to keep the aircraft aloft) is directly proportional to the square root of the quotient of its weight by its wing area. If a breakthrough in materials science allowed the construction of an aircraft with the same weight but twice the wing area, would the stall velocity increase or decrease? By what percent?

42. One of Kepler's three laws of planetary motion states that the square of the period, P, of a body orbiting the sun is proportional to the cube of its average distance, d, from the sun. The earth has a period of 365 days and its distance from the sun is approximately 93,000,000 miles.

(a) Find P as a function of d.

(b) The planet Jupiter has an average distance from the sun of 483,000,000 miles. How long in earth days is a Jupiter year?

43. A person's weight, w, on a planet of radius d is given by

$$w = kd^{-2}, \quad k > 0,$$

where the constant k depends on the masses of the person and the planet.

(a) A man weighs 180 lb on the surface of the earth. How much does he weigh on the surface of a planet whose mass is the same the earth's, but whose radius is three times as large? One-third as large?

(b) What fraction of the earth's radius must an equally massive planet have if, on this planet, the weight of the man in part (a) is one ton?

44. The following questions involve the behavior of the power function $y = x^{-p}$, for p a positive integer. If a distinction between even and odd values of p is significant, the significance should be indicated.

(a) What is the domain of $y = x^{-p}$? What is the range?

(b) What symmetries does the graph of $y = x^{-p}$ have?

(c) What is the behavior of $y = x^{-p}$ as $x \to 0$?

(d) What is the behavior of $y = x^{-p}$ for large positive values of x? For large negative values of x?

[7]Gillner, Thomas C., *Modern Ship Design*, (US Naval Institute Press, 1972).

45. Let $f(x) = 16x^4$ and $g(x) = 4x^2$.

  (a) If $f(x) = g(h(x))$, find a possible formula for $h(x)$, assuming $h(x) \leq 0$ for all x.

  (b) If $f(x) = j(2g(x))$, find a possible formula for $j(x)$, assuming $j(x)$ is a power function.

46. Consider the power function $y = t(x) = k \cdot x^{p/3}$ where

p is any integer, $p \neq 0$.

  (a) For what values of p does $t(x)$ have domain restrictions? What are those restrictions?

  (b) What is the range of $t(x)$ if p is even? If p is odd?

  (c) What symmetry does the graph of $t(x)$ exhibit if p is even? If p is odd?

9.2   POLYNOMIAL FUNCTIONS

A *polynomial function* is a sum of power functions whose exponents are nonnegative integers. We use what we learned about power functions to study polynomials.

Example 1   You make five separate deposits of $1000 each into a savings account, one deposit per year, beginning today. What annual interest rate gives a balance in the account of $6000 five years from today? (Assume the interest rate is constant over these five years.)

Solution   Let r be the annual interest rate. Our goal is to determine what value of r gives you $6000 in five years. In year $t = 0$, you make a $1000 deposit. One year later, you have $1000 plus the interest earned on that amount. At that time, you add another $1000.

To picture how this works, imagine the account pays 5% annual interest, compounded annually. Then, after one year, your balance would be

$$\text{Balance} = (100\% \text{ of Initial deposit}) + (5\% \text{ of Initial deposit}) + \text{Second deposit}$$
$$= 105\% \text{ of } \underbrace{\text{Initial deposit}}_{\$1000} + \underbrace{\text{Second deposit}}_{\$1000}$$
$$= 1.05(1000) + 1000.$$

Let x represent the annual growth factor, $1 + r$. For example, if the account paid 5% interest, then $x = 1 + 0.05 = 1.05$. We write the balance after one year in terms of x:

$$\text{Balance after one year} = 1000x + 1000.$$

After two years, you would have earned interest on the first-year balance. This gives

$$\text{Balance after earning interest} = \underbrace{(1000x + 1000)}_{\text{First-year balance}}x = 1000x^2 + 1000x.$$

The third $1000 deposit brings your balance to

$$\text{Balance after two years} = 1000x^2 + 1000x + \underbrace{1000.}_{\text{Third deposit}}$$

A year's worth of interest on this amount, plus the fourth $1000 deposit, brings your balance to

$$\text{Balance after three years} = \underbrace{(1000x^2 + 1000x + 1000)}_{\text{Second-year balance}}x + \underbrace{1000}_{\text{Fourth deposit}}$$
$$= 1000x^3 + 1000x^2 + 1000x + 1000.$$

The pattern is this: Each of the $1000 deposits grows to $1000x^n$ by the end of its nth year in the bank. Thus,

$$\text{Balance after five years} = 1000x^5 + 1000x^4 + 1000x^3 + 1000x^2 + 1000x.$$

If the interest rate is chosen correctly, then the balance will be $6000 in five years. This gives us

$$1000x^5 + 1000x^4 + 1000x^3 + 1000x^2 + 1000x = 6000.$$

Dividing by 1000 and moving the 6 to the left side, we have the equation

$$x^5 + x^4 + x^3 + x^2 + x - 6 = 0.$$

Solving this equation for x determines how much interest we must earn. Using a computer or calculator, we find where the graph of $Q(x) = x^5 + x^4 + x^3 + x^2 + x - 6$ crosses the x-axis. Figure 9.13 shows that this occurs at $x \approx 1.0614$. Since $x = 1 + r$, this means $r = 0.0614$. So the account must earn 6.14% annual interest[8] for the balance to be $6000 at the end of five years.

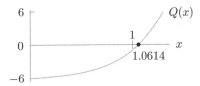

Figure 9.13: Finding where $Q(x)$ crosses the x-axis, for $x \geq 0$

You may wonder if Q crosses the x-axis more than once. For $x \geq 0$, graphing Q on a larger scale suggests that Q increases for all values of x and crosses the x-axis only once. For $x > 1$, we expect Q to be an increasing function, because larger values of x indicate higher interest rates and therefore larger values of $Q(x)$. Having crossed the axis once, the graph of Q does not "turn around" to cross it again.

The function $Q(x) = x^5 + x^4 + x^3 + x^2 + x - 6$ is the sum of power functions; Q is called a *polynomial*. (Note that the expression -6 can be written as $-6x^0$, so it, too, is a power function.)

A General Formula for the Family of Polynomial Functions

The general formula for a polynomial function can be written as

$$p(x) = a_n x^n + a_{n-1} x^{n-1} + \dots + a_1 x + a_0,$$

where n is called the *degree* of the polynomial and a_n is the *leading coefficient*. For example, the function

$$g(x) = 3x^2 + 4x^5 + x - x^3 + 1,$$

is a polynomial of degree 5 because the term with the highest power is $4x^5$. It is customary to write a polynomial with the powers in decreasing order from left to right:

$$g(x) = 4x^5 - x^3 + 3x^2 + x + 1.$$

The function g has one other term, $0 \cdot x^4$, which we don't bother to write down. The values of g's coefficients are $a_5 = 4, a_4 = 0, a_3 = -1, a_2 = 3, a_1 = 1$, and $a_0 = 1$. In summary:

---

[8]This is 6.14% interest per year, compounded annually.

The general formula for the family of polynomial functions can be written as

$$p(x) = a_n x^n + a_{n-1} x^{n-1} + \ldots + a_1 x + a_0,$$

where n is a positive integer called the **degree** of p and where $a_n \neq 0$.
- Each power function $a_n x^n$ in this sum is called a **term**.
- The constants $a_n, a_{n-1}, \ldots, a_0$ are called **coefficients**.
- The term a_0 is called the **constant term**. The highest-powered term, $a_n x^n$, is called the **leading term**.
- To write a polynomial in **standard form**, we arrange its terms from highest power to lowest power, going from left to right.

Like the power functions from which they are built, polynomials are defined for all values of x. Except for polynomials of degree zero (whose graphs are horizontal lines), the graphs of polynomials do not have horizontal or vertical asymptotes. The shape of the graph depends on its degree; typical graphs are shown in Figure 9.14.

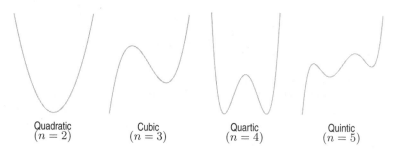

Quadratic   Cubic   Quartic   Quintic
($n = 2$)   ($n = 3$)   ($n = 4$)   ($n = 5$)

Figure 9.14: Graphs of typical polynomials of degree n

The Long-Run Behavior of Polynomial Functions

We have seen that, as x grows large, $y = x^2$ increases fast, $y = x^3$ increases faster, and $y = x^4$ increases faster still. In general, power functions with larger positive powers eventually grow much faster than those with smaller powers. This tells us about the behavior of polynomials for large x. For instance, consider the polynomial $g(x) = 4x^5 - x^3 + 3x^2 + x + 1$. Provided x is large enough, the absolute value of the term $4x^5$ is much larger than the absolute value of the other terms combined. For example, if $x = 100$,

$$4x^5 = 4(100)^5 = 40{,}000{,}000{,}000,$$

and the other terms in $g(x)$ are

$$-x^3 + 3x^2 + x + 1 = -(100)^3 + 3(100)^2 + 100 + 1$$
$$= -1{,}000{,}000 + 30{,}000 + 100 + 1 = -969{,}899.$$

Therefore $p(100) = 39{,}999{,}030{,}101$, which is approximately equal to the value of the $4x^5$ term. In general, if x is large enough, the most important contribution to the value of a polynomial p is made by the leading term; we can ignore the lower-powered terms.

When viewed on a large enough scale, the graph of the polynomial $p(x) = a_n x^n + a_{n-1}x^{n-1} + \cdots + a_1 x + a_0$ looks like the graph of the power function $y = a_n x^n$. This behavior is called the **long-run behavior** of the polynomial. Using limit notation, we write

$$\lim_{x \to \infty} p(x) = \lim_{x \to \infty} a_n x^n \quad \text{and} \quad \lim_{x \to -\infty} p(x) = \lim_{x \to -\infty} a_n x^n.$$

Example 2   Find a window in which the graph of $f(x) = x^3 + x^2$ resembles the power function $y = x^3$.

Solution   Figure 9.15 gives the graphs of $f(x) = x^3 + x^2$ and $y = x^3$. On this scale, f does not look like a power function. On the larger scale in Figure 9.16, the graph of f resembles the graph of $y = x^3$. On this larger scale, the "bumps" in the graph of f are too small to be seen. On an even larger scale, as in Figure 9.17, the graph of f is indistinguishable from the graph of $y = x^3$.

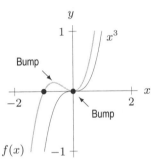

Figure 9.15: On this scale, $f(x) = x^3 + x^2$ does not look like a power function

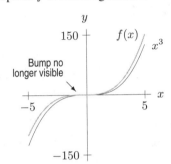

Figure 9.16: On this scale, $f(x) = x^3 + x^2$ resembles the power function $y = x^3$

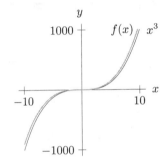

Figure 9.17: On this scale, $f(x) = x^3 + x^2$ is nearly indistinguishable from $y = x^3$

Zeros of Polynomials

The *zeros* of a polynomial p are values of x for which $p(x) = 0$. The zeros are also the x-intercepts, because they tell us where the graph of p crosses the x-axis. Factoring can sometimes be used to find the zeros of a polynomial; however, the numerical and graphical method of Example 1 can always be used. In addition, the long-run behavior of the polynomial can give us clues as to how many zeros (if any) there may be.

Example 3   Given the polynomial

$$q(x) = 3x^6 - 2x^5 + 4x^2 - 1,$$

where $q(0) = -1$, is there a reason to expect a solution to the equation $q(x) = 0$? If not, explain why not. If so, how do you know?

Solution   The equation $q(x) = 0$ must have at least two solutions. We know this because on a large scale, q looks like the power function $y = 3x^6$. (See Figure 9.18.) The function $y = 3x^6$ takes on large positive values as x grows large (either positive or negative). Since the graph of q is smooth and unbroken, it must cross the x-axis at least twice to get from $q(0) = -1$ to the positive values it attains as $x \to \infty$ and $x \to -\infty$.

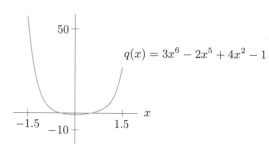

Figure 9.18: Graph must cross x-axis at least twice since $q(0) = -1$ and $q(x)$ looks like $3x^6$ for large x

A sixth degree polynomial such as q in Example 3 can have as many as six real zeros. We consider the zeros of a polynomial in more detail in Section 9.3.

Exercises and Problems for Section 9.2

Exercises

Are the functions in Exercises 1–6 polynomials? If so, of what degree?

1. $y = 5 + x$

2. $y = 5^x - 2$

3. $y = 4x^2 + 2$

4. $y = 4x^4 - 3x^3 + 2e^x$

5. $y = 4x^2 - 7\sqrt{x^9} + 10$

6. $y = 7t^6 - 8t + 7.2$

Describe in words the long-run behavior as $x \to \infty$ of the functions in Exercises 7–10. What power function does each resemble?

7. $y = 4x^4 - 2x^2 + 3$

8. $y = 16x^3 - 4023x^2 - 2$

9. $y = 3x^3 + 2x^2/x^{-7} - 7x^5 + 2$

10. $y = 5x^2/x^{3/2} + 2$

11. Find

    (a) $\displaystyle\lim_{x \to \infty} (3x^2 - 5x + 7)$ (b) $\displaystyle\lim_{x \to -\infty} (7x^2 - 9x^3)$

Problems

12. Estimate the zeros of $f(x) = x^4 - 3x^2 - x + 2$.

13. Estimate the minimum value of $g(x) = x^4 - 3x^3 - 8$.

14. Compare the graphs of $f(x) = x^3 + 5x^2 - x - 5$ and $g(x) = -2x^3 - 10x^2 + 2x + 10$ on a window that shows all intercepts. How are the graphs similar? Different? Discuss.

15. Find a possible formula for a polynomial with zeros at (and only at) $x = -2, 2, 5$, a y-intercept at $y = 5$, and long-run behavior of $y \to -\infty$ as $x \to \pm\infty$.

16. Let $u(x) = -\frac{1}{5}(x-3)(x+1)(x+5)$ and $v(x) = -\frac{1}{5}x^2(x-5)$.

    (a) Graph u and v for $-10 \le x \le 10$, $-10 \le y \le 10$. How are the graphs similar? How are they different?

    (b) Compare the graphs of u and v on the window $-20 \le x \le 20$, $-1600 \le y \le 1600$, the window $-50 \le x \le 50$, $-25,000 \le y \le 25,000$, and the window $-500 \le x \le 500$, $-25,000,000 \le y \le 25,000,000$. Discuss.

17. Find the equation of the line through the y-intercept of $y = x^4 - 3x^5 - 1 + x^2$ and the x-intercept of $y = 2x - 4$.

18. Let $f(x) = \left(\dfrac{1}{50,000}\right)x^3 + \left(\dfrac{1}{2}\right)x$.

    (a) For small values of x, which term of f is more important? Explain your answer.

    (b) Graph $y = f(x)$ for $-10 \le x \le 10$, $-10 \le y \le 10$. Is this graph linear? How does the appearance of this graph agree with your answer to part (a)?

    (c) How large a value of x is required for the cubic term of f to be equal to the linear term?

19. The polynomial function $f(x) = x^3 + x + 1$ is invertible—that is, this function has an inverse.

    (a) Graph $y = f(x)$. Explain how you can tell from the graph that f is invertible.

    (b) Find $f(0.5)$ and an approximate value for $f^{-1}(0.5)$.

20. If $f(x) = x^2$ and $g(x) = (x+2)(x-1)(x-3)$, find all x for which $f(x) < g(x)$.

21. Let V represent the volume in liters of air in the lungs during a 5-second respiratory cycle. If t is time in seconds, V is given by

$$V = 0.1729t + 0.1522t^2 - 0.0374t^3.$$

(a) Graph this function for $0 \leq t \leq 5$.
(b) What is the maximum value of V on this interval? What is the practical significance of the maximum value?
(c) Explain the practical significance of the t- and V-intercepts on the interval $0 \leq t \leq 5$.

22. Let $C(x)$ be a firm's total cost, in millions of dollars, for producing a quantity x thousand units of an item.

(a) Graph $C(x) = (x - 1)^3 + 1$.
(b) Let $R(x)$ be the revenue to the firm (in millions of dollars) for selling a quantity x thousand units of the good. Suppose $R(x) = x$. What does this tell you about the price of each unit?
(c) Profit equals revenue minus cost. For what values of x does the firm make a profit? Break even? Lose money?

23. The town of Smallsville was founded in 1900. Its population y (in hundreds) is given by the equation

$$y = -0.1x^4 + 1.7x^3 - 9x^2 + 14.4x + 5,$$

where x is the number of years since 1900. Use a the graph in the window $0 \leq x \leq 10$, $-2 \leq y \leq 13$.

(a) What was the population of Smallsville when it was founded?
(b) When did Smallsville become a ghost town (nobody lived there anymore)? Give the year and the month.
(c) What was the largest population of Smallsville after 1905? When did Smallsville reach that population? Again, include the month and year. Explain your method.

24. The volume, V, in milliliters, of 1 kg of water as a function of temperature T is given, for $0 \leq T \leq 30°C$, by:

$$V = 999.87 - 0.06426T + 0.0085143T^2 - 0.0000679T^3.$$

(a) Graph V.
(b) Describe the shape of your graph. Does V increase or decrease as T increases? Does the graph curve upward or downward? What does the graph tell us about how the volume varies with temperature?
(c) At what temperature does water have the maximum density? How does that appear on your graph? (Density = Mass/Volume. In this problem, the mass of the water is 1 kg.)

25. Let f and g be polynomial functions. Are the compositions

$$f(g(x)) \quad \text{and} \quad g(f(x))$$

also polynomial functions? Explain your answer.

26. Let $f(x) = x - \dfrac{x^3}{6} + \dfrac{x^5}{120}$.

(a) Graph $y = f(x)$ and $y = \sin x$ for $-2\pi \leq x \leq 2\pi$, $-3 \leq y \leq 3$.
(b) The graph of f resembles the graph of $\sin x$ on a small interval. Based on your graphs from part (a), give the approximate interval.
(c) Your calculator uses a function similar to f in order to evaluate the sine function. How reasonable an approximation does f give for $\sin(\pi/8)$?
(d) Explain how you could use the function f to approximate the value of $\sin \theta$, where $\theta = 18$ radians. [Hint: Use the fact that the sine function is periodic.]

27. Suppose f is a polynomial function of degree n, where n is a positive even integer. For each of the following statements, write *true* if the statement is always true, *false* otherwise. If the statement is false, give an example that illustrates why it is false.

(a) f is an even function.
(b) f has an inverse.
(c) f cannot be an odd function.
(d) If $f(x) \to +\infty$ as $x \to +\infty$, then $f(x) \to -\infty$ as $x \to -\infty$.

28. Let g be a polynomial function of degree n, where n is a positive odd integer. For each of the following statements, write *true* if the statement is always true, *false* otherwise. If the statement is false, give an example that illustrates why it is false.

(a) g is an odd function.
(b) g has an inverse.
(c) $\displaystyle \lim_{x \to \infty} g(x) = \infty$.
(d) If $\displaystyle \lim_{x \to -\infty} g(x) = -\infty$, then $\displaystyle \lim_{x \to \infty} g(x) = \infty$.

29. A function that is not a polynomial can often be approximated by a polynomial. For example, for certain x-values, the function $f(x) = e^x$ can be approximated by the fifth-degree polynomial

$$p(x) = 1 + x + \frac{x^2}{2} + \frac{x^3}{6} + \frac{x^4}{24} + \frac{x^5}{120}.$$

(a) Show that $p(1) \approx f(1) = e$. How good is the estimate?
(b) Calculate $p(5)$. How well does $p(5)$ approximate $f(5)$?
(c) Graph $p(x)$ and $f(x)$ together on the same set of axes. Based on your graph, for what range of values of x does $p(x)$ give a good estimate for $f(x)$?

30. Table 9.6 gives values of v, the speed of sound (in m/sec) in water as a function of the temperature T (in °C).[9]

(a) An approximate linear formula for v is given by $v = 1402.385 + 5.038813T$. Over what temperature range does this formula agree with the values in Table 9.6 to within 1°C?

(b) The formula in part (a) can be improved by adding the quadratic term $-5.799136 \cdot 10^{-2} T^2$. Repeat part (a) using this adjusted formula.

(c) The formula in part (b) can be further improved by adding the cubic term $3.287156 \cdot 10^{-4} T^3$. Repeat part (a) using this adjusted formula.

(d) The speed of sound in water at 50°C is 1542.6 m/s. If we want to improve our formula still further by adding a quartic (fourth-degree) term, should this term be positive or negative?

Table 9.6

T	0	5	10	15	20	25	30
v	1402.4	1426.2	1447.3	1466.0	1482.4	1496.7	1509.2

9.3 THE SHORT-RUN BEHAVIOR OF POLYNOMIALS

The long-run behavior of a polynomial is determined by its leading term. However, polynomials with the same leading term may have very different short-run behaviors.

Example 1   Compare the graphs of the polynomials f, g, and h given by

$$f(x) = x^4 - 4x^3 + 16x - 16, \quad g(x) = x^4 - 4x^3 - 4x^2 + 16x, \quad h(x) = x^4 + x^3 - 8x^2 - 12x.$$

Solution   Each of these functions is a fourth-degree polynomial, and each has x^4 as its leading term. Thus, all their graphs resemble the graph of x^4 on a large scale. See Figure 9.19.

However, on a smaller scale, the functions look different. See Figure 9.20. Two of the graphs go through the origin while the third does not. The graphs also differ from one another in the number of bumps each one has and in the number of times each one crosses the x-axis. Thus, polynomials with the same leading term look similar on a large scale, but may look dissimilar on a small scale.

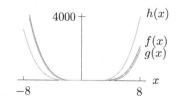
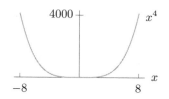

Figure 9.19: On a large scale, the polynomials f, g, and h resemble the power function $y = x^4$

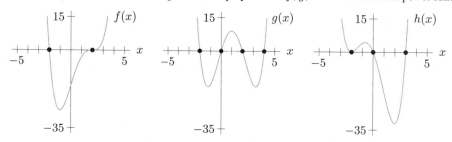

Figure 9.20: On a smaller scale, the polynomials f, g, and h look quite different from each other

[9]Data determined using the Marczak formula described at the UK National Physical Laboratory website, http://www.npl.co.uk.

Factored Form, Zeros, and the Short-Run Behavior of a Polynomial

To predict the long-run behavior of a polynomial, we write it in standard form. However, to determine the zeros and the short-run behavior of a polynomial, we write it in factored form, as a product of other polynomials. Some, but not all, polynomials can be factored.

Example 2   Investigate the short-run behavior of the third-degree polynomial $u(x) = x^3 - x^2 - 6x$.

(a) Rewrite $u(x)$ as a product of linear factors.
(b) Find the zeros of $u(x)$.
(c) Describe the graph of $u(x)$. Where does it cross the x-axis? the y-axis? Where is $u(x)$ positive? Negative?

Solution   (a) By factoring out an x and then factoring the quadratic, $x^2 - x - 6$, we rewrite $u(x)$ as

$$u(x) = x^3 - x^2 - 6x = x(x^2 - x - 6) = x(x - 3)(x + 2).$$

Thus, we have expressed $u(x)$ as the product of three linear factors, x, $x - 3$, and $x + 2$.

(b) The polynomial equals zero if and only if at least one of its factors is zero. We solve the equation:

$$x(x - 3)(x + 2) = 0,$$

giving

$$x = 0, \quad \text{or} \quad x - 3 = 0, \quad \text{or} \quad x + 2 = 0,$$

so

$$x = 0, \quad \text{or} \quad x = 3, \quad \text{or} \quad x = -2.$$

These are the zeros, or x-intercepts, of u. To check, evaluate $u(x)$ for these x-values; you should get 0. There are no other zeros.

(c) To describe the graph of u, we give the x- and y-intercepts, and the long-run behavior.
   The factored form, $u(x) = x(x - 3)(x + 2)$, shows that the graph crosses the x-axis at $x = 0, 3, -2$. The graph of u crosses the y-axis at $u(0) = 0^3 - 0^2 - 6 \cdot 0 = 0$; that is, at $y = 0$. For large values of x, the graph of $y = u(x)$ resembles the graph of its leading term, $y = x^3$. Figure 9.21 shows where u is positive and where u is negative.

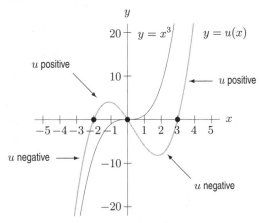

Figure 9.21: The graph of $u(x) = x^3 - x^2 - 6x$ has zeros at $x = -2$, 0, and 3. Its long-run behavior resembles $y = x^3$

In Example 2, each linear factor produced a zero of the polynomial. Now suppose that we do not know the polynomial p, but we do know that it has zeros at $x = 0, -12, 31$. Then we know that the factored form of the polynomial must include the factors $(x - 0)$ or x, and $(x - (-12))$ or $(x + 12)$, and $(x - 31)$. It may include other factors too. In summary:

> Suppose p is a polynomial. If the formula for p has a **linear factor**, that is, a factor of the form $(x - k)$, then p has a zero at $x = k$.
> Conversely, if p has a **zero** at $x = k$, then p has a linear factor of the form $(x - k)$.

The Number of Factors, Zeros, and Bumps

The number of linear factors is always less than or equal to the degree of a polynomial. For example, a fourth degree polynomial can have no more than four linear factors. This makes sense because if we had another factor in the product and multiplied out, the highest power of x would be greater than four. Since each zero corresponds to a linear factor, the number of zeros is less than or equal to the degree of the polynomial.

We can now say that there is a maximum number of bumps in the graph of a polynomial of degree n. Between any two consecutive zeros, there is a bump because the graph changes direction. In Figure 9.21, the graph, which decreases at $x = 1$, must come back up in order to cross the x-axis at $x = 3$. In summary:

> The graph of an nth degree polynomial has at most n zeros and turns at most $(n - 1)$ times.

Multiple Zeros

The functions $s(x) = (x - 4)^2$ and $t(x) = (x + 1)^3$ are both polynomials in factored form. Each is a horizontal shift of a power function. We refer to the zeros of s and t as *multiple zeros*, because in each case the factor contributing the value of $y = 0$ is repeated more than once. For instance, we say that $x = 4$ is a *double zero* of s, since

$$s(x) = (x - 4)^2 = \underbrace{(x - 4)(x - 4)}_{\text{Repeated twice}}.$$

Likewise, we say that $x = -1$ is a *triple zero* of t, since

$$t(x) = (x + 1)^3 = \underbrace{(x + 1)(x + 1)(x + 1)}_{\text{Repeated three times}}.$$

The graphs of s and t in Figures 9.22 and 9.23 show typical behavior near multiple zeros.

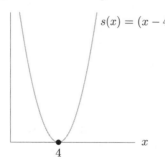

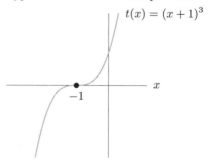

Figure 9.22: Double zero at $x = 4$ Figure 9.23: Triple zero at $x = -1$

In general:

> If p is a polynomial with a repeated linear factor, then p has a **multiple zero**.
> - If the factor $(x - k)$ is repeated an even number of times, the graph of $y = p(x)$ does not cross the x-axis at $x = k$, but "bounces" off the x-axis at $x = k$. (See Figure 9.22.)
> - If the factor $(x - k)$ is repeated an odd number of times, the graph of $y = p(x)$ crosses the x-axis at $x = k$, but it looks flattened there. (See Figure 9.23.)

Example 3   Describe in words the zeros of the 4th-degree polynomials $f(x)$, $g(x)$, and $h(x)$, in Figure 9.24.

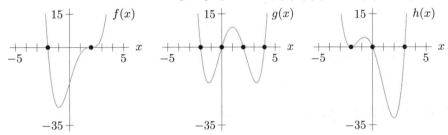

Figure 9.24

Solution   The graph suggests that f has a single zero at $x = -2$. The flattened appearance near $x = 2$ suggests that f has a multiple zero there. Since the graph crosses the x-axis at $x = 2$ (instead of bouncing off it), this zero must be repeated an odd number of times. Since f is 4th degree, f has at most 4 factors, so there must be a triple zero at $x = 2$.

   The graph of g has four single zeros. The graph of h has two single zeros (at $x = 0$ and $x = 3$) and a double zero at $x = -2$. The multiplicity of the zero at $x = -2$ is not higher than two because h is of degree $n = 4$.

Finding the Formula for a Polynomial from its Graph

The graph of a polynomial often enables us to find a possible formula for the polynomial.

Example 4   Find a possible formula for the polynomial function f graphed in Figure 9.25.

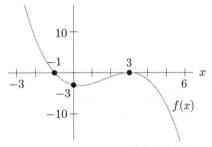

Figure 9.25: Features of the graph lead to a possible formula for this polynomial

Solution   Based on its long-run behavior, f is of odd degree greater than or equal to 3. The polynomial has zeros at $x = -1$ and $x = 3$. We see that $x = 3$ is a multiple zero of even power, because the graph bounces off the x-axis here instead of crossing it. Therefore, we try the formula

$$f(x) = k(x+1)(x-3)^2$$

where k represents a stretch factor. The shape of the graph shows that k must be negative.
To find k, we use the fact that $f(0) = -3$, so

$$f(0) = k(0+1)(0-3)^2 = -3$$

which gives

$$9k = -3 \qquad \text{so} \qquad k = -\frac{1}{3}.$$

Thus, $f(x) = -\frac{1}{3}(x+1)(x-3)^2$ is a possible formula for this polynomial.

The formula for f we found in Example 4 is the polynomial of least degree we could have chosen. However, there are other polynomials, such as $y = -\frac{1}{27}(x+1)(x-3)^4$, with the same overall behavior as the function shown in Figure 9.25.

Exercises and Problems for Section 9.3

Exercises

In Exercises 1–4, find the zeros of the functions.

1. $y = 7(x+3)(x-2)(x+7)$

2. $y = a(x+2)(x-b)$, where a, b are nonzero constants

3. $y = x^3 + 7x^2 + 12x$

4. $y = (x^2 + 2x - 7)(x^3 + 4x^2 - 21x)$

5. Use the graph of $g(x)$ in Figure 9.20 on page 402 to determine the factored form of
$$g(x) = x^4 - 4x^3 - 4x^2 + 16x.$$

6. Use the graph of $f(x)$ in Figure 9.20 on page 402 to determine the factored form of
$$f(x) = x^4 - 4x^3 + 16x - 16.$$

7. Use the graph of $h(x)$ in Figure 9.20 on page 402 to determine the factored form of
$$h(x) = x^4 + x^3 - 8x^2 - 12x.$$

8. Factor $f(x) = 8x^3 - 4x^2 - 60x$ completely, and determine the zeros of f.

Without a calculator, graph the polynomials in Exercises 9–10. Label all the x-intercepts and y-intercepts.

9. $f(x) = -5(x^2 - 4)(25 - x^2)$

10. $g(x) = 5(x-4)(x^2 - 25)$

Problems

11. (a) Let $f(x) = (2x-1)(3x-1)(x-7)(x-9)$. What are the zeros of this polynomial?
    (b) Is it possible to find a viewing window that shows all of the zeros and all of the the turning points of f?
    (c) Find two separate viewing windows which together show all the zeros and all the turning points of f.

12. (a) Experiment with various viewing windows to determine the zeros of $f(x) = 2x^4 + 9x^3 - 7x^2 - 9x + 5$. Then write f in factored form.
    (b) Find a single viewing window that clearly shows all of the turning points of f.

13. Let $p(x) = x^4 + 10x^3 - 68x^2 + 102x - 45$. By experimenting with various viewing windows, determine the zeros of p and use this information to write $p(x)$ in factored form.

14. Let $u(x) = \frac{1}{8}x^3$ and $v(x) = \frac{1}{8}x(x - 0.01)^2$. Do v and u have the exact same graph? Sketch u and v in the window $-10 \le x \le 10$, $-10 \le y \le 10$. Now do you think that v and u have the same graph? If so, explain why their formulas are different; if not, find a viewing window on which their graphs' differences are prominent.

15. Without using a calculator, decide which of the equations A–E best describes the polynomial in Figure 9.26.

A $y = (x + 2)(x + 1)(x - 2)(x - 3)$
B $y = x(x + 2)(x + 1)(x - 2)(x - 3)$
C $y = -\frac{1}{2}(x + 2)(x + 1)(x - 2)(x - 3)$
D $y = \frac{1}{2}(x + 2)(x + 1)(x - 2)(x - 3)$
E $y = -(x + 2)(x + 1)(x - 2)(x - 3)$

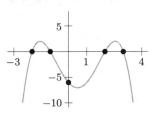

Figure 9.26

In Problems 16–21, find possible formulas for polynomials with the given properties.

16. f has degree ≤ 2, $f(0) = f(1) = f(2) = 1$.

17. f has degree ≤ 2, $f(0) = f(2) = 0$ and $f(3) = 3$.

18. f has degree ≤ 2, $f(0) = 0$ and $f(1) = 1$.

19. f is third degree with $f(-3) = 0$, $f(1) = 0$, $f(4) = 0$, and $f(2) = 5$.

20. g is fourth degree, g has a double zero at $x = 3$, $g(5) = 0$, $g(-1) = 0$, and $g(0) = 3$.

21. Least possible degree through the points $(-3, 0)$, $(1, 0)$, and $(0, -3)$.

Give a possible formula for the polynomials in Problems 22–35.

22.

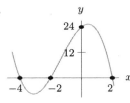

23.

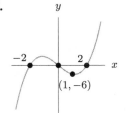

24.

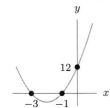

25.

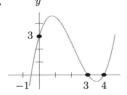

26.

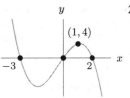

27.

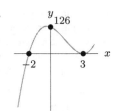

28.

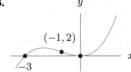

29.

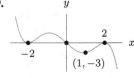

30.

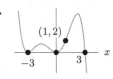

31.

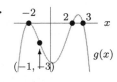

32.

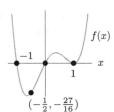

33.

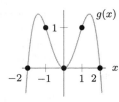

34.

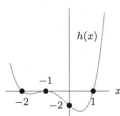

35.

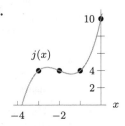

36. Which of these functions have inverses that are functions? Discuss.

(a) $f(x) = (x - 2)^3 + 4$.
(b) $g(x) = x^3 - 4x^2 + 2$.

For Problems 37–42, find the real zeros (if any) of the polynomials.

37. $y = x^2 + 5x + 6$

38. $y = x^4 + 6x^2 + 9$

39. $y = 4x^2 - 1$

40. $y = 4x^2 + 1$

41. $y = 2x^2 - 3x - 3$

42. $y = 3x^5 + 7x + 1$

43. An open-top box is to be constructed from a 6 in by 8 in rectangular sheet of tin by cutting out squares of equal size at each corner, then folding up the resulting flaps. Let x denote the length of the side of each cut-out square. Assume negligible thickness.

   (a) Find a formula for the volume of the box as a function of x.
   (b) For what values of x does the formula from part (a) make sense in the context of the problem?
   (c) Sketch a graph of the volume function.
   (d) What, approximately, is the maximum volume of the box?

44. You wish to pack a cardboard box inside a wooden crate. In order to have room for the packing materials, you need to leave a 0.5-ft space around the front, back, and sides of the box, and a 1-ft space around the top and bottom of the box. If the cardboard box is x feet long, $(x + 2)$ feet wide, and $(x - 1)$ feet deep, find a formula in terms of x for the amount of packing material needed.

45. Take an 8.5 by 11-inch piece of paper and cut out four equal squares from the corners. Fold up the sides to create an open box. Find the dimensions of the box that has maximum volume.

46. Consider the function $a(x) = x^5 + 2x^3 - 4x$.

   (a) Without using a calculator or computer, what can you say about the graph of a?
   (b) Use a calculator or a computer to determine the zeros of this function to three decimal places.
   (c) Explain why you think that you have all the possible zeros.
   (d) What are the zeros of $b(x) = 2x^5 + 4x^3 - 8x$? Does your answer surprise you?

47. (a) Sketch a graph of $f(x) = x^4 - 17x^2 + 36x - 20$ for $-10 \le x \le 10$, $-10 \le y \le 10$.

   (b) Your graph should appear to have a vertical asymptote at $x = -5$. Does f actually have a vertical asymptote here? Explain.
   (c) How many zeros does f have? Can you find a window in which all of the zeros of f are clearly visible?
   (d) Write the formula of f in factored form.
   (e) How many turning points does the graph of f have? Can you find a window in which all the turning points of f are clearly visible? Explain.

48. In each of the following cases, find a possible formula for the polynomial f.

   (a) Suppose f has zeros at $x = -2$, $x = 3$, $x = 5$ and a y-intercept of 4.
   (b) In addition to the properties in part (a), suppose f has the following long-run behavior: As $x \to \pm\infty$, $y \to -\infty$. [Hint: Assume f has a double zero.]
   (c) In addition to the properties in part (a), suppose f has the following long-run behavior: As $x \to \pm\infty$, $y \to +\infty$.

49. The following statements about $f(x)$ are true:

   - $f(x)$ is a polynomial function
   - $f(x) = 0$ at exactly four different values of x
   - $f(x) \to -\infty$ as $x \to \pm\infty$

For each of the following statements, write *true* if the statement must be true, *never true* if the statement is never true, or *sometimes true* if it is sometimes true and sometimes not true.

   (a) $f(x)$ is an odd function
   (b) $f(x)$ is an even function
   (c) $f(x)$ is a fourth degree polynomial
   (d) $f(x)$ is a fifth degree polynomial
   (e) $f(-x) \to -\infty$ as $x \to \pm\infty$
   (f) $f(x)$ is invertible

9.4 RATIONAL FUNCTIONS

The Average Cost of Producing a Therapeutic Drug

A pharmaceutical company wants to begin production of a new drug. The total cost C, in dollars, of making q grams of the drug is given by the linear function

$$C(q) = 2{,}500{,}000 + 2000q.$$

The fact that $C(0) = 2{,}500{,}000$ tells us that the company spends \$2,500,000 before it starts making the drug. This quantity is known as the *fixed cost* because it does not depend on how much of the drug is made. It represents the cost for research, testing, and equipment. In addition, the slope of C tells us that each gram of the drug costs an extra \$2000 to make. This quantity is known as the *variable cost* per unit. It represents the additional cost, in labor and materials, to make an additional gram of the drug.

The fixed cost of \$2.5 million is large compared to the variable cost of \$2000 per gram. This means that it is impractical for the company to make a small amount of the drug. For instance, the total cost for 10 grams is

$$C(10) = 2{,}500{,}000 + 2000 \cdot 10 = 2{,}520{,}000,$$

which works out to an average cost of \$252,000 per gram. The company would probably never sell such an expensive drug.

However, as larger quantities of the drug are manufactured, the initial expenditure of \$2.5 million seems less significant. The fixed cost averages out over a large quantity. For example, if the company makes 10,000 grams of the drug,

$$\text{Average cost} = \frac{\text{Cost of producing 10,000 grams}}{10{,}000} = \frac{2{,}500{,}000 + 2000 \cdot 10{,}000}{10{,}000} = 2250,$$

or \$2250 per gram of drug produced.

We define the average cost, $a(q)$, as the cost per gram to produce q grams of the drug:

$$a(q) = \frac{\text{Average cost of}}{\text{producing } q \text{ grams}} = \frac{\text{Total cost}}{\text{Number of grams}} = \frac{C(q)}{q} = \frac{2{,}500{,}000 + 2000q}{q}.$$

Figure 9.27 gives a graph of $y = a(q)$ for $q > 0$. The horizontal asymptote reflects the fact that for large values of q, the value of $a(q)$ is close to 2000. This is because, as more of the drug is produced, the average cost gets closer to \$2000 per gram. See Table 9.7.

The vertical asymptote of $y = a(q)$ is the y-axis, which tells us that the average cost per gram is very large if a small amount of the drug is made. This is because the initial \$2.5 million expenditure is averaged over very few units. We saw that producing only 10 grams costs a staggering \$252,000 per gram.

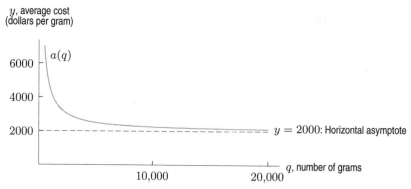

Figure 9.27: The graph of $y = a(q)$, a rational function, has a horizontal asymptote at $y = 2000$ and a vertical asymptote at $q = 0$

Table 9.7   *As quantity q increases, the average cost a(q) draws closer to $2000 per gram*

Quantity, q	Total cost, $C(q) = 2{,}500{,}000 + 2000q$	Average cost, $a(q) = C(q)/q$
10,000	$2{,}500{,}000 + 20{,}000{,}000 = 22{,}500{,}000$	2250
50,000	$2{,}500{,}000 + 100{,}000{,}000 = 102{,}500{,}000$	2050
100,000	$2{,}500{,}000 + 200{,}000{,}000 = 202{,}500{,}000$	2025
500,000	$2{,}500{,}000 + 1{,}000{,}000{,}000 = 1{,}002{,}500{,}000$	2005

What is a Rational Function?

The formula for $a(q)$ is the ratio of the polynomial $2{,}500{,}000 + 2000q$ and the polynomial q. Since $a(q)$ is given by the ratio of two polynomials, $a(q)$ is an example of a *rational function*. In general:

> If r can be written as the ratio of polynomial functions $p(x)$ and $q(x)$, that is, if
>
> $$r(x) = \frac{p(x)}{q(x)},$$
>
> then r is called a **rational function**. (We assume that $q(x)$ is not the constant polynomial $q(x) = 0$.)

The Long-Run Behavior of Rational Functions

In the long-run, every rational function behaves like a power function. For example, consider

$$f(x) = \frac{6x^4 + x^3 + 1}{-5x + 2x^2}.$$

Since the long-run behavior of a polynomial is determined by its highest power term, for large x the numerator behaves like $6x^4$ and the denominator behaves like $2x^2$. The long-run behavior of f is

$$f(x) = \frac{6x^4 + x^3 + 1}{-5x + 2x^2} \approx \frac{6x^4}{2x^2} = 3x^2,$$

so

$$\lim_{x \to \pm\infty} f(x) = \lim_{x \to \pm\infty} (3x^2) = \infty.$$

See Figure 9.28.

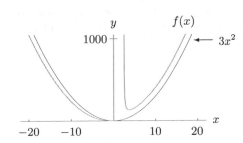

Figure 9.28: In the long-run, the graph of $f(x)$ looks like the graph of $3x^2$

In general, if r is any rational function, then for large enough values of x,

$$r(x) = \frac{a_n x^n + a_{n-1} x^{n-1} + \cdots + a_0}{b_m x^m + b_{m-1} x^{m-1} + \cdots + b_0} \approx \frac{a_n x^n}{b_m x^m} = \frac{a_n}{b_m} x^{n-m}.$$

This means that on a large scale r resembles the function $y = \left(\dfrac{a_n}{b_m}\right) x^{n-m}$, which is a power function of the form $y = kx^p$, where $k = a_n/b_m$ and $p = n - m$. In summary:

For large enough values of x (either positive or negative), the graph of the rational function r looks like the graph of a power function. If $r(x) = p(x)/q(x)$, then the **long-run behavior** of $y = r(x)$ is given by

$$y = \frac{\text{Leading term of } p}{\text{Leading term of } q}.$$

Using limits, we write

$$\lim_{x \to \pm\infty} \frac{p(x)}{q(x)} = \lim_{x \to \pm\infty} \frac{\text{Leading term of } p}{\text{Leading term of } q}.$$

Example 1   For positive x, describe the long-run behavior of the rational function

$$r(x) = \frac{x + 3}{x + 2}.$$

Solution   If x is a large positive number, then

$$r(x) = \frac{\text{Big number} + 3}{\text{Same big number} + 2} \approx \frac{\text{Big number}}{\text{Same big number}} = 1.$$

For example, if $x = 100$, we have

$$r(x) = \frac{103}{102} = 1.0098\ldots \approx 1.$$

If $x = 10,000$, we have

$$r(x) = \frac{10,003}{10,002} = 1.00009998\ldots \approx 1,$$

For large positive x-values, $r(x) \approx 1$. Thus, for large enough values of x, the graph of $y = r(x)$ looks like the line $y = 1$, its horizontal asymptote. We write $\lim_{x \to \infty} r(x) = 1$. See Figure 9.29. However, for $x > 0$, the graph of r is above the line since the numerator is larger than the denominator.

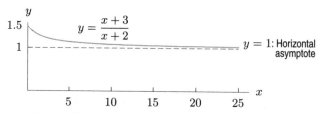

Figure 9.29: For large positive values of x, the graph of $r(x) = (x + 3)/(x + 2)$ looks like the horizontal line $y = 1$

Example 2   For positive x, describe the positive long-run behavior of the rational function

$$g(x) = \frac{3x + 1}{x^2 + x - 2}.$$

Solution   The leading term in the numerator is $3x$ and the leading term in the denominator is x^2. Thus for large enough values of x,

$$g(x) \approx \frac{3x}{x^2} = \frac{3}{x},$$

so

$$\lim_{x \to \infty} g(x) = \lim_{x \to \infty} \left(\frac{3}{x}\right) = 0.$$

Figure 9.30 shows the graphs of $y = g(x)$ and $y = 3/x$. For large values of x, the two graphs are nearly indistinguishable. Both graphs have a horizontal asymptote at $y = 0$.

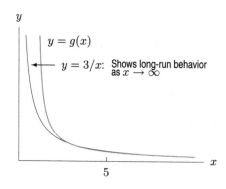

Figure 9.30: For large enough values of x, the function g looks like the function $y = 3x^{-1}$

What Causes Asymptotes?

The graphs of rational functions often behave differently from the graphs of polynomials. Polynomial graphs (except constant functions) cannot level off to a horizontal line like the graphs of rational functions can. In Example 1, the numerator and denominator are approximately equal for large x, producing the horizontal asymptote $y = 1$. In Example 2, the denominator grows faster than the numerator, driving the quotient toward zero.

The rapid rise (or fall) of the graph of a rational function near its vertical asymptote is due to the denominator becoming small (close to zero). It is tempting to assume that any function which has a denominator has a vertical asymptote. However, this is not true. To have a vertical asymptote, the denominator must become close to zero. For example, suppose that

$$r(x) = \frac{1}{x^2 + 3}.$$

The denominator is always greater than 3; it is never 0. We see from Figure 9.31 that r does not have a vertical asymptote.

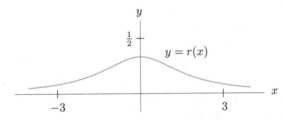

Figure 9.31: The rational function $r(x) = 1/(x^2 + 3)$ has no vertical asymptote

Exercises and Problems for Section 9.4

Exercises

Are the functions in Exercises 1–6 rational functions? If so, write them in the form $p(x)/q(x)$, the ratio of polynomials.

1. $f(x) = \dfrac{x^2}{2} + \dfrac{1}{x}$

2. $f(x) = \dfrac{\sqrt{x} + 1}{x + 1}$

3. $f(x) = \dfrac{4^x + 3}{3^x - 1}$

4. $f(x) = \dfrac{x^2 + 4}{e^x}$

5. $f(x) = \dfrac{x^2}{x - 3} - \dfrac{5}{x - 3}$

6. $f(x) = \dfrac{9x - 1}{4\sqrt{x} + 7} + \dfrac{5x^3}{x^2 - 1}$

7. Find

   (a) $\displaystyle\lim_{x \to \infty} \frac{2x + 1}{x - 5}$ **(b)** $\displaystyle\lim_{x \to -\infty} \frac{2 + 5x}{6x + 3}$

8. Find

   (a) $\displaystyle\lim_{x \to \infty} \frac{x(x^2 - 4)}{5 + 5x^3}$ **(b)** $\displaystyle\lim_{x \to -\infty} \frac{3x(x - 1)(x - 2)}{5 - 6x^4}$

Find the horizontal asymptote, if it exists, of the functions in Problems 9–11.

9. $f(x) = \dfrac{1}{1 + \dfrac{1}{x}}$

10. $g(x) = \dfrac{(1 - x)(2 + 3x)}{2x^2 + 1}$

11. $h(x) = 3 - \dfrac{1}{x} + \dfrac{x}{x + 1}$

12. Compare and discuss the long-run behaviors of the following functions:

$$f(x) = \frac{x^2 + 1}{x^2 + 5}, \quad g(x) = \frac{x^3 + 1}{x^2 + 5}, \quad h(x) = \frac{x + 1}{x^2 + 5}.$$

Problems

13. Let $r(x) = p(x)/q(x)$, where p and q are polynomial of degrees m and n, respectively. What conditions on m and n ensure that the following statements are true?

    (a) $\lim\limits_{x \to \infty} r(x) = 0$

    (b) $\lim\limits_{x \to \infty} r(x) = k$, with $k \neq 0$.

14. Give examples of rational functions with even symmetry, odd symmetry, and neither. How does the symmetry of $f(x) = p(x)/q(x)$ depend on the symmetry of $p(x)$ and $q(x)$?

15. Find a formula for $f^{-1}(x)$ given that

$$f(x) = \frac{4 - 3x}{5x - 4}.$$

16. Let t be the time in weeks. At time $t = 0$, organic waste is dumped into a pond. The oxygen level in the pond at time t is given by

$$f(t) = \frac{t^2 - t + 1}{t^2 + 1}.$$

Assume $f(0) = 1$ is the normal level of oxygen.

    (a) Graph this function.

    (b) Describe the shape of the graph. What is the significance of the minimum for the pond?

    (c) What eventually happens to the oxygen level?

    (d) Approximately how many weeks must pass before the oxygen level returns to 75% of its normal level?

17. The following procedure approximates the cube root of a number. If x is a guess for $\sqrt[3]{2}$, for example, then x^3 equals 2 only if the guess is correct. If $x^3 = 2$ we can also write $x = 2/x^2$. If our guess, x, is less than $\sqrt[3]{2}$, then $2/x^2$ is greater than $\sqrt[3]{2}$. If x is greater than $\sqrt[3]{2}$, then $2/x^2$ is less than $\sqrt[3]{2}$. In either case, if x is an estimate for $\sqrt[3]{2}$, then the average of x and $2/x^2$ provides a better estimate. Define $g(x)$ to be this improved estimate.

    (a) Find a possible formula for $g(x)$, expressed as one reduced fraction.

    (b) Use $1.26 \approx \sqrt[3]{2}$ as a first guess. Use the function $g(x)$ to estimate the value of $\sqrt[3]{2}$, accurate to five decimal places. Construct a table showing any intermediate results. Explain how you know you have reached the required accuracy.

18. Problem 17 outlines a method of approximating $\sqrt[3]{2}$. An initial guess, x, is averaged with $2/x^2$ to obtain a better guess, denoted by $g(x)$. A better method involves taking a weighted average of x and $2/x^2$.

    (a) Let x be a guess for $\sqrt[3]{2}$. Define $h(x)$ by

$$h(x) = \frac{1}{3}\left(x + x + \frac{2}{x^2}\right).$$

Express $h(x)$ as one reduced fraction. Explain why $h(x)$ is referred to as a weighted average.

    (b) Explain why $h(x)$ is a better function to use for estimating $\sqrt[3]{2}$ than is $g(x)$. Include specific, numerical examples in your answer.

19. Bronze is an alloy, or mixture, of copper and tin. The alloy initially contains 3 kg copper and 9 kg tin. You add x kg of copper to this 12 kg of alloy. The concentration of copper in the alloy is a function of x:

$$f(x) = \text{Concentration of copper} = \frac{\text{Total amount of copper}}{\text{Total amount of alloy}}.$$

    (a) Find a formula for f in terms of x, the amount of copper added.

    (b) Evaluate the following expressions and explain their significance for the alloy:

        (i) $f(\frac{1}{2})$ (ii) $f(0)$ (iii) $f(-1)$

        (iv) $f^{-1}(\frac{1}{2})$ (v) $f^{-1}(0)$

    (c) Graph $f(x)$ for $-5 \leq x \leq 5$, $-0.25 \leq y \leq 0.5$. Interpret the intercepts in the context of the alloy.

    (d) Graph $f(x)$ for $-3 \leq x \leq 100$, $0 \leq y \leq 1$. Describe the appearance of your graph for large x-values. Does the appearance agree with what you expect to happen when large amounts of copper are added to the alloy?

20. A chemist is studying the properties of a bronze alloy (mixture) of copper and tin. She begins with 2 kg of an alloy that is one-half tin. Keeping the amount of copper constant, she adds small amounts of tin to the alloy. Letting x be the total amount of tin added, define

$$C(x) = \text{Concentration of tin} = \frac{\text{Total amount of tin}}{\text{Total amount of alloy}}.$$

    (a) Find a formula for $C(x)$.

    (b) Evaluate $C(0.5)$ and $C(-0.5)$. Explain the physical significance of these quantities.

    (c) Graph $y = C(x)$, labeling all interesting features. Describe the physical significance of the features you have labeled.

21. The total cost $C(n)$ for a producer to manufacture n units of a good is given by

$$C(n) = 5000 + 50n.$$

The average cost of producing n units is $a(n) = C(n)/n$.

    (a) Evaluate and interpret the economic significance of:

        (i) $C(1)$ (ii) $C(100)$

        (iii) $C(1000)$ (iv) $C(10000)$

(b) Evaluate and interpret the economic significance of:

(i) $a(1)$ (ii) $a(100)$
(iii) $a(1000)$ (iv) $a(10000)$

(c) Based on part (b), what trend do you notice in the values of $a(n)$ as n gets large? Explain this trend in economic terms.

22. Figure 9.32 shows the cost function, $C(n)$, from Problem 21, together with a line, l, that passes through the origin.

(a) What is the slope of line l?
(b) How does line l relate to $a(n_0)$, the average cost of producing n_0 units (as defined in Problem 21)?

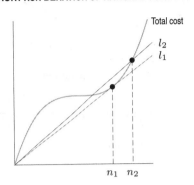

Figure 9.33

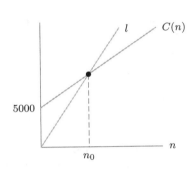

Figure 9.32

23. Typically, the average cost of production (as defined in Problem 21) decreases as the level of production increases. Is this always the case for the goods whose total cost function is graphed in Figure 9.33? Use the result of Problem 22 and explain your reasoning.

24. It costs a company $30,000 to begin production of a good, plus $3 for every unit of the good produced. Let x be the number of units produced by the company.

(a) Find a formula for $C(x)$, the total cost for the production of x units of the good.
(b) Find a formula for the company's average cost per unit, $a(x)$.
(c) Graph $y = a(x)$ for $0 < x \le 50{,}000$, $0 \le y \le 10$. Label the horizontal asymptote.
(d) Explain in economic terms why the graph of a has the long-run behavior that it does.
(e) Explain in economic terms why the graph of a has the vertical asymptote that it does.
(f) Find a formula for $a^{-1}(y)$. Give an economic interpretation of $a^{-1}(y)$.
(g) The company makes a profit if the average cost of its good is less than $5 per unit. Find the minimum number of units the company can produce and make a profit.

9.5   THE SHORT-RUN BEHAVIOR OF RATIONAL FUNCTIONS

The short-run behavior of a polynomial can often be determined from its factored form. The same is true of rational functions. If r is a rational function given by

$$r(x) = \frac{p(x)}{q(x)}, \qquad p, q \text{ polynomials,}$$

then the short-run behavior of p and q tell us about the short-run behavior of r.

The Zeros and Vertical Asymptotes of a Rational Function

A fraction is equal to zero if and only if its numerator equals zero (and its denominator does not equal zero). Thus, the rational function $r(x) = p(x)/q(x)$ has a zero wherever p has a zero, provided q does not have a zero there.

Just as we can find the zeros of a rational function by looking at its numerator, we can find the vertical asymptotes by looking at its denominator. A rational function is large wherever its denominator is small. This means that r has a vertical asymptote wherever its denominator has a zero, provided its numerator does not also have a zero there.

Example 1   Find the zeros and vertical asymptotes of the rational function $r(x) = \dfrac{x+3}{x+2}$.

Solution   We see that $r(x) = 0$ if

$$\frac{x+3}{x+2} = 0.$$

This ratio equals zero only if the numerator is zero (and the denominator is not zero), so

$$x + 3 = 0$$
$$x = -3.$$

The only zero of r is $x = -3$. To check, note that $r(-3) = 0/(-1) = 0$. The denominator has a zero at $x = -2$, so the graph of $r(x)$ has a vertical asymptote there.

Example 2   Graph $r(x) = \dfrac{25}{(x+2)(x-3)^2}$, showing all the important features.

Solution   Since the numerator of this function is never zero, r has no zeros, meaning that the graph of r never crosses the x-axis. The graph of r has vertical asymptotes at $x = -2$ and $x = 3$ because this is where the denominator is zero. What does the graph of r look like near its asymptote at $x = -2$? At $x = -2$, the numerator is 25 and the value of the factor $(x-3)^2$ is $(-2-3)^2 = 25$. Thus, near $x = -2$,

$$r(x) = \frac{25}{(x+2)(x-3)^2} \approx \frac{25}{(x+2)(25)} = \frac{1}{x+2}.$$

So, near $x = -2$, the graph of r looks like the graph of $y = 1/(x+2)$. Note that the graph of $y = 1/(x+2)$ is the graph of $y = 1/x$ shifted to the left by 2 units. We see that

$$\lim_{x \to -2^-} r(x) = -\infty \quad \text{and} \quad \lim_{x \to -2^+} r(x) = \infty.$$

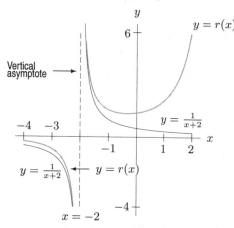

Figure 9.34: The rational function r resembles the shifted power function $1/(x+2)$ near the asymptote at $x = -2$

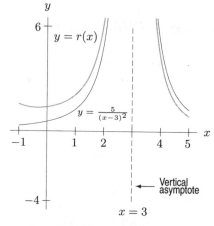

Figure 9.35: The rational function r resembles the shifted power function $5/(x-3)^2$ near the asymptote at $x = 3$

What does the graph of r look like near its vertical asymptote at $x = 3$? Near $x = 3$, the numerator is 25 and value of the factor $(x + 2)$ is approximately $(3 + 2) = 5$. Thus, near $x = 3$,

$$r(x) \approx \frac{25}{(5)(x - 3)^2} = \frac{5}{(x - 3)^2}.$$

Near $x = 3$, the graph of r looks like the the graph of $y = 5/(x - 3)^2$. We see that

$$\lim_{x \to 3} r(x) = \infty.$$

The graph of $y = 5/(x - 3)^2$ is the graph of $y = 5/x^2$ shifted to the right 3 units. Since

$$r(0) = \frac{25}{(0 + 2)(0 - 3)^2} = \frac{25}{18} \approx 1.4,$$

the graph of r crosses the y-axis at $25/18$. The long-run behavior of r is given by the ratio of the leading term in the numerator to the leading term in the denominator. The numerator is 25 and if we multiply out the denominator, we see that its leading term is x^3. Thus, the long-run behavior of r is given by $y = 25/x^3$, which has a horizontal asymptote at $y = 0$. See Figure 9.36. We see that

$$\lim_{x \to \pm\infty} r(x) = 0.$$

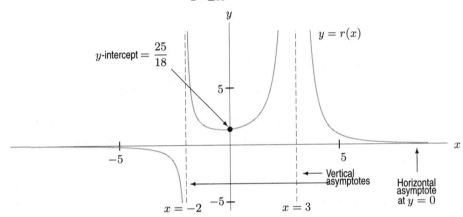

Figure 9.36: A graph of the rational function $r(x) = \dfrac{25}{(x + 2)(x - 3)^2}$, showing intercepts and asymptotes

The Graph of a Rational Function

We can now summarize what we have learned about the graphs of rational functions.

If r is a rational function given by $r(x) = \dfrac{p(x)}{q(x)}$, where p and q are polynomials with different zeros, then:
- The **long-run behavior** of r is given by the ratio of the leading terms of p and q.
- The **zeros** of r are the same as the zeros of the numerator, p.
- The graph of r has a **vertical asymptote** at each of the zeros of the denominator, q.

If p and q have zeros at the same x-values, the rational function may behave differently. See page 419.

Can a Graph Cross an Asymptote?

The graph of a rational function never crosses a vertical asymptote. However, the graphs of some rational functions cross their horizontal asymptotes. The difference is that a vertical asymptote occurs where the function is undefined, so there can be no y-value there, whereas a horizontal asymptote represents the limiting value of the function as $x \to \pm\infty$. There is no reason that the function cannot take on this limiting y-value for some finite x-value. For example, the graph of $r(x) = \dfrac{x^2 + 2x - 3}{x^2}$ crosses the line $y = 1$, its horizontal asymptote; the graph does not cross the vertical asymptote, the y-axis. See Figure 9.37.

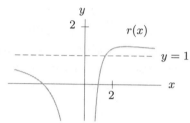

Figure 9.37: A rational function can cross its horizontal asymptote

Rational Functions as Transformations of Power Functions

The average cost function on page 409 can be written as

$$a(q) = \frac{2{,}500{,}000 + 2000q}{q} = 2{,}500{,}000q^{-1} + 2000.$$

Thus, the graph of a is the graph of the power function $y = 2{,}500{,}000q^{-1}$ shifted up 2000 units. Many rational functions can be viewed as translations of power functions.

Finding a Formula for a Rational Function from its Graph

The graph of a rational function can give a good idea of its formula. Zeros of the function correspond to factors in the numerator and vertical asymptotes correspond to factors in the denominator.

Example 3   Find a possible formula for the rational function, $g(x)$, graphed in Figure 9.38.

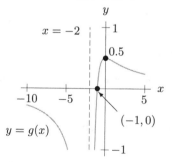

Figure 9.38: The graph of $y = g(x)$ a rational function

Solution   From the graph, we see that g has a zero at $x = -1$ and a vertical asymptote at $x = -2$. This means that the numerator of g has a zero at $x = -1$ and the denominator of g has a zero at $x = -2$. The zero of g does not seem to be a multiple zero because the graph crosses the x-axis instead of bouncing and does not have a flattened appearance. Thus, we conclude that the numerator of g has one factor of $(x + 1)$.

The values of $g(x)$ have the same sign on both sides of the vertical asymptote. Thus, the behavior of g near its vertical asymptote is more like the behavior of $y = 1/(x + 2)^2$ than like $y = 1/(x + 2)$. We conclude that the denominator of g has a factor of $(x + 2)^2$. This suggests

$$g(x) = k \cdot \frac{x + 1}{(x + 2)^2},$$

where k is a stretch factor. To find the value of k, use the fact that $g(0) = 0.5$. So

$$0.5 = k \cdot \frac{0 + 1}{(0 + 2)^2}$$

$$0.5 = k \cdot \frac{1}{4}$$

$$k = 2.$$

Thus, a possible formula for g is $g(x) = \dfrac{2(x + 1)}{(x + 2)^2}$.

When Numerator and Denominator Have the Same Zeros: Holes

The rational function $h(x) = \dfrac{x^2 + x - 2}{x - 1}$ is undefined at $x = 1$ because the denominator equals zero at $x = 1$. However, the graph of h does not have a vertical asymptote at $x = 1$ because the numerator of h also equals zero at $x = 1$. At $x = 1$,

$$h(1) = \frac{x^2 + x - 2}{x - 1} = \frac{1^2 + 1 - 2}{1 - 1} = \frac{0}{0},$$

and this ratio is undefined. What does the graph of h look like? Factoring the numerator of h gives

$$h(x) = \frac{(x - 1)(x + 2)}{x - 1} = \frac{x - 1}{x - 1}(x + 2).$$

For any $x \neq 1$, we can cancel $(x - 1)$ top and bottom and rewrite the formula for h as

$$h(x) = x + 2, \qquad \text{provided } x \neq 1.$$

Thus, the graph of h is the line $y = x + 2$ except at $x = 1$, where h is undefined. The line $y = x + 2$ contains the point $(1, 3)$, but the graph of h does not. Therefore, we say that the graph of h has a *hole* in it at the point $(1, 3)$. See Figure 9.39.

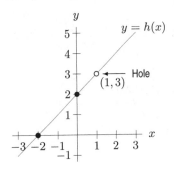

Figure 9.39: The graph of $y = h(x)$ is the line $y = x + 2$, except at the point $(1, 3)$, where it has a hole

Exercises and Problems for Section 9.5

Exercises

For the rational functions in Exercises 1–4, find all zeros and vertical asymptotes and describe the long-run behavior. Then graph the function without a calculator.

1. $y = \dfrac{x+3}{x+5}$

2. $y = \dfrac{x+3}{(x+5)^2}$

3. $y = \dfrac{x-4}{x^2-9}$

4. $y = \dfrac{x^2-4}{x-9}$

In Exercises 5–8, what are the x-intercepts, y-intercepts, and horizontal and vertical asymptotes (if any)?

5. $f(x) = \dfrac{x-2}{x-4}$

6. $g(x) = \dfrac{x^2-9}{x^2+9}$

7. $h(x) = \dfrac{x^2-4}{x^3+4x^2}$

8. $k(x) = \dfrac{x(4-x)}{x^2-6x+5}$

9. Let $f(x) = \dfrac{1}{x-3}$.

(a) Complete Table 9.8 for x-values close to 3. What happens to the values of $f(x)$ as x approaches 3 from the left? From the right?

Table 9.8

x	2	2.9	2.99	3	3.01	3.1	4
$f(x)$							

(b) Complete Tables 9.9 and 9.10. What happens to the values of $f(x)$ as x takes very large positive values? As x takes very large negative values?

Table 9.9

x	5	10	100	1000
$f(x)$				

Table 9.10

x	-5	-10	-100	-1000
$f(x)$				

(c) Without a calculator, graph $y = f(x)$. Give equations for the horizontal and vertical asymptotes.

10. Let $g(x) = \dfrac{1}{(x+2)^2}$.

(a) Complete Table 9.11 for x-values close to -2. What happens to the values of $g(x)$ as x approaches -2 from the left? From the right?

Table 9.11

x	-3	-2.1	-2.01	-2	-1.99	-1.9	-1
$g(x)$							

(b) Complete Tables 9.12 and 9.13. What happens to the values of $g(x)$ as x takes very large positive values? As x takes very large negative values?

Table 9.12

x	5	10	100	1000
$g(x)$				

Table 9.13

x	-5	-10	-100	-1000
$g(x)$				

(c) Without a calculator, graph $y = g(x)$. Give equations for the horizontal and vertical asymptotes.

Problems

Graph the functions in Exercises 11–12 without a calculator.

11. $y = 2 + \dfrac{1}{x}$

12. $y = \dfrac{2x^2 - 10x + 12}{x^2 - 16}$

In Problems 13–14, estimate the one-sided limits

(a) $\lim\limits_{x \to a^+} f(x)$

(b) $\lim\limits_{x \to a^-} f(x)$

13. $f(x) = \dfrac{x}{5-x}$ with $a = 5$

14. $f(x) = \dfrac{5-x}{(x-2)^2}$ with $a = 2$

In Problems 15–16,

(a) Estimate $\lim\limits_{x \to \infty} f(x)$ and $\lim\limits_{x \to -\infty} f(x)$.

(b) What does the vertical asymptote tell you about limits?

15.

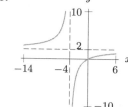

16.

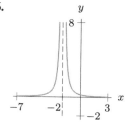

17. Without a calculator, match the functions (a)–(f) with their graphs in (i)–(vi) by finding the zeros, asymptotes, and end behavior for each function.

(a) $y = \dfrac{-1}{(x-5)^2} - 1$ **(b)** $y = \dfrac{x-2}{(x+1)(x-3)}$

(c) $y = \dfrac{2x+4}{x-1}$ **(d)** $y = \dfrac{1}{x+1} + \dfrac{1}{x-3}$

(e) $y = \dfrac{1-x^2}{x-2}$ **(f)** $y = \dfrac{1-4x}{2x+2}$

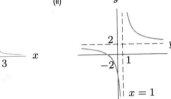
(i)

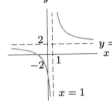
(ii)

(iii)   (iv)

(v)   (vi)

18. Let $f(x) = x^2 + 5x + 6$ and $g(x) = x^2 + 1$.

(a) What are the zeros of f and g?

(b) Let $r(x) = f(x)/g(x)$. Graph r. Does r have zeros? Vertical asymptotes? What is its long-run behavior as $x \to \pm\infty$?

(c) Let $s(x) = g(x)/f(x)$. If you graph s in the window $-10 \le x \le 10$, $-10 \le y \le 10$, it appears to have a zero near the origin. Does it? Does s have a vertical asymptote? What is its long-run behavior?

19. Suppose that n is a constant and that $f(x)$ is a function defined when $x = n$. Complete the following sentences.

(a) If $f(n)$ is large, then $\dfrac{1}{f(n)}$ is ...

(b) If $f(n)$ is small, then $\dfrac{1}{f(n)}$ is ...

(c) If $f(n) = 0$, then $\dfrac{1}{f(n)}$ is ...

(d) If $f(n)$ is positive, then $\dfrac{1}{f(n)}$ is ...

(e) If $f(n)$ is negative, then $\dfrac{1}{f(n)}$ is ...

20. **(a)** Use the results of Problem 19 to graph $y = 1/f(x)$ given the graph of $y = f(x)$ in Figure 9.40.

(b) Find a possible formula for the function in Figure 9.40. Use this formula to check your graph for part (a).

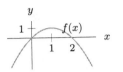

Figure 9.40

21. Use the graph of f in Figure 9.41 to graph

(a) $y = -f(-x) + 2$ **(b)** $y = \dfrac{1}{f(x)}$

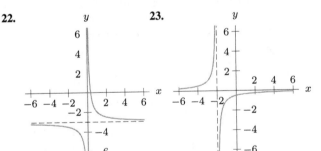

Figure 9.41

Problems 22–24 show a translation of $y = 1/x$.

(a) Find a possible formula for the graph.

(b) Write the formula from part (a) as the ratio of two linear polynomials.

(c) Find the coordinates of the intercepts of the graph.

22.   **23.**

24.

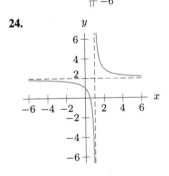

Problems 25–27 show a translation of $y = 1/x^2$.

(a) Find a formula for the graph.

(b) Write the formula from part (a) as the ratio of two polynomials.

(c) Find the coordinates of any intercepts of the graph.

32. Cut four equal squares from the corners of a $8.5'' \times 11''$ piece of paper. Fold up the sides to create an open box. Find the dimensions of the box with the maximum volume per surface area.

Find possible formulas for the functions in Problems 33–39.

25.
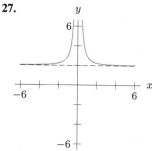

26.

27.

33.
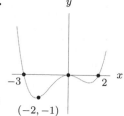

34.
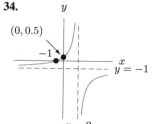

35.
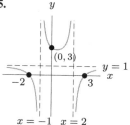

36.
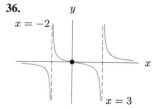

37.
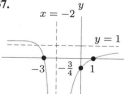

38.
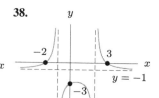

Problems 28–31 give values of translations of either $y = 1/x$ or $y = 1/x^2$. In each case

(a) Determine if the values are from a translation of $y = 1/x$ or $y = 1/x^2$. Explain your reasoning.

(b) Find a possible formula for the function.

39.
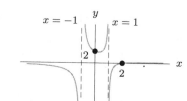

28.

x	y
2.7	12.1
2.9	101
2.95	401
3	Undefined
3.05	401
3.1	101
3.3	12.1

29.

x	y
-1000	0.499
-100	0.490
-10	0.400
10	0.600
100	0.510
1000	0.501

30.

x	y
-1000	1.000001
-100	1.00001
-10	1.01
10	1.01
100	1.0001
1000	1.000001

31.

x	y
1.5	-1.5
1.9	-9.5
1.95	-19.5
2	Undefined
2.05	20.5
2.1	10.5
2.5	2.5

In Problems 40–42, find a possible formula for the rational functions.

40. The graph of $y = f(x)$ has one vertical asymptote, at $x = -1$, and a horizontal asymptote at $y = 1$. The graph of f crosses the y-axis at $y = 3$ and crosses the x-axis once, at $x = -3$.

41. The graph of $y = g(x)$ has two vertical asymptotes: one at $x = -2$ and one at $x = 3$. It has a horizontal asymptote of $y = 0$. The graph of g crosses the x-axis once, at $x = 5$.

42. The graph of $y = h(x)$ has two vertical asymptotes: one at $x = -2$ and one at $x = 3$. It has a horizontal asymptote of $y = 1$. The graph of h touches the x-axis once, at $x = 5$.

9.6 COMPARING POWER, EXPONENTIAL, AND LOG FUNCTIONS

In preceding chapters, we encountered exponential, power, and logarithmic functions. In this section, we compare the long and short-run behaviors of these functions.

Comparing Power Functions

For power functions $y = kx^p$ for large x, the higher the power of x, the faster the function climbs. See Figure 9.42. Not only are the higher powers larger, but they are *much* larger. This is because if $x = 100$, for example, 100^5 is one hundred times as big as 100^4, which is one hundred times as big as 100^3. As x gets larger (written as $x \to \infty$), any positive power of x grows much faster than all lower powers of x. We say that, as $x \to \infty$, higher powers of x *dominate* lower powers.

As x approaches zero (written $x \to 0$), the story is entirely different. Figure 9.43 is a close-up view near the origin. For x between 0 and 1, x^3 is bigger than x^4, which is bigger than x^5. (Try $x = 0.1$ to confirm this.) For values of x near zero, smaller powers dominate.

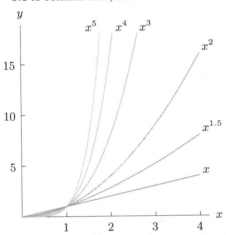

Figure 9.42: For large x: Large powers of x dominate

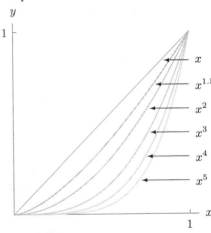

Figure 9.43: For $0 \le x \le 1$: Small powers of x dominate

In Chapter 5 we saw the effect of k on the graph of $f(x) = kx^p$. The coefficient k stretches or compresses the graph vertically; if k is negative, the graph is reflected across the x-axis. How does the value of k affect the long-term growth rate of $f(x) = kx^p$? Is the growth of a power function affected more by the size of the coefficient or by the size of the power?

Example 1 Let $f(x) = 100x^3$ and $g(x) = x^4$ for $x > 0$. Compare the long-term behavior of these two functions using graphs.

Solution For $x < 10$, Figure 9.44 suggests that f is growing faster than g and that f dominates g. Eventually, however, the fact that g has a higher power than f asserts itself. In Figure 9.45, we see that $g(x)$ has caught up to $f(x)$ at $x = 100$. In Figure 9.46, we see that for $x > 100$, values of g are larger than values of f.

Could the graphs of f and g intersect again for some value of $x > 100$? To show that this cannot be the case, solve the equation $g(x) = f(x)$:

$$x^4 = 100x^3$$
$$x^4 - 100x^3 = 0$$
$$x^3(x - 100) = 0.$$

Since the only solutions to this equation are $x = 0$ and $x = 100$, the graphs of f and g do not cross for $x > 100$.

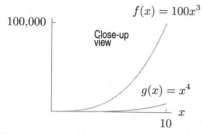

Figure 9.44: On this interval, f climbs faster than g

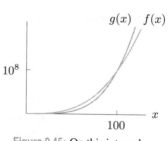

Figure 9.45: On this interval, g catches up to f

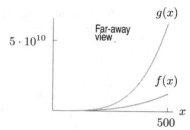

Figure 9.46: On this interval, g ends up far ahead of f

Comparing Exponential Functions and Power Functions

Both power functions and exponential functions can increase at phenomenal rates. For example, Table 9.14 shows values of $f(x) = x^4$ and $g(x) = 2^x$.

Table 9.14   *The exponential function* $g(x) = 2^x$ *eventually grows faster than the power function* $f(x) = x^4$

x	0	5	10	15	20
$f(x) = x^4$	0	625	10,000	50,625	160,000
$g(x) = 2^x$	1	32	1024	32,768	1,048,576

Despite the impressive growth in the value of the power function $f(x) = x^4$, in the long run $g(x) = 2^x$ grows faster. By the time $x = 20$, the value of $g(20) = 2^{20}$ is over six times as large as $f(20) = 20^4$. Figure 9.47 shows the exponential function $g(x) = 2^x$ catching up to $f(x) = x^4$.

But what about a more slowly growing exponential function? After all, $y = 2^x$ increases at a 100% growth rate. Figure 9.48 compares $y = x^4$ to the exponential function $y = 1.005^x$. Despite the fact that this exponential function creeps along at a 0.5% growth rate, at around $x = 7000$, it overtakes the power function. In summary,

> *Any* positive increasing exponential function eventually grows faster than *any* power function.

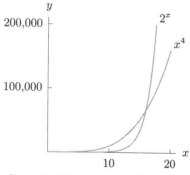

Figure 9.47: The exponential function $y = 2^x$ dominates the power function $y = x^4$

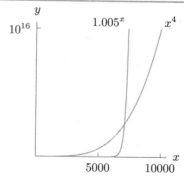

Figure 9.48: The exponential function $y = 1.005^x$ dominates the power function $y = x^4$

Decreasing Exponential Functions and Decreasing Power Functions

Just as an increasing exponential function eventually outpaces any increasing power function, an exponential decay function wins the race toward the x-axis. In general:

> *Any* positive decreasing exponential function eventually approaches the horizontal axis faster than any positive decreasing power function.

For example, let's compare the long term behavior of the decreasing exponential function $y = 0.5^x$ with the decreasing power function $y = x^{-2}$. By rewriting

$$y = 0.5^x = \left(\frac{1}{2}\right)^x = \frac{1}{2^x} \qquad \text{and} \qquad y = x^{-2} = \frac{1}{x^2}$$

we can see the comparison more easily. In the long run, the smallest of these two fractions is the one with the largest denominator. The fact that 2^x is eventually larger than x^2 means that $1/2^x$ is eventually smaller than $1/x^2$.

Figure 9.49 shows $y = 0.5^x$ and $y = x^{-2}$. Both graphs have the x-axis as a horizontal asymptote. As x increases, the exponential function $y = 0.5^x$ approaches the x-axis faster than the power function $y = x^{-2}$. Figure 9.50 shows what happens for large values of x. The exponential function approaches the x-axis so rapidly that it becomes invisible compared to $y = x^{-2}$.

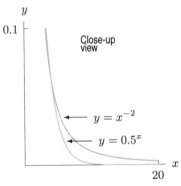

Figure 9.49: Graphs of $y = x^{-2}$ and $y = 0.5^x$

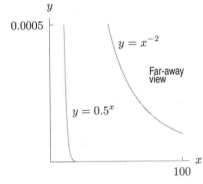

Figure 9.50: Graphs of $y = x^{-2}$ and $y = 0.5^x$

Comparing Log and Power Functions

Power functions like $y = x^{1/2}$ and $y = x^{1/3}$ grow quite slowly. However, they grow rapidly in comparison to log functions. In fact:

> *Any* positive increasing power function eventually grows more rapidly than $y = \log x$ and $y = \ln x$.

For example, Figure 9.51 shows the graphs of $y = x^{1/2}$ and $y = \log x$. The fact that exponential functions grow so fast should alert you to the fact that their inverses, the logarithms, grow very slowly. See Figure 9.52.

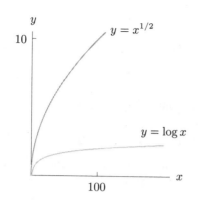

Figure 9.51: Graphs of $y = x^{1/2}$ and $y = \log x$

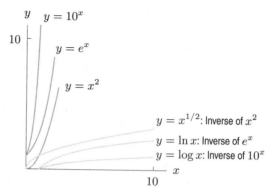

Figure 9.52: Graphs of $y = 10^x$, $y = e^x$, $y = x^2$, $y = x^{1/2}$, $y = \ln x$, and $y = \log x$

Exercises and Problems for Section 9.6

Exercises

Can the formulas in Exercises 1–6 be written in the form of an exponential function or a power function? If not, explain why the function does not fit either form.

1. $m(x) = 3(3x + 1)^2$

2. $n(x) = 3 \cdot 2^{3x+1}$

3. $p(x) = (5^x)^2$

4. $q(x) = 5^{(x^2)}$

5. $r(x) = 2 \cdot 3^{-2x}$

6. $s(x) = \dfrac{4}{5x^{-3}}$

7. Without a calculator, match the following functions with the graphs in Figure 9.53.

(i) $y = x^5$ (ii) $y = x^2$ (iii) $y = x$ (iv) $y = x^3$

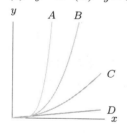

Figure 9.53

8. Without a calculator, match the following functions with the graphs in Figure 9.54.

(i) $y = x^5$ (ii) $y = x^2$ (iii) $y = x$ (iv) $y = x^3$

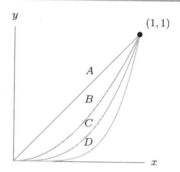

Figure 9.54

9. Let $f(x) = 3^x$ and $g(x) = x^3$.

(a) Complete the following table of values:

x	-3	-2	-1	0	1	2	3
$f(x)$							
$g(x)$							

(b) Describe the long-run behaviors of f and g as $x \to -\infty$ and as $x \to +\infty$.

In Exercises 10–13, which function dominates as $x \to \infty$?

10. $y = 50x^{1.1}$, $y = 1000x^{1.08}$

11. $y = 4e^x$, $y = 2x^{50}$

12. $y = 7(0.99)^x$, $y = 6x^{35}$

13. $y = ax^3$, $y = bx^2$, $a, b > 0$

Problems

14. The functions $y = x^{-3}$ and $y = 3^{-x}$ both approach zero as $x \to \infty$. Which function approaches zero faster? Support your conclusion numerically.

15. The functions $y = x^{-3}$ and $y = e^{-x}$ both approach zero as $x \to \infty$. Which function approaches zero faster? Support your conclusion numerically.

16. Let $f(x) = x^x$. Is f a power function, an exponential function, both, or neither? Discuss.

In Problems 17–19, find a possible formula for f if f is

(a) Linear   **(b)** Exponential   **(c)** Power function.

17. $f(1) = 18$ and $f(3) = 1458$

18. $f(1) = 16$ and $f(2) = 128$

19. $f(-1) = \frac{3}{4}$ and $f(2) = 48$

20. (a) Match the functions $f(x) = x^2, g(x) = 2x^2$, and $h(x) = x^3$ to their graphs in Figure 9.55.
   (b) Do graphs A and B intersect for $x > 0$? If so, for what value(s) of x? If not, explain how you know.
   (c) Do graphs C and A intersect for $x > 0$? If so, for what value(s) of x? If not, explain how you know.

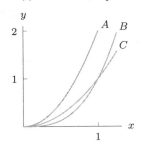

Figure 9.55

21. Match the graphs in Figure 9.56 with the functions $y = kx^{9/16}, y = kx^{3/8}, y = kx^{5/7}, y = kx^{3/11}$.

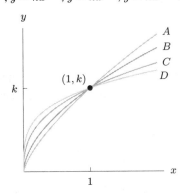

Figure 9.56

22. In Figure 9.57, find the values of m, t, and k.

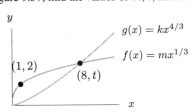

Figure 9.57

23. (a) Given $t(x) = x^{-2}$ and $r(x) = 40x^{-3}$, find v such that $t(v) = r(v)$.
   (b) For $0 < x < v$, which is greater, $t(x)$ or $r(x)$?
   (c) For $x > v$, which is greater, $t(x)$ or $r(x)$?

What is the long-run behavior of the functions in Problems 24–35?

24. $y = \dfrac{x^2 + 5}{x^8}$

25. $y = \dfrac{5 - t^2}{(7 + t + \sqrt{t})t^5}$

26. $y = \dfrac{x(x + 5)(x - 7)}{4 + x^2}$

27. $y = \dfrac{2^x + 3}{x^2 + 5}$

28. $y = \dfrac{2^t + 7}{5^t + 9}$

29. $y = \dfrac{3^{-t}}{4^t + 7}$

30. $y = \dfrac{e^x + 5}{x^{100} + 50}$

31. $y = \dfrac{e^{2t}}{e^{3t} + 5}$

32. $y = \dfrac{\ln x}{\sqrt{x} + 5}$

33. $y = \dfrac{e^t + t^2}{\ln |t|}$

34. $y = \dfrac{e^x - e^{-x}}{2}$

35. $y = \dfrac{e^x - e^{-x}}{e^x + e^{-x}}$

36. Table 9.15 gives approximate values for three functions, f, g, and h. One is exponential, one is trigonometric, and one is a power function. Determine which is which and find possible formulas for each.

Table 9.15

x	-2	-1	0	1	2
$f(x)$	4	2	4	6	4
$g(x)$	20.0	2.5	0.0	-2.5	-20.0
$h(x)$	1.33	0.67	0.33	0.17	0.08

37. (a) The functions in Table 9.16 are of the form $y = a \cdot r^{3/4}$ and $y = b \cdot r^{5/4}$. Explain how you can tell which is which from the values in the table.
   (b) Determine the constants a and b.

Table 9.16

r	2.5	3.2	3.9	4.6
$y = g(r)$	15.9	19.1	22.2	25.1
$y = h(r)$	9.4	12.8	16.4	20.2

38. A woman opens a bank account with an initial deposit of $1000. At the end of each year thereafter, she deposits an additional $1000.

  (a) The account earns 6% annual interest, compounded annually. Complete Table 9.17.
  (b) Does the balance of this account grow linearly, exponentially, or neither? Justify your answer.

Table 9.17

Years elapsed	Start-of-year balance	End-of-year deposit	End-of-year interest
0	$1000.00	$1000	$60.00
1	$2060.00	$1000	$123.60
2	$3183.60	$1000	
3		$1000	
4		$1000	
5		$1000	

39. Suppose the annual percentage rate (APR) paid by the account in Problem 38 is r, where r does not necessarily equal 6%. Define $p_n(r)$ as the balance of the account after n years have elapsed. (For example, $p_2(0.06) = \$3183.60$, because, according to Table 9.17, the balance after 2 years is $3183.60 if the APR is 6%.)

  (a) Find formulas for $p_5(r)$ and $p_{10}(r)$.
  (b) What is APR if the woman in Problem 38 has $10,000 in 5 years?

40. Values of f and g are in Table 9.18 and 9.19. One function is of the form $y = a \cdot d^{p/q}$ with $p > q$; the other is of the form $y = b \cdot d^{p/q}$ with $p < q$. Which is which? How can you tell?

Table 9.18

d	2	2.2	2.4	2.6	2.8
$f(d)$	151.6	160.5	169.1	177.4	185.5

Table 9.19

d	10	10.2	10.4	10.6	10.8
$g(d)$	7.924	8.115	8.306	8.498	8.691

9.7   FITTING EXPONENTIALS AND POLYNOMIALS TO DATA

In Section 1.6 we used linear regression to find the equation for a line of best fit for a set of data. In this section, we fit an exponential or a power function to a set of data.

The Spread of AIDS

The data in Table 9.20 give the total number of deaths in the US from AIDS from 1981 to 1996. Figure 9.58 suggests that a linear function may not give the best possible fit for these data.

Table 9.20   *Domestic deaths from AIDS, 1981–96*

t	N	t	N
1	159	9	90039
2	622	10	121577
3	2130	11	158193
4	5635	12	199287
5	12607	13	243923
6	24717	14	292586
7	41129	15	340957
8	62248	16	375904

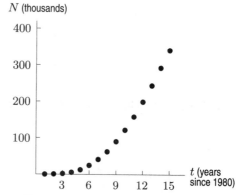

Figure 9.58: Domestic deaths from AIDS, 1981–96

Fitting an Exponential

We first fit an exponential function to the data[10] in Table 9.20

$$N = ae^{kt},$$

where N is the total number of deaths t years after 1980.

Using exponential regression on a calculator or computer, we obtain

$$N \approx 630e^{0.47t}.$$

Figure 9.59 on page 429 shows how the graph of this formula fits the data points.

Fitting a Power Function

Now we fit the AIDS data with a power function of the form

$$N = at^p,$$

where a and p are constants. Some scientists have suggested that a power function may be a better model for the growth of AIDS than an exponential function.[11] Using power function regression on a calculator or a computer, we obtain

$$N \approx 107t^{3.005}.$$

Figure 9.59 shows the graph of this power function with the data.

Which Function Best Fits the Data?

Both the exponential function

$$N = 630e^{0.47t}$$

and the power function

$$N = 107t^{3.005}$$

fit the AIDS data reasonably well. By visual inspection alone, the power function arguably provides the better fit. If we fit a linear function to the original data we get

$$N = -97311 + 25946t.$$

Even this linear function gives a possible fit for $t \geq 4$, that is, for 1984 to 1996. (See Figure 9.59.)

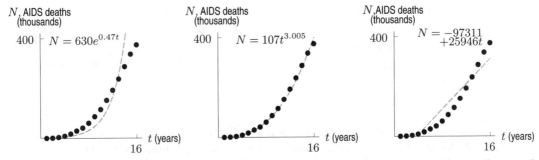

Figure 9.59: The AIDS data since 1980 together with an exponential model, a power-function model, and a linear model

[10] *HIV/AIDS Surveillance Report*, Year-end Edition, Vol 9, No 2, Table 13, US Department of Health and Human Services, Centers for Disease Control and Prevention, Atlanta. 2000–2004 data from *HIV/AIDS Surveillance Report*, Vol 16, at www.cdc.gov/hiv/stats/hastlink.htm, accessed January 15, 2006. Data does not include 450 people whose dates of death are unknown.

[11] " Risk behavior-based model of the cubic growth of acquired immunodeficiency syndrome in the United States", by Stirling A. Colgate, E. Ann Stanley, James M. Hyman, Scott P. Layne, and Alifford Qualls, in *Proc. Natl. Acad. Sci. USA*, Vol 86, June 1989, Population Biology.

Despite the fact that all three functions fit the data reasonably well up to 1996, it's important to realize that they give wildly different predictions for the future. If we use each model to estimate the total number of AIDS deaths by the year 2010 (when $t = 30$), the exponential model gives

$$N = 630e^{(0.47)30} \approx 837{,}322{,}467, \quad \text{about triple the current US population;}$$

the power model gives

$$N = 107(30)^{3.005} \approx 2{,}938{,}550, \quad \text{or about 1\% of the current population;}$$

and the linear model gives

$$N = -97311 + 25946 \cdot 30 \approx 681{,}069, \quad \text{or about 0.25\% of the current population.}$$

Which function is the best predictor of the future? To explore this question, let us add some more recent data to our previous data on AIDS deaths. See Table 9.21.

Table 9.21
Domestic deaths from AIDS, 1997–2004

t	N
17	406,444
18	424,841
19	442,013
20	457,258
21	462,653
22	501,669
23	524,060
24	529,113

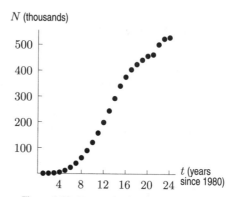

Figure 9.60: Domestic deaths from AIDS, 1981–2004

When data from the entire period from 1981 to 2004 are plotted together (see Figure 9.60), we see that the rate of increase of AIDS deaths reaches a peak sometime around 1995 and then begins to taper off. Since none of the three types of functions we have used to model AIDS deaths exhibit this type of behavior, some other type of function is needed to describe the number of AIDS deaths accurately over the entire 23-year period.

This example illustrates that while a certain type of function may fit a set of data over a short period of time, care must be taken when using a mathematical model to make predictions about the future. An understanding of the processes leading to the data is crucial in answering any long-term question.

Exercises and Problems for Section 9.7

1. Find a formula for the power function $f(x)$ such that $f(1) = 1$ and $f(2) = c$.

2. Find a formula for the power function $g(x)$.

x	2	3	4	5
$g(x)$	4.5948	7.4744	10.5561	13.7973

3. Find a formula for an exponential function $h(x)$.

x	2	3	4	5
$h(x)$	4.5948	7.4744	10.5561	13.7973

4. Anthropologists suggest that the relationship between the body weight and brain weight of primates can be modeled with a power function. Table 9.22 lists various body weights and the corresponding brain weights of different primates.[12]

   (a) Using Table 9.22, find a power function that gives the brain weight, Q (in mg), as a function of the body weight, b (in gm).
   (b) The Erythrocebus (Patas monkey) has a body weight of 7800 gm. Estimate its brain weight.

Table 9.22

b	6667	960	6800	9500	1088
Q	56,567	18,200	110,525	120,100	20,700
b	2733	3000	6300	1500	665
Q	78,250	58,200	96,400	31,700	25,050

5. Students in the School of Forestry & Environmental Studies at Yale University collected data measuring Sassafras trees. Table 9.23 lists the diameter at breast height (dbh, in cm) and the total dry weight (w, in gm) of different trees.[13]

   (a) Find a power function that fits the data.
   (b) Predict the total weight of a tree with a dbh of 20 cm.
   (c) If a tree has a total dry weight of 100,000 gm, what is its expected dbh?

Table 9.23

dbh	5	23.4	11.8	16.7	4.2	5.6
w	5,353	169,290	30,696	76,730	3,436	5,636
dbh	3.8	4.3	6.5	21.9	17.7	25.5
w	14,983	2,098	7,364	177,596	100,848	171,598

6. According to the National Marine Fisheries Service, the Maine lobster catch (in millions of pounds) has greatly increased in the past 30 years.[14] See Table 9.24. With t in years since 1965, use a calculator or computer to fit the data with

   (a) A power function of the form $y = at^b$.
   (b) A quadratic function of the form $y = at^2 + bt + c$.
   (c) Discuss which is a better fit and why.

Table 9.24

Year	1970	1975	1980	1985	1990	1995	2000
t	5	10	15	20	25	30	35
Lobster	17	19	22	20	27	36	56

In Exercises 7–12, find an equation for y in terms of x.

7.
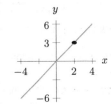

8.
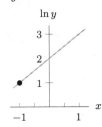

9.
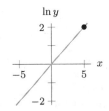

10.
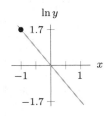

11.
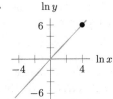

12.
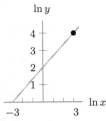

---

[12] http://mac-huwis.lut.ac.uk/ wis/lectures/primate-adaptation/10PrimateBrains.pdf (December 15, 2002).

[13] www.yale.edu/fes519b/totoket/allom/allom.htm (December 15, 2002).

[14] Adapted from *The New York Times*, p.16, May 31, 2001.

Problems

13. An analog radio dial can be measured in millimeters from left to right. Although the scale of the dial can be different from radio to radio, Table 9.25 gives typical measurements.

(a) Which radio band data appear linear? Graph and connect the data points for each band.

(b) Which radio band data appear exponential?

(c) Find a possible formula for the FM station number in terms of x.

(d) Find a possible formula for the AM station number in terms of x.

Table 9.25

x, millimeters	5	15	25	35	45	55
FM (mhz)	88	92	96	100	104	108
AM (khz/10)	53	65	80	100	130	160

14. (a) Find a linear function that fits the data in Table 9.26. How good is the fit?

(b) The data in the table was generated using the power function $y = 5x^3$. Explain why (in this case) a linear function gives such a good fit to a power function. Does the fit remain good for other values of x?

Table 9.26

x	2.00	2.01	2.02	2.03	2.04	2.05
y	40.000	40.603	41.212	41.827	42.448	43.076

15. In this problem you will fit a quartic polynomial to the AIDS data.

(a) With N as the total number of AIDS deaths t years after 1980, use a calculator or computer to fit the data in Table 9.20 on page 428 with a polynomial of the form

$$N = at^4 + bt^3 + ct^2 + dt + e.$$

(b) Graph the data and your quartic for $0 \le t \le 16$. Comment on the fit.

(c) Graph the data and your quartic for $0 \le t \le 30$. Comment on the predictions made by this model.

16. The managers of a furniture store have compiled data showing the daily demand for recliners at various prices.

(a) In Table 9.27, fill in the revenue generated by selling the number of recliners at the corresponding price.

(b) Find the quadratic function that best fits the data.

(c) According to the function you found, what price should the store charge for their recliners to maximize revenue? What is the maximum revenue?

Table 9.27

Recliner price ($)	399	499	599	699	799
Demand (recliners)	62	55	47	40	34
Revenue ($)					

17. Cellular telephone use has increased over the past two decades. Table 9.28 gives the number of cellular telephone subscriptions, in thousands, from 1985 to 2004.[15]

(a) Fit an exponential function to this data with time in years since 1985.

(b) Based on your model, by what percent was the number of cell subscribers increasing each year?

(c) In the long-run, what do you expect of the rate of growth? What does this mean in terms of the shape of the graph?

Table 9.28

Year	1985	1990	1995	2000	2004
Subscriptions	340	5283	33786	109478	182140

18. The use of one-way pagers declined as cell phones became more popular.[16] The number of users is given in Table 9.29 and plotted in Figure 9.61, along with a quadratic regression function.

(a) How well does the graph of the quadratic function fit the data?

(b) Find a cubic regression function. Does it fit better?

Table 9.29

Year	1990	1991	1992	1993	1994	1995
Users, millions	10	12	15	19	25	32
Year	1996	1997	1998	1999	2000	
Users, millions	38	43	44	43	37	

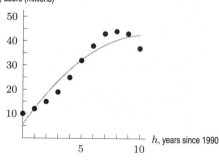

Figure 9.61

---

[15]World Almanac and Book of Fact, 2006. pg.380
[16]*The New York Times*, p.16, April 11, 2002.

19. Table 9.30 gives the estimated population, in thousands, of the American Colonies from 1650 to 1770.[17]

  (a) Make a scatterplot of the data using $t = 0$ to represent the year 1650.

  (b) Fit an exponential function to the data.

  (c) Explain the meaning of the parameters in your model.

  (d) Use your function to predict the population in 1750. Is it high or low?

  (e) According to the US Census Bureau, the US population in 1800 was 5,308,483.[18] Use your function to make a prediction for 1800. Is it high or low?

Table 9.30

Year	1650	1670	1690	1700
Population	50.4	111.9	210.4	250.9

Year	1720	1740	1750	1770
Population	466.2	905.6	1170.8	2148.1

20. The US Census Bureau began recording census data in 1790. Table 9.31 gives the population of the US in millions from 1790 to 1860.[19]

  (a) With t = 0 representing the number of years since 1790, fit an exponential function to the data.

  (b) The 1800 census value is 5.3 million. Find the population predicted by your function for 1800. Problem 19 gave a prediction of 5.5 million using the data for 1650 to 1750. Using the two data sets, explain the difference in predicted values.

  (c) Use your function to project the population of the US in 2000. Is this prediction reasonable?

Table 9.31

Year	1790	1800	1810	1820
Population	3.929	5.308	7.240	9.638

Year	1830	1840	1850	1860
Population	12.861	17.063	23.192	31.443

21. Table 9.32 gives N, the number of transistors per integrated circuit chip, t years after 1970.[20]

  (a) Plot N versus t and fit an exponential curve to the data.

  (b) According to the formula of your curve of best fit, approximately how often does the number of transistors double?

Table 9.32

Chip name	t	N
4004	1	2,300
8008	2	2,500
8080	4	4,500
8086	8	29,000
Intel286	12	134,000
Intel386	15	275,000
Intel486	19	1,200,000
Pentium	23	3,100,000
Pentium II	27	7,500,000
Pentium III	29	9,500,000
Pentium 4	30	42,000,000
Itanium	31	25,000,000
Itanium 2	33	220,000,000
Itanium 2 (9MB cache)	34	592,000,000
Dual Core Itanium	36	1,720,000,000

22. The US export of edible fishery produce, in thousands of metric tons, is shown in Table 9.33.[21] With t in years since 1935, fit the data with a function of the form

  (a) $y = at^b$ (b) $y = ab^t$ (c) $y = at^2 + bt + c$

  (d) Discuss the reliability for estimating 2010 exports with each function.

Table 9.33

Year	1940	1945	1950	1955	1960	1965	1970
Fish export	66	62	55	50	31	50	73
Year	1975	1980	1985	1990	1995	2000	2005
Fish export	109	275	305	883	929	982	1329

23. The data in Table 9.33 show a big jump in fish exports between 1985 and 1990. This suggests fitting a piecewise defined function. With t in years since 1935, fit a quadratic function to the data from

  (a) 1940 to 1985   (b) 1990 to 2005

  (c) Write a piecewise defined function using parts (a) and (b). Graph the function and the data.

[17] *The World Almanac and Book of Facts, 2002*, New York, NY, p. 376.
[18] http://www.census.gov/, January 15, 2003.
[19] http://www.census.gov/, January 15, 2003.
[20] The Intel Corporation, http://www.intel.com/museum/archives/history_docs/mooreslaw.htm.
[21] www.st.nmfs.gov/st1/trade/trade2001.pdf, accessed December 15, 2002 and www.st.nmfs.gov/st1/trade/documents/TRADE2005.pdf, accessed July 25, 2006.

24. (a) Using the data in Table 9.20 on page 428, plot $\ln N$ against t. If the original data were exponential, the points would lie on a line.
(b) Fit a line to the graph from part (a).
(c) From the equation of the line, obtain the formula for N as an exponential function of t.

25. (a) Let $N = at^p$, with a, p constant. Explain why if you plot $\ln N$ against $\ln t$, you get a line.
(b) To decide if a function of the form $N = at^p$ fits some data, you plot $\ln N$ against $\ln t$. Explain why this plot is useful.

26. (a) Using the data in Table 9.20 on page 428, plot $\ln N$ against $\ln t$. If a power function fitted the original data, the points would lie on a line
(b) Fit a line to the graph from part (a).
(c) From the equation of the line, obtain the formula for N as a power function of t.

27. According to the US Census Bureau, the 2004 mean income by age is given in Table 9.34. [22]

(a) Choose the best type of function to fit the data: linear, exponential, power, or quadratic.
(b) Using a mid-range age value for each interval, find an equation to fit the data.
(c) Interpolation estimates incomes for ages within the range of the data. Predict the income of a 37-year old.
(d) Extrapolation estimates incomes outside the range of data. Use your function to predict the income of a 10-year old. Is it reasonable?

Table 9.34

Age	Mean income, dollars
15 to 24	12,789
25 to 34	31,987
35 to 44	42,582
45 to 54	45,179
55 to 64	40,788
65 to 74	27,579
75+ years	19,955

28. German physicist Arnd Leike of the University of Munich won the 2002 Ig Nobel prize in Physics for experiments with beer foam conducted with his students. [23]

The data in Table 9.35 give the height (in cm) of beer foam after t seconds for three different types of beer, Erdinger Weissbier, Augustinerbräu München, and Budweiser Budvar. The heights are denoted h_e, h_a, and h_b, respectively.

(a) Plot these points and fit exponential functions to them. Give the equations in the form $h = h_0 e^{-t/\tau}$.
(b) What does the value of h_0 tell you for each type of beer? What does the value of τ tell you for each type of beer?

Table 9.35

t	h_e	h_a	h_b	t	h_e	h_a	h_b
0	17.0	14.0	14.0	120	10.7	6.0	7.0
15	16.1	11.8	12.1	150	9.7	5.3	6.2
30	14.9	10.5	10.9	180	8.9	4.4	5.5
45	14.0	9.3	10.0	210	8.3	3.5	4.5
60	13.2	8.5	9.3	240	7.5	2.9	3.5
75	12.5	7.7	8.6	300	6.3	1.3	2.0
90	11.9	7.1	8.0	360	5.2	0.7	0.9
105	11.2	6.5	7.5				

29. Table 9.36 gives the development time t (in days) for eggs of the pea weevil (*Bruchus pisorum*) at temperature H (°C). [24]

(a) Plot these data and fit a power function.
(b) Ecologists define the development rate $r = 1/t$ where t is the development time. Plot r against H, and fit a linear function.
(c) At a certain temperature, the value of r drops to 0 and pea weevil eggs will not develop. What is this temperature according to the model from part (a)? part (b)? Which model's prediction do you think is more reasonable?

Table 9.36

H, °C	10.7	14.4	16.2	18.1	21.4	23.7	24.7	26.9
t, days	38.0	19.5	15.6	9.6	9.5	7.3	4.5	4.5

---

[22] www.census.gov/hhes/www/income/histinc/p10ar.html, accessed July 25, 2006.
[23] http://ignobel.com/ig/ig-pastwinners.html. The Ig Nobel prize is a spoof of the Nobel prize and honors researchers whose achievements "cannot or should not be reproduced." The data here is taken from *Demonstration of the Exponential Decay Law Using Beer Froth*, Arnd Leike, European Journal of Physics, vol. 23, January 2002, pp. 21-26.
[24] From website created by A. Sharov, http://www.ento.vt.edu/ sharov/PopEcol/lec8/quest8.html. The site attributes the data to Smith, A. M., 1992, Environ. Entomol. 21:314-321.

30. In this problem, we will determine whether or not the compact disc data from Table 4.7 on page 180 can be well modeled using a power function of the form $l = kc^p$, where l and c give the number of LPs and CDs (in millions) respectively, and where k and p are constant.

(a) Based on the plot of the data in Figure 4.23 on page 180, what do you expect to be true about the sign of the power p?

(b) Fit a power function to the data. One data point may have to be omitted. Which point and why?

(c) Let $y = \ln l$ and $x = \ln c$. Find a linear formula for y in terms of x by making substitutions in the equation $l = kc^p$.

(d) Transform the data in Table 4.7 to create a table comparing $x = \ln c$ and $y = \ln l$. What data point must be omitted?

(e) Plot your transformed data from part (d). Based on your plot, do you think a power function gives a good fit to the data? Explain.

CHAPTER SUMMARY

- **Proportionality**
  Direct and indirect.

- **Power Functions**
  $y = kx^p$.

- **Polynomials**
  General formula: $p(x) = a_n x^n + a_{n-1} x^{n-1} + \cdots + a_1 x + a_0$.
  All terms have non-negative, integer exponents. Leading term $a_n x^n$; coefficients $a_0, \ldots, a_n$.
  Long-run behavior: Like $y = a_n x^n$.
  Short-run behavior: Zeros corresponding to each factor; multiple zeros.

- **Rational Functions**
  Ratio of polynomials: $r(x) = \dfrac{p(x)}{q(x)}$.
  Long-run behavior: Horizontal asymptote of $r(x)$:
      Given by ratio of highest-degree terms.
  Short-run behavior: Vertical asymptote of $r(x)$:
      At zeros of $q(x)$ (if $p(x) \neq 0$).
  Short-run behavior: Zeros of $r(x)$:
      At zeros of $p(x)$ (if $q(x) \neq 0$).
  Using limits to understand short- and long-run behavior

- **Comparing Functions**
  Exponential functions eventually dominate power functions. Power functions eventually dominate logs.

- **Fitting Exponentials and Polynomials to Data**

REVIEW EXERCISES AND PROBLEMS FOR CHAPTER NINE

Exercises

In Exercises 1–6, is y a power function of x? If so, write it in the form $y = kx^p$.

1. $y = 6x^3 + 2$

2. $3y = 9x^2$

3. $y - 9 = (x+3)(x-3)$

4. $y = 4(x-2)(x+2)+16$

5. $y = 4(x+7)^2$

6. $y - 1 = 2x^2 - 1$

Do the power functions in Exercises 7–8 appear to have odd, even, or fractional powers?

7.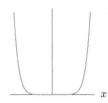

8.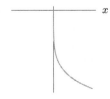

In Exercises 9–10, find possible formulas for the power functions with the properties given.

9. $f(1) = \frac{3}{2}$ and $f(2) = \frac{3}{8}$

10. $g\left(-\frac{1}{5}\right) = 25$ and $g(2) = -\frac{1}{40}$

11. Show that the function $u(x) = x(x-3)(x+2)$ is a polynomial. What is its degree?

For the polynomials in Exercises 12–14, state the degree, the number of terms, and describe the long-run behavior.

12. $y = 2x^3 - 3x + 7$

13. $y = 1 - 2x^4 + x^3$

14. $y = (x+4)(2x-3)(5-x)$

In Exercises 15–16, find the zeros of the functions.

15. $y = (x^2 - 8x + 12)(x - 3)$

16. $y = ax^2(x^2 + 4)(x+3)$, where a is a nonzero constant.

Are the functions in Exercises 17–18 rational functions? If so, write them in the form $p(x)/q(x)$, the ratio of polynomials.

17. $f(x) = \dfrac{x^3}{2x^2} + \dfrac{1}{6}$

18. $f(x) = \dfrac{x^4 + 3^x - x^2}{x^3 - 2}$

In Exercises 19–20, which function dominates as $x \to \infty$?

19. $y = 12x^3, \quad y = 7/x^{-4}$

20. $y = 4/e^{-x}, \quad y = 17x^{43}$

Evaluate the limits in Exercises 21–24.

21. $\lim\limits_{x \to \infty} \left(2x^{-3} + 4\right)$

22. $\lim\limits_{x \to \infty} \left(3x^{-2} + 5x + 7\right)$

23. $\lim\limits_{x \to \infty} \dfrac{4x + 3x^2}{4x^2 + 3x}$

24. $\lim\limits_{x \to -\infty} \dfrac{3x^2 + x}{2x^2 + 5x^3}$

Problems

In Problems 25–28, find a viewing window on which the graph of $f(x) = x^3 + x^2$ resembles the plot.

25.

26.

27.

28.

29. Without a calculator, match graphs (i)–(iv) with the functions in Table 9.37.

(i)

(ii)

(iii)

(iv)

Table 9.37

(A) $y = 0.5\sin(2x)$	(J) $y = 2\sin(0.5x)$
(B) $y = -\ln x$	(K) $y = \ln(x-1)$
(C) $y = 10(0.6)^x$	(L) $y = 2e^{-0.2x}$
(D) $y = 2\sin(2x)$	(M) $y = 1/(x-6)$
(E) $y = \ln(-x)$	(N) $y = (x-2)/(x^2-9)$
(F) $y = -15(3.1)^x$	(O) $y = 1/(x^2-4)$
(G) $y = 0.5\sin(0.5x)$	(P) $y = x/(x-3)$
(H) $y = \ln(x+1)$	(Q) $y = (x-1)/(x+3)$
(I) $y = 7(2.5)^x$	(R) $y = 1/(x^2+4)$

30. Without a calculator, match each graph (i)–(viii) with a functions in Table 9.38.

(i)
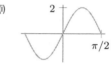

(ii)

(iii)

(iv)

(v)
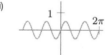

(vi)

(vii)
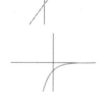

(viii)

Table 9.38

(A) $y = 0.5\sin(2x)$	(M) $y = (x+3)/(x^2-4)$
(B) $y = 2\sin(2x)$	(N) $y = (x^2-4)/(x^2-1)$
(C) $y = 0.5\sin(0.5x)$	(O) $y = (x+1)^3 - 1$
(D) $y = 2\sin(0.5x)$	(P) $y = -2x - 4$
(E) $y = (x-2)/(x^2-9)$	(Q) $y = 3e^{-x}$
(F) $y = (x-3)/(x^2-1)$	(R) $y = -3e^x$
(G) $y = (x-1)^3 - 1$	(S) $y = -3e^{-x}$
(H) $y = 2x - 4$	(T) $y = 3e^{-x^2}$
(I) $y = -\ln x$	(U) $y = 1/(4-x^2)$
(J) $y = \ln(-x)$	(V) $y = 1/(x^2+4)$
(K) $y = \ln(x+1)$	(W) $y = (x+1)^3 + 1$
(L) $y = \ln(x-1)$	(X) $y = 2(x+2)$

Find possible polynomial formulas in Problems 31–36.

31.

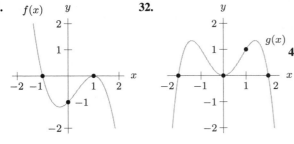

32.

33.

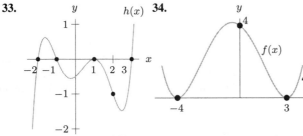

34.

35.

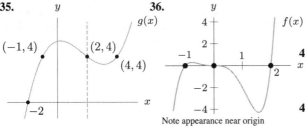

36.

Note appearance near origin

37. For each of the following functions, state whether it is even, odd, or neither.

(a) $f(x) = x^2 + 3$ (b) $g(x) = x^3 + 3$
(c) $h(x) = 5/x$ (d) $j(x) = |x - 4|$
(e) $k(x) = \log x$ (f) $l(x) = \log(x^2)$
(g) $m(x) = 2^x + 2$ (h) $n(x) = \cos x + 2$

38. Assume that $x = a$ and $x = b$ are zeros of the second degree polynomial, $y = q(x)$.

(a) Explain what you know and don't know about the graph of q. (Intercepts, vertex, end behavior.)

(b) Explain why a possible formula for $q(x)$ is $q(x) = k(x - a)(x - b)$, with k unknown.

39. (a) Suppose $f(x) = ax^2 + bx + c$. What must be true about the coefficients if f is an even function?

(b) Suppose $g(x) = ax^3 + bx^2 + cx + d$. What must be true about the coefficients if g is an odd function?

40. The gravitational force exerted by a planet is inversely proportional to the square of the distance to the center of the planet. Thus, the weight, w, of an object at a distance, r, from a planet's center is given by

$$w = \frac{k}{r^2}, \quad \text{with } k \text{ constant.}$$

A gravitational force of one ton (2000 lbs) will kill a 150-pound person. Suppose the earth's radius were to shrink with its mass remaining the same. What is the smallest radius at which the 150-pound person could survive? Give your answer as a percentage of the earth's radius.

41. The period, p, of the orbit of a planet whose average distance (in millions of miles) from the sun is d, is given by $p = kd^{3/2}$, where k is a constant. The average distance from the earth to the sun is 93 million miles.

(a) If the period of the earth's orbit were twice the current 365 days, what would be the average distance from the sun to earth?

(b) Is there a planet in our solar system whose period is approximately twice the earth's?

42. Refer to Problem 41. If the distance between the sun and the earth were halved, how long (in earth days) would a "year" be?

43. Ship designers usually construct scale models before building a real ship. The formula that relates the speed u to the hull length l of a ship is

$$u = k\sqrt{l},$$

where k is a positive constant. This constant k varies depending on the ship's design, but scale models of a real ship have the same k as the real ship after which they are modeled.[25]

(a) How fast should a scale model with hull length 4 meters travel to simulate a real ship with hull length 225 meters traveling 9 meters/sec?

(b) A new ship is to be built whose speed is to be 10% greater than the speed of an existing ship with the same design. What is the relationship between the hull lengths of the new ship and the existing ship?

[25]R. McNeill Alexander, *Dynamics of Dinosaurs and Other Extinct Giants*. (New York: Columbia University Press, 1989).

44. An alcohol solution consists of 5 gallons of pure water and x gallons of alcohol, $x > 0$. Let $f(x)$ be the ratio of the volume of alcohol to the total volume of liquid. [Note that $f(x)$ is the concentration of the alcohol in the solution.]

(a) Find a possible formula for $f(x)$.

(b) Evaluate and interpret $f(7)$ in the context of the mixture.

(c) What is the zero of f? Interpret your result in the context of the mixture.

(d) Find an equation for the horizontal asymptote of f. Explain its significance in the context of the mixture.

45. The function $f(x)$ defined in Problem 44 gives the concentration of a solution of x gallons of alcohol and 5 gallons of water.

(a) Find a formula for $f^{-1}(x)$.

(b) Evaluate and interpret $f^{-1}(0.2)$ in the context of the mixture.

(c) What is the zero of f^{-1}? Interpret your result in the context of the mixture.

(d) Find an equation for the horizontal asymptote of f^{-1}. Explain its significance in the context of the mixture.

Find possible formulas for the polynomials and rational functions in Problems 46–50.

46. The zeros of f are $x = -3$, $x = 2$, and $x = 5$, and the y-intercept is $y = -6$.

47. This function has zeros at $x = -3$, $x = 2$, $x = 5$, and a double-zero at $x = 6$. It has a y-intercept of 7.

48. This function has zeros at $x = 2$ and $x = 3$. It has a vertical asymptote at $x = 5$. It has a horizontal asymptote of $y = -3$.

49. The polynomial $h(x) = 7$ at $x = -5, -1, 4$, and the y-intercept is 3. [Hint: Visualize h as a vertically shifted version of another polynomial.]

50. The graph of w intercepts the graph of $v(x) = 2x + 5$ at $x = -4, 1, 3$ and has a y-intercept of 2. [Hint: Let $w(x) = p(x) + v(x)$ where p is another polynomial.]

51. The ancient Greeks placed great importance on a number known as the *golden ratio*, ϕ, which is defined geometrically as follows. Starting with a square, add a rectangle to one side of the square, so that the resulting rectangle has the same proportions as the rectangle that was added. The golden ratio is defined as the ratio of either rectangle's length to its width. (See Figure 9.62.) Given this information, show that $\phi = (1 + \sqrt{5})/2$.

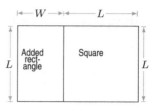

Figure 9.62: Large rectangle has the same proportions as small rectangle

52. The number ϕ, defined in Problem 51, has the property:

$$\phi^k + \phi^{k+1} = \phi^{k+2}.$$

(a) Check that the property holds true for $k = 3$ and $k = 10$.

(b) Show that this property follows from the definition of ϕ.

53. The resolution, r %, of a gamma ray telescope depends on the energy v (in millions of electron volts, or MeVs) of the detected gamma rays.[26] The smaller the value of r, the better the telescope is at distinguishing two gamma ray photons of slightly different energies, and the more detailed observations that can be made. Table 9.39 gives values of r for gamma rays at different energies.

(a) Plot the data in Table 9.39, with r on the vertical axis.

(b) Based on this data, is the telescope better able to distinguish between high-energy photons or low-energy photons?

(c) Fit both power and exponential functions to the data, and give their formulas. Which appears to give the better fit?

(d) The telescope is predicted to grow rapidly worse and worse at distinguishing photons as the energy level drops toward 0 MeV. Which curve, power or exponential, is most consistent with this prediction?

Table 9.39

v, MeV	0.5	0.7	0.9	1.3	1.8	4.0	4.4
r, %	16.0	13.5	12.0	8.5	7.0	4.5	4.0

[26]*The LXeGRIT Compton Status and Future Prospects*, E. Aprile, et al., posted at http://arxiv.org as arXiv:astro-ph/0212005v2, December 4, 2002.

54. We launch an unpowered spacecraft, initially in free space, so that it hits a planet of radius R. When viewed from a distance, the planet looks like a disk of area πR^2. In the absence of gravity, we would need to aim the spacecraft directly at this disk. However, because of gravity, the planet draws the spacecraft toward it, so that even if we are somewhat off the mark, the spacecraft might still hit its target. Thus, the area we must aim for is actually larger than the apparent area of the planet. This area is called the planet's *capture cross-section*. The more massive the planet, the larger its capture cross-section, because it exerts a stronger pull on passing objects.

A spacecraft with a large initial velocity has a greater chance of slipping past the planet even if its aim is only slightly off, whereas a spacecraft with a low initial velocity has a good chance of drifting into the planet even if its aim is poor. Thus, the planet's capture cross-section is a function of the initial velocity of the spacecraft, v. If the planet's capture cross-section is denoted by A and M is the planet's mass, then it can be shown that, for a positive constant G,

$$A(v) = \pi R^2 \left(1 + \frac{2MG/R}{v^2} \right).$$

(a) Show from the formula for $A(v)$ that, for any initial velocity v,
$$A(v) > \pi R^2.$$
Explain why this makes sense physically.

(b) Consider two planets: The first is twice as massive as the second, and the radius of the second is twice the radius of the first. Which has the larger capture cross-section?

(c) The graph of $A(v)$ has both horizontal and vertical asymptotes. Find their equations, and explain their physical significance.

55. A group of x people is tested for the presence of a certain virus. Unfortunately, the test is imperfect and incorrectly identifies some healthy people as being infected and some sick people as being noninfected. There is no way to know when the test is right and when it is wrong. Since the disease is so rare, only 1% of those tested are actually infected.

(a) Write expressions in terms of x for the number of people tested that are actually infected and the number who are not.

(b) The test correctly identifies 98% of all infected people as being infected. (It incorrectly identifies the remaining 2% as being healthy.) Write, in terms of x, an expression representing the number of infected people who are correctly identified as being infected. (This group is known as the *true-positive* group.)

(c) The test incorrectly identifies 3% of all healthy people as being infected. (It correctly identifies the remaining 97% as being healthy.) Write, in terms of x, an expression representing the number of noninfected people who are incorrectly identified as being infected. (This group is known as the *false-positive* group.)

(d) Write, in terms of x, an expression representing the total number of people the test identifies as being infected, including both true- and false-positives.

(e) Write, in terms of x, an expression representing the fraction of those testing positive who are actually infected. Can this expression be evaluated without knowing the value of x?

(f) Suppose you are among the group of people who test positive for the presence of the virus. Based on your test result, do you think it is likely that you are actually infected?

CHECK YOUR UNDERSTANDING

Are the statements in Problems 1–47 true or false? Give an explanation for your answer.

1. All quadratic functions are power functions.

2. The function $y = 3 \cdot 2^x$ is a power function.

3. Let $g(x) = x^p$. If p is a positive, even integer, then the graph of g passes through the point $(-1, 1)$.

4. Let $g(x) = x^p$. If p is a positive, even integer, then the graph of g is symmetric about the y-axis.

5. Let $g(x) = x^p$. If p is a positive, even integer, then the graph of g is concave up.

6. The graph of $f(x) = x^{-1}$ passes through the origin.

7. The graph of $f(x) = x^{-2}$ has the x-axis as its only asymptote.

8. If $f(x) = x^{-1}$ then $f(x)$ approaches $+\infty$ as x approaches zero.

9. As x grows very large, the values of $f(x) = x^{-1}$ approach zero.

10. The function 2^x eventually grows faster than x^b for any b.

11. The function $f(x) = x^{0.5}$ eventually grows faster than $g(x) = \ln x$.

12. We have $2^x \geq x^2$ on the interval $0 \leq x \leq 4$.

13. The function $f(x) = x^{-3}$ approaches the x-axis faster than $g(x) = e^{-x}$ as x grows very large.

14. The function $f(x) = 3^x$ is an example of a power function.

15. The function $y = 3x$ is an example of a power function.

16. Every quadratic function is a polynomial function.

17. The power of the first term of a polynomial is its degree.

18. Far from the origin, the graph of a polynomial looks like the graph of its highest degree term.

19. A zero of a polynomial p is the value $p(0)$.

20. The zeros of a polynomial are the x-coordinates where its graph intersects the x-axis.

21. The y-intercept of a polynomial $y = p(x)$ can be found by evaluating $p(0)$.

22. For very large x-values $f(x) = 1000x^3 + 345x^2 + 17x + 394$ is less than $g(x) = 0.01x^4$.

23. If $y = f(x)$ is a polynomial of degree n, where n is a positive even number, then f has an inverse.

24. If $y = f(x)$ is a polynomial of degree n, where n is a positive odd number, then f has an inverse.

25. If $p(x)$ is a polynomial and $x - a$ is a factor of p, then $x = a$ is a zero of p.

26. A polynomial of degree n cannot have more than n zeros.

27. The polynomial in Figure 9.63 has a multiple zero at $x = -2$.

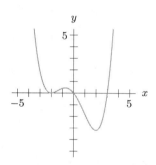

Figure 9.63

28. The polynomial in Figure 9.63 has a multiple zero at $x = 0$.

29. A rational function is the quotient of two polynomials. We assume the denominator is not equal to zero.

30. The function $f(x) = \dfrac{1}{x}$ is a rational function.

31. In order to determine the long-run behavior of a rational function, it is sufficient to consider only the ratio of the highest degree term in the numerator to the highest degree term in the denominator.

32. As x grows through large positive values, $y = \dfrac{x + 18}{x + 9}$ approaches $y = 2$.

33. As x grows through large positive values, $y = \dfrac{2x + 125}{x^2 - 1}$ approaches $y = 0$.

34. As x grows through large positive values, $y = \dfrac{x^3 + 4x^2 - 16x + 12}{4x^3 - 16x + 1}$ has an asymptote at $y = 4$.

35. As x grows through large positive values, $y = \dfrac{1 - 4x^2}{x^2 + 1}$ approaches $y = 0$.

36. As x grows through large positive values, $y = \dfrac{5x}{x + 1}$ approaches $y = -5$.

37. As x grows through large positive values, $y = \dfrac{3x^4 - 6x^3 + 10x^2 - 16x + 7}{-3x + x^2}$ behaves like $y = -x^3$.

38. As x decreases through large negative values, $f(x) = \dfrac{x^3 - 7x^2 + 28x + 76}{-x^2 - 101x + 72}$ approaches positive infinity.

39. A fraction is equal to zero if and only if its numerator equals zero and its denominator does not.

40. The zeros of a function $y = f(x)$ are the values of x that make $y = 0$.

41. The function $f(x) = \dfrac{x + 4}{x - 3}$ has a zero at $x = -4$.

42. The rational function $y = \dfrac{x + 2}{x^2 - 4}$ has a zero at $x = -2$.

43. The rational function $g(w) = \dfrac{12}{(w - 2)(w + 3)}$ has exactly two zeros.

44. If $p(x)$ and $q(x)$ have no zeros in common, then the rational function $r(x) = \dfrac{p(x)}{q(x)}$ has an asymptote at each of the zeros of $p(x)$.

45. In general, the rational function $r(x) = \dfrac{p(x)}{q(x)}$ must have at least one zero.

46. Rational functions can never cross an asymptote.

47. The rational function $g(w) = \dfrac{3w - 3}{(w - 12)(w + 4)}$ has a vertical asymptote at $w = 1$.

TOOLS FOR CHAPTER 9: ALGEBRAIC FRACTIONS

Algebraic fractions are combined in the same way as numeric fractions according to the following rules:

Add numerators when denominators are equal: $\dfrac{a}{c} + \dfrac{b}{c} = \dfrac{a+b}{c}$

Find a common denominator: $\dfrac{a}{b} + \dfrac{c}{d} = \dfrac{a \cdot d}{b \cdot d} + \dfrac{b \cdot c}{b \cdot d} = \dfrac{ad + bc}{bd}$

Multiply numerators and denominators for a product: $\dfrac{a}{b} \cdot \dfrac{c}{d} = \dfrac{ac}{bd}$

To divide by a fraction, multiply by its reciprocal: $\dfrac{a/b}{c/d} = \dfrac{a}{b} \cdot \dfrac{d}{c} = \dfrac{ad}{bc}$

The sign of a fraction is changed by changing the sign of the numerator or the denominator (but not both):

$$-\frac{a}{b} = \frac{-a}{b} = \frac{a}{-b}$$

We assume that no denominators are zero, since we cannot divide by zero; that is, $a/0$ is not defined.

We can simplify a fraction in which either the numerator or denominator is itself a fraction as follows:

$$\frac{a/b}{c} = \frac{a/b}{c/1} = \frac{a}{b} \cdot \frac{1}{c} = \frac{a}{bc} \quad \text{and} \quad \frac{a}{b/c} = \frac{a/1}{b/c} = \frac{a}{1} \cdot \frac{c}{b} = \frac{ac}{b}.$$

Example 1   Perform the indicated operations and express the answers as a single fraction.

(a) $\dfrac{4}{x^2 + 1} - \dfrac{1 - x}{x^2 + 1}$

(b) $\dfrac{M}{M^2 - 2M - 3} + \dfrac{1}{M^2 - 2M - 3}$

(c) $\dfrac{-H^2 P}{17} \cdot \dfrac{\left(PH^{1/3}\right)^2}{K^{-1}}$

(d) $\dfrac{2z/w}{w(w - 3z)}$

Solution   (a) $\dfrac{4}{x^2 + 1} - \dfrac{1 - x}{x^2 + 1} = \dfrac{4 - (1 - x)}{x^2 + 1} = \dfrac{3 + x}{x^2 + 1}$

(b) $\dfrac{M}{M^2 - 2M - 3} + \dfrac{1}{M^2 - 2M - 3} = \dfrac{M + 1}{(M^2 - 2M - 3)} = \dfrac{M + 1}{(M + 1)(M - 3)} = \dfrac{1}{M - 3}$

(c) $\dfrac{-H^2 P}{17} \cdot \dfrac{\left(PH^{1/3}\right)^2}{K^{-1}} = \dfrac{-H^2 P \left(P^2 H^{2/3}\right)}{17 K^{-1}} = -\dfrac{H^{8/3} P^3 K}{17}$

(d) $\dfrac{2z/w}{w(w - 3z)} = \dfrac{2z}{w} \cdot \dfrac{1}{w(w - 3z)} = \dfrac{2z}{w^2(w - 3z)}$

Example 2   Simplify the following expressions, giving your answer as a single fraction.

(a) $2x^{-1/2} + \dfrac{\sqrt{x}}{3}$

(b) $2\sqrt{t + 3} + \dfrac{1 - 2t}{\sqrt{t + 3}}$

Solution

(a) $2x^{-1/2} + \dfrac{\sqrt{x}}{3} = \dfrac{2}{\sqrt{x}} + \dfrac{\sqrt{x}}{3} = \dfrac{2 \cdot 3 + \sqrt{x}\sqrt{x}}{3\sqrt{x}} = \dfrac{6 + x}{3\sqrt{x}} = \dfrac{6 + x}{3x^{1/2}}$

(b) $2\sqrt{t+3} + \dfrac{1 - 2t}{\sqrt{t+3}} = \dfrac{2\sqrt{t+3}}{1} + \dfrac{1 - 2t}{\sqrt{t+3}}$

$= \dfrac{2\sqrt{t+3}\sqrt{t+3} + 1 - 2t}{\sqrt{t+3}}$

$= \dfrac{2(t+3) + 1 - 2t}{\sqrt{t+3}}$

$= \dfrac{7}{\sqrt{t+3}} = \dfrac{7}{(t+3)^{1/2}}$

Finding a Common Denominator

We can multiply (or divide) both the numerator and denominator of a fraction by the same nonzero number without changing the fraction's value. This is equivalent to multiplying by a factor of $+1$. We are using this rule when we add or subtract fractions with different denominators. For example, to add $\dfrac{x}{3a} + \dfrac{1}{a}$, we multiply $\dfrac{1}{a} \cdot \dfrac{3}{3} = \dfrac{3}{3a}$. Then

$$\frac{x}{3a} + \frac{1}{a} = \frac{x}{3a} + \frac{3}{3a} = \frac{x+3}{3a}.$$

Example 3   Perform the indicated operations:

(a) $3 - \dfrac{1}{x - 1}$

(b) $\dfrac{2}{x^2 + x} + \dfrac{x}{x + 1}$

Solution

(a) $3 - \dfrac{1}{x-1} = 3\dfrac{(x-1)}{(x-1)} - \dfrac{1}{x-1} = \dfrac{3(x-1) - 1}{x - 1} = \dfrac{3x - 3 - 1}{x - 1} = \dfrac{3x - 4}{x - 1}$

(b) $\dfrac{2}{x^2 + x} + \dfrac{x}{x + 1} = \dfrac{2}{x(x+1)} + \dfrac{x}{x+1} = \dfrac{2}{x(x+1)} + \dfrac{x(x)}{(x+1)(x)} = \dfrac{2 + x^2}{x(x + 1)}$

Note: We can multiply (or divide) the numerator and denominator by the same nonzero number because this is the same as multiplying by a factor of $+1$, and multiplying by a factor of 1 does not change the value of the expression. However, we cannot perform any other operation that would change the value of the expression. For example, we cannot add the same number to the numerator and denominator of a fraction nor can we square both, take the logarithm of both, etc., without changing the fraction.

Reducing Fractions: Canceling

We can reduce a fraction when we have the same (nonzero) factor in both the numerator and the denominator. For example,

$$\frac{ac}{bc} = \frac{a}{b} \cdot \frac{c}{c} = \frac{a}{b} \cdot 1 = \frac{a}{b}.$$

Example 4   Reduce the following fractions (if possible).

(a) $\dfrac{2x}{4y}$

(b) $\dfrac{2+x}{2+y}$

(c) $\dfrac{5n-5}{1-n}$

(d) $\dfrac{x^2(4-2x)-(4x-x^2)2x}{x^4}$

Solution   (a) $\dfrac{2x}{4y} = \dfrac{2}{2}\cdot\dfrac{x}{2y} = \dfrac{x}{2y}$

(b) $\dfrac{2+x}{2+y}$ cannot be reduced further.

(c) $\dfrac{5n-5}{1-n} = \dfrac{5(n-1)}{(-1)(n-1)} = -5$

(d)

$$\frac{x^2(4-2x)-\left(4x-x^2\right)2x}{x^4} = \frac{x^2(4-2x)-(4-x)2x^2}{x^4}$$

$$= \frac{(4-2x)-2(4-x)}{x^2}\left(\frac{x^2}{x^2}\right)$$

$$= \frac{4-2x-8+2x}{x^2} = \frac{-4}{x^2}.$$

Complex Fractions

A *complex fraction* is a fraction whose numerator or denominator (or both) contains one or more fractions. To simplify a complex fraction, we change the numerator and denominator to single fractions and then divide.

Example 5   Write the following as simple fractions in reduced form.

(a) $\dfrac{\dfrac{1}{x+h}-\dfrac{1}{x}}{h}$

(b) $\dfrac{a+b}{a^{-2}-b^{-2}}$

Solution   (a) $\dfrac{\dfrac{1}{x+h}-\dfrac{1}{x}}{h} = \dfrac{\dfrac{x-(x+h)}{x(x+h)}}{h} = \dfrac{\dfrac{-h}{x(x+h)}}{h} = \dfrac{-h}{x(x+h)}\cdot\dfrac{1}{h} = \dfrac{-1}{x(x+h)}\dfrac{(h)}{(h)} = \dfrac{-1}{x(x+h)}$

(b) $\dfrac{a+b}{a^{-2}-b^{-2}} = \dfrac{a+b}{\dfrac{1}{a^2}-\dfrac{1}{b^2}} = \dfrac{a+b}{\dfrac{b^2-a^2}{a^2b^2}} = \dfrac{a+b}{1}\cdot\dfrac{a^2b^2}{b^2-a^2} = \dfrac{(a+b)(a^2b^2)}{(b+a)(b-a)} = \dfrac{a^2b^2}{b-a}$

Splitting Expressions

We can reverse the rule for adding fractions to split up an expression into two fractions,

$$\frac{a+b}{c} = \frac{a}{c}+\frac{b}{c}.$$

Example 6   Split $\dfrac{3x^2+2}{x^3}$ into two reduced fractions.

Solution $\dfrac{3x^2+2}{x^3} = \dfrac{3x^2}{x^3}+\dfrac{2}{x^3} = \dfrac{3}{x}+\dfrac{2}{x^3}$

Sometimes we can alter the form of the fraction even further if we can create a duplicate of the denominator within the numerator. This technique is useful when graphing some rational functions. For example, we may rewrite the fraction $\dfrac{x+3}{x-1}$ by creating a factor of $(x-1)$ within the numerator. To do this, we write

$$\frac{x+3}{x-1} = \frac{x-1+1+3}{x-1}$$

which can be written as

$$\frac{(x-1)+4}{x-1}.$$

Then, splitting this fraction, we have

$$\frac{x+3}{x-1} = \frac{x-1}{x-1} + \frac{4}{x-1} = 1 + \frac{4}{x-1}.$$

Note: It is not possible to split a sum that occurs in the denominator of a fraction. For example,

$$\frac{a}{b+c} \text{ does not equal } \frac{a}{b} + \frac{a}{c}.$$

Exercises to Tools for Chapter 9

For Exercises 1–35, perform the operations. Express answers in reduced form.

1. $\dfrac{3}{5} + \dfrac{4}{7}$

2. $\dfrac{7}{10} - \dfrac{2}{15}$

3. $\dfrac{1}{2x} - \dfrac{2}{3}$

4. $\dfrac{6}{7y} + \dfrac{9}{y}$

5. $\dfrac{-2}{yz} + \dfrac{4}{z}$

6. $\dfrac{-2z}{y} + \dfrac{4}{y}$

7. $\dfrac{2}{x^2} - \dfrac{3}{x}$

8. $\dfrac{6}{y} + \dfrac{7}{y^3}$

9. $\dfrac{3/4}{7/20}$

10. $\dfrac{5/6}{15}$

11. $\dfrac{3/x}{x^2/6}$

12. $\dfrac{3/x}{6/x^2}$

13. $\dfrac{13}{x-1} + \dfrac{14}{2x-2}$

14. $\dfrac{14}{x-1} + \dfrac{13}{2x-2}$

15. $\dfrac{4z}{x^2y} - \dfrac{3w}{xy^4}$

16. $\dfrac{10}{y-2} + \dfrac{3}{2-y}$

17. $\dfrac{8y}{y-4} + \dfrac{32}{y-4}$

18. $\dfrac{8y}{y-4} + \dfrac{32}{4-y}$

19. $\dfrac{\dfrac{1}{x} - \dfrac{2}{x^2}}{\dfrac{2x-4}{x^5}}$

20. $\dfrac{9}{x^2+5x+6} + \dfrac{12}{x+3}$

21. $\dfrac{8}{3x^2-x-4} - \dfrac{9}{x+1}$

22. $\dfrac{5}{(x-2)^2(x+1)} - \dfrac{18}{(x-2)}$

23. $\dfrac{15}{(x-3)^2(x+5)} + \dfrac{7}{(x-3)(x+5)^2}$

24. $\dfrac{3}{x-4} - \dfrac{2}{x+4}$

25. $\dfrac{x^2}{x-1} - \dfrac{1}{1-x}$

26. $\dfrac{1}{2r+3} + \dfrac{3}{4r^2+6r}$

27. $u + a + \dfrac{u}{u+a}$

28. $\dfrac{1}{\sqrt{x}} - \dfrac{1}{(\sqrt{x})^3}$

29. $\dfrac{1}{e^{2x}} + \dfrac{1}{e^x}$

30. $\dfrac{a+b}{2} \cdot \dfrac{8x+2}{b^2-a^2}$

31. $\dfrac{0.07}{M} + \dfrac{3}{4}M^2$

32. $\dfrac{1}{r_1} + \dfrac{1}{r_2} + \dfrac{1}{r_3}$

33. $\dfrac{8y}{y-4} - \dfrac{32}{y-4}$

34. $\dfrac{a}{a^2-9} + \dfrac{1}{a-3}$

35. $\dfrac{x^3}{x-4} \Big/ \dfrac{x^2}{x^2-2x-8}$

In Exercises 36–49, simplify, if possible.

36. $\dfrac{1/(x+y)}{x+y}$

37. $\dfrac{(w+2)/2}{w+2}$

38. $\dfrac{\dfrac{1}{(x+h)^2} - \dfrac{1}{x^2}}{h}$

39. $\dfrac{a^{-2} + b^{-2}}{a^2 + b^2}$

40. $\dfrac{a^2 - b^2}{a^2 + b^2}$

41. $\dfrac{4 - (x+h)^2 - (4 - x^2)}{h}$

42. $\dfrac{b^{-1}(b - b^{-1})}{b+1}.$

43. $\dfrac{1 - a^{-2}}{1 + a^{-1}}.$

44. $\dfrac{x^{-1} + x^{-2}}{1 - x^{-2}}.$

45. $p - \dfrac{q}{\dfrac{p}{q} + \dfrac{q}{p}}$

46. $\dfrac{\dfrac{3}{xy} - \dfrac{5}{x^2 y}}{\dfrac{6x^2 - 7x - 5}{x^4 y^2}}$

47. $\dfrac{\dfrac{1}{x}\left(3x^2\right) - (\ln x)(6x)}{(3x^2)^2}$

48. $\dfrac{2x(x^3 + 1)^2 - x^2(2)(x^3 + 1)(3x^2)}{[(x^3 + 1)^2]^2}$

49. $\dfrac{\frac{1}{2}(2x - 1)^{-1/2}(2) - (2x - 1)^{1/2}(2x)}{(x^2)^2}$

In Exercises 50–55, split into a sum or difference of reduced fractions.

50. $\dfrac{26x + 1}{2x^3}$

51. $\dfrac{\sqrt{x} + 3}{3\sqrt{x}}$

52. $\dfrac{6l^2 + 3l - 4}{3l^4}$

53. $\dfrac{7 + p}{p^2 + 11}$

54. $\dfrac{\frac{1}{3}x - \frac{1}{2}}{2x}$

55. $\dfrac{t^{-1/2} + t^{1/2}}{t^2}$

In Exercises 56–61, rewrite in the form $1 + (A/B)$.

56. $\dfrac{x - 2}{x + 5}$

57. $\dfrac{q - 1}{q - 4}$

58. $\dfrac{R + 1}{R}$

59. $\dfrac{3 + 2u}{2u + 1}$

60. $\dfrac{\cos x + \sin x}{\cos x}$

61. $\dfrac{1 + e^x}{e^x}$

Are the statements in Exercises 62–67 true or false?

62. $\dfrac{a + c}{a} = 1 + c$

63. $\dfrac{rs - s}{s} = r - 1$

64. $\dfrac{y}{y + z} = 1 + \dfrac{y}{z}$

65. $\dfrac{2u^2 - w}{u^2 - w} = 2$

66. $\dfrac{x^2 yz}{2x^2 y} = \dfrac{z}{2}$

67. $x^{5/3} - 3x^{2/3} = \dfrac{x^2 - 3x}{x^{1/3}}$

Section 1.1

1 2.9

3 0, 4, 8

5 $m = f(v)$

7 (a) (I), (III), (IV), (V)
    (VII), (VIII)
  (b)   (i) (V) and (VI)
        (ii) (VIII)
  (c) (III) and (IV)

9 (a) 40
  (b) 2

11 (a) w
   (b) $(-4, 10)$
   (c) $(6, 1)$

13 P (millions)

t (years)

15 p, pressure (lbs/in^2)

v, volume (in^3)

17 (a) $f(s) = 0.1s$
   (b) $f(5) = 0.5$
   (c) $s = 50$

19 (a) 100.3 m. own phones in 2000
   (b) 20 m. own phones a years after 1990
   (c) b m. own phones in 2010
   (d) n m. own phones t years after 1990

21 $200 \le s \le 1000$

23 (a) 69°F
   (b) July 17 and 20
   (c) Yes
   (d) No

27 (a) Yes
   (b) No
   (c) 8 female senators in 104th Congress
   (d) 14 female senators in 108th Congress

29 temperature

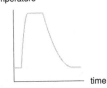
time

31 $S = 6\pi r^2$

33 (a) (ii)
   (b) (i)
   (c) (v)
   (d) (iv)
   (e) (ii)

35 $T(d) = d/5 + (10 - d)/8$

Section 1.2

1 $G(3) - G(-1) > 0$

3 0.513

5 0.513

7 (a) Negative
  (b) Positive

9 Decreasing

11 (a) 300, -150 people/yr
   (b) 167, -83 people/yr
   (c) 235, -118 people/yr

13 Between 3000 and
    4000 years ago

15 (a) 2
   (b) Increasing
   (c) Increasing everywhere

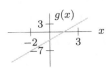

17 (a) 1/2
   (c) 1/4

19 (a)   (i) 1/2
        (ii) 1/2
       (iii) 1/2
   (b) Always 1/2

21 (a) 9
   (b) $(n - k)/(m - j)$
   (c) $6x + 3h$

23 (a) 10
   (b) 30, 30, 55, 29
   (c) No; $\Delta G/\Delta t$ not constant

25 (a) 0°C/meter
   (b) -0.008°C/meter
   (c) 0.009°C/meter.

Section 1.3

1 Not linear

3 No

5 Yes

7 Vert int: 54.25 thousand; Slope: $-2/7$ thousand/yr

9 Vert int: $-\$3000$; Slope: \$0.98/item

11 $P = 18{,}310 + 58t$

15 (a) \$5350, \$5700, \$6750,
        \$8500, \$12,000

C, total cost (\$1000s)

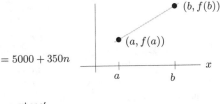
$C = 5000 + 350n$
n, number of horses

(b) $C = 5000 + 350n$
(c) \$350/horse

17 (a) Radius and circumference
   (c) 2π

19 (a) inches

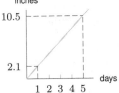
days

(b) gallons

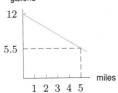
miles

21 (a) No
   (b) Looks linear

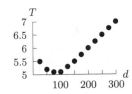

(c) $\Delta T/\Delta d = 0.01$°C/meter

23 (a) $T = \$1900$
   (b) $C = 7$
   (d) Twelve credits
   (e) Fixed costs that do not depend on the number of credits taken

25 (a) $m = -0.62$, $A = 16.2$
   (b) $f(15) = 15.27$
   (c) 0.93 acres
   (d) $t = 67.7$

29 No

31 (a)

$(b, f(b))$
$(a, f(a))$

(b) $(f(b) - f(a))/(b - a)$

Section 1.4

1 $y = 4/5 - x$

3 $y = 180 - 10x$

5 $y = -0.3 + 5x$

7 $y = -40/3 - 2/3x$

9 $y = 21 - x$

11 Yes; $F(P) = 13 + (-1/8)P$

13 Yes; $C(r) = 0 + 2\pi r$

15 Yes; $f(x) = n^2 + m^2 x$

17 $y = 8 + 3x$

19 $y = (11 + 2x)/3$

21 $y = 0.03 + 0.1x$

23 $f(x) = 3 - 2x$

25 $q = 2500 - 2000p$

27 $y = 459.7 + 1x$

29 $u = (1/12)n$

31 $y = -4 + 4x$

33 $h(t) = 254 - 248t$

35 $y = \frac{16 + 5\sqrt{7}}{2 + \sqrt{7}} - \frac{3}{2 + \sqrt{7}}x$ or
$y = (1 + 2\sqrt{7}) + (2 - \sqrt{7})x$

37 (a) 1000, 990.2, 980.4, 970.6, 960.8
(b) v decreasing at constant rate
(c) Slope: -9.8 meter/sec^2
v-intercept: 1000 meters/sec
t-intercept: 102.04 sec

39 (b) $p = 12 - s$
(c)

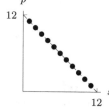

41 (a) $q = 170 - 50p$

43 (a)

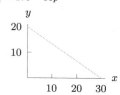

(b) $f(x) = 20 - (2/3)x$
(d)

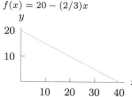

45 (a) $r = 0.005H - 0.03$
(b) $S = 200$

Section 1.5

1 (a) (ii)
(b) (iii)
(c) (i)

3 (a) $y = -2 + 3x$
(b) $y = -1 + 2x$

5 (a) $y = (1/4)x$
(b) $y = 1 - 6x$

7 A, h
B, f
C, g
D, j
E, k

9 Parallel

11 Parallel

13 Neither

15 $y = 24 - 4x$

17 (a) $y = 9 - \frac{2}{3}x$
(b) $y = -4 + \frac{3}{2}x$
(c)

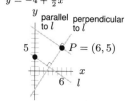

19 (b) $y = 0$

21 (d) Steepness appears to decrease as vertical height of window increases

23 Slope $= -2/5$
$y = -(2/5)x + 3$
(answers may vary)

25 $y = (3/2)x$

27 $\beta = 5$

29 $y = -2x - 3$

31 (a) Company A: $20 + 0.2x$
Company B: $35 + 0.1x$
Company C: 70
(b)

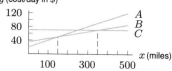

(c) Slope: mileage rate
Vertical intercept: fixed cost/day
(d) A for $x < 150$
B for $150 < x < 350$
C for $x > 350$

33 (a) $y = -7065.9 + 3.65t$
(b) 307.1 million tons

35 (a) $m_1 = m_2$ and $b_1 \neq b_2$
(b) $m_1 = m_2$ and $b_1 = b_2$
(c) $m_1 \neq m_2$
(d) Not possible

Section 1.6

1 (a) $r = 1$
(b) $r = 0.7$
(c) $r = 0$
(d) $r = -0.98$
(e) $r = -0.25$
(f) $r = -0.5$

3 (a) and (b)

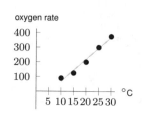

(c) $y = 15x - 80$
(e) Strong positive correlation

5 (a) and (b)

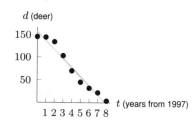

(c) $y = -20x + 157$
(e) Strong negative correlation.

7 (a) A column of zeros

Chapter 1 Review

1 Neither

3 Both

5 Both

7 (a) 9
(b) $\dfrac{n - k}{m - j}$
(c) $6x + h$

9 Yes

11 $f(t) = 2.2 - 1.22t$

13 (a) $y = 7 + 2x$
(b) $y = 8 - 15x$

15 Neither

17 Perpendicular

19 $f(x) = -12.5 - 1.5x$

21 $h(t) = 12{,}000 + 225t$

23 $y = 6 - (3/5)x$

25 Parallel line:
$y = -4x + 9$
Perpendicular line:
$y = 0.25x + 4.75$

27 $\pi(n) = -10{,}000 + 127n$

29 (a) $r_m(0) - r_h(0) = 22$

(b) $r_m(9) - r_h(9) = -2$
(c) $r_m(t) < r_a(t)$ for $t = 5$ to $t = 9$

31 (a) Yes
(b) No

33 hair length
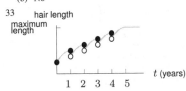

35 $0.945P$

37 (a) 10.71 gallons
(b) 0.25 gallons
(c) 55 mph

39 (a) $x + y$
(b) $0.15x + 0.18y$
(c) $(15x + 18y)/(x + y)$

41 (a) \$11,375
(b) \$125
(c) \$5

43 $C(n) = 10,500 + 5n$

45 (b) (i)
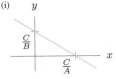

(ii)
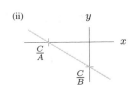

(iii)
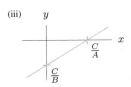

Ch. 1 Understanding

1 False
3 True
5 True
7 True
9 True
11 True
13 True
15 True
17 False
19 False
21 False
23 True

25 True
27 False
29 True
31 False
33 False
35 True
37 False
39 False
41 True
43 False
45 True
47 True
49 False
51 True
53 True

Chapter 1 Tools

1 $x = 5$
3 $z = 11/2$
5 $y = 26$
7 $x = 9$
9 $t = 45/13$
11 $x = 20$
13 $y = -17/16$
15 $r = 10$
17 $s = -0.115$
19 $r = C/(2\pi)$
21 $F = (9/5)C + 32$
23 $a = 2(h - v_0t)/t^2$
25 $x = (c - ab)/(2a)$
27 $v = (3w - 2u - z)/(u + w - z)$
29 $x = -a(b + 1)/(ad - c)$
31 $y' = 4/(y + 2x)$
33 $x = 4, y = -1$
35 $x = 4, y = 3$
37 $x = -55, y = 39$
39 $x = 13.5; y = -12$
41 $x = 3/2, y = 3/2$
43 $x = 3, y = 6$
45 $A = (17, 23); B = (0, 40); C = (-17, 23)$
47 $A = (3, 21)$
49 $B = (7, 4), A = (11, 0)$
51 $A = (2, 5), B = (5, 8)$

Section 2.1

1 $f(-7) = -9/2$
3 $-3/31; 1$
5 $32; \sqrt[3]{9/4}$
7 (a) 1
(b) $-1/2$
9 (a) 6
(b) 2, 3
11 2/3

13 -8
15 (a) $1/(x + 3)$
(b) $(1/x) + (1/3)$
17 (a) $2, 0, -2$
(b) $x = -1$
19 100
21 6π cubic inches
23 $p(-1) = 1; -p(1) = -3$; Not equal
25 (a) $t = 6$
(b) $t = 1, t = 2$
27 (a) (i) $1/(1 - t)$
(ii) $-1/t$
(b) $x = 3/2$
29 (a) 24
(b) 10
(c) -7
(d) 0
(e) 20
31 (a) -1
(b) $x = \pm 3$
(c) 0
(d) -1
(e) $3, -3$
33 (a) 48 feet for both
(b) 4 sec, 64 ft
35 (a) $s(2) = 146$
(b) Solve $v(t) = 65$
(c) At 3 hours
37 (b) No
(c) $f(0) = 0$
$f(-1) = 1$
$f(-2) = -1$
$f(0.5)$: undefined

Section 2.2

1 $f(x) \leq -(1/2)$ or $f(x) \geq (1/2)$
3 $-4 \leq f(x) \leq 5$
5 Domain: all real x
Range: all real $f(x)$
7 Domain: all real x
Range: $f(x) \leq 9$
9 Domain: $x \leq 8$
Range: $f(x) \geq 0$
11 Domain: $x, x \neq -1$
Range: $f(x) < 0$
13 D: $1 \leq x \leq 7$; R: $2 \leq f(x) \leq 18$
15 Domain: $x \geq 3$ or $x \leq -3$
Range: $q(x) \geq 0$
17 Domain: all real numbers
Range: all real numbers
19 D: all real numbers; R: all real numbers ≤ 7
21 D: all real numbers; R: all real numbers ≥ 2
23 D and R: all real numbers
25 $y = \frac{1}{x-3} + \sqrt{x}$
27 D: $0 \leq t \leq 12$
R: $0 \leq f(t) \leq 200$
29 Domain: integers $0 \leq n \leq 200$
Range: $0, 4, 8, \ldots, 800$
31 (a) 162 calories

(c) (i) Calories $=$
      $0.025 \times$ weight

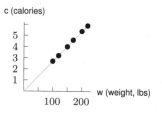

c (calories)

(ii) (0,0) is the number of calories burned
      by a weightless runner
(iii) Domain $0 < w$; range $0 < c$
(iv) 3.6

33 D: all real numbers $\geq b$;
    R: all real numbers ≥ 6

35 (a) $p(0) = 50$
        $p(10) \approx 131$
        $p(50) \approx 911$
   (c) $50 \leq p(t) < 1000$

Section 2.3

1

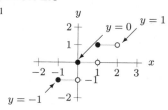

3

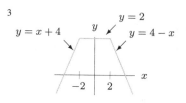

5 Domain: all reals;
   Range: $G(x) < 0$ and $G(x) \geq 3$

7 $y = \begin{cases} 5 - x & \text{for } x < 3 \\ -1 + (1/2)x & \text{for } x \geq 3 \end{cases}$

9 $y = \begin{cases} 4 - \frac{1}{2}x & \text{for } 1 \leq x \leq 3 \\ -9 + 2x & \text{for } 5 \leq x \leq 8 \end{cases}$

11 (a) Yes
   (b) No
   (c) $y = 1, 2, 3, 4$

13 (c) Domain: all $x, x \neq 0$
        Range: -1 and 1
   (d) False, $u(0)$ is undefined

15 (a)

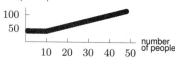

cost (dollars)

(b) Integers from 1 to 50
     Even integers from 40 to 120

17 (a) $n(L) = 2L + 10$
   (b) Domain: $L \geq 5$
        Range: $n(L) =$
        $20, 21, 22, 23, \ldots$

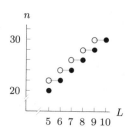

(c) Domain: All real numbers
     Range: All real numbers

19 (a) $1.12
        $1.26
   (b) Domain: All positive integers
        Range: All positive multiples of 0.14

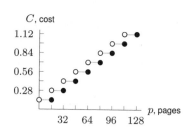

Section 2.4

1 Area in sq cm at time t
3 Acceleration in m/sec^2 at wind speed w
5 10
7 5
9 $4x^2 + 12x + 10$
11 $x^4 + 2x^2 + 2$
13 Year pop is P; years
15 Days for N inches snow; days
17 Interest rate for I interest; %/year
19 $f^{-1}(Q) = (Q - 3)^{1/3}$
21 $f^{-1}(P) = (P + 2)/14.$
23 (a) b
   (b) a
   (c) a
   (d) b
25 $f^{-1}(f(A)) = A$
    $f(f^{-1}(n)) = n$
27 $g^{-1}(7) = 1, g^{-1}(12) = 2, g^{-1}(13) = 3,$
    $g^{-1}(19) = 4, g^{-1}(22) = 5$
29 $f^{-1}(V) = \sqrt[3]{3V/4\pi}$
31 (a) 12, perimeter for $s = 3$

(b) 5; side for $P = 20$
(c) $f^{-1}(P) = P/4$

33 (a) $s = f(A) = +\sqrt{\frac{A}{6}}$
   (b) $V = g(f(A)) = \left(\sqrt{A/6}\right)^3.$

35 (a) 5000 loaves cost $653
   (b) 620 loaves $80
   (c) $790 for 6300 loaves
   (d) 1200 loaves for $150

37 $f(t) = 4\pi(50 - 2.5t)^3/3$

39 (a) Domain: $0 \leq t \leq 5$, range: $365 \leq C(t) \leq 375$
   (b) $C(4)$ is the concentration in 2002
   (c) $C^{-1}(370)$ is number of years after 1998
        when the concentration was 370 ppm

41 (a) $P = f(s) = 4s$
   (b) $f(s + 4) = 4(s + 4) = 4s + 16$
   (c) $f(s) + 4 = 4s + 4$
   (d) Meters

Section 2.5

1 Concave down
3 Concave up
5 Concave up
7 Concave up
9 Rates of change: 4.35, 4.10, 3.80; Concave down
11 Possible graph:

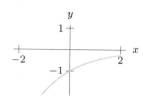

13 Increasing;
    concave up
15 Increasing;
    concave up then down
17 Increasing;
    concave up then down
19 (a) F, IV
   (b) G, I
   (c) E, II
   (d) H, III
21 (a) From A to F
   (b) From O to A
   (c) From D to E
   (d) From F to I

Section 2.6

1 Yes; $f(x) = 2x^2 - 28x + 99$
3 Yes; $g(m) = -2m^2 + \sqrt{3}m + 42$
5 Not quadratic
7 Yes; $T(n) = (\sqrt{3} - 1/2)n^2 + \sqrt{5}$
9 $x \approx -0.541$ and $x \approx 5.541$

11 (a) $x \approx 0.057$, $x \approx 1.943$
   (b) No real solutions

13 $x = 2, 3/2$

15 $x = 2$, $x = -1$

17 $x = -1/3$

19 $x = (-1 \pm \sqrt{6})/5$

21 $x = (23 \pm \sqrt{1821})/(-34) \approx 1.932$ or -0.579

23 No zeros

25 4.046 sec

27 Rates of change: $0, -4, -8$; Concave up

29
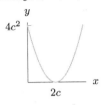

31 (a) 4 meters per second
   (b) 2 seconds
   (c) Concave up

33 (a) Similar shape, end behavior, Different intercepts, vertices
   (b) Differences in intercepts become less significant
   (c) Graphs look more like each other as the scale causes the distances between intercepts to decrease

35 (a) $y = 0.01x^2 + 2x + 1$
   (b) $y = 2.03x + 0.98$
   (c) 0.02
   (d) 23.52
   (e) $-0.791 \le x \le 3.791$

Chapter 2 Review

1 54

3 (a) $h(1) = b + c + 1$
   (b) $h(b+1) = 2b^2 + 3b + c + 1$

5 $l = 0$ and $l = 7$

7 Domain: all real numbers
   Range: $h(x) \ge -16$

9 Domain: $4 \le x \le 20$
   Range: $0 \le r(x) \le 2$

11 (a) $-3(x^2 + x)$
   (b) $2 - x$
   (c) $x^2 + x + \pi$
   (d) $\sqrt{(x^2 + x)}$
   (e) $2/(x + 1)$
   (f) $(x^2 + x)^2$

13 $3x^3 - 4$

15 $f^{-1}(y) = (y + 7)/3$

17 (a) 1.5
   (b) 2.2
   (c) 2.2
   (d) 1.5

19 Time, yrs, at which pop is P mil

21 $(0, 2)$

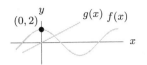

23 Intersect at $x = 2$

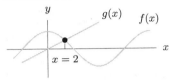

25 $a/2$

27 $a/(a - a^2 + 1)$

29 (a) 5000 loaves cost $653
   (b) 620 loaves $80
   (c) $790 for 6300 loaves
   (d) 1200 loaves for $150

31 (a) $-17.778°C$
   (b) $32°F$
   (c) $37.778°C$
   (d) $212°F$

33 $f^{-1}(T) = gT^2/(4\pi^2)$;
   Length for period T

35 (a) 7000
   (b) 8500; 4 weeks after the beginning of the epidemic
   (c) $w = 1$, $w = 10$
   (d) $1.5 \le w \le 8$

37 (a) 2
   (b) Unknown
   (c) 5

39 (a) $f(1) = 2$
     $g(3) = 4$
   (c) $f(5) = 14$
     $f(-2) = -7$
     $g(5) = 16$
     $g(-2) = 9$
   (d) $f(x) = -1 + 3x$
     $g(x) = (x - 1)^2$

41 (a) 2 lbs cost $4.98
   (b) 0.5 lb costs $1.25
   (c) $0.62 buys 1/4 lb
   (d) $12.45 buys 5 lb

43 (a)   (i) 6
      (ii) 5
      (iii) Not defined
   (b)   (i) $50 \le s \le 75$
      (ii) $76 \le s \le 125$

47 (a) $A = 2\pi r^2 + 710/r$
   (b) A (cm²)

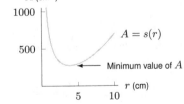

   (c) Domain: $r > 0$
   Approximate range: $A > 277.5$ cm²
   (d) ≈ 277.5 cm²
     $r \approx 3.83$ cm
     $h \approx 7.7$ cm

Ch. 2 Understanding

1 False

3 False

5 False

7 False

9 True

11 True

13 False

15 False

17 True

19 True

21 True

23 False

25 True

27 True

29 True

31 True

33 False

35 True

37 True

39 True

41 True

43 True

45 False

47 False

49 False

51 False

Chapter 2 Tools

1 $3x + 6$

3 $6x - 14$

5 $12x + 12y$

7 $2x^2 + 5x$

9 $-50r^2 - 60r^2s$

11 $5xz - 10z - 3x + 6$

13 $x^2 + 4x - 12$

15 $3x^2 - 2x - 16$

17 $96wy + 84y - 40w - 35$

19 $x - 7$

21 $4x^2 + 11x - 20$

23 $Pp^2 - 6Ppq + 9Pq^2$

25 $4x^2 - 24x + 43$

27 $2^u + u2^{2u}$

29 $3(y + 5)$

31 $2(2t - 3)$

33 $u(u - 2)$

35 $3u^2(u^5 + 4)$

37 $7rs(2r^3s - 3t)$

39 Cannot be factored

41 Cannot be factored

43 $(x-3)(x+1)$

45 $(x+3)(x-1)$

47 $(3x-4)(x+1)$

49 $(x+7)(x-4)$

51 $x(x+3)(x-1)$

53 $(x+2y)(x+3z)$

55 $(ax-b)(ax+b)$

57 $(B-6)(B-4)$

59 Cannot be factored.

61 $(t-1)(t+7)$

63 $(a-2)(a^2+3)$

65 $(d+5)(d-5)(c+3)(c-3)$

67 $(r+2)(r-s)$

69 $xe^{-3x}(x+2)$

71 $(s+2t+2p)(s+2t-2p)$

73 $(x-3+2z)(x-3-2z)$

75 $(r-2)(\pi r+3)$

77 $x=-6$ or $x=-1$

79 $w=(-5/2)$ or $w=2$

81 $x=(7/16)$

83 $y=170$

85 $x=(37/2)$

87 $t=3\pm2\sqrt{3}$

89 $g=3,-2,$ or 2

91 $p=3, p=-3, p=-1/2$

93 $t=0, t=\pm8$

95 $x=4, x=-3/4$

97 $n=5,-2,$ or 2

99 $y=-2\pm\sqrt{6}$

101 $x=\pm1$

103 $q=\pm\sqrt{2}$

105 $x=-1/8$

107 $v=700\pi$

109 $l=gT^2/4\pi^2$

111 $x=3, x=-4$

113 $x=3$ and $y=-3$, or $x=-1$ and $y=-3$

115 $x=(3\pm\sqrt{63})/2,$
     $y=(-3\pm\sqrt{63})/2$

117 $x=2.081, y=8.013$
     $x=4.504, y=90.348$

119 $(4,3), (-3,-4)$

Section 3.1

1 1.03 (per year)

3 0.99 (per day)

5 550

7 495

9 411.8

11 $a=1750; b=1.593; r=59.3\%$

13 $a=79.2; b=1.002; r=0.2\%$

15 (a) III
   (b) I
   (c) II

(d) VI

(e) V

(f) IV

17 20%; 2%.

19 $P=2200(0.968)^t$

21

Yr	2006	2007	2008	2009	2010
$	73	80.30	88.33	97.16	106.88

23 $Q=726(0.94374)^t$

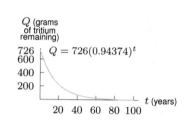

25 \$109,272.70

27 (a) $P=7.50(1.035)^t$
   (b) $\approx\$14.92$

29 (a) $C=100(0.84)^t$
   (b) 41.821 mg

31 $f(n)=P_0(0.8)^n$

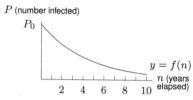

33 $L=420(0.15)^n$

35 (a) \$573.60 per month
   (b) \$440.40 per month
   (c) \$645.00 per month
   (d) \$12,852
   (e) \$55,296

37 $b(b^4-1)$

39 (a) $R=Nr$
   (b) $A=R/P=Nr/P$
   (c) $N_{new}=1.02N$
        $r_{new}=1.03r$
   (d) $R_{new}=1.0506R$; 5.06%
   (e) $A_{new}=(0.9728)A$; average revenue falls
        by 2.7%

41 b_0

43 t_0 decreases

Section 3.2

1 B, C, D exponential

3 (a) $P=100+10t$.
  (b) $P=100(1.10)^t$.

(c)

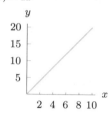

5 $f(x)=16{,}384(1/4)^x$

7 (a) $g(x)$ is linear
  (b) $g(x)=2x$

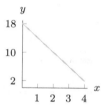

9 (a) $i(x)$ is linear
  (b) $i(x)=18-4x$

11 $h(x)=3(5)^x$

13 $g(x)=2(4)^x$

15 $g(x)=14.20(0.6024)^x$

17 (a) $f(x)=\frac{31}{8}x+\frac{49}{4}$
   (b) $f(x)=5(2)^x$

19 $y=(1/2)^x$

21 $y=\frac{1}{5}(3)^x$

23 $y=2(0.8)^x$

25 $p=20(1.0718)^x; q=160(0.8706)^x$

27 Exponential: $q(x)=82.6446\cdot1.03228^x$

29 Exponential; $g(t)=1024\cdot0.5^t$

31 (a) $P(t)=2.58+0.09t$,
        increases by 90,000 people per year
   (b) $P(t)=2.68(1.026)^t$,
        increases by 2.6% per year

33 (a) $P=1154.160(1.20112)^t$
   (b) \$1154.16
   (c) 20.112%

35 (a) $S=91(1.52)^t$
   (b) Increasing by 52%/yr
   (c) No

37 $N=10(1.13)^t$; 13%/yr

39 (a) $V=(61{,}055)(0.916)^t$
   (b) $V=61{,}055-4012.19t$
   (c) Linear

41 (a) Penalty A: \$291 million
        Penalty B: \$5.369 million
   (b) $A(t)=(1+10t)10^6$ dollars
        $B(t)=(0.01)2^t$ dollars
   (c) $t\approx35.032$ days

Section 3.3

1 (b)

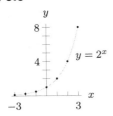

3 $h(x)$ top; $g(x)$ middle; $f(x)$ bottom

5 D

7 D

9 $x = 7.158$

11 $w = 1.246$

13 Zero

15 (a) $P = 651(0.9925)^t$
   (b) 603,790
   (c) $t = 22.39$

17 (a) $y = (10,000) \cdot (0.9)^t$
   (b) ≈ 5905 cases
   (c) ≈ 21.854 years

19 (a) All
   (b) b
   (c) b, a, c, p
   (d) $a = c$
   (e) d and q

21 y_0 decreases , $y_0 > 0$

23 t_0 decreases

27

29

31 (a) 5
   (b) -3

33 (a) 0
   (b) 0
   (c) 0.7

35 $y = 8$

39 (a)

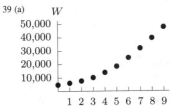

   (b) $W = 4710(1.306)^t$; answers may vary
   (c) 30.6%/yr

41 Domain: all t
   Range: $Q > 0$

43 (a)

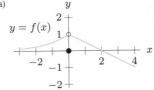

   (b) $f(x) < 1$
   (c) $(0,0)$ $(2,0)$
   (d) As $x \to +\infty$, $f(x) \to -\infty$
       As $x \to -\infty$, $f(x) \to 0$
   (e) Increasing for $x < 0$, decreasing for $x > 0$

Section 3.4

1 Bottom to top:
   $y = e^x, y = 2e^x, y = 3e^x$

3 (a)=(II); (b)=(III); (c)=(IV); (d)=(I)

5 $f(x) = e^{-x}$
   $g(x) = e^x$
   $h(x) = -e^x$

7 (a)=(I); (b)=(II); (c)=(III); (d)=(IV)

9 46.210 years

11 0

13 2

15 $a > 0, k > 0$

17 (a) $4157.86
   (b) $4234.00

19 (a) $P(t) = 25,000e^{0.075t}$
   (b) 7.788%

21 (a) $A = 50e^{-0.14t}$
   (b) 12.330 mg
   (c) 2016

23 (a) $P = 77.2e^{0.016t}$
   (b) 84.979 million tons
   (c) Middle of 2013

25 (a) Increasing, 2.7169239,
       2.7181459, 2.7182682, 2.7182805
   (b) Approximately 10^7
   (c) $(1 + 1/10^{16})^{10^{16}}$ appears to be 1

27 (a)

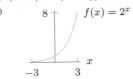

   (b) 0.69
   (c) 1.10
   (d) $e \approx 2.72$

Section 3.5

1 (a) $505
   (b) $505.02
   (c) $505.03
   (d) $505.03

3 (a) $525
   (b) $525.62
   (c) $525.64

   (d) $525.64

5 A is continuous, B is annual
   Initial deposit is $500

7 (a) $7401.22
   (b) $7459.12

9 5.127%

11 (a) Nom: 1% Eff: 1%
   (b) Nom: 1% Eff: 1.004%
   (c) Nom: 1% Eff: 1.005%
   (d) Nom: 1% Eff: 1.005%

13 (a) Nom: 3% Eff: 3%
   (b) Nom: 3% Eff: 3.034%
   (c) Nom: 3% Eff: 3.045%
   (d) Nom: 3% Eff: 3.045%

15 (a)   (i) 6.14%

        (ii) 6.17%

        (iii) 6.18%

        (iv) 6.18%

   (b) 1.0618
       The highest possible APR is 6.18%.

17 (i) (b)
   (ii) (a)
   (iii) (c)
   (iv) (b), (c) and (d)
   (v) (a) and (e)

19 From best to worst: B, C, A

21 (a) The effective annual yield is 7.763%
   (b) The nominal annual rate is 7.5%

23 $27,399.14

25 5.387%

Chapter 3 Review

1 Yes; $g(w) = 2(1/2)^w$

3 Yes; $f(x) = (1/4)9^x$

5 Yes; $q(r) = -4(1/3)^r$

7 Yes; $Q(t) = 2^t$

9 Not exponential

11 (a) Starts at 200, grows at 2.8%/yr
   (b) Starts at 50, shrinks at continuous rate of 17%/yr
   (c) Starts at 1000, shrinks by 11%/yr
   (d) Starts at 600, grows at continuous rate of 20%/yr
   (e) Starts at 2000, shrinks by 300 animals/yr
   (f) Starts at 600, grows by 50 animals/yr

13 $y = 10(1.260)^x$

15 $y = (1/2)(1/3)^x$

17 $y = 4(0.1)^x$ or $y = 4(10)^{-x}$

19 (a) (ii)
   (b) (i)
   (c) (iv)
   (d) (ii)
   (e) (iii)
   (f) (i)

21

23

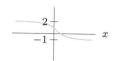

25

27 0

29 5.1

31 ∞

33 $Q = 70.711(0.966)^t$

35 $f(x) = 2(1/3)^x$

37 $Q = 0.7746 \cdot (0.3873)^t$

39 $Q = 1149.4641(0.935)^t$

41 $V = 2500e^{0.042t}$

43 Linear, $Q(t) = 7 + 0.17t$

45 Neither

47 (a) $N = 178.8 + 0.84t$
   (b) $N = 178.8(1.0046)^t$

49 (a) Initial balance = \$1100
       Effective yield = 5%
   (b) Initial balance = \$1500
       Effective yield $\approx$ 5.13%

51 $a > c$

53 $x_1 < x_3 < x_2$

55 (a) 10.409%
   (b) 10.503%
   (c) 42.576%
   (d) 48.770%

57 (a) Exponential
   (b) $P(t) = 20,000(1.0414)^t$

59 (a) $a = 12, \quad b = 0.841$
   (b) $C = 11.914(0.840)^t$

61 (a) $15.269(1.122)^t$
   (b) 108,066
   (c) Not useful

63 (a) $P(t) = 0.755 (1.194)^t$

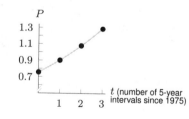

   (b) 20 years; 2135

65 (a) $f(x) = p_0(2,087,372,982)^x$
   (b) 8.55
   (c) BAC of 0.051

Ch. 3 Understanding

1 True

3 True

5 False

7 True

9 True

11 False

13 False

15 True

17 True

19 False

21 True

23 False

25 True

27 False

29 True

31 False

Chapter 3 Tools

1 64

3 121

5 1

7 5

9 1,000

11 1

13 4

15 16

17 49

19 -1

21 -18

23 2100

25 4

27 8

29 1024

31 -5

33 -6

35 4

37 1/9

39 1/25

41 1/125

43 0.5

45 y^4

47 $x^{5/2}y^2$

49 $7w^{9/2}$

51 $|r|$

53 r^2

55 $8s^{7/2}$

57 $4\sqrt{3}u^5v^6y^{5/2}$

59 $6s^{3/2}t^4v^4$

61 3^{x+1}

63 $70w^{5/6}$

65 e^x

67 e^{kt+4}

69 $9x^5$

71 e^{2y}/y^4

73 $64A$

75 $4u^4v^2w^4$

77 $25(2b+1)^{20}$

79 -8

81 Not a real number

83 $1/512$

85 Not a real number

87 $x = 0.585$

89 $x = 1.842$

91 $x = \pm 0.1$

93 $(2.5, 31.25)$

95 False

97 False

99 True

101 False

103 True

105 $x = r + s$

107 $x = 5/a$

109 $x = 3/a$

111 $x = b/a$

Section 4.1

1 $19 = 10^{1.279}$

3 $26 = e^{3.258}$

5 $P = 10^t$

7 $8 = \log 100,000,000$

9 $v = \log \alpha$

11 $(\log 11)/(\log 2) = 3.459$

13 $(\ln 100)/(0.12) = 38.376$

15 $(\log(48/17))/(\log(2.3)) = 1.246$

17 $2\log(0.00012)/(-3) = 2.614$

19 (a) 0
   (b) -1
   (c) 0
   (d) 1/2
   (e) 5
   (f) 2
   (g) $-1/2$
   (h) 100
   (i) 1
   (j) 0.01

21 3.47712

23 (a) 0
   (b) $\sqrt{2} - 1$
   (c) $\frac{31}{30}$
   (d) 27
   (e) $\frac{1}{4}$
   (f) 1

25 (a) $2x$
   (b) $3x + 2$
   (c) $-5x$
   (d) $\frac{1}{2}x$

27 (a) False
   (b) True
   (c) False
   (d) False

29 (a) 10^p

(b) 10^{3q}
(c) $p + 3q$
(d) $p/2$

31 (a) $25; 7.5\%$
(b) $t \approx 19$
(c) $t = (\log 4)/(\log 1.075) = 19.169$

33 $S(x) = 42.0207(0.8953)^x$

35 $\log(7/4)/\log(1.171/1.088)$

37 $\log(17/3)/\log 2$

39 $(\ln 7 - 5)/(1 - \ln 2)$

41 $(\log c - \log a)/\log b$

43 $(\ln Q - \ln P)/k$

45 $\frac{1}{4}(\ln(30/58) - 1)$

47 $(\ln 50 - \ln 44)/(0.15 - \ln 1.2)$

49 $-2, 1/3, -1/3$

51 (a) $(\ln(0.5))/2 = -0.347$
(b) $(\ln(b/3))/3$

53 $0 < A < 1 < A^2 B^2 < 100 < B^2$

Section 4.2

1 $a = 230, r = 18.2\%, k = 16.72\%$

3 $a = 0.81, r = 100\%$, and $k = 69.31\%$

5 $a = 12.1, r = -22.38\%, k = -25.32\%$

7 $a = 5.4366, b = 0.4724, r = -52.76\%, k = -3/4$

9 $Q = 4e^{1.946t}$

11 $Q = 4e^{2.703t}$

13 $Q = 4 \cdot 1096.633^t$

15 $Q = (14/5)1.030^t$

17 $y = 25(1.0544)^t$,
5.44%/yr, 5.3%/yr

19 $y = 6000e^{-0.1625t}$,
-15%/yr, -16.25%/yr

21 $t \approx 3.466$

23 About 26 years

25 About 12.3 years

27 6.301 minutes

29 $Q = 28.9101(1.0074)^t$

31 (a) 5.726%
(b) 5.568%

33 3.053%/yr

35
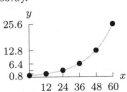

37 $10^{(\log 5)/(4\log 3)}$

39 No solution

41 2

43 (a) 1.3%
(b) 5.4 million
(c) 84.509 years
(d) 1192.455 years ago; No

45 (a) $P = 3(3.218)^t$

(b) 0.940 hours

47 (a) 13.9% per year
(b) 7.9 years

49 (a) $o(t) = 245 \cdot 1.03^t$
(b) $h(t) = 63 \cdot 2^{t/10} \approx 63 \cdot (1.072)^t$
(c) 34.162 years

51 5092.013 years ago

53 2.291 hours

55 Yes, after 108.466 years

57 (a) $190°$F; $100°$F; $77.5°$F
(b) 1.292 hours; 2.292 hours

59 t_0 decreases

61 s must increase

Section 4.3

1 $y = 0, y = 0, x = 0$

3 $A: y = 10^x$, $B: y = e^x$
$C: y = \ln x$, $D: y = \log x$

5 (a) 0
(b) $-\infty$

7

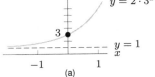
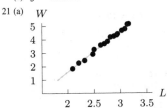

9
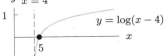

11 Vertical asymptote at 3,
Domain $(3, \infty)$

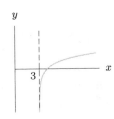

13 10^{-13} moles/l

15 5.012×10^{-9} moles/l

17 1 mole/l

19 (a) is (III)
(b) is (IV)
(c) is (I)
(d) is (I) or (II)

23 $y = b^x, 0 < b < 1$

25 $y = \ln x$

27 $y = -b^x, b > 1$

29 $x > 0$

31 $x > 3$

33 (a) $1.01 \cdot 10^{-5}$ moles/liter
(b) 4.996

35 37

37 (a) $M_2 - M_1 = \log(W_2/W_1)$
(b) 40

Section 4.4

1 Log

3 Linear

7 (a) $y = -3582.145 + 236.314x$; $r \approx 0.7946$
(b) $y = 4.797(1.221)^x$; $r \approx 0.9998$
(c) Exponential is better fit

9 $10^{-3.65}$ million years ago

17 Yes

19 (a) $y = 14.227 - 0.233x$
(b) $\ln y = 2.682 - 0.0253x$
(c) $y = 14.614e^{-.0253x}$

21 (a)
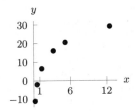

(b) $W = 3.06L - 4.54$
(c) $w = 0.011\ell^{3.06}$

23 (a) Log function

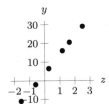

(c) Linear; $y = 4 + 9.9z$
(d) $y = 4 + 9.9\ln x$
(e) $x = 0.67e^{0.1y}$;
Exponential function of y

Chapter 4 Review

1 $Q = 12e^{-0.105t}$

3 $Q = 14e^{-0.208t}$

5 $Q = 7(0.0000454)^t$

7 $(\ln 50)/(\ln 3) = 3.561$

9 $(\ln 0.3)/(-0.2) = 6.020$

11 $a = 0.05, b = 1.13, r = 0.13, k = \ln 1.13$

13 (a) $3\%, 2.96\%$
   (b) $3.05\%, 3\%$
   (c) Decay: $6\%, 6.19\%$
   (d) Decay: $4.97\%, 5.1\%$
   (e) $3.93\%, 3.85\%$
   (f) Decay: $2.73\%, 2.77\%$

15 $\ln(1328/400)/\ln 1.112$

17 $\ln(28/55)/(-0.223)$

19 $x = \ln(55/5)/\ln 1.1$

21 $x = 0.25$

23 $(1/0.049) \cdot \ln(25/13) \approx 13.345$

25 $x = 1000$

27 $2(x + 1)$

29 $\ln(AB)$

31 $g(t) = 97.1187(0.9762)^t$

33 $p(t) = 5000(1.0234)^t$

35 $x < -2$ and $x > 3$

37 In 1969

39 (a) $W(t) = 50(1.029)^t$, $C(t) = 45(1.032)^t$
   (b) 36.191 years
   (c) 274.287 years

41 (a) 1412 bacteria
   (b) 10.011 hours
   (c) 1.005 hours

43 (a) 13.333%
   (b) 2.534%
   (c) 2.503%

45 (a) $Q(t) = 2e^{-0.04t}$
   (b) 3.921%
   (c) After 51.986 hours
   (d) 54.931 hrs after second injection

47 (a) $\ln 8 - 3 \approx -0.9206$
   (b) $\log 1.25/ \log 1.12 \approx 1.9690$
   (c) $-\dfrac{\ln 4}{0.13} \approx -10.6638$
   (d) 105
   (e) $\frac{1}{3}e^{3/2} \approx 1.4939$
   (f) $e^{1/2}/(e^{1/2} - 1) \approx 2.5415$
   (g) -1.599 or 2.534
   (h) 2.478 or 3
   (i) 0.653

49 Predicted (yrs):
   70, 35, 14, 10, 7
   Actual (yrs):
   69.661, 35.003, 14.207, 10.245, 7.273

51 100 months

53 About 12:53 pm

55 (a) Use $e < 3 < 4$
   (b) Use $e < 4 < e^2$

Ch. 4 Understanding

1 True

3 False

5 True

7 False

9 True

11 True

13 True

15 True

17 True

19 False

21 False

23 False

25 True

27 False

29 False

Chapter 4 Tools

1 0

3 -4

5 3

7 0

9 2

11 $\log 100{,}000 = 5$

13 $\log 3 = 0.477$

15 $\ln 0.135 = -2$

17 $10^{-2} = 0.01$

19 $e^{-1} = x$

21 $\log 2 + \log x$

23 Cannot be rewritten

25 $\log(x^2 + 1) - 3 \log x$

27 Cannot be rewritten

29 $\log(x + y) + \log(x - y)$

31 $(2 \ln x)/ \ln(x + 2)$

33 $\ln x^5$

35 $\log(\sqrt{x}y^4)$

37 $\log(2/5)$

39 $\ln(((x^2)y + 4xy)/2z)$

41 $(5x)^{-1}$

43 $2\sqrt{x}$

45 $t^2/2$

47 1

49 $(1/2) \ln(x^2 + 16)$

51 $1/2$

53 $x = (\log 9)/(\log 4) \approx 1.585$

55 $x = (\log 3)/(\log 5) \approx 0.683$

57 $x = \ln 8 \approx 2.079$

59 $x = -(\ln 9)/5 \approx -0.439$

61 $x = (\log 3)/(5 \log 12 - 2 \log 15) \approx 0.157$

63 $x = 93/2$

65 $x = (10^{3/2} - 17)/9 \approx 1.625$

67 $x = (e^5 - 4)/3 \approx 48.138$

Section 5.1

1 (a) $-3, 0, 2, 1, -1$
   One unit right
   (b) $-3, 0, 2, 1, -1$
   One unit left

(c) $0, 3, 5, 4, 2$
   Up three units
(d) $0, 3, 5, 4, 2$
   One right and three up

3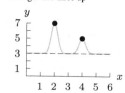

5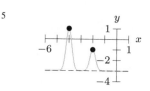

9 (a) $(3, 1)$
   (b) $(-2, -4)$
   (c) $(6, -6)$

11 $-50 \le R(s) - 150 \le 50$

13 $(1/2)n^2 + n + 1/2$

15 $(1/2)n^2 - 3.7n + 6.845$

17 $(1/2)n^2 + 2\sqrt{2}n + 4$

19 $(1/2)n^2 - 17n - 29/2$

21 3^{w-3}

23 $3^{w+\sqrt{5}}$

25 $3^{w-1.5} - 0.9$

27 (a) $g(x) + 3$
   (b) $g(x - 2)$

29 (a) Population 100 people larger than original
   (b) Population same as 100 years earlier

31 $x = 0$ and $x = 3$

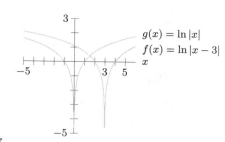

$g(x) = \ln |x|$
$f(x) = \ln |x - 3|$

33 Shift up 3

35 Shift left 4

37 Shift left b, down a

39 (a) $T(d) = S(d) + 1$
   (b) $P(d) = S(d - 1)$

41 (a) $H(t + 15) = 68 + 93(0.91)^{t+15}$
   $H(t) + 15 = 83 + 93(0.91)^t$

(b)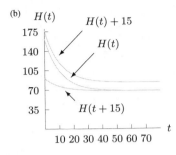

(d) $H(t+15)$ and $H(t)$ approach $68°$F

43 $H(t) = 280(0.97)^t + 70$

45 $-\ln 5$

Section 5.2

1 (a) $(-2,-3)$
   (b) $(2,3)$

3 -7

5 $y = -e^x$

9 Reflected across x-axis;
   $-g(x) = -(1/3)^x$

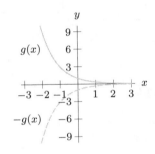

11 $-m(n) = -(n)^2 + 4n - 5$

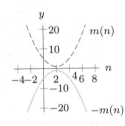

13 $-m(-n) + 3 = -n^2 - 4n - 2$

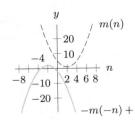

15 $-k(w) = -3^w$

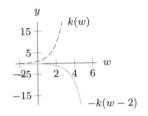

17 $-k(w-2) = -3^{w-2}$

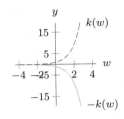

19 $-k(-w) - 1 = -3^{-w} - 1$

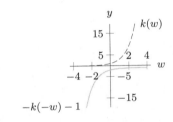

21 Odd

23 Neither

25 (a) $y = 2^{-x} - 3$

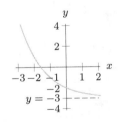

(b) $y = 2^{-x} - 3$

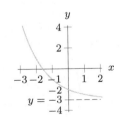

(c) Yes

27 Reflections across x-axis

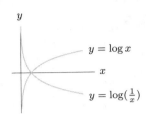

29 (i) c
   (ii) d
   (iii) e
   (iv) f
   (v) a
   (vi) b

31 (a)

(b)

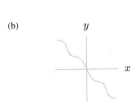

(c)

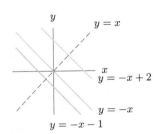

33 $y = x$. $y = -x + b$, where b is an arbitrary constant

37 If $f(x)$ is odd, then $f(0) = 0$

41 Yes, $f(x) = 0$

Section 5.3

1 $y = 10f(x - 2)$

3 $-0.25 \le 0.25C(x) \le 0.25$

5
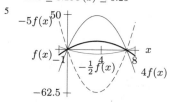

7
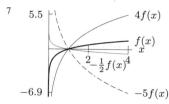

9 (d) All three

11
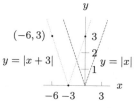

13
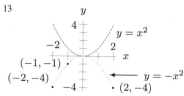

15
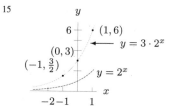

17 (i) i
   (ii) c
   (iii) b
   (iv) g
   (v) d

19 35 mph

21
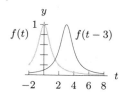

23
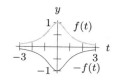

25 (a) (iii)
   (b) (i)
   (c) (ii)

29
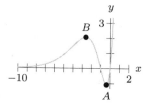

31
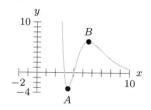

33
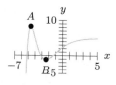

35 (a) $y = -2f(x)$
   (b) $y = f(x) + 2$
   (c) $y = 3f(x - 2)$

Section 5.4

1 $(1, 3)$

3 Same function values for
   $x = -6, -4, -2, 0, 2, 4, 6$

5
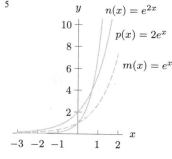

7
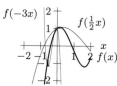

9
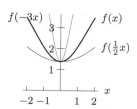

11 $2/3$

13 $(a/d, b + c)$

15

17 $r(t)$: half the level
    $s(t)$: half the rate

19 (a) III
   (b) II
   (c) I
   (d) IV

21 $y = -f(-\frac{1}{2}x)$

23
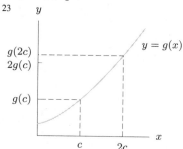

25

d	20	45	70	95
$h(d)$	5.5	5.2	5.1	5.1
d	120	145	170	195
$h(d)$	5.3	5.5	5.75	6

27

d	25	50	75	100
$n(d)$	8.25	7.8	7.65	7.65
d	125	150	175	200
$n(d)$	7.95	8.25	8.63	9

29

d	25	50	75	100
$q(d)$	10.25	9.8	9.65	9.65
d	125	150	175	200
$q(d)$	9.95	10.25	10.63	11

Section 5.5

1. $(1, 2)$; $x = 1$; opens upward

3. (a) $a = 1, b = 0, c = 3$
   Axis of symmetry: y-axis
   Vertex: $(0, 3)$
   No zeros
   y-intercept: $y = 3$

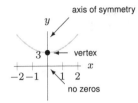

   (b) $a = -2, b = 4, c = 16$
   Axis of symmetry: $x = 1$
   Vertex: $(1, 18)$
   Zeros: $x = -2, 4$
   y-intercept: $y = 16$

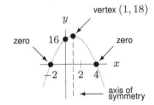

5. Vertex is $(-5, 106)$
   Axis of symmetry is $x = -5$

7. $k = 4$

9. $y = -(3/16)(x - 4)^2 + 7$

11. $y = (1/3)x^2 - (2/3)x - 1$

13. $y = -(5/12)x^2 - (5/3)x + 5$

15. $f(x) = (x + 4)^2 - 13$;
    Vertex: $(-4, -13)$; axis: $x = -4$

17. $y = -3(x - 2)^2 + 5$

19. $y = (1/4)(x - 4)^2 + 2$

21. $y = (-2/49)(x - 4)^2 + 2$

23. $y = (7/4)(x + 2)^2$

25. Shift $y = x^2$ right by 5 units to get $y = (x - 5)^2 = x^2 - 10x + 25$

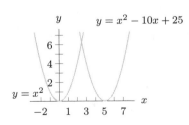

27. (a)

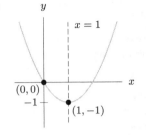

   (b) $y = (x - 1)^2 - 1$ or $y = x^2 - 2x$
   (c) Range: $y \geq -1$
   (d) The other zero is $(2, 0)$

29. Yes. $f(x) = -(x - 1)^2 + 4$

31. (a)

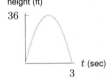

   (b) $t = 0, 3$; being thrown; hitting the ground
   (c) 1.5 seconds
   (d) 36 feet

33. 12.5 cm by 12.5 cm; $k/4$ by $k/4$

35. (b) Maximum height: $t = T/2$

Chapter 5 Review

1. (a) 4
   (b) 1
   (c) 5
   (d) -2

3. (a) $(6, 5)$
   (b) $(2, 1)$
   (c) $(1/2, 5)$
   (d) $(2, 20)$

5. Odd

7. Neither

9. Even

11. (a) $f(2x) = 1 - 2x$
    (b) $f(x + 1) = -x$
    (c) $f(1 - x) = x$
    (d) $f(x^2) = 1 - x^2$
    (e) $f(1/x) = (x - 1)/x$
    (f) $f(\sqrt{x}) = 1 - \sqrt{x}$

13. $y = (x + 1)(x - 3)$

15. $y = -(x - 2)^2$

17.

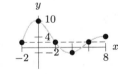

19. $y = f(t + 4) - 8$

21. (b) Decreasing

23. (a) VI
    (b) V
    (c) III
    (d) IV
    (e) I
    (f) II

25. (a) $-16t^2 + 23$
    $-16t^2 + 48t + 2$
    (b)

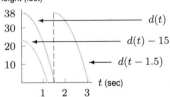

   (d) 1.541 secs
       1.199 secs
   (e) 3.041 secs

27. $y = -(x + 1)^3 + 1$

29. $y = (1/2)h(x + 6) + 1$

31. $p \approx 15, q \approx 7190$

35.

37. $y = 3h(x)$

39. $y = -h(2 - 2x)$

41. 1/2 second

Ch. 5 Understanding

1. True

3. True

5. True

7. False

9. True

11. False

13. False

15. True

17. True

19. False

21. False

23. True

25. True

27. False

29. True

Chapter 5 Tools

1. $(x + 4)^2 - 16$

3. $(w + (7/2))^2 - (7/2)^2$

5. $(s + 3)^2 - 17$

7. $(a - 1)^2 - 5$

9 $(c + 3/2)^2 - 37/4$

11 $4(s + 1/8)^2 + 31/16$

13 $(x - 1)^2 - 4$

15 $-(x - 3)^2 + 7$

17 $(-3, -6)$

19 $(-4, 18)$

21 $(1/2, -23/4)$

23 $(1, -2)$

25 $(7/4, -25/8)$

27 $r = 4, 2$

29 $p = 1 \pm \sqrt{7}$

31 $d = 2, -1$

33 $s = -5/2 \pm \sqrt{27}/2$

35 $r = 3/14 \pm \sqrt{177}/14$

37 $n = 6, -2$

39 $k = -1/3, -3/2$

41 $z = -2 \pm \sqrt{10}$

43 $r = 4, -2$

45 $n = -5, 1$

47 $z = -2, \pm\sqrt{3}$

49 $u = (3 \pm \sqrt{5})/5$

51 $y = 1 \pm \sqrt{7}$

53 $w = 3, 2, -2$

55 $m = (-5 \pm \sqrt{3})/7$

Section 6.1

1 Yes

3 No

5 No

7 Yes

9 4

11 3

13
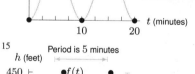

15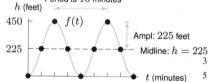

17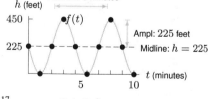

19 3 (or 9) o'clock; rising; 4 minutes; 30 meters; 5 meters; 11 minutes

21 3 (or 9) o'clock; upward; 5 minutes; 40 meters; 0 meters; 11.25 minutes

23 Midline: $y = 10$;
Period: 1;
Amplitude: 4;
Minimum: 6 cm;
Maximum: 14 cm

25 Graph is same except starts at a peak

27 (b) Period: 1/60 seconds;
Amplitude: 155.6 volts;
Midline: $V = 0$

29 (a) Periodic
(b) Not periodic
(c) Not periodic
(d) Not periodic
(e) Periodic
(f) Not periodic
(g) Periodic

31 Midline: $h = 2$;
Amplitude: 1;
Period: 1

Section 6.2

1 (a) $(-0.174, 0.985)$
(b) $(-0.940, -0.342)$
(c) $(-0.940, 0.342)$
(d) $(0.707, -0.707)$
(e) $(0.174, -0.985)$
(f) $(1, 0)$

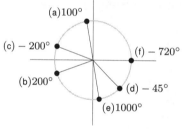

3 $-720°$

5 $S = (-0.707, -0.707)$, $T = (0, -1)$, $U = (0.866, -0.5)$

7 $A = (0.866, 0.5)$, $B = (-0.707, 0.707)$, $C = (0.866, -0.5)$

9 $S = (-3.536, -3.536)$
$T = (0, -5)$
$U = (4.330, -2.5)$

11 $(0, 3.8)$

13 $(-3.8, 0)$

15 $(0, 3.8)$

17 $(3.687, -0.919)$

19 $(3.8\sqrt{2}/2, 3.8\sqrt{2}/2)$ or $(2.687, 2.687)$

21 $(-3.8\sqrt{2}/2, -3.8\sqrt{2}/2)$ or $(-2.687, -2.687)$

23 $(3.742, -0.660)$

27 (a) $307°$
(b) $127°$

29 (a)

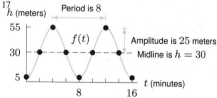

(b)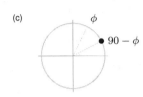

180 − φ   φ

(c)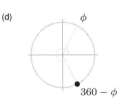

φ

90 − φ

(d)

φ

360 − φ

33 4/3 minutes

35 (a) 90°
(b) 90°
(c) 180°
(d) 180°
(e) A

Section 6.3

1 $\pi/3$

3 1.7453 radians

5 $5\pi/6$

7 $-3\pi/2$

9 630°

11 $16{,}200/\pi \approx 5156.620°$

13 $8100/\pi \approx 2578.310°$

15 (a) I
(b) II
(c) II
(d) III
(e) IV
(f) IV
(g) I
(h) II
(i) II
(j) III

17 -4π

19 8.54π

21 $6.2\pi/4 \approx 4.869$

23 $6.2a\pi/180$

25 5π feet

27 $\pi/9$ radians or 20°

29 $r = \sqrt{65}$; $\theta = 0.5191$ rad $= 29.7449°$;
$s = 4.185$; $P = (7, 4)$

31 $r = 12$; $\theta = 1.3$ rad $= 74.485°$;
$s = 15.6$; $P = (3.2100, 11.5627)$

33 $\theta = 0.4$ rad $= 22.918°$; $P = (0.9211r, 0.3894r)$

35 (a) Negative
(b) Negative
(c) Positive
(d) Positive

37 $\sin\theta = 0.6$;
$\cos\theta = -0.8$

39 $(-0.99, 0.14)$

41 $\pi/6$ feet

43 3998.310 miles

45 $t \approx 0.739$

Section 6.4

1 Mid: $y = 0$; Amp: 1

3 Mid: $y = -4$; Amp: 7

5 Mid: $y = -2$; Amp: 3

7 Mid: at 185 cm; Amp: 15cm

9 (a) (i) $0 < t < \pi$ and
$2\pi < t < 3\pi$
(ii) $-\frac{\pi}{2} < t < \frac{\pi}{2}$ and
$\frac{3\pi}{2} < t < \frac{5\pi}{2}$
(iii) $-\pi < t < 0$ and
$\pi < t < 2\pi$
(b) $t = 0, 2\pi$

11 They are equal

13 $\sqrt{3}/2$

15 $\sqrt{3}/2$

17 $g(x) = \cos x$, $a = \pi/2$, $b = 1$

19 $f(x) = \sin(x + \frac{\pi}{2})$
$g(x) = \sin(x - \frac{\pi}{2})$

23 (a) $1/\sqrt{2}$
(b) $1/2$
(c) $-\sqrt{3}/2$
(d) $-1/2$
(e) $1/\sqrt{2}$

25 $(-5\sqrt{3}, -5)$

27 (a) (i) p
(ii) s
(iii) q
(iv) r
(b)

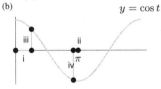

$y = \cos t$

iii   ii
i   π
iv

29 (a) $m = (\cos b - \cos a)/(b - a)$
(b) $-6(1 + \sqrt{2})/(13\pi)$

Section 6.5

1 Mid: $y = 0$; Amp: 6; Per: 2π

3 Mid: $y = 1$; Amp: $1/2$; Per: $\pi/4$

5 Hor: $-4/3$; Phs: -4

7 Both f and g have periods of 1, amplitudes of 1, and midlines $y = 0$

9 Period: 6; Amp: 5; Mid: 0

11 $h(t) = 4\sin(2\pi t)$

13 $g(t) = -2\cos(t/2) + 2$

15 $y = 4000 + 4000\sin((2\pi/60)x)$

17 $y = -2\sin(\pi\theta/6) + 2$

19

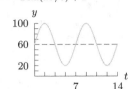

y
100
60
20
7   14
t

21

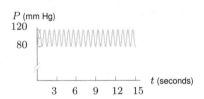

y
0.004
0.001
1000   2000 x
-0.002

23 $1/4$, $g(x) = 3\sin((\pi/4)x - \pi/2)$

25 $f(x) = \sin x$, $a = \pi/2$, $b = \pi$,
$c = 3\pi/2$, $d = 2\pi$, $e = 1$

27 Amplitude: 20
Period: 3/4 seconds

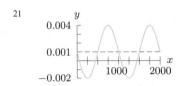

P (mm Hg)
120
80
3   6   9   12   15 t (seconds)

29 $f(t) = 14 + 10\sin(\pi t + \pi/2)$

31 $f(t) = 20 + 15\sin((\pi/2)t + \pi/2)$

33 (a) 12°/min
(b) $\theta = (12t - 90)°$
(c) $f(t) = 225 + 225\sin(12t - 90)°$
(d) Amp = Midline = 225 feet
Period = 30 min

35 (a) $P = f(t) = -450\cos(\pi t/6) + 1750$
(c) $t_1 \approx 1.9$; $t_2 \approx 10.1$

37 $y = 3f(x)$

39 $y = -f(2x)$

41 Amplitude: 41.5;
Period: 12 months

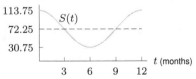

blanket sales (thousands)
113.75
72.25 $S(t)$
30.75
3   6   9   12 t (months)

43 $f(t) = -100\cos(\pi t) + 100$ (for $0 \le t \le 1$)
$10\cos(4\pi t) + 190$ (for $1 < t \le 2$)

45 (a) $T(^\circ F)$

[graph with midline Temperature dashed line at 60, values 20, 40, 60, 80 on t (months) axis 2 4 6 8 10 12]

(b) 23.2°; 12 months
(c) $T = f(t) =$
   $-23.2\cos((\pi/6)t) + 58.6$
(d) $T = f(9) \approx 58.6^\circ$

47 $f(t) = 3\sin((\pi/6)(t - 74)) + 15$

BTU (quadrillions)

[scatter graph with values 12, 14, 16, 18, 20 on axis; year (since 1900) 75 80 85 90]

Section 6.6

1 $0, 1, 0$
3 1
5 -1
7 -1
9 1
11 $-\sqrt{3}$
13 $-\sqrt{2}$
15 $2/\sqrt{3}$
17 $\sec\theta = 2$
   $\tan\theta = \sqrt{3}$
19 $\sec\theta = 3/\sqrt{8}$
   $\tan\theta = 1/\sqrt{8}$
21 $f(\theta) = (1/2)\tan\theta$
23 (a) $\sin\alpha = -\sqrt{22}/5$,
      $\tan\alpha = \sqrt{22/3}$
   (b) $\sin\beta = -4/5$,
      $\cos\beta = -3/5$
25 $\cos\theta = \sqrt{1 - y^2}$
29 $\sin\theta = \sqrt{x^2 - 16}/x$,
   $\tan\theta = \sqrt{x^2 - 16}/4$
31 $\cos\theta = 9/\sqrt{x^2 + 81}$,
   $\sin\theta = x/\sqrt{x^2 + 81}$
33 $y = y_0 + (\tan\theta)(x - x_0)$
35 No

[graph of y vs x with curve, axis markers $-\pi$, π, and $y = 1, -1$; open circles]

37 $u = -5\cos 2$
   $v = 5\sin 2$
   $w = 5\sqrt{2(1 - \cos 2)}$

Section 6.7

1 1.570
3 1.330
5 -1.447
7 $3\pi/2$
9 π
11 $\pi/4, 5\pi/4$
13 $\pi/3, 4\pi/3$
15 (a) $1.88, 4.41$
   (b) $1.88, 4.41$
17 $\pi/6$
19 $\pi/3$
21 $\pi/3$
23 0.850
25 (a) $-1/2$
   (b) $\sqrt{2}/2$
   (c) $-\sqrt{2}/2$
   (d) $-\sqrt{3}/2$
27 $\theta = 0.708, 2.434$
29 $t = 1.813, 4.473$
31 $0.340, 2.802$
33 $0.152, 2.989, 3.294, 6.131$
35 $1.914, 4.653$
37 $0.305, 2.837$
39 $4.069, 5.356, 10.352, 11.639$
41 $\theta = \pi/6 + 2\pi k, 11\pi/6 + 2\pi k$, k an integer
43 $\theta \approx 1.893$
45 $t = \pi/6, 5\pi/6,$
   $7\pi/6$, or $11\pi/6$
47 $t = \pi/2, 3\pi/2,$
   $\pi/6$, or $5\pi/6$
49 $\approx 39.806^\circ$
51 (a) $f(t) = 40,000\cos\left(\frac{\pi}{6}t + \frac{\pi}{6}\right) + 60,000$
   (b) $f(3) = \$40,000$
   (c) Mid-March and mid-September
53 $P: x \approx 0.819$;
   $Q: x \approx 3.181$
55 (a) $\pi/3$
   (b) π
   (c) ≈ 0.1
57 (a) $t_1 \approx 0.161$ and $t_2 \approx 0.625$.
   (b) $t_1 = \arcsin(3/5)/4$ and
      $t_2 = \pi/4 - \arcsin(3/5)/4$
59 Statement II is always true;
   statement I is not always true
61 (a) $d = \sqrt{2rx + x^2}$
   (b) $d = 25,238.776$ meters

Chapter 6 Review

1 (i) is B; (ii) is C; (iii) is A
3 (a) I
   (b) I and III
   (c) II and IV
   (d) IV

(e) III
5 $7\pi/4$
7 $\pi^2/30 \approx 0.329$
9 $32,400/\pi \approx 10,313.240^\circ$
11 8π
13 32.8π
15 $6.2 \cdot 17\pi/180 \approx 1.840$
17 12.4
19 Mid: 3; amp: 1; per:2π
21 Mid: 7; Amp: 2; Per: 2
23 Amplitude: 20
   Period: 1/2
   Phase shift: 0
   Horizontal shift: 0

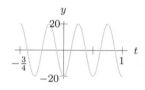

25 Amplitude: 3;
   Period: 1/2;
   Phase Shift: -6π;
   Horizontal Shift: $-3/2$ (left)

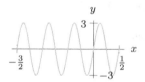

27 Amp: 30; mid: $y = 60$; per: 20
29 Amp: 50; mid: $y = 50$; per: 64
31 [graph of y vs t, markers 1, -1 on y; 2π, 4π on t]

33 [graph of y vs t, values 4, 5, 6 on y; π, 2π on t]

35 -1
37 $\sqrt{3}$
39 0.412

41 0.979

43 (a) $y = 600 - 300\cos(2\pi x/80)$
   (b) $x = 14.5279, 65.4721, 94.5279$

45 $f_1(x) = 6\cos((1/2)(x - 3\pi)) + 2, f_2(x) = -6\cos((1/2)(x - \pi)) + 2, f_3(x) = 6\sin((1/2)(x - 2\pi)) + 2, f_4(x) = -6\sin((1/2)x) + 2$; answers may vary

47 $f_1(x) = 5\cos((\pi/6)(x+2))+3, f_2(x) = -5\cos((\pi/6)(x - 4)) + 3, f_3(x) = 5\sin((\pi/6)(x - 7)) + 3, f_4(x) = -5\sin((\pi/6)(x - 1)) + 3$; answers may vary

49 $\pi/6, 7\pi/6$

51 2.897, 6.038

53 0, π, 1.107, 4.249

55 69.115 miles

57 Outer edge: 3770 cm/min;
   Inner edge: 471 cm/min

59 0.1345 radians

61 $f(t) = -900\cos((\pi/4)t) + 2100$

63 $y = 30\sin(105t - \pi/2) + 150$

Ch. 6 Understanding

1 True

3 False

5 True

7 True

9 False

11 False

13 True

15 False

17 True

19 True

21 False

23 True

25 True

27 True

29 False

31 True

33 False

35 True

37 True

39 True

41 False

43 False

45 True

47 False

49 True

51 True

53 True

55 False

57 False

59 False

61 True

63 True

65 True

67 True

69 True

71 False

73 True

75 True

77 False

79 False

81 False

83 False

85 True

87 False

Chapter 6 Tools

1 (a) $\tan\theta = 2$
   (b) $\sin\theta = 2/\sqrt{5}$
   (c) $\cos\theta = 1/\sqrt{5}$

3 (a) $5/\sqrt{125}$
   (b) $10/\sqrt{125}$
   (c) $10/\sqrt{125}$
   (d) $5/\sqrt{125}$
   (e) $1/2$
   (f) 2

5 (a) $\sqrt{45}/7$
   (b) $2/7$
   (c) $\sqrt{45}/2$

7 (a) $8/12$
   (b) $\sqrt{80}/12$
   (c) $8/\sqrt{80}$

9 (a) $\sqrt{117}/11$
   (b) $2/11$
   (c) $\sqrt{117}/2$

11 $r = 7\sin 17°; q = 7\cos 17°$

13 $r = 6/\cos 37°; q = 6\tan 37°$

15 $r = 9/\tan 77°; q = 9/\sin 77°$

17 $c = 34.409; A = 35.538°, B = 54.462°$

19 $B = 62°; a = 9.389; b = 17.659$

21 Height = 46.174 ft;
   Incline = 205.261 ft

23 $h = 400$ feet; $x = 346.410$ feet

25 74.641 feet

27 $d = 35000/\tan\theta$ feet

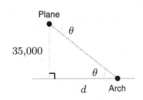

29 $d = 3\tan\phi$ miles

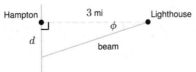

31 $d \approx 15.877$ feet

Section 7.1

1 $A = 25.922°, B = 37.735°, C = 116.343°$

3 $b = 31.762, A = 38.458°, C = 60.542°$

5 $c = 10.954, A = 54.010°, B = 45.990°$

7 $c = 7.2605; A = 21.4035°; B = 126.597°$

9 $a = 15.860, b = 2.569, C = 66°$

11 $a = 10.026, b = 6.885, C = 61°$

13 $a = 2.079, b = 3.090, B = 18°$

15 $a = 1.671, b = 4.639, B = 166°$

17 $a = 13.667, A = 90.984°, C = 17.016°$

19 $a = 12.070, A = 135.109°, C = 27.891°$
   or
   $a = 3.231, A = 10.891°, C = 152.109°$

21 $b = 0.837$ m, $c = 2.720$ m; $\gamma = 143.7°$

23 $\alpha \approx 41.410°, \beta \approx 82.819°, \gamma \approx 55.771°$

25 (a) $\sin\theta = 0.282$
   (b) $\theta \approx 16.374°$
   (c) 12.077 cm^2

27 Length of arc ≈ 0.174533 feet;
   Length of chord ≈ 0.174524 feet

29 B closer by 2.387 miles

31 396.004 miles

33 $(18.876, 10.071)$

37 (a) First; 3.062 feet closer
   (b) 157.279 feet to home
       113.218 feet to third

39 158.926 feet

Section 7.2

1 $\sin x$

3 $2\sin\alpha$

5 $\cos t - \sin t$

7 0

9 $\cos^2\theta + \sin^2\theta = 1$; $\cos 2\theta = \cos^2\theta - \sin^2\theta = 2\cos^2\theta - 1 = 1 - 2\sin^2\theta$

17 $\pi/2, 7\pi/6, 11\pi/6$

19 $0, 3\pi/4, \pi, 7\pi/4, 2\pi$

21 (a) (x, y)

23 (a) $(x, -y)$

25 Not an identity

27 Not an identity

29 Not an identity

31 Identity

33 Identity

35 Identity

37 Not an identity

39 Not an identity

41 (a) $\theta = 60°$, $180°$, and $300°$
   (b) $\theta = \frac{7\pi}{6}, \frac{3\pi}{2}, \frac{11\pi}{6}$

43 (a) $\sqrt{1 - y^2}$
   (b) $y/(\sqrt{1 - y^2})$
   (c) $1 - 2y^2$
   (d) y
   (e) $1 - y^2$

45 $\sin 2\theta = \frac{2x}{9}\sqrt{9 - x^2}$

47 (a) $2x\sqrt{1 - x^2}/(2x^2 - 1)$
   (b) $2x/(1 + x^2)$

49 $\sin 4\theta = 4(\sin\theta \cos\theta)(2\cos^2\theta - 1)$

Section 7.3

1 $10\sin(t - 0.644)$

3 $\sqrt{2}\sin(t + 3\pi/4)$

5 $\sin 15° = \cos 75° = (\sqrt{6} - \sqrt{2})/4$
   $\cos 15° = \sin 75° = (\sqrt{6} + \sqrt{2})/4$

7 $\sqrt{6}/2$

9 $(\sqrt{6} + \sqrt{2})/4$

11 (a) 1.585
   (b) 0.053
   (c) 1.216
   (d) -0.069

19 $\cos 3\theta = 4\cos^3\theta - 3\cos\theta$

Section 7.4

1 All integral multiples of π

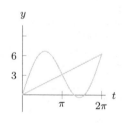

3 (a) $m = 2.5$; $b = 20$; $A = 10$
   (b) Roughly in January and December
   (c) Roughly between May and September

5 (a) $y = 1$
   (b) f oscillates faster and faster between -1 and 1 as t increases.
   (c) ≈ 0.540
   (d) $t_1 = \ln(\pi/2)$
   (e) $t_2 = \ln(3\pi/2)$

9 (a) $h = f(t) = 25 + 15\sin(\pi t/3) + 10\sin(\pi t/2)$
   (b) $f(t)$ is periodic with period 12

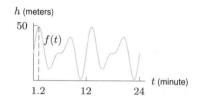

(c) $h = f(1.2) = 48.776$ m

Section 7.5

1 IV

3 II

5 III

7 I

9 IV

11 $90°$ to $180°$

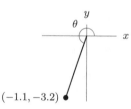

13 $180°$ to $270°$

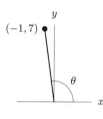

15 $(1, \pi)$

17 $(2, 5\pi/6)$

19 $(-\sqrt{6}/2, -\sqrt{6}/2)$

21 $(-\sqrt{3}, 1)$

23 $x^2 + y^2 = 6x$

25 $y = x^2 - 2x$

27 $r = \sqrt{5}$

29 $r = 1/\sqrt{2\cos\theta\sin\theta}$

31 $H: x = 3, y = 0; r = 3, \theta = 0$
   $M: x = 0, y = 4; r = 4, \theta = \pi/2$

33 $H: x = 3/2, y = 3\sqrt{3}/2; r = 3, \theta = \pi/3$
   $M: x = 0, y = 4; r = 4, \theta = \pi/2$

35 $H: x = -1.5, y = -3\sqrt{3}/2; r = 3, \theta = 4\pi/3$
   $M: x = 0, y = 4; r = 4, \theta = \pi/2$

37 $H: x \approx -2.974, y \approx 0.392; r = 3, \theta = 172.5\pi/180$
   $M: x = 4, y = 0; r = 4, \theta = 0$

39 $0 \leq r \leq 2$ and $-\pi/6 \leq \theta \leq \pi/6$

41 (b)

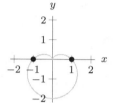

(c) Cartesian:
   $(\sqrt{3}/4, 1/4)$;
   $(-\sqrt{3}/4, 1/4)$ or polar:
   $r = 1/2, \theta = \pi/6$ or $5\pi/6$

(d)

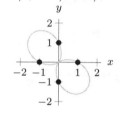

43 Looks the same

45 Rotated by $90°$ clockwise

47 $\pi/4 \leq \theta \leq 5\pi/4$;
   $0 \leq \theta \leq \pi/4$ and $5\pi/4 \leq \theta \leq 2\pi$

Section 7.6

1 $5e^{i\pi}$

3 $0e^{i\theta}$, for any θ.

5 $5e^{i4.069}$

7 $-5 + 12i$

9 $-3 - 4i$

11 $-\frac{1}{2} + i\frac{\sqrt{3}}{2}$

13 $\frac{\sqrt{3}}{2} + \frac{i}{2}$

15 (a) $e^{i\pi/2}$

17 $\sqrt{2} + i\sqrt{2}$

19 $\frac{\sqrt{3}}{2} + \frac{i}{2}$

21 $\sqrt{2}/2 + i\sqrt{2}/2$

23 $\sqrt{2}\cos\frac{\pi}{12} + i\sqrt{2}\sin\frac{\pi}{12}$

25 $2.426 + 4.062i$

27 $A_1 = 2 - i$
   $A_2 = -2 + 2i$

29 $p = -b$ and $q = \sqrt{c - b^2}$

Chapter 7 Review

1 (a) $a = 4$; $c = 2$; $B = 60°$
   (b) $A \approx 73.740°$; $B \approx 16.260°$; $b = 7$

3 3.004, 5.833; $31°$

5 14.188, 9.829; $105°$

7 $\cos\theta$

9 $2\cos\phi$

11 $-\sqrt{2}/2$

13 $(\sqrt{2}-\sqrt{6})/4$

15 I

17 I

19 $(1.571,0)$

21 $(0,0)$

25 $\cos\theta = 3/\sqrt{14}$

27 (a) $\cos\theta = -\sqrt{48}/7$
(b) $\theta \approx 2.998$ radians

29 $\sin(\ln(xy)) \approx 0.515$

35 $(\tan^2 x)(\sin^2 x) = \tan^2 x - \sin^2 x$

37 (a)

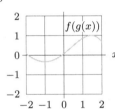

(b) $\sqrt{2}\sin(\theta - \pi/4)$
$\sqrt{2}\cos(\theta - 3\pi/4)$

39 $\theta = 101.068°$

43 Height: 541.723 ft;
Distance between: 718.891 ft

45 (b) 12 o'clock $\rightarrow$ $(x,y) = (1,1)$ and
$(r,\theta) = (\sqrt{2}, \pi/4)$,
3 o'clock $\rightarrow$ $(x,y) = (2,0)$ and $(r,\theta) = (2,0)$,
6 o'clock $\rightarrow$ $(x,y) = (1,-1)$ and
$(r,\theta) = (\sqrt{2}, -\pi/4)$,
9 o'clock $\rightarrow$ $(x,y) = (0,0)$ and $(r,\theta) = (0, \text{any angle})$

Ch. 7 Understanding

1 True

3 False

5 True

7 True

9 True

11 True

13 False

15 True

17 True

19 True

21 False

23 False

25 False

27 False

29 False

31 True

33 False

35 True

37 True

39 True

41 False

43 False

45 True

47 True

49 False

51 True

53 True

55 True

57 True

Section 8.1

1 $r(0) = 4, r(1) = 5, r(2) = 2, r(3) = 0, r(4) = 3, r(5)$ undefined

3 $\pi/2, \pi/3, \pi/4, \pi/6, 0$

5 $2^{x^2}; 4^x$

7 $(x^2 - 6x + 10)/(x^2 - 6x + 9)$

9 $x + 1$

11 $(x - 3)/(10 - 3x)$

13 $\sin x$

15 $x^3 + 3x + 1$

17 $5 + 1/x$

19 Length in terms of time

21 Time in terms of temp

25 (a) 4
(b) 1
(c) 4
(d) 0

27

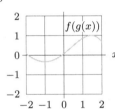

29

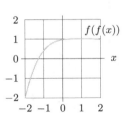

33 (a)

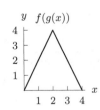

(b) $0 < x < 2$
(c) $2 < x < 4$

37 $1/2$

39 $2x + h + 1$

41 $-1/(x(x+h))$

43 $f(x) = 2x$

45 $f(x) = \ln x$

47 (a) $v(x) = -\sqrt{x}$
(b) $u(x) = e^{-x}$

49 (a) $v(x) = 2^x$
(b) $u(x) = 2^{1-x}$

51 (a) $v(x) = 2\cos x$
(b) $u(x) = e^{2x}$

53 $u(x) = \sin x, \quad v(x) = x^2$

55 $u(x) = e^x + x, \quad v(x) = \sin x$

57 $u(x) = 2/x, v(x) = 1 + \sqrt{x}$

59 $u(x) = 8 - 2x, v(x) = |x|$

61 (a) $f(x) = 114.64x$
$g(x) = 0.829x$
$h(x) = 0.00723x$
(b) $1000 trades for yen,
then for 828.8472 euros

Section 8.2

1 Not invertible

3 Not invertible

5 Not invertible

11 Yes, $f(f^{-1}(x)) = f^{-1}(f(x)) = x$

13 Yes, $f(f^{-1}(x)) = f^{-1}(f(x)) = x$

15 $h^{-1}(x) = \sqrt[3]{x/12}$

17 $k^{-1}(x) = \frac{1}{2}\ln(x/3)$

19 $n^{-1}(x) = 10^x + 3$

21 $h^{-1}(x) = (x/(1-x))^2$

23 $f^{-1}(x) = (4x^2 - 4)/(x^2 - 7)$

25 $f^{-1}(x) = 1/(e^x - 1)$

27 $q^{-1}(x) = (3 + 5e^x)/(e^x - 1)$

29 (a) $p(q(t)) = q(p(t)) = t$; inverses
(b) Line $y = t$

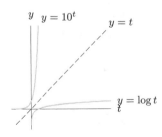

31 $f^{-1}(P) = 50\ln(P/10)$

33 $f^{-1}(N) = I_0 10^{N/10}$

35 $x = (\ln 3 / \ln 2) - 5$

37 $x = e^{1.8} - 3$

39 $x = (19 - \sqrt{37})/2$

41 $f^{-1}(3) < f(3) < 0 < f(0) < f^{-1}(0) < 3$

43 $1 - t^2$

45 (a) $A = \pi r^2$

(b)

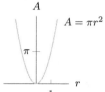

(c) $r \geq 0$

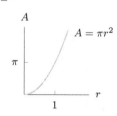

(d) $f^{-1}(A) = \sqrt{A/\pi}$

(e)

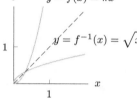

(f) Yes

47 (a) $P(t) = 150(1.1)^t$

(b) $P^{-1}(y) = (\log(y) - \log(150))/(\log(1.1))$

(c) 10.3 years

49 (a) 36 m

(b) 6 seconds

(c) One possibility: $3 \leq t \leq 6$

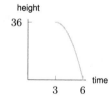

(e)

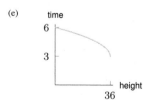

51 (a) A (wrong) guess is 0.99 ml

(b) $x = C^{-1}(0.98)$

(c) 50 ml

59 $f^{-1}(L) = -\frac{1}{k} \ln(1 - L/L_\infty)$

$f^{-1}(L) =$ Age of fish of length L

Domain: $0 \leq L \leq L_\infty$

Section 8.3

1 (a) $f(x) + g(x) = 3x^2 + x + 1$

(b) $f(x) - g(x) = -3x^2 + x + 1$

(c) $f(x)g(x) = 3x^3 + 3x^2$

(d) $f(x)/g(x) = (x + 1)/(3x^2)$

3 (a) $f(x) + g(x) = 2x$

(b) $f(x) - g(x) = 10$

(c) $f(x)g(x) = x^2 - 25$

(d) $f(x)/g(x) = (x + 5)/(x - 5)$

5 (a) $f(x) + g(x) = x^3 + x^2$

(b) $f(x) - g(x) = x^3 - x^2$

(c) $f(x)g(x) = x^5$

(d) $f(x)/g(x) = x$

7 $3x^2 + x$

9 $2x\sqrt{x + 2}$

11 $3x/2 - 1/2$

13 $f(x) = e^x(2x + 1) = 2xe^x + e^x$

15 $h(x) = 4e^{2x} + 4e^x + 1$

17 $\sin x + x^2$

19 $(\sin x)/x^2$

21 $\sin^2 x$

23 (a)

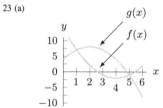

(c)

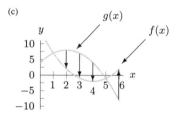

(f) $f(x) = x^2 - 8x + 14$;
$g(x) = -x^2 + 4x + 4$;
$f(x) - g(x) = 2x^2 - 12x + 10$

(g) Yes

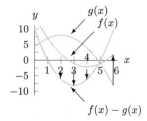

25 (a)

t (yrs)	0	1	2
$f(t)$ ($)	109,366	111,958	111,581
$g(t)$	13.61	13.68	13.03

t (yrs)	3	4	5
$f(t)$ ($)	114,931	119,162	122,499
$g(t)$	13.42	13.73	13.63

27 (a)

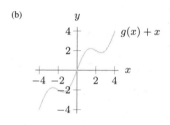

(b)

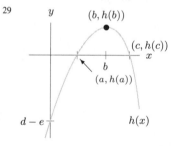

29

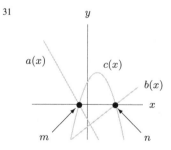

31

33 (a) $h(x) = x^2 + x, h(3) = 12$
(b) $j(x) = x^2 - 2x - 3, j(3) = 0$
(c) $k(x) = x^3 + x^2 - x - 1, k(3) = 32$
(d) $m(x) = x - 1$ for $x \neq -1, m(3) = 2$
(e) $n(x) = 2x + 2, n(3) = 8$

35 (a) $f(\theta) = (\tan \theta)/(1 + \tan \theta)$
(b)

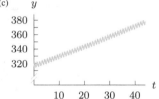

$\theta = -\frac{\pi}{4}$ $\theta = \frac{3\pi}{4}$

(c) $f(\theta)$ is periodic

37 40

39 (a) Even
(b) Odd
(c) Neither

41 (a) $A(t) = 316.75(1.004)^t$
(b) $V(t) = 3.25 \sin 2\pi t$; other answers possible
(c)

43 (b) $p(t) = (f_{CA}(t) \cdot g_{CA}(t) + f_{FL}(t) \cdot g_{FL}(t))/(f_{US}(t) \cdot g_{US}(t))$

Chapter 8 Review

1 $\sqrt{27x - 6}$
3 $3x$
5 $108x^2 - 2$
7 $2^{x/(x+1)}$
9 $2e^x - 1$
11 $4x - 3$
13 $\sqrt{x}e^{2x-1}$
15 (a) $f(2x) = 4x^2 + 2x$
(b) $g(x^2) = 2x^2 - 3$
(c) $h(1 - x) = (1 - x)/x$
(d) $(f(x))^2 = (x^2 + x)^2$
(e) $g^{-1}(x) = (x + 3)/2$
(f) $(h(x))^{-1} = (1 - x)/x$
(g) $f(x)g(x) = (x^2 + x)(2x - 3)$
(h) $h(f(x)) = (x^2 + x)/(1 - x^2 - x)$
17 $x/(1 + e^{2x})$
19 $x^{3/2} \tan 2x$
21 $\tan((3x - 1)^2/2) - 27x^{3/2}$
23 $f^{-1}(x) = (x + 7)/3$
25 $h^{-1}(x) = (2x + 1)/(3x - 2)$
27 $g^{-1}(x) = e^{(5+7x)/(1-2x)}$
29 $f^{-1}(x) = (\arccos x)^2$

31

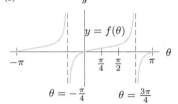

t	u	v	w
0	2	3	1
1	3	4	2
2	1	1	4
3	4	2	0
4	0	0	3

33 $g(x) = x^2$, $h(x) = x + 3$
35 $g(x) = x^2 + x$, $h(x) = 3x$
37 65
39

41

43 (a) II
(b) I
(c) None
(d) None
(e) IV
(f) None
(g) None
45 (a) $x \neq 3$
(b) $x \leq 2$
47 $r^{-1}(x) = (x + 1)/(2 - 2x)$
49 $u(x) = 0.5\sqrt{x}$
51 (a) $f(t) = 800 - 14t$ gals
(b) (i) 800 gals
(ii) 57.143 days
(iii) 28.571 days
(iv) 14t
53 (a) $N(20,000) = 380$
(b) $N(x) = \frac{1}{250}x + 300$
(d) $N^{-1}(500) = 50,000$
55 Ace estimates 2000 ft² of office space costs $200,000.
57 $f(2x) < 2f(x)$
59 Space estimates 1500 ft² of office space costs $200,000
61 Ace seems to be a better value
63 Decreasing
65 Increasing

Ch. 8 Understanding

1 False
3 True
5 True
7 True
9 True
11 False
13 False
15 True
17 False
19 False
21 False
23 False
25 True
27 True
29 True
31 False
33 True
35 True
37 True

Section 9.1

1 Yes; $g(x) = (-1/6)x^9$
3 Yes; $Q(t) = (1/8)t^{-3/2}$
5 Yes; $T(s) = 6es^{-5}$
7 Odd
9 Odd
11 $y = 0.7x^{1.252}$
13 $y = 2x^{1.194}$
15 $k = 3/2; y = (3x)/2; x = 5.33$
17 $k = 5; c = 5d^2; c = 125$
19 $j(x) = 2x^3$
21 $g(x) = -\frac{1}{6}x^3$
23 (a) 0
(b) 0
27 (a) $x^{-3} \to +\infty, x^{1/3} \to 0$
(b) $x^{-3} \to 0, x^{1/3} \to \infty$
29 (a) No
(b) No new deductions
(c) All points satisfying the equation $y = -3x^5$
31 (a) $f(x) = x^{1/n}$
    $g(x) = x^n$
(b) $(1, 1)$
33 $c = 81.67x; 326.68$
35 $y = 1350/n; 14$
37 $d = 0.1x; 32.5$ miles
39 (a) $T = kR^2D^4$
(b) Increases by factor of 4
(c) Increases by factor of 16
(d) Reduce to 44.4%
41 Decrease by 29.289%
43 (a) 20 lbs; 1620 lbs
(b) 3/10
45 (a) $h(x) = -2x^2$
(b) $j(x) = \frac{1}{4}x^2$

Section 9.2

1 Yes, 1

3 Yes, 2

5 No

7 $y \to \infty$; like $4x^4$

9 $y \to \infty$; like $2x^9$

11 (a) ∞

(b) ∞

13 -16.543

15 $y = (-1/8)(x+2)(x-2)^2(x-5)$;
$y = (-1/20)(x+2)(x-2)(x-5)^2$

17 $y = \frac{1}{2}x - 1$

19 (a)

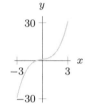

(b) $f(0.5) = 1.625$;
$f^{-1}(0.5) \approx -0.424$.

21 (a)

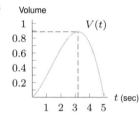

(b) $V \approx .886$ at $t \approx 3.195$

(c) $(0,0)$ and $(5,0)$;
Lungs empty at beginning and end

23 (a) 500 people

(b) May of 1908

(c) 790; February of 1907

25 Yes

27 (a) False

(b) False

(c) True

(d) False

29 (c)

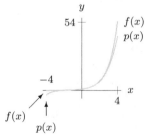

Section 9.3

1 $-3, 2, -7$

3 $0, -4, -3$

5 $x(x+2)(x-2)(x-4)$

7 $h(x) = x(x+2)^2(x-3)$

9

11 (a) $1/2, 1/3, 7$, and 9

(b) No

(c) $0 \le x \le 10, -500 \le y \le 1500$ and
$0 \le x \le 1, -2 \le y \le 2$

13 $p(x) = (x+15)(x-1)^2(x-3)$

15 C

17 $f(x) = x^2 - 2x$

19 $f(x) = -\frac{1}{2}(x+3)(x-1)(x-4)$

21 $p(x) = x^2 + 2x - 3$

23 $y = \frac{1}{2}(x+\frac{1}{2})(x-3)(x-4)$

25 $y = 2x(x+2)(x-2)$

27 $y = 7(x+2)(x-3)^2$

29 $y = -\frac{1}{3}(x+2)^2(x)(x-2)^2$

31 $g(x) = -\frac{1}{4}(x+2)^2(x-2)(x-3)$

33 $g(x) = -\frac{1}{3}(x+2)(x-2)x^2$

35 $j(x) = (x+3)(x+2)(x+1) + 4$

37 $x = -2$ or $x = -3$

39 $x = \pm\frac{1}{2}$

41 $x = (3 \pm \sqrt{33})/4$

43 (a) $V(x) = x(6-2x)(8-2x)$

(b) $0 < x < 3$

(c)

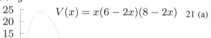

(d) ≈ 24.26 in^3

45 7.83 by 5.33 by 1.585 inches

47 (a)

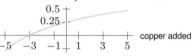

(b) No

(c) $3; -6 \le x \le 3, -3 \le y \le 3$

(d) $f(x) = (x+5)(x-1)(x-2)^2$

(e) 3; No

49 (a) Never true

(b) Sometimes true

(c) Sometimes true

(d) Never true

(e) True

(f) Never true

Section 9.4

1 Rational; $(x^3+2)/(2x)$

3 Not rational

5 Rational; $(x^2-5)/(x-3)$

7 (a) 2

(b) 5/6

9 $y = 1$

11 $y = 4$

13 (a) $n > m$

(b) $n = m$

15 $f^{-1}(x) = (4x+4)/(5x+3)$

17 (a) $g(x) = (x^3+2)/(2x^2)$

19 (a) $f(x) = (3+x)/(12+x)$

(b) (i) 28%

(ii) 25%

(iii) $\approx 18.2\%$

(iv) 6

(v) -3

(c)

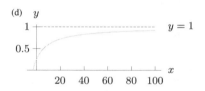

(d)

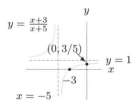

21 (a) (i) $C(1) = 5050$

(ii) $C(100) = 10,000$

(iii) $C(1000) = 55,000$

(iv) $C(10000) = 505,000$

(b) (i) $a(1) = 5050$

(ii) $a(100) = 100$

(iii) $a(1000) = 55$

(iv) $a(10000) = 50.5$

(c) $a(n)$ gets closer to $50

23 No

Section 9.5

1 Zero: $x = -3$;
Asymptote: $x = -5$;
$y \to 1$ as $x \to \pm\infty$

3 Zeros: $x = 4$;
   Asymptote: $x = \pm3$;
   $y \to 0$ as $x \to \pm\infty$

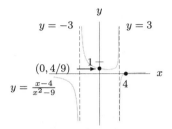

$y = -3$ $y = 3$
$(0, 4/9)$
$y = \dfrac{x-4}{x^2-9}$
4
x

5 x-int: $x = 2$
   y-int: $y = 1/2$
   Horiz asy: $y = 1$
   Vert asy: $x = 4$

7 x-int: $x = \pm2$
   y-int: None
   Horiz asy: $y = 0$
   Vert asy: $x = 0, x = -4$

9 (c) Horizontal: $y = 0$
      Vertical: $x = 3$

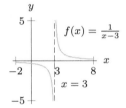

$f(x) = \dfrac{1}{x-3}$
$x = 3$

11

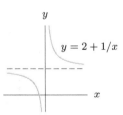

$y = 2 + 1/x$
x

13 (a) $-\infty$
   (b) $+\infty$

15 (a) $2, 2$
   (b) $\lim_{x \to -4+} f(x) = -\infty$;
       $\lim_{x \to -4-} f(x) = \infty$

17 (a) (iii)
   (b) (i)
   (c) (ii)
   (d) (iv)
   (e) (vi)
   (f) (v)

19 (a) Small
   (b) Large
   (c) Undefined
   (d) Positive
   (e) Negative

21 (a)

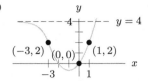

$y = 4$
$(-3, 2)$ $(0, 0)$ $(1, 2)$
-3 1 x

(b)
$x = -1$ y $x = 3$
4
x
$y = -\frac{1}{2}$

23 (a) $y = -1/(x + 2)$
   (b) $y = -1/(x + 2)$
   (c) $(0, -1/2)$

25 (a) $y = -1/(x - 3)^2$
   (b) $y = -1/(x^2 - 6x + 9)$
   (c) $(0, -1/9)$

27 (a) $y = (1/x^2) + 2$
   (b) $y = (2x^2 + 1)/x^2$
   (c) None

29 (a) $1/x$
   (b) $y = (1/x) + 2$

31 (a) $y = 1/x$
   (b) $y = x/(2x - 4)$

33 $y = \frac{1}{16}x^2(x + 3)(x - 2)$

35 $y = (x + 2)(x - 3)/((x - 2)(x + 1))$

37 $y = ((x + 3)(x - 1))/(x + 2)^2$

39 $y = (x - 2)/((x + 1)(x - 1))$

41 $g(x) = (x - 5)/((x + 2)(x - 3))$

Section 9.6

1 Neither

3 $p(x) = 25^x$

5 $r(x) = 2(\frac{1}{9})^x$

7 A - (i)
   B - (iv)
   C - (ii)
   D - (iii)

11 $y = 4e^x$

13 $y = ax^3$

15 $y = e^{-x}$

17 (a) $f(x) = 720x - 702$
   (b) $f(x) = 2(9)^x$
   (c) $f(x) = 18x^4$

19 (a) $f(x) = y = \dfrac{63}{4}x + \dfrac{33}{2}$
   (b) $f(x) = 3 \cdot 4^x$
   (c) $f(x) = \frac{3}{4}x^6$

21 $A: kx^{5/7}$; $B: kx^{9/16}$;
    $C: kx^{3/8}$; $D: kx^{3/11}$

23 (a) $v = 40$
   (b) $r(x) > t(x)$
   (c) $t(x) > r(x)$

25 $y \to 0$ as $x \to \pm\infty$

27 $y \to \infty$ as $x \to \infty$
    $y \to 0$ as $x \to -\infty$

29 $y \to 0$ as $t \to \infty$
    $y \to \infty$ as $t \to -\infty$

31 $y \to 0$ as $t \to \infty$
    $y \to 0$ as $t \to -\infty$

33 $y \to \infty$ as $t \to \pm\infty$

35 $y \to 1$ as $x \to \infty$
    $y \to -1$ as $x \to -\infty$

37 (a) $h(r) = b \cdot r^{5/4}$;
       $g(r) = a \cdot r^{3/4}$
   (b) $a \approx 8$; $b \approx 3$

39 (a) $p_5(r) = 1000[(1 + r)^5 + (1 + r)^4 + (1 + r)^3 + (1 + r)^2 + (1 + r) + 1]$;
       $p_{10}(r) = 1000[(1 + r)^{10} + (1 + r)^9 + (1 + r)^8 + (1 + r)^7 + (1 + r)^6 + (1 + r)^5 + (1 + r)^4 + (1 + r)^3 + (1 + r)^2 + (1 + r) + 1]$
   (b) 20.279%

Section 9.7

1 $f(x) = x^{\ln c / \ln 2}$

3 $h(x) = 2.35(1.44)^x$

5 (a) $f(x) = 201.353x^{2.111}$
   (b) $f(20) = 112{,}313.62$ gm
   (c) $x = 18.930$ cm

7 $y = \frac{3}{2}x$

9 $y = e^{0.4x}$

11 $y = x^{\frac{3}{2}}$

13 (a) FM

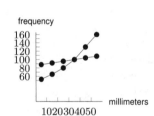

frequency
160
140
120
100
80
60
millimeters
1020304050

(b) AM
(c) $y = 86 + 0.4x$
(d) $y = 46.5e^{0.023x}$

15 (a) $N = -14t^4 + 433t^3 - 2255t^2 + 5634t - 4397$
   (b) Good fit

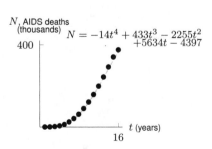

N, AIDS deaths (thousands)
$N = -14t^4 + 433t^3 - 2255t^2 + 5634t - 4397$
400
t (years)
16

(c) Model fails for $t > 20$

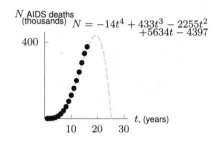

$N = -14t^4 + 433t^3 - 2255t^2 + 5634t - 4397$

17 (a) $C(t) = 664.769(1.388)^t$
(b) 38.8% per year
(c) slower growth; concave down

19 (a)
Population (thousands)

(b) $P(t) = 56.108(1.031)^t$, answers may vary
(c) 56.108 is 1650 population, 1.031 means 3.1% annual growth
(d) $P(100) = 1194.308$, Slightly higher
(e) $P(150) = 5510.118$, higher

21 (a) $N = 1271.2e^{0.3535t}$

(b) About 1.96 years

23 (a) $y = 0.310t^2 - 12.177t + 144.517$
(b) $y = 3.01t^2 - 348.43t + 10,955.75$

25 (b) Points lie on a line

27 (a) Quadratic
(b) $y = -31.798x^2 + 3218.719x - 37,169.5$; answers may vary
(c) $38,392; answers may vary
(d) Age 10, −$8162, not reasonable; answers may vary

29 (a) $t = 8966.1H^{-2.3}$

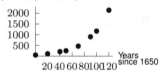

(b) $r = 0.0124H - 0.1248$

(c) $H = 0°C$; $H = 10.1°C$; model (b)

Chapter 9 Review

1 No
3 Yes; $y = x^2$
5 No
7 Even
9 $f(x) = (3/2) \cdot x^{-2}$
11 3rd degree
13 Degree: 4; Terms: 3; $x \to \pm\infty: y \to -\infty$
15 6, 2, 3
17 Rational; $(3x + 1)/6$
19 $y = 7/x^{-4}$
21 4
23 3/4
25 $-0.1 \le x \le 0.1, 0 \le y \le 0.011$
27 $-1.1 \le x \le 0.3, -0.121 \le y \le 0.117$
29 Graph (i): J; Graph (ii): L; Graph (iii): O; Graph (iv): H
31 $f(x) = -(x + 1)(x - 1)^2$
33 $h(x) = \frac{1}{12}(x + 2)(x + 1)(x - 1)^2(x - 3)$
35 $g(x) = \frac{1}{6}(x + 1)(x - 2)(x - 4) + 4$
37 (a) Even (b) Neither (c) Odd (d) Neither (e) Neither (f) Even (g) Neither (h) Even
39 (a) $b = 0$ (b) $b = d = 0$
41 (a) 147.628 million miles (b) Yes
43 (a) 1.2 meters/sec (b) 21% longer than the existing ship
45 (a) $f^{-1}(x) = 5x/(1 - x)$ (b) $f^{-1}(0.2) = 1.25$ (c) $x = 0$ (d) $y = -5$
47 $p(x) = \frac{7}{1080}(x + 3)(x - 2)(x - 5)(x - 6)^2$
49 $h(x) = (1/5)(x + 5)(x + 1)(x - 4) + 7$

53 (a) Exponential $r = 15.597e^{-0.323v}$; Power $r = 10.53v^{-0.641}$
(b) High-energy photons
(c) $r = 15.597e^{-0.323v}$; $r = 10.53v^{-0.641}$ (best fit)
(d) Power function

55 (a) $I(x) = 0.01x$ (number infected); $N(x) = 0.99x$ (number not infected)
(b) $T(x) = 0.0098x$
(c) $F(x) = 0.0297x$
(d) $P(x) = 0.0395x$
(e) $0.01x/(0.0395x) \approx 0.253$
(f) No

Ch. 9 Understanding

1 False
3 True
5 True
7 False
9 True
11 True
13 False
15 True
17 False
19 False
21 True
23 False
25 True
27 True
29 True
31 True
33 True
35 False
37 False
39 True
41 True
43 False
45 False
47 False

Chapter 9 Tools

1 41/35
3 $(3 - 4x)/6x$
5 $-2(1 - 2y)/yz$
7 $(2 - 3x)/x^2$
9 15/7
11 $18/x^3$
13 $20/(x - 1)$
15 $(4y^3z - 3wx)/(x^2y^4)$
17 $(8(y + 4))/(y - 4)$

19 $x^3/2$

21 $(-27x + 44)/((x + 1)(3x - 4))$

23 $2(11x + 27)/((x - 3)^2(x + 5)^2)$

25 $(x^2 + 1)/(x - 1)$

27 $\left((u + a)^2 + u\right)/(u + a)$

29 $(1 + e^x)/e^{2x}$

31 $(0.28 + 3M^3)/(4M)$

33 8

35 $x(x + 2)$

37 $1/2$

39 $1/(a^2 b^2)$

41 $-2x - h$

43 $1 - (1/a)$

45 $p^3/(p^2 + q^2)$

47 $(1 - 2\ln x)/\left(3x^3\right)$

49 $(-4x^2 + 2x + 1)/(x^4\sqrt{2x - 1})$

51 $1/3 + 1/\sqrt{x}$

53 $7/(p^2 + 11) + p/(p^2 + 11)$

55 $1/t^{5/2} + 1/t^{3/2}$

57 $1 + 3/(q - 4)$

59 $1 + 2/(2u + 1)$

61 $1 + 1/e^x$

63 True

65 False

67 True

Section 10.1

1 Scalar

3 Scalar

5 $\vec{p} = 2\vec{w}$
$\vec{q} = -\vec{u}$
$\vec{r} = \vec{u} + \vec{w}$
$\vec{s} = 2\vec{w} - \vec{u}$
$\vec{t} = \vec{u} - \vec{w}$

7

9
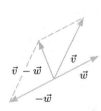
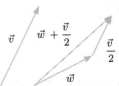

11
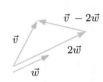

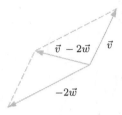

13 5.116 miles; $14.639°$ east of north

15 (a) 1.710 miles
    (b) 5.848 miles

17 13,757 meters at an angle of
    $67.380°$ north of west and
    $19.093°$ from the horizontal

19 7.431 ft/sec and $16.588°$; 3.576 ft/sec and
    $36.387°$

Section 10.2

1 $10\vec{i} - 4\vec{j}$

3 $3\vec{i} - 7\vec{j}$

5 $-3\vec{i} - 4\vec{j}$

7 $\vec{w} \approx -0.725\vec{i} - 0.95\vec{j}$

9 $\sqrt{6} \approx 2.449$

11 7.649

13 (a) $50\vec{i}$
    (b) $-50\vec{j}$
    (c) $(25\sqrt{2})\vec{i} - (25\sqrt{2})\vec{j}$
    (d) $-(25\sqrt{2})\vec{i} + (25\sqrt{2})\vec{j}$

15 $45°$ or $\pi/4$

17 $-140.847\vec{i} + 140.847\vec{j} + 18\vec{k}$

19 $21\vec{j} + 35\vec{k}$

21 $\vec{u}$ and $\vec{w}$; $\vec{v}$ and $\vec{q}$.

23 3.982 mph; $51.116°$

25 $\vec{i} + 4\vec{j}$

27 $-\vec{i}$

Section 10.3

1 $(6, 7, 9, 11, 14, 18)$

3 $(3, 5, 0, -5, -17, -36)$

5 $(12.872, 15.233, 18.661, 22.089,$
    $26.584, 32.146)$

7 $(3.63, 1.44, 6.52, 1.43, 1.20, 0.74)$

9 $(3.467, 1.277, 6.357, 1.267, 1.037, 0.577)$

11 $(79.000, 79.333, 89.000, 68.333, 89.333)$

13 $3.378°$ north of east

15 (a) $\vec{v} = 4.330\vec{i} + 2.500\vec{j}$
    For the second leg of his journey, $\vec{w} = x\vec{i}$

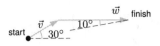

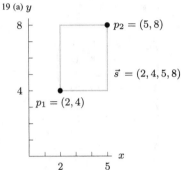

    (b) $x = 9.848$
    (c) 14.397

17 (a) $\sqrt{34}$
    (b) 17.6
    (c) $(9.065, 15.086)$

19 (a) y

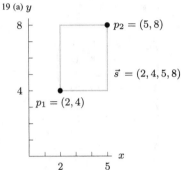

    (b)   (i) 1 unit right
          (ii) 1 unit left
         (iii) 2 right, 3 up
          (iv) 1 right, 1 up
           (v) k right, k up

Section 10.4

1 -7

3 -14

5 -22

7 -2

9 185

11 (a) 6 ft-lb
    (b) -10 ft-lb

13 Parallel:
    $3\vec{i} + \sqrt{3}\,\vec{j}$ and $\sqrt{3}\,\vec{i} + \vec{j}$
    Perpendicular:
    $\sqrt{3}\,\vec{i} + \vec{j}$ and $\vec{i} - \sqrt{3}\,\vec{j}$
    $3\vec{i} + \sqrt{3}\,\vec{j}$ and $\vec{i} - \sqrt{3}\,\vec{j}$

15 Perpendicular: $t = 2$ or -1
    No values of t make $\vec{u}$ parallel to $\vec{v}$

17 No

23 Bantus

25 (a) $\sqrt{2}$
    (b) 0.32

Section 10.5

1 (a) $\begin{pmatrix} 15 & 35 \\ 10 & -5 \end{pmatrix}$

(b) $\begin{pmatrix} -2 & 10 \\ 0 & -16 \end{pmatrix}$

(c) $\begin{pmatrix} 4 & 2 \\ 2 & 7 \end{pmatrix}$

(d) $\begin{pmatrix} -8 & -26 \\ -6 & 11 \end{pmatrix}$

(e) $\begin{pmatrix} 13 & 45 \\ 10 & -21 \end{pmatrix}$

(f) $\begin{pmatrix} k & -5k \\ 0 & 8k \end{pmatrix}$

3 (a) $\begin{pmatrix} 12 & 8 & 20 & 4 \\ 16 & 24 & 28 & 12 \\ 4 & 36 & 20 & 32 \\ 0 & -8 & 16 & 24 \end{pmatrix}$

(b) $\begin{pmatrix} -2 & -12 & -8 & -4 \\ -6 & -10 & 2 & -14 \\ -18 & -8 & -14 & -6 \\ -4 & -16 & -8 & -10 \end{pmatrix}$

(c) $\begin{pmatrix} 2 & -4 & 1 & -1 \\ 1 & 1 & 8 & -4 \\ -8 & 5 & -2 & 5 \\ -2 & -10 & 0 & 1 \end{pmatrix}$

(d) $\begin{pmatrix} 6 & -12 & 3 & -3 \\ 3 & 3 & 24 & -12 \\ -24 & 15 & -6 & 15 \\ -6 & -30 & 0 & 3 \end{pmatrix}$

(e) $\begin{pmatrix} 4 & 8 & 9 & 3 \\ 7 & 11 & 6 & 10 \\ 10 & 13 & 12 & 11 \\ 2 & 6 & 8 & 11 \end{pmatrix}$

(f) $\begin{pmatrix} 10 & -4 & 12 & 0 \\ 10 & 14 & 30 & -2 \\ -14 & 28 & 6 & 26 \\ -4 & -24 & 8 & 14 \end{pmatrix}$

5 (a) $(51, 15, 38)$
(b) $(-8, -11, 33)$
(c) $(70, 20, 22)$
(d) $(11, -6, 17)$
(e) 681
(f) $\begin{pmatrix} 24 & 60 & 84 \\ 48 & -72 & 36 \\ 192 & -60 & 0 \end{pmatrix}$

7 (a) $\mathbf{T} = \begin{pmatrix} 0.90 & 0 & 0 \\ 0.10 & 0.50 & 0.02 \\ 0 & 0.50 & 0.98 \end{pmatrix}$

(b) $\vec{p_1} = (1.8, 0.2, 0)$,
$\vec{p_2} = (1.62, 0.28, 0.1)$,
$\vec{p_3} = (1.458, 0.304, 0.238)$

9 (a) $\mathbf{T} = \begin{pmatrix} 0.97 & 0.05 \\ 0.03 & 0.95 \end{pmatrix}$

(b) $\vec{p}_{2006} = (214, 386)$,
$\vec{p}_{2007} = (226.88, 373.12)$.

11 (a) $\vec{v} = \begin{pmatrix} 11 \\ 19 \end{pmatrix}$

(b) $\vec{v} = \begin{pmatrix} 5 \\ 11 \end{pmatrix}$

(c) $\vec{v} = \begin{pmatrix} 2a + b \\ 3a + 2b \end{pmatrix}$

13 (a) $\lambda_2 = -1$
(b) $\lambda_3 = -1$
(c) $\mathbf{A}\vec{v} = \lambda\vec{v}$, and $\mathbf{A}\vec{v}$ is parallel to $\vec{v}$

15 (a) $\begin{pmatrix} 3 & 5 \\ 2 & 4 \end{pmatrix}\begin{pmatrix} a \\ b \end{pmatrix} = a\begin{pmatrix} 3 \\ 2 \end{pmatrix} + b\begin{pmatrix} 5 \\ 4 \end{pmatrix}$

(b) $\vec{v} = \begin{pmatrix} -8.5 \\ 5.5 \end{pmatrix}$

(c) $\vec{v} = -8.5\vec{c_1} + 5.5\vec{c_2}$

Chapter 10 Review

1 $(3, 3, 6)$

3 $(-3, -2, 9)$

5 $(7, 8, -21)$

7 $(4, -2, 18)$

9 $-4.5\vec{i} + 8\vec{j} + 0.5\vec{k}$

11 13

13 6

15 $6\vec{i} + 6\vec{j} + 6\vec{k}$

17 $\vec{a} = \vec{b} = \vec{c} = 3\vec{k}$
$\vec{d} = 2\vec{i} + 3\vec{k}$
$\vec{e} = \vec{j}$
$\vec{f} = -2\vec{i}$

19 $\|\vec{u}\| = \sqrt{6}$
$\|\vec{v}\| = \sqrt{5}$

21 (a) Yes
(b) No

23 (a) $\vec{L} = (11, 7, 11, 7, 13)$
(b) $\vec{F} = (32, 36, 21, 8, 4)$,
$\vec{G} = (3, 3, 2, 0, 7)$

25 $F = g\sin\theta$

29 $0.4v\vec{i} + 0.693v\vec{j}$

31 (a) $\overrightarrow{AB} = 2\vec{i} - 2\vec{j} - 7\vec{k}$
$\overrightarrow{AC} = -2\vec{i} + 2\vec{j} - 7\vec{k}$
(b) $\theta = 44.003°$

35 $\overrightarrow{AB} = -\vec{u}$; $\overrightarrow{BC} = 3\vec{v}$; $\overrightarrow{AC} = \overrightarrow{AB} + \overrightarrow{BC} = -\vec{u} + 3\vec{v}$; $\overrightarrow{AD} = 3\vec{v}$

37 $3\vec{n} - 3\vec{m}$;
$3\vec{m} + \vec{n}$;
$4\vec{m} - \vec{n}$;
$\vec{m} - 2\vec{n}$

Ch. 10 Understanding

1 False

3 False

5 False

7 False

9 True

11 True

13 False

15 True

17 True

19 False

21 True

23 False

25 True

Section 11.1

1 Arithmetic

3 Not arithmetic

5 Not arithmetic

7 Arithmetic, $a_n = -0.9 - 0.1n$

9 Geometric

11 Geometric

13 Geometric; $4 \cdot 3^{n-1}$

15 Geometric; $2(-2)^{n-1}$

17 Geometric; $1/(1.2)^{n-1}$

19 $10.8, 64.8, 4.8 + 1.2n$

21 $7.9, 57.4, 2.4 + 1.1n$

23 $1.661, 7(0.75)^{n-1}$

25 $486, 2 \cdot 3^{n-1}$

27 (a) $646.7, 650.580, 654.484, 658.411$
(b) $367.7, 396.748, 428.091, 461.911$
(c) 2012

29 (a) $17.960, 18.314, 18.675$
(b) $17.960(1.0197)^n$
(c) 36.5 years

31 Arithmetic, $d > 0$

33 Arithmetic, $d < 0$

35 $2, 7, 12, 17; a_n = -3 + 5n$

37 $3, 7, 15, 31;$
$a_n = 2^{n-1} \cdot 3 + 2^{n-2} + 2^{n-3} + \cdots + 1$

39 (a) $\$256$
(b) $d_n = 4^n$

Section 11.2

1 Not arithmetic

3 Not arithmetic

5 $a_1 = 2, d = 5$

7 $a_1 = 7, d = 3$

9 $a_1 = 6, d = 11$

11 $11^2 + 12^2 + 13^2 + \cdots + 21^2$

13 $-6 - 3 + 0 + 3 + 6 + 9$

15 $(-1)^0 2^1 + (-1)^1 2^2 + (-1)^2 2^3 + \cdots (-1)^6 2^7$

17 $\sum_{n=0}^{4}(10 + 3n)$

19 $\sum_{n=0}^{5}(30 - 5n)$

21 $500,500$

23 2625

25 -561

27 -111.3

29 -132

31 (a)   (i) $24,717; 41,129; 62,248$; total

number of deaths up to that year

    (ii) 12,110; 16,412; 21,119; deaths in each year

(b) a_{n+1}; deaths in year $n + 1$

33   0

35   20

•37   784

39   $16n^2$

41 (a) $1, n$
    (b) $n, n(n + 1)/2$

43 (a)   297

Section 11.3

1   Yes, $a = 2$, ratio $= 1/2$

3   No. Ratio between successive terms is not constant

5   1,572,768

7   5.997

9   781.248

11   7.199

13   $\sum_{n=1}^{6} (-1)^{n+1}(3^n)$

15   $\sum_{n=0}^{5} (-1)^n 32(\frac{1}{2})^n$

17 (a)   \$64,735.69
    (b)   \$65,358.46

19   \$26,870.37

21 (a)   \$12,351.86
    (b)   Shortly before 20th deposit

Section 11.4

1   Yes, $a = y^2$, ratio $= y$

3   Yes, $a = 1$, ratio $= -x$

5   $y^2/(1 - y), |y| < 1$

7   $-4/3$

9   0.011

11   $32/3$

13 (a) $0.23 + 0.23(0.01) + 0.23(0.01)^2 + \cdots$
    (b) $0.23/(1 - 0.01) = 23/99$

15   $613/99$

17   $431/900$

19   $Q_3 = 260.400$
    $Q_{40} = 260.417$
    Approaches 260.417 mg

23   \$926.40

25 (a)   \$1000
    (b)   When the interest rate is 5%, the present value equals the principal.
    (c)   The value of the bond.
    (d)   Because the present value is more than the principal.

Chapter 11 Review

1 (a) $1 + 5 + 9 + 13 + 17$
    (b)   45

3   $\sum_{n=0}^{10} (100 - 10n)$

5   Yes, $a = 1$, ratio $= -y^2$

7   $1/(1 + y^2), |y| < 1$

9 (a) $1, 4, 9, 16$; n^2
    (b) $1, 3, 5, 7, 2n - 1$

11 (b) $c_n = 300 + \frac{1}{2}(n - 1)(3n - 46)$
    $c_{12} = 245, c_{50} = 2848$
    (c)   19

13   8160, 8323, 8490, 8787, 9094, 9413, 9742, 10,083, 10,436, 10,801

15 (a) $\sum_{n=1}^{25} 81(1.012)^{n-1}$
    (b)   2345.291 bn barrels

17 (a)   Increase
    (b)   \$121,609.86
    (c)   \$2912.62

19 (a)   1365 people
    (b)   1,398,101
    (c)   6 stages

23 (a)

    (b) $1 + \frac{1}{2} + \frac{1}{4} + \cdots + \frac{1}{2^{n-1}}$
    (c)   2

Ch. 11 Understanding

1   True

3   True

5   True

7   True

9   True

11   False

13   True

15   False

17   False

19   False

21   True

23   False

25   False

27   True

29   False

31   False

33   False

Section 12.1

1   $y = 11 - 2x$

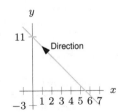

3   $y = 2x^2 + 1$

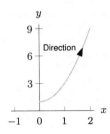

5   $y = (x + 4)^2$

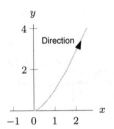

7   $y = x^{3/2}$

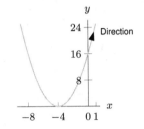

9   $y = (2/3)\ln x, x > 0$

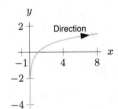

11   $(x^2/4) + (y^2/9) = 1$

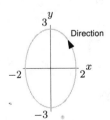

586

13 Lines from $(0,0)$ to $(2,0)$ to $(2,1)$ to $(0,1)$ to $(0,0)$

15 Lines from $(2,0)$ to $(1.5,1)$ to $(0.5,-1)$ to $(0,0)$ to $(0.5,1)$ to $(1.5,-1)$ to $(2,0)$

17 Clockwise for all t.

19 Clockwise: $t < 0$,
Counter-clockwise: $t > 0$.

23 (a) $x = t, y = t^2$
$x = t + 1, y = (t+1)^2$
(b) $x = t, y = (t+2)^2 + 1$
$x = t + 1, y = (t+3)^2 + 1$

25

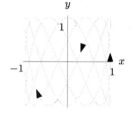

27

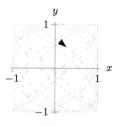

29 (a) Line $y = x$
(b) Circle, with starting point $(1,0)$ and period 2π
(c) Ellipse, with starting point $(1,0)$ and period 2π

31 $x = t, y = -4t + 7$

33

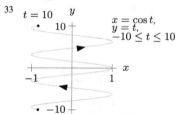

35 (a) $x = t, y = -16t^2 + 48t + 6$
(b)

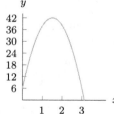

(c) 6 feet
(d) 3 seconds
(e) 42 feet

Section 12.2

1 $(0,0)$; $3/2$

3 $(-1,-3)$; 4

5 $x = 3\sin t, y = 3\cos t, 0 \le t \le 2\pi$

7 $x = -7\cos t, y = -7\sin t, 0 \le t \le 2\pi$

9 $x = 3+4\sin t, y = 1+4\cos t, 0 \le t \le 2\pi$

11 $x = -1 - 3\cos t, y = -2 - 3\sin t,$ $0 \le t \le 2\pi$

13 (a) Center $(2,-4)$, radius $\sqrt{20}$
(b) Center $(-1,2)$, radius $\sqrt{11}$

15 Parabola:
$y = (x-2)^2, 1 \le x \le 3$

17 $x = 4(y-3)^2, 2 \le y \le 4.$

19 Implicit: $xy = 1, x > 0$
Explicit: $y = 1/x, x > 0$
Parametric: $x = t, y = 1/t, t > 0$

21 Explicit: $y = \sqrt{4 - x^2}$
Implicit: $y^2 = 4 - x^2$ or $x^2 + y^2 = 4, y > 0$
Parametric: $x = 4\cos t, y = 4\sin t,$ with $0 \le t \le \pi$

23 (a) $x = t, y = 1$
(b) $x = t + \cos t, y = 1 - \sin t$

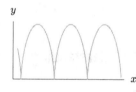

Section 12.3

1 (a) $(0,0); 24; 10$
(b) $(x^2/144) + (y^2/25) = 1$

3 (a) $(-2,-1); 6; 10$
(b) $((x+2)^2/9) + ((y+1)^2/25) = 1$

5 $x = 12\cos t, y = 5\sin t, 0 \le t \le 2\pi$

7 $x = -2 - 3\cos t, y = -1 + 5\sin t,$ $0 \le t \le 2\pi$

9 Same ellipse; traced opposite direction

11 $((x + 2)^2/9) + ((y + 5)^2/25) = 1;$ $(-2,-5); 3; 5$

13 $(x - 1/2)^2 + (y+1)^2/4 = 1; (1/2,-1);$ $1; 2$

15 $((x-3)^2/4) + ((y-2)^2/9) = 1; (3,2);$ $2; 3$

17 (a) Center $(-1,3)$, major axis $a = \sqrt{6}$, minor axis $b = 2$

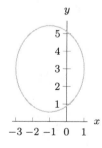

(b) Center $(3/2, -1)$, major axis $a = \sqrt{39}/2$, minor axis $b = \sqrt{13/2}$

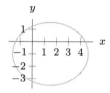

19 $h < k < 0 < a < b$

21 (b) Min$= r_0/(1 + \epsilon)$
Max$= r_0/(1 - \epsilon)$
(c) Center$= (8,0)$

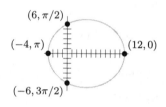

(d) $2r_0/(1 - \epsilon^2)$

23 (a) $\left(\dfrac{2x - r_m + r_e}{r_e + r_m}\right)^2 + \dfrac{y^2}{b^2} = 1$
(b) $b = \sqrt{r_e r_m}$

Section 12.4

1 (a) $(5,0); (-5,0); (0,0)$
(b) $y = x/5; y = -x/5$
(c) $(x^2/25) - y^2 = 1$

3 (a) $(2,7); (2,-1); (2,3)$
(b) $y = (4x+1)/3; y = (-4x + 17)/3$
(c) $(y^2/16) - ((x-2)^2/9) = 1$

5 $x = 5/\cos t, y = \tan t;$
Right half: $0 \le t < \pi/2, 3\pi/2 < t < 2\pi$

7 $x = 2 + 4\tan t, y = 3 + 3/\cos t;$
Lower half: $\pi/2 < t < 3\pi/2$

9 I; $0 < b < k < h < a.$

11 (a) Center $(-5,2)$; Vertices $(-5 \pm \sqrt{6}, 2)$; Asymptotes $y = \pm(2/\sqrt{6})(x + 5) + 2$
(b) Center $(-1,-2)$; Vertices $(-1 \pm \sqrt{14}, -2)$; Asymptotes $y = \pm(x+1) - 2$

13 $((y + 1)^2/4) - ((x - 2)^2/9) = 1$
$(2,-1);$ up-down; 3; 2

15 $((x - 2)^2/4) - ((y - 1)^2/9) = 1$
$(2,1);$ right-left; 2; 3

17 $((y + 1/3)^2/8) - ((x + 3/2)^2/9) = 1$
$(-3/2, -1/3);$ up-down; 3; $2\sqrt{2}$

380

Section 12.5

1 $\sqrt{10}$

3 (a), (b), (c)

5 $(0, \pm\sqrt{7})$

7 Hyperbola; x-axis

9 Parabola; x-axis

11 (a), (b), (c)

13 $(\pm\sqrt{2}, 0)$

15 $y = -(1/12)x^2$

17 $(-2, 1); (-2, 9/4)$

19 $(1/2, 3/4); (1/2, 1)$

21 $y = (3/4)(x-2)^2 - 3; (2, -8/3); y = -10/3$

23 $(0, 3); (0, 3 \pm \sqrt{24})$

25 $x^2/25 + y^2/(50/3) = 1; (\pm 5/\sqrt{3}, 0)$

27 $(2, -2 \pm 5); (2, -2 \pm \sqrt{29})$

29 $(-4, -7 \pm \sqrt{20}); (-4, -7 \pm 10)$

31 $(x-3)^2 - (y-4)^2/9 = 1; (3 \pm \sqrt{10}, 4)$

33 $x^2/25 + y^2/21 = 1$

35 Yes

37 Distance doubles

39 (a) 298 million km
    (b) $(x-3)^2/149^2 + y^2/148.970^2 = 1$

41 (a) Hyperbola
    (b) $y^2/196 - x^2/64 = 1; y^2/49 - x^2/64 = 1$
    (c) $y = 14\sqrt{1 + x^2/64}; y = -7\sqrt{1 + x^2/64}$

Section 12.6

3 $\sinh x \to (e^x)/2$ as $x \to \infty$
   $\sinh x \to -(e^{-x})/2$ as $x \to -\infty$

5 $x = \sinh t, y = -\cosh t, -\infty < t < \infty$

7 $x = 2 + \cosh t, y = 3 + \sinh t, -\infty < t < \infty$

9 $x = 1 + 2\cosh t, y = -1 + 3\sinh t, -\infty < t < \infty$

11 $x = -3 + (\cosh t)/2, y = 1 + \sinh t, -\infty < t < \infty$

13 $x = 1 + (1/\sqrt{2})\cosh t, y = -2 + \sqrt{2}\sinh t, -\infty < t < \infty$

15 $x = 1 + \cosh t, y = 2 + \sinh t, -\infty < t < \infty$

17 $x = 1 + \sqrt{2}\sinh t, y = -2\sqrt{2}\cosh t, -\infty < t < \infty$

19 $x = h + a\cosh t$ and $y = k + b\sinh t$

21 Yes, $\cosh 2x = \cosh^2 x + \sinh^2 x$

25 $\sin(ix) = i\sinh x$

Chapter 12 Review

1 $x = 3\cos t, y = -3\sin t, 0 \le t \le 2\pi$

3 $x = -2\cos t, y = 2\sin t, 0 \le t \le 2\pi$

5 $x = 5\cos t, y = 7\sin t, 0 \le t \le 2\pi$

7 $x = -3\cos t, y = -7\sin t, 0 \le t \le 2\pi$

9 Circle; $(0, 3); \sqrt{5}$

11 Hyperbola, $(0, 1); 2; 3$; left-right

13 Ellipse, $(5, 0); 2; 3$

15 Hyperbola, $(-1/3, 1/2); \sqrt{3}; \sqrt{2}$; up-down

17 $(\pm\sqrt{21}, 0)$

19 $(0, 1/20); y = -1/20$

21 $x = \cos t, y = \sin t$

23 Circle; $(-1, 0); 1$

25 Ellipse; $(1, -\frac{1}{3}); 1; \sqrt{2/3}$

27 No, since $(0, 1)$ not on curve

29 (a) $x = 10\cos t, y = 10\sin t$
    (b) $x = 10\cos t + 3\cos 8t$
         $y = 10\sin t + 3\sin 8t$
    (c)

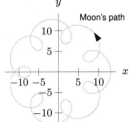

Ch. 12 Understanding

1 True

3 True

5 False

7 False

9 False

11 True

13 False

15 True

17 True

19 True

21 False

23 False

25 True

27 False

29 False

31 True

33 False

Select Chapters
from the
Student Solutions Manual

CHAPTER ONE

Solutions for Section 1.1

Exercises

1. $f(6.9) = 2.9$.

5. $m = f(v)$.

9. (a) Since the vertical intercept is $(0, 40)$, we have $f(0) = 40$.
   (b) Since the horizontal intercept is $(2, 0)$, we have $f(2) = 0$.

13. Appropriate axes are shown in Figure 1.1.

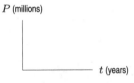

Figure 1.1

Problems

17. (a) When there is no snow, it is equivalent to no rain. Thus, the vertical intercept is 0. Since every ten inches of snow is equivalent to one inch of rain, we can specify the slope as

$$\frac{\Delta \text{rain}}{\Delta \text{snow}} = \frac{1}{10} = 0.1$$

We have a vertical intercept of 0 and a slope of 0.1. Thus, the equation is: $r = f(s) = 0.1s$.
   (b) By substituting 5 in for s, we get $f(5) = 0.1(5) = 0.5$ This tells us that five inches of snow is equivalent to approximately 1/2 inch of rain.
   (c) Substitute 5 inches for $r = f(s)$ in the equation: $5 = 0.1s$. Solving gives $s = 50$. Five inches of rain is equivalent to approximately 50 inches of snow.

21. Judging from the table, $r(s) \geq 116$ for $200 \leq s \leq 1000$. This tells us that the wind speed is at least 116 mph between 200 m and 1000 m above the ground.

25. (a) Figure 1.2 shows the plot of R versus t. R is a function of t because no vertical line intersects the graph in more than one place.
   (b) Figure 1.3 shows the plot of F versus t. F is a function of t because no vertical line intersects the graph in more than one place.

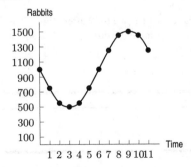

Figure 1.2: The graph of R versus t

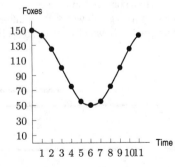

Figure 1.3: The graph of F versus t

(c) Figure 1.4 shows the plot of F versus R. We have also drawn the vertical line corresponding to $R = 567$. This tells us that F is not a function of R because there is a vertical line that intersects the graph twice. In fact the lines $R = 567$, $R = 750$, $R = 1000$, $R = 1250$, and $R = 1433$ all intersect the graph twice. However, the existence of any one of them is enough to guarantee that F is not a function of R.

(d) Figure 1.5 shows the plot of R versus F. We have drawn the vertical line corresponding to $F = 57$. This tells us that R is not a function of F because there is a vertical line that intersects the graph twice. In fact the lines $F = 57$, $F = 75$, $F = 100$, $F = 125$, and $F = 143$ all intersect the graph twice. However, the existence of any one of them is enough to guarantee that R is not a function of F.

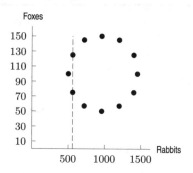

Figure 1.4: The graph of F versus R

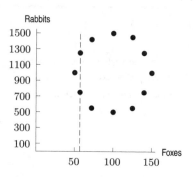

Figure 1.5: The graph of R versus F

29. A possible graph is shown in Figure 1.6.

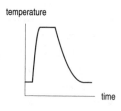

Figure 1.6

33. (a) Since the person starts out 5 miles from home, the vertical intercept on the graph must be 5. Thus, (i) and (ii) are possibilities. However, since the person rides 5 mph away from home, after 1 hour the person is 10 miles from home. Thus, (ii) is the correct graph.

(b) Since this person also starts out 5 miles from home, (i) and (ii) are again possibilities. This time, however, the person is moving at 10 mph and so is 15 miles from home after 1 hour. Thus, (i) is correct.

(c) The person starts out 10 miles from home so the vertical intercept must be 10. The fact that the person reaches home after 1 hour means that the horizontal intercept is 1. Thus, (v) is correct.

(d) Starting out 10 miles from home means that the vertical intercept is 10. Being half way home after 1 hour means that the distance from home is 5 miles after 1 hour. Thus, (iv) is correct.

(e) We are looking for a graph with vertical intercept of 5 and where the distance is 10 after 1 hour. This is graph (ii). Notice that graph (iii), which depicts a bicyclist stopped 10 miles from home, does not match any of the stories.

Exercises

1. We have $G(3) - G(-1) > 0$.

5. Using the points on g

$$\text{Average rate of change } = \frac{g(6.1) - g(2.2)}{6.1 - 2.2} = \frac{4.9 - 2.9}{6.1 - 2.2} = 0.513.$$

9. To decide if CD sales are an increasing or decreasing function of LP sales, we must read the table in the direction in which LP sales increase. This means we read the table from right to left. As the number of LP sales increases, the number of CD sales decrease. Thus, CD sales are a decreasing function of LP sales.

Problems

13. According to the table in the text, the tree has $139\mu g$ of carbon-14 after 3000 years from death and $123\mu g$ of carbon-14 after 4000 years from death. Because the function $L = g(t)$ is decreasing, the tree must have died between 3,000 and 4,000 years ago.

17. (a) From the graph, we see that $g(4) \approx 2$ and $g(0) \approx 0$. Thus,

$$\frac{g(4) - g(0)}{4 - 0} \approx \frac{2 - 0}{4 - 0} = \frac{1}{2}.$$

(b) The line segment joining the points in part (a), as well as the line segment in part (d), is shown on the graph in Figure 1.7.

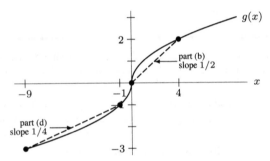

Figure 1.7

(c) From the graph, $g(-9) \approx -3$ and $g(-1) \approx -1$. Thus,

$$\frac{g(b) - g(a)}{b - a} \approx \frac{-1 - (-3)}{-1 - (-9)} = \frac{2}{8} = \frac{1}{4}.$$

(d) The line segment in part (c) with slope $(1/4)$ is shown in Figure 1.7.

21. (a) Average rate of change $= \dfrac{\Delta y}{\Delta x} = \dfrac{13 - 4}{2 - 1} = 9$

(b) Average rate of change $= \dfrac{\Delta y}{\Delta x} = \dfrac{n - k}{m - j}$

(c) The average rate of change is

$$\begin{aligned}
\frac{\Delta y}{\Delta x} &= \frac{f(x+h) - f(x)}{(x+h) - x} = \frac{(3(x+h)^2 + 1) - (3x^2 + 1)}{(x+h) - x} \\
&= \frac{(3(x^2 + 2xh + h^2) + 1) - (3x^2 + 1)}{h} \\
&= \frac{3x^2 + 6xh + 3h^2 + 1 - 3x^2 - 1}{h} \\
&= \frac{6xh + 3h^2}{h} \\
&= 6x + 3h.
\end{aligned}$$

25. **(a)** We have

$$\frac{f(150) - f(25)}{150 - 25} = \frac{5.50 - 5.50}{125} = 0°\text{C/meter}.$$

This tells us that on average the temperature changes by 0°C per meter of depth between 25 meters and 150 meters.

(b) We have

$$\frac{f(75) - f(25)}{75 - 25} = \frac{5.10 - 5.50}{50} = -0.008°\text{C/meter}.$$

This tells us that on average the temperature drops by 0.008°C per meter of depth, or by 0.8°C per 100 meters of depth, on this interval.

(c) We have

$$\frac{f(200) - f(100)}{200 - 100} = \frac{6.00 - 5.10}{100} = 0.009°\text{C/meter}.$$

This tells us that on average the temperature rises by 0.009°C per meter of depth, or by 0.9°C per 100 meters of depth, on this interval.

Solutions for Section 1.3

Exercises

1. The function g is not linear even though $g(x)$ increases by $\Delta g(x) = 50$ each time. This is because the value of x does not increase by the same amount each time. The value of x increases from 0 to 100 to 300 to 600 taking steps that get larger each time.

5. This table could represent a linear function because the rate of change of $p(\gamma)$ is constant. Between consecutive data points, $\Delta \gamma = -1$ and $\Delta p(\gamma) = 10$. Thus, the rate of change is $\Delta p(\gamma)/\Delta \gamma = -10$. Since this is constant, the function could be linear.

9. The vertical intercept is -3000, which tells us that if no items are sold, the company loses $3000. The slope is 0.98. Since

$$\text{Slope} = \frac{\Delta \text{profit}}{\Delta \text{number}} = \frac{0.98}{1},$$

this tells us that, for each item the company sells, their profit increases by $0.98.

Problems

13. The 78.9 tells us that there were approximately 79 cases on March 17. The 30.1 tells us that the number of cases increased by about 30 a day.

17. We know that the area of a circle of radius r is

$$\text{Area} = \pi r^2$$

while its circumference is given by

$$\text{Circumference} = 2\pi r.$$

Thus, a table of values for area and circumference is

Table 1.1

Radius	0	1	2	3	4	5	6
Area	0	π	4π	9π	16π	25π	36π
Circumference	0	2π	4π	6π	8π	10π	12π

(a) In the area function we see that the rate of change between pairs of points does not remain constant and thus the function is not linear. For example, the rate of change between the points $(0, 0)$ and $(2, 4\pi)$ is not equal to the rate of change between the points $(3, 9\pi)$ and $(6, 36\pi)$. The rate of change between $(0, 0)$ and $(2, 4\pi)$ is

$$\frac{\Delta\text{area}}{\Delta\text{radius}} = \frac{4\pi - 0}{2 - 0} = \frac{4\pi}{2} = 2\pi$$

while the rate of change between $(3, 9\pi)$ and $(6, 36\pi)$ is

$$\frac{\Delta\text{area}}{\Delta\text{radius}} = \frac{36\pi - 9\pi}{6 - 3} = \frac{27\pi}{3} = 9\pi.$$

On the other hand, if we take only pairs of points from the circumference function, we see that the rate of change remains constant. For instance, for the pair $(0, 0)$, $(1, 2\pi)$ the rate of change is

$$\frac{\Delta\text{circumference}}{\Delta\text{radius}} = \frac{2\pi - 0}{1 - 0} = \frac{2\pi}{1} = 2\pi.$$

For the pair $(2, 4\pi)$, $(4, 8\pi)$ the rate of change is

$$\frac{\Delta\text{circumference}}{4 - 2} = \frac{4\pi}{2} = 2\pi.$$

For the pair $(1, 2\pi)$, $(6, 12\pi)$ the rate of change is

$$\frac{\Delta\text{circumference}}{\Delta\text{radius}} = \frac{12\pi - 2\pi}{6 - 1} = \frac{10\pi}{5} = 2\pi.$$

Picking any pair of data points would give a rate of change of 2π.

(b) The graphs for area and circumference as indicated in Table 1.1 are shown in Figure 1.8 and Figure 1.9.

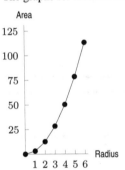

Figure 1.8

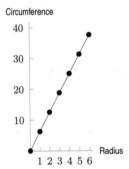

Figure 1.9

(c) From part (a) we see that the rate of change of the circumference function is 2π. This tells us that for a given circle, when we increase the length of the radius by one unit, the length of the circumference would increase by 2π units. Equivalently, if we decreased the length of the radius by one unit, the length of the circumference would decrease by 2π.

21. (a) No. The values of $f(d)$ first drop, then rise, so f is not linear.

(b) For $d \geq 150$, the graph looks linear. See Figure 1.10.

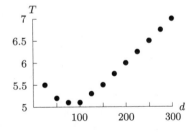

Figure 1.10

(c) For $d \geq 150$ the average rate of change appears to be constant. Each time the depth goes up by $\Delta d = 25$ meters, the temperature rises by $\Delta T = 0.25°C$, so the average rate of change is $\Delta T/\Delta d = 0.25/25 = 0.01°C/meter$. In other words, the temperature rises by $0.01°C$ for each extra meter in depth.

25. (a) The slope is $m = -0.062$, which tells us that the glacier area in the park goes down by 0.062 km^2/year. The A-intercept is $b = 16.2$, which tells us that in the year 2000, the area was 16.2 km^2.

(b) We have $f(15) = 16.2 - 0.062(15) = 15.27$, which tells us that in the year 2015, the area is predicted to be 15.27 km^2.

(c) Letting $\Delta t = 15$, we have

$$m = \frac{\Delta A}{\Delta t} = -0.062$$
$$\underline{\Delta A}$$

Solutions for Section 1.4

Exercises

1. Rewriting in slope-intercept form:

$$5(x + y) = 4$$
$$5x + 5y = 4$$
$$5y = 4 - 5x$$
$$\frac{5y}{5} = \frac{4}{5} - \frac{5x}{5}$$
$$y = \frac{4}{5} - x$$

5. Rewriting in slope-intercept form:

$$y - 0.7 = 5(x - 0.2)$$
$$y - 0.7 = 5x - 1$$
$$y = 5x - 1 + 0.7$$
$$y = 5x - 0.3$$
$$y = -0.3 + 5x$$

9. Rewriting in slope-intercept form:

$$\frac{x+y}{7} = 3$$
$$x + y = 21$$
$$y = 21 - x$$

13. Yes. Write the function as

$$C(r) = 0 + 2\pi r,$$

so $C(r)$ is linear with $b = 0$ and $m = 2\pi$.

17. We can put the slope $m = 3$ and y-intercept $b = 8$ directly into the general equation $y = b + mx$ to get $y = 8 + 3x$.

21. Since the slope is $m = 0.1$, the equation is

$$y = b + 0.1x.$$

Substituting $x = -0.1$, $y = 0.02$ to find b gives

$$0.02 = b + 0.1(-0.1)$$
$$0.02 = b - 0.01$$
$$b = 0.03.$$

The equation is $y = 0.03 + 0.1x$.

25. Since the function is linear, we can choose any two points to find its formula. We use the form

$$q = b + mp$$

to get the number of bottles sold as a function of the price per bottle. We use the two points $(0.50, 1500)$ and $(1.00, 500)$. We begin by finding the slope, $\Delta q / \Delta p = (500 - 1500)/(1.00 - 0.50) = -2000$. Next, we substitute a point into our equation using our slope of -2000 bottles sold per dollar increase in price and solve to find b, the q-intercept. We use the point $(1.00, 500)$:

$$500 = b - 2000 \cdot 1.00$$
$$2500 = b.$$

Therefore,

$$q = 2500 - 2000p.$$

29. Since the function is linear, we can use any two points (from the graph) to find its formula. We use the form

$$u = b + mn$$

to get the meters of shelf space used as a function of the number of different medicines stocked. We use the two points $(60, 5)$ and $(120, 10)$. We begin by finding the slope, $\Delta u / \Delta n = (10 - 5)/(120 - 60) = 1/12$. Next, we substitute a point into our equation using our slope of $1/12$ meters of shelf space per medicine and solve to find b, the u-intercept. We use the point $(60, 5)$:

$$5 = b + (1/12) \cdot 60$$
$$0 = b.$$

Therefore,

$$u = (1/12)n.$$

The fact that $b = 0$ is not surprising, since we would expect that, if no medicines are stocked, they should take up no shelf space.

Problems

33. Using our formula for j, we have

$$h(-2) = j(-2) = 30(0.2)^{-2} = 750$$
$$h(1) = j(1) = 30(0.2)^1 = 6.$$

This means that $h(t) = b + mt$ where

$$m = \frac{h(1) - h(-2)}{1 - (-2)} = \frac{6 - 750}{3} = -248.$$

Solving for b, we have

$$h(-2) = b - 248(-2)$$
$$b = h(-2) + 248(-2) = 750 + 248(-2) = 254,$$

so $h(t) = 254 - 248t$.

37. (a) The results are in Table 1.2.

Table 1.2

t	0	1	2	3	4
$v = f(t)$	1000	990.2	980.4	970.6	960.8

(b) The speed of the bullet is decreasing at a constant rate of 9.8 meters/sec every second. To confirm this, calculate the rate of change in velocity over every second. We get

$$\frac{\Delta v}{\Delta t} = \frac{990.2 - 1000}{1 - 0} = \frac{980.4 - 990.2}{2 - 1} = \frac{970.6 - 980.4}{3 - 2} = \frac{960.8 - 970.6}{4 - 3} = -9.8.$$

Since the value of $\Delta v / \Delta t$ comes out the same, -9.8, for every interval, we can say that the bullet is slowing down at a constant rate. This makes sense as the constant force of gravity acts to slow the upward moving bullet down at a constant rate.

(c) The slope, -9.8, is the rate at which the velocity is changing. The v-intercept of 1000 is the initial velocity of the bullet. The t-intercept of $1000/9.8 = 102.04$ is the time at which the bullet stops moving and starts to head back to Earth.

(d) Since Jupiter's gravitational field would exert a greater pull on the bullet, we would expect the bullet to slow down at a faster rate than a bullet shot from earth. On earth, the rate of change of the bullet is -9.8, meaning that the bullet is slowing down at the rate of 9.8 meters per second. On Jupiter, we expect that the coefficient of t, which represents the rate of change, to be a more negative number (less than -9.8). Similarly, since the gravitational pull near the surface of the moon is less, we expect that the bullet would slow down at a lesser rate than on earth. So, the coefficient of t should be a less negative number (greater than -9.8 but less than 0).

41. (a) Since q is linear, $q = b + mp$, where

$$m = \frac{\Delta q}{\Delta p} = \frac{65 - 45}{2.10 - 2.50}$$
$$= \frac{20}{-0.40} = -50 \text{ gallons/dollar.}$$

Thus, $q = b - 50p$ and since $q = 65$ if $p = 2.10$,

$$65 = b - 50(2.10)$$
$$65 = b - 105$$
$$b = 65 + 105 = 170.$$

So,

$$q = 170 - 50p.$$

(b) The slope is $m = -50$ gallons per dollar, which tells us that the quantity of gasoline demanded in one time period decreases by 50 gallons for each \$1 increase in price.

(c) If $p = 0$ then $q = 170$, which means that if the price of gas were \$0 per gallon, then the quantity demanded in one time period would be 170 gallons per month. This means if gas were free, a person would want 170 gallons. If $q = 0$ then $170 - 50p = 0$, so $170 = 50p$ and $p = 170/50 = 3.40$. This tells us that (according to the model), at a price of \$3.40 per gallon there will be no demand for gasoline. In the real world, this is not likely.

45. (a) We know that $r = 1/t$. Table 1.3 gives values of r. From the table, we see that $\Delta r/\Delta H \approx 0.01/2 = 0.005$, so $r = b + 0.005H$. Solving for b, we have

$$0.070 = b + 0.005 \cdot 20$$
$$b = 0.070 - 0.1 = -0.03.$$

Thus, a formula for r is given by $r = 0.005H - 0.03$.

Table 1.3 *Development time t (in days) for an organism as a function of ambient temperature H (in °C)*

H, °C	20	22	24	26	28	30
r, rate	0.070	0.080	0.090	0.100	0.110	0.120

(b) From Problem 44, we know that if $r = b + kH$ then the number of degree-days is given by $S = 1/k$. From part (a) of this problem, we have $k = 0.005$, so $S = 1/0.005 = 200$.

Solutions for Section 1.5

Exercises

1. (a) $f(x)$ has a y-intercept of 1 and a positive slope. Thus, (ii) must be the graph of $f(x)$.
(b) $g(x)$ has a y-intercept of 1 and a negative slope. Thus, (iii) must be the graph of $g(x)$.
(c) $h(x)$ is a constant function with a y intercept of 1. Thus, (i) must be the graph of $h(x)$.

5. (a) Since the slopes are $\frac{1}{4}$ and -6, we see that $y = \frac{1}{4}x$ has the greater slope.
(b) Since the y-intercepts are 0 and 1, we see that $y = 1 - 6x$ has the greater y-intercept.

9. These lines are parallel because they have the same slope, 5.

13. These lines are neither parallel nor perpendicular. They do not have the same slopes, nor are their slopes negative reciprocals (if they were, one of the slopes would be negative).

Problems

17. (a) This line, being parallel to l, has the same slope. Since the slope of l is $-\frac{2}{3}$, the equation of this line is

$$y = b - \frac{2}{3}x.$$

To find b, we use the fact that $P = (6, 5)$ is on this line. This gives

$$5 = b - \frac{2}{3}(6)$$
$$5 = b - 4$$
$$b = 9.$$

So the equation of the line is

$$y = 9 - \frac{2}{3}x.$$

(b) This line is perpendicular to line l, and so its slope is given by

$$m = \frac{-1}{-2/3} = \frac{3}{2}.$$

Therefore its equation is

$$y = b + \frac{3}{2}x.$$

We again use point P to find b:

$$5 = b + \frac{3}{2}(6)$$
$$5 = b + 9$$
$$b = -4.$$

This gives

$$y = -4 + \frac{3}{2}x.$$

(c) Figure 1.11 gives a graph of line l together with point P and the two lines we have found.

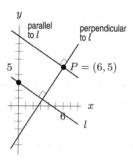

Figure 1.11: Line l and two lines through P, one parallel and one perpendicular to l

21.

(a)
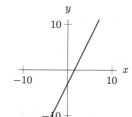

(b)
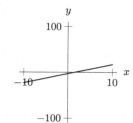

(c)
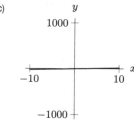

Figure 1.12

(d) If the width of the window remains constant and the height of the window increases, then the graph will appear less steep.

25. We see in the figure from the problem that line l_2 is perpendicular to line l_1. We can find the slope of line l_1 because we are given the x-intercept $(3, 0)$ and the y-intercept $(0, 2)$.

$$m_1 = \frac{2 - 0}{0 - 3} = \frac{2}{-3} = \frac{-2}{3}$$

Therefore, we know that the slope of line l_2 is

$$m_2 = \frac{-1}{\frac{-2}{3}} = \frac{3}{2}$$

We also know that l_2 passes through the origin $(0,0)$ and therefore has a y-intercept of zero.
Hence, the equation of l_2 is

$$y = \frac{3}{2}x.$$

29. The altitude is perpendicular to the side $\overline{BC}$. The slope of $\overline{BC}$ is

$$\frac{8-2}{9-(-3)} = \frac{6}{12} = \frac{1}{2}.$$

Therefore the slope of the altitude is the negative reciprocal of $1/2$, which is -2, and it passes through the point $(-4, 5)$. Using the point-slope formula, we find the equation $y - 5 = -2(x + 4)$, or $y = -2x - 3$.

33. (a) We are looking at the amount of municipal solid waste, W, as a function of year, t, and the two points are $(1960, 88.1)$ and $(2000, 234)$. For the model, we assume that the quantity of solid waste is a linear function of year. The slope of the line is

$$m = \frac{234 - 88.1}{2000 - 1960} = \frac{145.9}{40} = 3.65 \frac{\text{millions of tons}}{\text{year}}.$$

This slope tells us that the amount of solid waste generated in the cities of the US has been going up at a rate of 3.65 million tons per year. To find the equation of the line, we must find the vertical intercept. We substitute the point $(1960, 88.1)$ and the slope $m = 3.65$ into the equation $W = b + mt$:

$$W = b + mt$$
$$88.1 = b + (3.65)(1960)$$
$$88.1 = b + 7154$$
$$-7065.9 = b.$$

The equation of the line is $W = -7065.9 + 3.65t$, where W is the amount of municipal solid waste in the US in millions of tons, and t is the year.

(b) How much solid waste does this model predict in the year 2020? We can graph the line and find the vertical coordinate when $t = 2020$, or we can substitute $t = 2020$ into the equation of the line, and solve for W:

$$W = -7065.9 + 3.65t$$
$$W = -7065.9 + (3.65)(2020) = 307.1.$$

The model predicts that in the year 2020, the solid waste generated by cities in the US will be 307.1 million tons.

Solutions for Section 1.6

1. (a) Since the points lie on a line of positive slope, $r = 1$.
(b) Although the points do not lie on a line, they are tending upward as x increases. So, there is a positive correlation and a reasonable guess is $r = 0.7$.
(c) The points are scattered all over. There is neither an upward nor a downward trend, so there is probably no correlation between x and y, so $r = 0$.
(d) These points are very close to lying on a line with negative slope, so the best correlation coefficient is $r = -0.98$.
(e) Although these points are quite scattered, there is a downward slope, so $r = -0.25$ is probably a good answer.
(f) These points are less scattered than those in part (e). The best answer here is $r = -0.5$.

5. (a) See Figure 1.13.

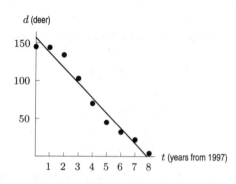

Figure 1.13

(b) Estimates vary, but should be roughly $d = -20t + 157$.
(c) A calculator gives $d = -20t + 157$.
(d) The slope of -20 tells us that, on average, 20 deer die per year. The vertical intercept value is the initial population and should be close to 145. The horizontal intercept is the number of years until all the deer have died.
(e) There is a strong negative correlation, $(r \approx -0.98)$.

Solutions for Chapter 1 Review

Exercises

1. Any w value can give two z values. For example, if $w = 0$,

$$7 \cdot 0^2 + 5 = z^2$$
$$\pm\sqrt{5} = z,$$

so there are two z values (one positive and one negative) for $w = 0$. Thus, z is not a function of w.
A similar argument shows that w is not a function of z.

5. Both of the relationships are functions because any quantity of gas determines the quantity of coffee that can be bought, and vice versa. For example, if you buy 30 gallons of gas, spending $60, you buy 4 pounds of coffee.

9. This table could represent a linear function, because, for the values shown, the rate of change of $a(t)$ is constant. For the given data points, between consecutive points, $\Delta t = 3$, and $\Delta a(t) = 2$. Thus, in each case, the rate of change is $\Delta a(t)/\Delta t = 2/3$. Since the rate of change is constant, the function could be linear.

13. (a) Since the slopes are 2 and -15, we see that $y = 7 + 2x$ has the greater slope.
(b) Since the y-intercepts are 7 and 8, we see that $y = 8 - 15x$ has the greater y-intercept.

17. These lines are perpendicular because one slope, $-\frac{1}{3}$, is the negative reciprocal of the other, 3.

Problems

21. The starting value is $b = 12{,}000$, and the growth rate is $m = 225$, so $h(t) = 12{,}000 + 225t$.

25. The line $y + 4x = 7$ has slope -4. Therefore the parallel line has slope -4 and equation $y - 5 = -4(x - 1)$ or $y = -4x + 9$. The perpendicular line has slope $\frac{-1}{(-4)} = \frac{1}{4}$ and equation $y - 5 = \frac{1}{4}(x - 1)$ or $y = 0.25x + 4.75$.

29. (a) We have $r_m(0) - r_h(0) = 29 - 7 = 22$. This tells us that in 1995 (year $t = 0$), the name Hannah was ranked 22 places higher than Madison on the list of most popular names. (Recall that the lower the ranking, the higher a name's position on the list.)

(b) We have $r_m(9) - r_h(9) = 3 - 5 = -2$. This tells us that in 2004 (year $t = 9$), the name Hannah was ranked 2 places lower than Madison on the list of most popular names.

(c) We have $r_m(t) < r_a(t)$ for $t = 5$ to $t = 9$. This tells us that the name Madison was ranked higher than the name Alexis on the list of most popular names in the years 2000 to 2004.

33. In Figure 1.14 the graph of the hair length is steepest just after each haircut, assumed to be at the beginning of each year. As the year progresses, the growth is slowed by split ends. By the end of the year, the hair is breaking off as fast as it is growing, so the graph has leveled off. At this time the hair is cut again. Once again it grows until slowed by the split ends. Then it is cut. This continues for five years when the longest hairs fall out because they have come to the end of their natural lifespan.

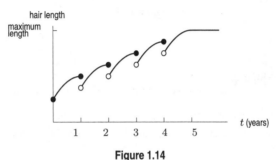

Figure 1.14

37. (a) At 40 mph, fuel consumption is about 28 mpg, so the fuel used is $300/28 = 10.71$ gallons.

(b) At 60 mph, fuel consumption is about 29 mpg. At 70 mph, fuel consumption is about 28 mpg. Therefore, on a 200 mile trip

$$\text{Fuel saved} = \frac{200}{28} - \frac{200}{29} = 0.25 \text{ gallons.}$$

(c) The most fuel-efficient speed is where mpg is a maximum, which is about 55 mph.

41. (a) $C(175) = 11,375$, which means that it costs \$11,375 to produce 175 units of the good.

(b) $C(175) - C(150) = 125$, which means that the cost of producing 175 units is \$125 greater than the cost of producing 150 units. That is, the cost of producing the additional 25 units is an additional \$125.

(c) $\dfrac{C(175) - C(150)}{175 - 150} = \dfrac{125}{25} = 5$, which means that the average per-unit cost of increasing production to 175 units from 150 units is \$5.

45. (a) Since $y = f(x)$, to show that $f(x)$ is linear, we can solve for y in terms of $A, B, C,$ and x.

$$Ax + By = C$$
$$By = C - Ax, \text{ and, since } B \neq 0,$$
$$y = \frac{C}{B} - \frac{A}{B}x$$

Because C/B and $-A/B$ are constants, the formula for $f(x)$ is of the linear form:

$$f(x) = y = b + mx.$$

Thus, f is linear, with slope $m = -(A/B)$ and y-intercept $b = C/B$.

To find the x-intercept, we set $y = 0$ and solve for x:

$$Ax + B(0) = C$$
$$Ax = C, \text{ and, since } A \neq 0,$$
$$x = \frac{C}{A}.$$

Thus, the line crosses the x–axis at $x = C/A$.

(b) (i) Since $A > 0, B > 0, C > 0$, we know that C/A (the x-intercept) and C/B (the y-intercept) are both positive and we have Figure 1.15.

(ii) Since only $C < 0$, we know that C/A and C/B are both negative, and we obtain Figure 1.16.

(iii) Since $A > 0, B < 0, C > 0$, we know that C/A is positive and C/B is negative. Thus, we obtain Figure 1.17.

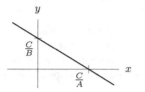

Figure 1.15

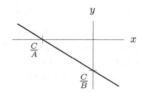

Figure 1.16

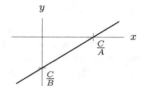

Figure 1.17

CHECK YOUR UNDERSTANDING

1. False. $f(t)$ is functional notation, meaning that f is a function of the variable t.

5. True. The number of people who enter a store in a day and the total sales for the day are related, but neither quantity is uniquely determined by the other.

9. True. A circle does not pass the vertical line test.

13. True. This is the definition of an increasing function.

17. False. Parentheses must be inserted. The correct ratio is $\dfrac{(10 - 2^2) - (10 - 1^2)}{2 - 1} = -3$.

21. False. Writing the equation as $y = (-3/2)x + 7/2$ shows that the slope is $-3/2$.

25. True. A constant function has slope zero. Its graph is a horizontal line.

29. True. At $y = 0$, we have $4x = 52$, so $x = 13$. The x-intercept is $(13, 0)$.

33. False. Substitute the point's coordinates in the equation: $-3 - 4 \neq -2(4 + 3)$.

37. False. The first line does but the second, in slope-intercept form, is $y = (1/8)x + (1/2)$, so it crosses the y-axis at $y = 1/2$.

41. True. The point $(1, 3)$ is on both lines because $3 = -2 \cdot 1 + 5$ and $3 = 6 \cdot 1 - 3$.

45. True. The slope, $\Delta y / \Delta x$ is undefined because Δx is zero for any two points on a vertical line.

49. False. For example, in children there is a high correlation between height and reading ability, but it is clear that neither causes the other.

53. True. There is a perfect fit of the line to the data.

Solutions to Tools for Chapter 1

1.
$$3x = 15$$
$$\frac{3x}{3} = \frac{15}{3}$$
$$x = 5$$

5.
$$y - 5 = 21$$
$$y = 26$$

9.
$$13t + 2 = 47$$
$$13t = 45$$
$$\frac{13t}{13} = \frac{45}{13}$$
$$t = \frac{45}{13}$$

13. We first distribute $\frac{5}{3}(y + 2)$ to obtain:

$$\frac{5}{3}(y + 2) = \frac{1}{2} - y$$
$$\frac{5}{3}y + \frac{10}{3} = \frac{1}{2} - y$$
$$\frac{5}{3}y + y = \frac{1}{2} - \frac{10}{3}$$
$$\frac{5}{3}y + \frac{3y}{} \quad \frac{}{6} - \frac{20}{6}$$
$$\frac{8y}{3} = -\frac{17}{16}$$
$$\left(\frac{3}{8}\right)\frac{8y}{3} = \left(\frac{3}{8}\right)\left(-\frac{17}{6}\right)$$
$$y = -\frac{17}{16}.$$

17. Expanding yields

$$1.06s - 0.01(248.4 - s) = 22.67s$$
$$1.06s - 2.484 + 0.01s = 22.67s$$
$$-21.6s = 2.484$$
$$s = -0.115.$$

21. We have

$$C = \frac{5}{9}(F - 32)$$
$$\frac{9C}{5} = F - 32$$
$$F = \frac{9}{5}C + 32$$

25. We collect all terms involving x and then divide by $2a$:

$$ab + ax = c - ax$$
$$2ax = c - ab$$
$$x = \frac{c - ab}{2a}.$$

29. Solving for x:

$$\frac{a - cx}{b + dx} + a = 0$$

$$\frac{a - cx}{b + dx} = -a$$

$$a - cx = -a(b + dx) = -ab - adx$$

$$adx - cx = -ab - a$$

$$(ad - c)x = -a(b + 1)$$

$$x = -\frac{a(b + 1)}{ad - c}.$$

33. Adding the two equations to eliminate y, we have

$$2x = 8$$

$$x = 4.$$

Using $x = 4$ in the first equation gives

$$4 + y = 3,$$

so

$$y = -1.$$

37. We substitute the expression $-\frac{3}{5}x + 6$ for y in the first equation.

$$2x + 3y = 7$$

$$2x + 3\left(-\frac{3}{5}x + 6\right) = 7$$

$$2x - \frac{9}{5}x + 18 = 7 \quad \text{or}$$

$$\frac{10}{5}x - \frac{9}{5}x + 18 = 7$$

$$\frac{1}{5}x = -11$$

$$x = -55$$

$$y = -\frac{3}{5}(-55) + 6$$

$$y = 39$$

41. We set the equations $y = x$ and $y = 3 - x$ equal to one another.

$$x = 3 - x$$

$$2x = 3$$

$$x = \frac{3}{2} \quad \text{and} \quad y = \frac{3}{2}$$

So the point of intersection is $x = 3/2$, $y = 3/2$.

45. The figure is a square, so $A = (17, 23)$; $B = (0, 40)$; $C = (-17, 23)$.

49. The radius is 4, so $B = (7, 4)$, $A = (11, 0)$.

CHAPTER TWO

Solutions for Section 2.1

Exercises

1. To evaluate when $x = -7$, we substitute -7 for x in the function, giving $f(-7) = -\dfrac{7}{2} - 1 = -\dfrac{9}{2}$.

5. We have
$$y = f(4) = 4 \cdot 4^{3/2} = 4 \cdot 2^3 = 4 \cdot 8 = 32.$$

Solve for x:

$$4x^{3/2} = 6$$
$$x^{3/2} = 6/4$$
$$x^3 = 36/16 = 9/4$$
$$x = \sqrt[3]{9/4}.$$

9. (a) Substituting $x = 0$ gives $g(0) = 0^2 - 5(0) + 6 = 6$.
   (b) Setting $g(x) = 0$ and solving gives $x^2 - 5x + 6 = 0$.
   Factoring gives $(x - 2)(x - 3) = 0$, so $x = 2, 3$.

13. Substituting 4 for t gives
$$P(4) = 170 - 4 \cdot 4 = 154.$$

Similarly, with $t = 2$,
$$P(2) = 170 - 4 \cdot 2 = 162,$$

so
$$P(4) - P(2) = 154 - 162 = -8.$$

17. (a) Reading from the table, we have $f(1) = 2$, $f(-1) = 0$, and $-f(1) = -2$.
   (b) When $x = -1$, $f(x) = 0$.

Problems

21. Substituting $r = 3$ and $h = 2$ gives
$$V = \frac{1}{3}\pi 3^2 \cdot 2 = 6\pi \text{ cubic inches.}$$

25. (a) The table shows $f(6) = 3.7$, so $t = 6$. In a typical June, Chicago has 3.7 inches of rain.
   (b) First evaluate $f(2) = 1.8$. Solving $f(t) = 1.8$ gives $t = 1$ or $t = 2$. Chicago has 1.8 inches of rain in January and in February.

29. (a) In order to find $f(0)$, we need to find the value which corresponds to $x = 0$. The point $(0, 24)$ seems to lie on the graph, so $f(0) = 24$.
   (b) Since $(1, 10)$ seems to lie on this graph, we can say that $f(1) = 10$.
   (c) The point that corresponds to $x = b$ seems to be about $(b, -7)$, so $f(b) = -7$.
   (d) When $x = c$, we see that $y = 0$, so $f(c) = 0$.
   (e) When your input is d, the output is about 20, so $f(d) = 20$.

33. (a) Substituting into $h(t) = -16t^2 + 64t$, we get

$$h(1) = -16(1)^2 + 64(1) = 48$$
$$h(3) = -16(3)^2 + 64(3) = 48$$

Thus the height of the ball is 48 feet after 1 second and after 3 seconds.

(b) The graph of $h(t)$ is in Figure 2.1. The ball is on the ground when $h(t) = 0$. From the graph we see that this occurs at $t = 0$ and $t = 4$. The ball leaves the ground when $t = 0$ and hits the ground at $t = 4$ or after 4 seconds. From the graph we see that the maximum height is 64 ft.

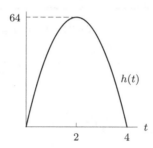

Figure 2.1

37. (a)

n	1	2	3	4	5	6	7	8	9	10	11	12
$f(n)$	1	1	2	3	5	8	13	21	34	55	89	144

(b) We note that for every value of n, we can find a unique value for $f(n)$ (by adding the two previous values of the function). This satisfies the definition of function, so $f(n)$ is a function.

(c) Using the pattern, we can figure out $f(0)$ from the fact that we must have

$$f(2) = f(1) + f(0).$$

Since $f(2) = f(1) = 1$, we have

$$1 = 1 + f(0),$$

so

$$f(0) = 0.$$

Likewise, using the fact that $f(1) = 1$ and $f(0) = 0$, we have

$$f(1) = f(0) + f(-1)$$
$$1 = 0 + f(-1)$$
$$f(-1) = 1.$$

Similarly, using $f(0) = 0$ and $f(-1) = 1$ gives

$$f(0) = f(-1) + f(-2)$$
$$0 = 1 + f(-2)$$
$$f(-2) = -1.$$

However, there is no obvious way to extend the definition of $f(n)$ to non-integers, such as $n = 0.5$. Thus we cannot easily evaluate $f(0.5)$, and we say that $f(0.5)$ is undefined.

41. In $r(s) = 0.75v_0$, the variable s is the height (or heights) at which the wind speed is 75% of the maximum wind speed.

Solutions for Section 2.2

Exercises

1. The graph of $f(x) = 1/x$ for $-2 \leq x \leq 2$ is shown in Figure 2.2. From the graph, we see that $f(x) = -(1/2)$ at $x = -2$. As we approach zero from the left, $f(x)$ gets more and more negative. On the other side of the y-axis, $f(x) = (1/2)$ at $x = 2$. As x approaches zero from the right, $f(x)$ grows larger and larger. Thus, on the domain $-2 \leq x \leq 2$, the range is $f(x) \leq -(1/2)$ or $f(x) \geq (1/2)$.

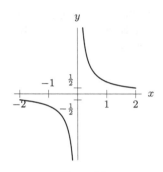

Figure 2.2

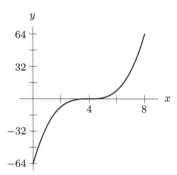

Figure 2.3

5. The graph of $f(x) = (x - 4)^3$ is given in Figure 2.3.
The domain is all real x; the range is all real $f(x)$.

9. The graph of $f(x) = \sqrt{8 - x}$ is given in Figure 2.4.

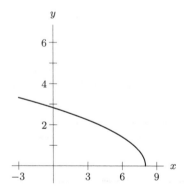

Figure 2.4

The domain is all real $x \leq 8$; the range is all $f(x) \geq 0$.

13. The domain is $1 \leq x \leq 7$. The range is $2 \leq f(x) \leq 18$.

Problems

17. Since for any value of x that you might choose you can find a corresponding value of $m(x)$, we can say that the domain of $m(x) = 9 - x$ is all real numbers.
For any value of $m(x)$ there is a corresponding value of x. So the range is also all real numbers.

21. Any number can be squared, so the domain is all real numbers. Since x^2 is always greater than or equal to zero, we see that $f(x) = x^2 + 2 \geq 2$. Thus, the range is all real numbers ≥ 2.

25. One way to do this is to combine two operations, one of which forces x to be non-negative, the other of which forces x not to equal 3. One possibility is

$$y = \frac{1}{x-3} + \sqrt{x}.$$

The fraction's denominator must not equal 0, so x must not equal 3. Further, the input of the square root function must not be negative, so x must be greater than or equal to zero. Other possibilities include

$$y = \frac{\sqrt{x}}{x-3}.$$

29. We know that the theater can hold anywhere from 0 to 200 people. Therefore the domain of the function is the integers, n, such that $0 \le n \le 200$.

We know that each person who enters the theater must pay \$4.00. Therefore, the theater makes $(0) \cdot (\$4.00) = 0$ dollars if there is no one in the theater, and $(200) \cdot (\$4.00) = \$800.00$ if the theater is completely filled. Thus the range of the function would be the integer multiples of 4 from 0 to 800. (That is, $0, 4, 8, \dots$.)

The graph of this function is shown in Figure 2.5.

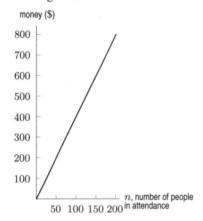

Figure 2.5

33. Since $(x-b)^{1/2} = \sqrt{x-b}$, we know that $x - b \ge 0$. Thus, $x \ge b$. If $x = b$, then $(x-b)^{1/2} = 0$, which is the minimum value of $\sqrt{x-b}$, since it can't be negative. Thus, the range is all real numbers greater than or equal to 6.

Solutions for Section 2.3

Exercises

1. $f(x) = \begin{cases} -1, & -1 \le x < 0 \\ 0, & 0 \le x < 1 \\ 1, & 1 \le x < 2 \end{cases}$ is shown in Figure 2.6.

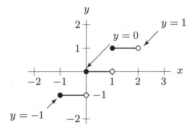

Figure 2.6

5. Since $G(x)$ is defined for all x, the domain is all real numbers. For $x < -1$ the values of the function are all negative numbers. For $-1 \geq x \geq 0$ the functions values are $4 \geq G(x) \geq 3$, while for $x > 0$ we see that $G(x) \geq 3$ and the values increase to infinity. The range is $G(x) < 0$ and $G(x) \geq 3$.

9. We find the formulas for each of the lines. For the first, we use the two points we have, $(1, 3.5)$ and $(3, 2.5)$. We find the slope: $(2.5 - 3.5)/(3 - 1) = -\frac{1}{2}$. Using the slope of $-\frac{1}{2}$, we solve for the y-intercept:

$$3.5 = b - \frac{1}{2} \cdot 1$$
$$4 = b.$$

Thus, the first line is $y = 4 - \frac{1}{2}x$, and it is for the part of the function where $1 \leq x \leq 3$.

We follow the same method for the second line, using the points $(5, 1)$ and $(8, 7)$. We find the slope: $(7-1)/(8-5) = 2$. Using the slope of 2, we solve for the y-intercept:

$$1 = b + 2 \cdot 5$$
$$-9 = b.$$

Thus, the second line is $y = -9 + 2x$, and it is for the part of the function where $5 \leq x \leq 8$.

Therefore, the function is:

$$y = \begin{cases} 4 - \frac{1}{2}x & \text{for } 1 \leq x \leq 3 \\ -9 + 2x & \text{for } 5 \leq x \leq 8. \end{cases}$$

Problems

13. **(a)** Figure 2.7 shows the function $u(x)$. Some graphing calculators or computers may show a near vertical line close to the origin. The function seems to be -1 when $x < 0$ and 1 when $x > 0$.

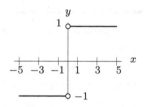

Figure 2.7

(b) Table 2.1 is the completed table. It agrees with what we found in part (a). The function is undefined at $x = 0$.

Table 2.1

x	-5	-4	-3	-2	-1	0	1	2	3	4	5
$|x|/x$	-1		-1	-1	-1		1	1	1	1	1

(c) The domain is all x except $x = 0$. The range is -1 and 1.
(d) $u(0)$ is undefined, not 0. The claim is false.

17. **(a)** The depth of the driveway is 1 foot or 1/3 of a yard. The volume of the driveway is the product of the three dimensions, length, width and depth. So,

$$\begin{array}{c} \text{Volume of} \\ \text{gravel needed} \end{array} = \text{Length} \cdot \text{Width} \cdot \text{Depth} = (L)(6)(1/3) = 2L.$$

Since he buys 10 cubic yards more than needed,

$$n(L) = 2L + 10.$$

(b) The length of a driveway is not less than 5 yards, so the domain of n is all real numbers greater than or equal to 5. The contractor can buy only 1 cubic yd at a time so the range only contains integers. The smallest value of the range occurs for the shortest driveway, when $L = 5$. If $L = 5$, then $n(5) = 2(5) + 10 = 20$. Although very long driveways are highly unlikely, there is no upper limit on L, so no upper limit on $n(L)$. Therefore the range is all integers greater than or equal to 20. See Figure 2.8.

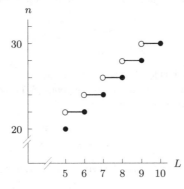

Figure 2.8

(c) If $n(L) = 2L + 10$ was not intended to represent a quantity of gravel, then the domain and range of n would be all real numbers.

Solutions for Section 2.4

Exercises

1. $A(f(t))$ is the area, in square centimeters, of the circle at time t minutes.

5. $f(g(0)) = f(2 \cdot 0 + 3) = f(3) = 3^2 + 1 = 10$.

9. $f(g(x)) = f(2x + 3) = (2x + 3)^2 + 1 = 4x^2 + 12x + 10$.

13. The inverse function, $f^{-1}(P)$, gives the year in which population is P million. Units of $f^{-1}(P)$ are years.

17. The inverse function, $f^{-1}(I)$, gives the interest rate that gives \$$I$ in interest. Units of $f^{-1}(I)$ is percent per year.

21. Since $P = 14q - 2$, solving for q gives

$$14q - 2 = P$$
$$q = \frac{P + 2}{14}$$
$$f^{-1}(P) = \frac{P + 2}{14}.$$

Problems

25. Since $f(A) = A/250$ and $f^{-1}(n) = 250n$, we have

$$f^{-1}(f(A)) = f^{-1}\left(\frac{A}{250}\right) = 250\frac{A}{250} = n.$$

To interpret these results, we use the fact that $f(A)$ gives the number of gallons of paint needed to cover an area A, and $f^{-1}(n)$ gives the area covered by n gallons. Thus $f^{-1}(f(A))$ gives the area which can be covered by $f(A)$ gallons; that is, A square feet. Similarly, $f(f^{-1}(n))$ gives the number of gallons needed for an area of $(f^{-1}(n))$; that is, n gallons.

29. We solve the equation $V = f(r) = \frac{4}{3}\pi r^3$ for r. Divide both sides by $\frac{4}{3}\pi$ and then take the cube root to get

$$r = \sqrt[3]{\frac{3V}{4\pi}}.$$

So

$$f^{-1}(V) = \sqrt[3]{\frac{3V}{4\pi}}.$$

33. (a) To write s as a function of A, we solve $A = 6s^2$ for s

$$s^2 = \frac{A}{6} \qquad \text{so} \qquad s = f(A) = +\sqrt{\frac{A}{6}} \qquad \text{Because the length of a side of a cube is positive.}$$

The function f gives the side of a cube in terms of its area A.

(b) Substituting $s = f(A) = \sqrt{A/6}$ in the formula $V = g(s) = s^3$ gives the volume, V, as a function of surface area, A,

$$V = g(f(A)) = s^3 = \left(\sqrt{\frac{A}{6}}\right)^3.$$

37. Since $V = \frac{4}{3}$

$$\frac{4}{3}\pi(50 - 2.5t)^3.$$

41. (a) $P = f(s) = 4s$.
(b) $f(s + 4) = 4(s + 4) = 4s + 16$. This the perimeter of a square whose side is four meters larger than s.
(c) $f(s) + 4 = 4s + 4$. This is the perimeter of a square whose side is s, plus four meters.
(d) Meters.

Solutions for Section 2.5

Exercises

1. To determine concavity, we calculate the rate of change:

$$\frac{\Delta f(x)}{\Delta x} = \frac{1.3 - 1.0}{1 - 0} = 0.3$$

$$\frac{\Delta f(x)}{\Delta x} = \frac{1.7 - 1.3}{3 - 1} = 0.2$$

$$\frac{\Delta f(x)}{\Delta x} = \frac{2.2 - 1.7}{6 - 3} \approx 0.167.$$

The rates of change are decreasing, so we expect the graph of $f(x)$ to be concave down.

5. The slope of $y = x^2$ is always increasing, so its graph is concave up. See Figure 2.9.

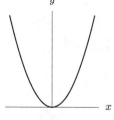

Figure 2.9

9. The rate of change between $t = 0.2$ and $t = 0.4$ is

$$\frac{\Delta p(t)}{\Delta t} = \frac{-2.32 - (-3.19)}{0.4 - 0.2} = 4.35.$$

Similarly, we have

$$\frac{\Delta p(t)}{\Delta t} = \frac{-1.50 - (-2.32)}{0.6 - 0.4} = 4.10$$

$$\frac{\Delta p(t)}{\Delta t} = \frac{-0.74 - (-1.50)}{0.8 - 0.6} = 3.80.$$

Thus, the rate of change is decreasing, so we expect the graph to be concave down.

Problems

13. This function is increasing throughout and the rate of increase is increasing, so the graph is concave up.

17. Since new people are always trying the product, it is an increasing function. At first, the graph is concave up. After many people start to use the product, the rate of increase slows down and the graph becomes concave down.

21. **(a)** From O to A, the rate is zero, so no water is flowing into the reservoir, and the volume remains constant. From A to B, the rate is increasing, so the volume is going up more and more quickly. From B to C, the rate is holding steady, but water is still going into the reservoir—it's just going in at a constant rate. So volume is increasing on the interval from B to C. Similarly, it is increasing on the intervals from C to D and from D to E. Even on the interval from E to F, water is flowing into the reservoir; it is just going in more and more slowly (the *rate* of flow is decreasing, but the total amount of water is still increasing). So we can say that the volume of water increases throughout the interval from A to F.

(b) The volume of water is constant when the rate is zero, that is from O to A.

(c) According to the graph, the rate at which the water is entering the reservoir reaches its highest value at $t = D$ and stays at that high value until $t = E$. So the volume of water is increasing most rapidly from D to E. (Be careful. The rate itself is increasing most rapidly from C to D, but the volume of water is increasing fastest when the rate is at its highest points.)

(d) When the rate is negative, water is leaving the reservoir, so its volume is decreasing. Since the rate is negative from F to I, we know that the volume of water *decreases* on that interval.

Solutions for Section 2.6

Exercises

1. Yes. We rewrite the function giving

$$f(x) = 2(7 - x)^2 + 1$$
$$= 2(49 - 14x + x^2) + 1$$
$$= 98 - 28x + 2x^2 + 1$$
$$= 2x^2 - 28x + 99.$$

So $f(x)$ is quadratic with $a = 2$, $b = -28$ and $c = 99$.

5. No. We rewrite the function giving

$$R(q) = \frac{1}{q^2}(q^2 + 1)^2$$
$$= \frac{1}{q^2}(q^4 + 2q^2 + 1)$$

$$= q^2 + 2 + \frac{1}{q^2}$$
$$= q^2 + 2 + q^{-2}.$$

So $R(q)$ is not quadratic since it contains a term with q to a negative power.

9. We solve for x in the equation $5x - x^2 + 3 = 0$ using the quadratic formula with $a = -1$, $b = 5$ and $c = 3$.

$$x = \frac{-5 \pm \sqrt{(-5)^2 - 4(-1)3}}{2(-1)}$$
$$x = \frac{-5 \pm \sqrt{37}}{-2}.$$

The solutions are $x \approx -0.541$ and $x \approx 5.541$.

13. Setting the factors equal to zero, we have

$$2 - x = 0$$
$$x = 2$$
$$\text{and} \quad 3 - 2x = 0$$
$$x = 3/2,$$

so the zeros are $x = 2, 3/2$.

17. To find the zeros, we solve the equation

$$0 = 9x^2 + 6x + 1.$$

We see that this is factorable, as follows:

$$y = (3x + 1)(3x + 1)$$
$$y = (3x + 1)^2.$$

Therefore, there is only one zero at $x = -\frac{1}{3}$.

21. To find the zeros, we solve the equation $0 = -17x^2 + 23x + 19$. This does not appear to be factorable. Thus, we use the quadratic formula with $a = -17$, $b = 23$, and $c = 19$:

$$x = \frac{-23 \pm \sqrt{23^2 - 4(-17)(19)}}{2(-17)}$$
$$x = \frac{-23 \pm \sqrt{1821}}{-34}.$$

Therefore, the zeros occur where $x = (-23 \pm \sqrt{1821})/(-34) \approx 1.932$ or -0.579.

Problems

25. We solve the equation $f(t) = -16t^2 + 64t + 3 = 0$ using the quadratic formula

$$-16t^2 + 64t + 3 = 0$$
$$t = \frac{-64 \pm \sqrt{64^2 - 4(-16)3}}{2(-16)}.$$

Evaluating gives $t = -0.046$ sec and $t = 4.046$ sec; the value $t = 4.046$ sec is the time we want. The baseball hits the ground 4.046 sec after it was hit.

29. Factoring gives $y = -4cx + x^2 + 4c^2 = x^2 - 4ck + 4c^2 = (x - 2c)^2$. Since $c > 0$, this is the graph of $y = x^2$ shifted to the right $2c$ units. See Figure 2.10.

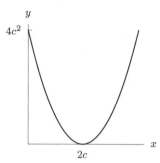

Figure 2.10: $y = -4cx + x^2 + 4c^2$ for $c > 0$

33. (a) In this window we see the expected parabolic shapes of $f(x)$ and $g(x)$. Both graphs open upward, so their shapes are similar and the end behaviors are the same. The differences in $f(x)$ and $g(x)$ are apparent at their vertices and intercepts. The graph of $f(x)$ has one intercept at $(0,0)$. The graph of $g(x)$ has x-intercepts at $x = -4$ and $x = 2$, and a y-intercept at $y = -8$. See Figure 2.11.

(b) As we extend the range to $y = 100$, the difference between the y-intercepts for $f(x)$ and $g(x)$ becomes less significant. See Figure 2.12.

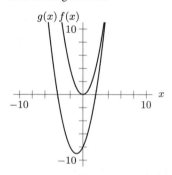

Figure 2.11

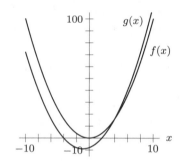

Figure 2.12

(c) In the window $-20 \le x \le 20, -10 \le y \le 400$, the graphs are still distinguishable from one another, but all intercepts appear much closer. In the next window, the intercepts appear the same for $f(x)$ and $g(x)$. Only a thickening along the sides of the parabola gives the hint of two functions. In the last window, the graphs appear identical. See Figure 2.13.

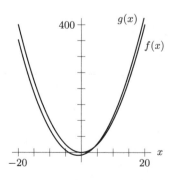 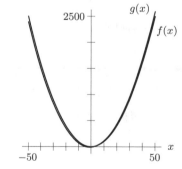 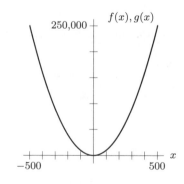

Figure 2.13

Solutions for Chapter 2 Review

Exercises

1. To evaluate $p(7)$, we substitute 7 for each r in the formula:

$$p(7) = 7^2 + 5 = 54.$$

5. We solve for l in the equation $7l - l^2 = 0$ by factoring to obtain $l(7 - l) = 0$, so $l = 0$ and $l = 7$ are the zeros.

9. We know that $x \geq 4$, for otherwise $\sqrt{x - 4}$ would be undefined. We also know that $4 - \sqrt{x - 4}$ must not be negative. Thus we have

$$4 - \sqrt{x - 4} \geq 0$$
$$4 \geq \sqrt{x - 4}$$
$$4^2 \geq \left(\sqrt{x - 4}\right)^2$$
$$16 \geq x - 4$$
$$20 \geq x.$$

Thus, the domain of $r(x)$ is $4 \leq x \leq 20$.

We use a computer or graphing calculator to find the range of $r(x)$. Graphing over the domain of $r(x)$ gives Figure 2.14.

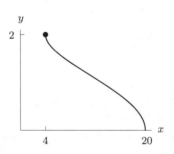

Figure 2.14

Because $r(x)$ is a decreasing function, we know that the maximum value of $r(x)$ occurs at the left end point of the domain, $r(4) = \sqrt{4 - \sqrt{4 - 4}} = \sqrt{4 - 0} = 2$, and the minimum value of $r(x)$ occurs at the right end point, $r(20) = \sqrt{4 - \sqrt{20 - 4}} = \sqrt{4 - \sqrt{16}} = \sqrt{4 - 4} = 0$. The range of $r(x)$ is thus $0 \leq r(x) \leq 2$.

13. $f(g(x)) = f(x^3 + 1) = 3(x^3 + 1) - 7 = 3x^3 - 4$.

17. (a) Since the vertical intercept of the graph of f is $(0, 1.5)$, we have $f(0) = 1.5$.

(b) Since the horizontal intercept of the graph of f is $(2.2, 0)$, we have $f(2.2) = 0$.

(c) The function f^{-1} goes from y-values to x-values, so to evaluate $f^{-1}(0)$, we want the x-value corresponding to $y = 0$. This is $x = 2.2$, so $f^{-1}(0) = 2.2$.

(d) Solving $f^{-1}(?) = 0$ means finding the y-value corresponding to $x = 0$. This is $y = 1.5$, so $f^{-1}(1.5) = 0$.

Problems

21.

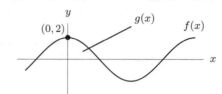

25. $f(a) = \dfrac{a \cdot a}{a + a} = \dfrac{a^2}{2a} = \dfrac{a}{2}.$

29. **(a)** The cost of producing 5000 loaves is $653.
   (b) $C^{-1}(80)$ is the number of loaves of bread that can be made for $80, namely 0.62 thousand or 620.
   (c) The solution is $q = 6.3$ thousand. It costs $790 to make 6300 loaves.
   (d) The solution is $x = 150$ dollars, so 1.2 thousand, or 1200, loaves can be made for $150.

33. Since

$$T = 2\pi\sqrt{\frac{l}{g}},$$

solving for l gives

$$T^2 = 4\pi^2\frac{l}{g}$$

$$l = \frac{gT^2}{4\pi^2}.$$

Thus,

$$f^{-1}(T) = \frac{gT^2}{4\pi^2}.$$

The function $f^{-1}(T)$ gives the length of a pendulum of period T.

37. **(a)** Since $f(2) = 3$, $f^{-1}(3) = 2$.
   (b) Unknown
   (c) Since $f^{-1}(5) = 4$, $f(4) = 5$.

41. **(a)** $f(2) = 4.98$ means that 2 pounds of apples cost $4.98.
   (b) $f(0.5) = 1.25$ means that 1/2 pound of apples cost $1.25.
   (c) $f^{-1}(0.62) = 0.25$ means that $0.62 buys 1/4 pound of apples.
   (d) $f^{-1}(12.45) = 5$ means that $12.45 buys 5 pounds of apples.

45. This represents the change in average hurricane intensity at current CO_2 levels if sea surface temperature rises by $1°C$.

CHECK YOUR UNDERSTANDING

1. False. $f(2) = 3 \cdot 2^2 - 4 = 8$.

5. False. $W = (8 + 4)/(8 - 4) = 3$.

9. True. A fraction can only be zero if the numerator is zero.

13. False. The domain consists of all real numbers x, $x \neq 3$

17. True. Since f is an increasing function, the domain endpoints determine the range endpoints. We have $f(15) = 12$ and $f(20) = 14$.

21. True. $|x| = |-x|$ for all x.

25. True. If $x < 0$, then $f(x) = x < 0$, so $f(x) \neq 4$. If $x > 4$, then $f(x) = -x < 0$, so $f(x) \neq 4$. If $0 \leq x \leq 4$, then $f(x) = x^2 = 4$ only for $x = 2$. The only solution for the equation $f(x) = 4$ is $x = 2$.

29. True. To find $f^{-1}(R)$, we solve $R = \frac{2}{3}S + 8$ for S by subtracting 8 from both sides and then multiplying both sides by $(3/2)$.

33. False. Since

$$f(g(x)) = 2\left(\frac{1}{2}x - 1\right) + 1 = x - 1 \neq x,$$

the functions do not undo each other.

37. True. Since the function is concave up, the average rate of change increases as we move right.

41. True. For $x > 0$, the function $f(x) = -x^2$ is both decreasing and concave down.

45. False. It has a minimum but no maximum.

49. False. For example, $x^2 + 1 = 0$ has no solutions, and $x^2 = 0$ has one solution.

Solutions to Tools for Chapter 2

1. $3(x + 2) = 3x + 6$

5. $12(x + y) = 12x + 12y$

9. $-10r(5r + 6rs) = -50r^2 - 60r^2 s$

13. $(x - 2)(x + 6) = x^2 + 6x - 2x - 12 = x^2 + 4x - 12$

17. $(12y - 5)(8w + 7) = 96wy + 84y - 40w - 35$

21. First we multiply 4 by the terms $3x$ and $-2x^2$, and expand $(5 + 4x)(3x - 4)$. Therefore,

$$\left(3x - 2x^2\right)(4) + (5 + 4x)(3x - 4) = 12x - 8x^2 + 15x - 20 + 12x^2 - 16x$$
$$= 4x^2 + 11x - 20.$$

25. The order of operations tells us to expand $(x - 3)^2$ first and then multiply the result by 4. Therefore,

$$4(x - 3)^2 + 7 = 4(x - 3)(x - 3) + 7$$
$$= 4(x^2 - 3x - 3x + 9) + 7 = 4(x^2 - 6x + 9) + 7$$
$$= 4x^2 - 24x + 36 + 7 = 4x^2 - 24x + 43.$$

29. $3y + 15 = 3(y + 5)$

33. $u^2 - 2u = u(u - 2)$

37. $14r^4 s^2 - 21rst = 7rs(2r^3 s - 3t)$

41. Can be factored no further.

45. $x^2 + 2x - 3 = (x + 3)(x - 1)$

49. $x^2 + 3x - 28 = (x + 7)(x - 4)$

53. $x^2 + 2xy + 3xz + 6yz = x(x + 2y) + 3z(x + 2y) = (x + 2y)(x + 3z)$.

57. We notice that the only factors of 24 whose sum is -10 are -6 and -4. Therefore,

$$B^2 - 10B + 24 = (B - 6)(B - 4).$$

61. This example is factored as the difference of perfect squares. Thus,

$$(t + 3)^2 - 16 = ((t + 3) - 4)((t + 3) + 4)$$
$$= (t - 1)(t + 7).$$

Alternatively, we could arrive at the same answer by multiplying the expression out and then factoring it.

65.

$$
\begin{aligned}
c^2d^2 - 25c^2 - 9d^2 + 225 &= c^2(d^2 - 25) - 9(d^2 - 25) \\
&= (d^2 - 25)(c^2 - 9) \\
&= (d + 5)(d - 5)(c + 3)(c - 3).
\end{aligned}
$$

69. The common factor is xe^{-3x}. Therefore,

$$
x^2e^{-3x} + 2xe^{-3x} = xe^{-3x}(x + 2).
$$

73. $x^2 - 6x + 9 - 4z^2 = (x - 3)^2 - (2z)^2 = (x - 3 + 2z)(x - 3 - 2z)$.

77.

$$
\begin{aligned}
x^2 + 7x + 6 &= 0 \\
(x + 6)(x + 1) &= 0 \\
x + 6 = 0 \quad &\text{or} \quad x + 1 = 0 \\
x = -6 \quad &\text{or} \quad x = -1
\end{aligned}
$$

81.

$$
\begin{aligned}
\frac{2}{x} + \frac{3}{2x} &= 8 \\
\frac{4 + 3}{2x} &= 8 \\
16x &= 7 \\
x &= \frac{7}{16}
\end{aligned}
$$

85.

$$
\begin{aligned}
\sqrt{2x - 1} + 3 &= 9 \\
\sqrt{2x - 1} &= 6 \\
2x - 1 &= 36 \\
2x &= 37 \\
x &= \frac{37}{2}
\end{aligned}
$$

89. Rewrite the equation $g^3 - 4g = 3g^2 - 12$ with a zero on the right side and factor completely.

$$
\begin{aligned}
g^3 - 3g^2 - 4g + 12 &= 0 \\
g^2(g - 3) - 4(g - 3) &= 0 \\
(g - 3)(g^2 - 4) &= 0 \\
(g - 3)(g + 2)(g - 2) &= 0.
\end{aligned}
$$

So, $g - 3 = 0$, $g + 2 = 0$, or $g - 2 = 0$. Thus, $g = 3, -2$, or 2.

93. Do not divide both sides by t, because you would lose the solution $t = 0$ in that case. Instead, set one side $= 0$ and factor.

$$
\begin{aligned}
\frac{1}{64}t^3 &= t \\
\frac{1}{64}t^3 - t &= 0 \\
t\left(\frac{1}{64}t^2 - 1\right) &= 0 \\
t = 0 \quad \text{or} \quad \frac{1}{64}t^2 - 1 &= 0
\end{aligned}
$$

The second equation still needs to be solved for t:

$$\frac{1}{64}t^2 = 1$$
$$t^2 = 64$$
$$t = \pm 8.$$

So the final answer is $t = 0$ or $t = 8$ or $t = -8$.

97. Rewrite the equation $n^5 + 80 = 5n^4 + 16n$ with a zero on the right side and factor completely.

$$n^5 - 5n^4 - 16n + 80 = 0$$
$$n^4(n - 5) - 16(n - 5) = 0$$
$$(n - 5)(n^4 - 16) = 0$$
$$(n - 5)(n^2 - 4)(n^2 + 4) = 0$$
$$(n - 5)(n + 2)(n - 2)(n^2 + 4) = 0.$$

So, $n - 5 = 0$, $n + 2 = 0$, $n - 2 = 0$, or $n^2 + 4 = 0$. Note that $n^2 + 4 = 0$ has no real solutions, so, $n = 5, -2$, or 2.

101. First we combine like terms in the numerator.

$$\frac{x^2 + 1 - 2x^2}{(x^2 + 1)^2} = 0$$
$$\frac{-x^2 + 1}{(x^2 + 1)^2} = 0$$
$$-x^2 + 1 = 0$$
$$-x^2 = -1$$
$$x^2 = 1$$
$$x = \pm 1$$

105. We can solve this equation by cubing both sides of this equation.

$$\frac{1}{\sqrt[3]{x}} = -2$$
$$\left(\frac{1}{\sqrt[3]{x}}\right)^3 = (-2)^3$$
$$\frac{1}{x} = -8$$
$$x = -\frac{1}{8}$$

109. We begin by squaring both sides of the equation in order to eliminate the radical.

$$T = 2\pi\sqrt{\frac{l}{g}}$$
$$T^2 = 4\pi^2\left(\frac{l}{g}\right)$$
$$\frac{gT^2}{4\pi^2} = l$$

113. We substitute -3 for y in the first equation.

$$y = 2x - x^2$$
$$-3 = 2x - x^2$$
$$x^2 - 2x - 3 = 0$$
$$(x - 3)(x + 1) = 0$$
$$x = 3 \quad \text{and} \quad y = 2(3) - 3^2 = -3 \quad \text{or}$$
$$x = -1 \quad \text{and} \quad y = 2(-1) - (-1)^2 = -3$$

117. These equations cannot be solved exactly. A calculator gives the solutions as

$$x = 2.081, \quad y = 8.013 \quad \text{and} \quad x = 4.504, \quad y = 90.348.$$

CHAPTER THREE

Solutions for Section 3.1

Exercises

1. The annual growth factor is $1+$ the growth rate, so we have 1.03.

5. For a 10% increase, we multiply by 1.10 to obtain $500 \cdot 1.10 = 550$.

9. For a 42% increase, we multiply by 1.42 to obtain $500 \cdot 1.42 = 710$. For a 42% decrease, we multiply by $1 - 0.42 = 0.58$ to obtain $710 \cdot 0.58 = 411.8$.

13. Since $Q = 79.2(1.002)^t$, we have $a = 79.2$, $b = 1.002$, and $r = b - 1 = 0.002 = 0.2\%$.

17. The percent of change is given by

$$\text{Percent of change} = \frac{\text{Amount of change}}{\text{Old amount}} \cdot 100\%.$$

So in these two cases,

$$\text{Percent of change from 10 to 12} = \frac{12 - 10}{10} \cdot 100\% = 20\%$$

$$\text{Percent of change from 100 to 102} = \frac{102 - 100}{100} \cdot 100\% = 2\%$$

Problems

21. In 2007, the cost of tickets will be 1.1 times their cost in 2006, (i.e. 10% greater). Thus, the price in 2007 is $1.1 \cdot \$73 = \$80.30$. The price in 2008 is then $1.1 \cdot \$80.30 = \$88.33$, and so forth. See Table 3.1.

Table 3.1

Year	2006	2007	2008	2009	2010
Cost (\$)	73	80.30	88.33	97.16	106.88

25. Since, after one year, 3% of the investment is added on to the original amount, we know that its value is 103% of what it had been a year earlier. Therefore, the growth factor is 1.03.

$$\text{So, after one year,} \quad V = 100,000(1.03)$$
$$\text{After two years,} \quad V = 100,000(1.03)(1.03) = 100,000(1.03)^2$$
$$\text{After three years,} \quad V = 100,000(1.03)(1.03)(1.03) = 100,000(1.03)^3 = \$109,272.70$$

29. (a) We have $C = C_0(1 - r)^t = 100(1 - 0.16)^t = 100(0.84)^t$, so

$$C = 100(0.84)^t.$$

(b) At $t = 5$, we have $C = 100(0.84)^5 = 41.821$ mg

33. Since each filter removes 85% of the remaining impurities, the rate of change of the impurity level is $r = -0.85$ per filter. Thus, the growth factor is $B = 1 + r = 1 - 0.85 = 0.15$. This means that each time the water is passed through a filter, the impurity level L is multiplied by a factor of 0.15. This makes sense, because if each filter removes 85% of the impurities, it will leave behind 15% of the impurities. We see that a formula for L is

$$L = 420(0.15)^n,$$

because after being passed through n filters, the impurity level will have been multiplied by a factor of 0.15 a total of n times.

37. Using the formula for slope, we have

$$\text{Slope} = \frac{f(5) - f(1)}{5 - 1} = \frac{4b^5 - 4b^1}{4} = \frac{4b(b^4 - 1)}{4} = b(b^4 - 1).$$

41. The graph $a_0(b_0)^t$ climbs faster than that of $a_1(b_1)^t$, so $b_0 > b_1$.

Solutions for Section 3.2

Exercises

1. The formula $P_A = 200 + 1.3t$ for City A shows that its population is growing linearly. In year $t = 0$, the city has 200,000 people and the population grows by 1.3 thousand people, or 1,300 people, each year.

The formulas for cities B, C, and D show that these populations are changing exponentially. Since $P_B = 270(1.021)^t$, City B starts with 270,000 people and grows at an annual rate of 2.1%. Similarly, City C starts with 150,000 people and grows at 4.5% annually.

Since $P_D = 600(0.978)^t$, City D starts with 600,000 people, but its population decreases at a rate of 2.2% per year. We find the annual percent rate by taking $b = 0.978 = 1 + r$, which gives $r = -0.022 = -2.2\%$. So City D starts out with more people than the other three but is shrinking.

Figure 3.1 gives the graphs of the three exponential populations. Notice that the P-intercepts of the graphs correspond to the initial populations (when $t = 0$) of the towns. Although the graph of P_C starts below the graph of P_B, it eventually catches up and rises above the graph of P_B, because City C is growing faster than City B.

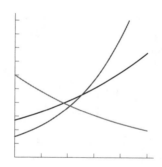

$$\frac{}{f(1)}, \frac{f(5)}{f(4)}, \text{ and } \frac{f(9)}{f(8)}.$$

We find

$$\frac{f(2)}{f(1)} = \frac{f(5)}{f(4)} = \frac{f(9)}{f(8)} = \frac{1}{4}.$$

With $f(x) = ab^x$ we also have

$$\frac{f(2)}{f(1)} = \frac{f(5)}{f(4)} = \frac{f(9)}{f(8)} = b,$$

so $b = \frac{1}{4}$. Using $f(1) = 4096$ we find $4096 = ab = a\left(\frac{1}{4}\right)$, so $a = 16{,}384$. Thus, $f(x) = 16{,}384\left(\frac{1}{4}\right)^x$.

9. (a) If a function is linear, then the differences in successive function values will be constant. If a function is exponential, the ratios of successive function values will remain constant. Now

$$i(1) - i(0) = 14 - 18 = -4$$

and

$$i(2) - i(1) = 10 - 14 = -4.$$

Checking the rest of the data, we see that the differences remain constant, so $i(x)$ is linear.

(b) We know that $i(x)$ is linear, so it must be of the form

$$i(x) = b + mx,$$

where m is the slope and b is the y-intercept. Since at $x = 0$, $i(0) = 18$, we know that the y-intercept is 18, so $b = 18$. Also, we know that at $x = 1$, $i(1) = 14$, we have

$$i(1) = b + m \cdot 1$$
$$14 = 18 + m$$
$$m = -4.$$

Thus, $i(x) = 18 - 4x$. The graph of $i(x)$ is shown in Figure 3.2.

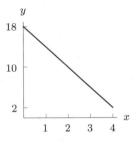

Figure 3.2

Problems

13. Since $g(x) = ab^x$, we can say that $g(\frac{1}{2}) = ab^{1/2}$ and $g(\frac{1}{4}) = ab^{1/4}$. Since we know that $g(\frac{1}{2}) = 4$ and $g(\frac{1}{4}) = 2\sqrt{2}$, we can conclude that

$$ab^{1/2} = 4 = 2^2$$

and

$$ab^{1/4} = 2\sqrt{2} = 2 \cdot 2^{1/2} = 2^{3/2}.$$

Forming ratios, we have

$$\frac{ab^{1/2}}{ab^{1/4}} = \frac{2^2}{2^{3/2}}$$
$$b^{1/4} = 2^{1/2}$$
$$(b^{1/4})^4 = (2^{1/2})^4$$
$$b = 2^2 = 4.$$

Now we know that $g(x) = a(4)^x$, so $g(\frac{1}{2}) = a(4)^{1/2} = 2a$. Since we also know that $g(\frac{1}{2}) = 4$, we can say

$$2a = 4$$
$$a = 2.$$

Therefore $g(x) = 2(4)^x$.

17. (a) If f is linear, then $f(x) = b + mx$, where m, the slope, is given by:

$$m = \frac{\Delta y}{\Delta x} = \frac{f(2) - f(-3)}{(2) - (-3)} = \frac{20 - \frac{5}{8}}{5} = \frac{\frac{155}{8}}{5} = \frac{31}{8}.$$

Using the fact that $f(2) = 20$, and substituting the known values for m, we write

$$20 = b + m(2)$$
$$20 = b + \left(\frac{31}{8}\right)(2)$$
$$20 = b + \frac{31}{4}$$

which gives

$$b = 20 - \frac{31}{4} = \frac{49}{4}$$

$$\frac{}{8}x + \frac{49}{4}.$$

(b) If f is exponential, then $f(x) = ab^x$. We know that $f(2) = ab^2$ and $f(2) = 20$. We also know that $f(-3) = ab^{-3}$ and $f(-3) = \frac{5}{8}$. So

$$\frac{f(2)}{f(-3)} = \frac{ab^2}{ab^{-3}} = \frac{20}{\frac{5}{8}}$$

$$b^5 = 20 \times \frac{8}{5} = 32$$

$$b = 2.$$

Thus, $f(x) = a(2)^x$. Solve for a by using $f(2) = 20$ and (with $b = 2$), $f(2) = a(2)^2$.

$$20 = a(2)^2$$
$$20 = 4a$$
$$a = 5.$$

Thus, $f(x) = 5(2)^x$.

21. The formula is of the form $y = ab^x$. Since the points $(-1, 1/15)$ and $(2, 9/5)$ are on the graph, so

$$\frac{1}{15} = ab^{-1}$$
$$\frac{9}{5} = ab^2.$$

Taking the ratio of the second equation to the first we obtain

$$\frac{9/5}{1/15} = \frac{ab^2}{ab^{-1}}$$
$$27 = b^3$$
$$b = 3.$$

Substituting this value of b into $\frac{1}{15} = ab^{-1}$ gives

$$\frac{1}{15} = a(3)^{-1}$$
$$\frac{1}{15} = \frac{1}{3}a$$
$$a = \frac{1}{15} \cdot 3$$
$$a = \frac{1}{5}.$$

Therefore $y = \frac{1}{5}(3)^x$ is a possible formula for this function.

25. We have $p = f(x) = ab^x$. From the figure, we see that the starting value is $a = 20$ and that the graph contains the point $(10, 40)$. We have

$$f(10) = 40$$
$$20b^{10} = 40$$
$$b^{10} = 2$$
$$b = 2^{1/10}$$
$$= 1.0718,$$

so $p = 20(1.0718)^x$.

We have $q = g(x) = ab^x$, $g(10) = 40$, and $g(15) = 20$. Using the ratio method, we have

$$\frac{ab^{15}}{ab^{10}} = \frac{g(15)}{g(10)}$$
$$b^5 = \frac{20}{40}$$
$$b = \left(\frac{20}{40}\right)^{1/5}$$
$$= (0.5)^{1/5} = 0.8706.$$

Now we can solve for a:

$$a((0.5)^{1/5})^{10} = 40$$
$$a = \frac{40}{\rule{2cm}{0.4pt}}$$

$\frac{}{2} = 0.5$. We can solve for a by substituting in $(1, 512)$ (or any other point):

$$512 = a \cdot 0.5^1$$
$$512 = a \cdot 0.5$$
$$1024 = a.$$

Thus, a possible formula to describe the data in the table is $g(t) = 1024 \cdot 0.5^t$.

33. (a) Since this function is exponential, its formula is of the form $f(t) = ab^t$, so

$$f(3) = ab^3$$
$$f(8) = ab^8.$$

From the graph, we know that

$$f(3) = 2000$$
$$f(8) = 5000.$$

So

$$\frac{f(8)}{f(3)} = \frac{ab^8}{ab^3} = \frac{5000}{2000}$$
$$b^5 = \frac{5}{2} = 2.5$$
$$(b^5)^{1/5} = (2.5)^{1/5}$$
$$b = 1.20112.$$

We now know that $f(t) = a(1.20112)^t$. Using either of the pairs of values on the graph, we can find a. In this case, we use $f(3) = 2000$. According to the formula,

$$f(3) = a(1.20112)^3$$
$$2000 = a(1.20112)^3$$
$$a = \frac{2000}{(1.20112)^3} \approx 1154.160.$$

The formula we want is $f(t) = 1154.160(1.20112)^t$ or $P = 1154.160(1.20112)^t$.

(b) The initial value of the account occurs when $t = 0$.

$$f(0) = 1154.160(1.20112)^0 = 1154.160(1) = \$1154.16.$$

(c) The value of b, the growth factor, is related to the growth rate, r, by

$$b = 1 + r.$$

We know that $b = 1.20112$, so

$$1.20112 = 1 + r$$
$$0.20112 = r$$

Thus, in percentage terms, the annual interest rate is 20.112%.

37. Since $N = 10$ when $t = 0$, we use $N = 10b^t$ for some base b. Since $N = 20000$ when $t = 62$, we have

$$N = 10b^t$$
$$20000 = 10b^{62}$$
$$b^{62} = \frac{20000}{10} = 2000$$
$$b = (2000)^{1/62} = 1.13.$$

An exponential formula for the brown tree snake population is

$$N = 10(1.13)^t.$$

The population has been growing by about 13% per year.

41. (a) Under Penalty A, the total fine is $1 million for August 2 and $10 million for each day after August 2 . By August 31, the fine had been increasing for 29 days so the total fine would be $1 + 10(29) = \$291$ million.

Under the Penalty B, the penalty on August 2 is 1 cent. On August 3, it is $1(2)$ cents; on August 4, it is $1(2)(2)$ cents; on August 5, it is $1(2)(2)(2)$ cents. By August 31, the fine has doubled 29 times, so the total fine is $(1) \cdot (2)^{29}$ cents, which is 536,870,912 cents or $5,368,709.12 or, approximately, $5.37 million.

(b) If t represents the number of days after August 2, then the total fine under Penalty A would be $1 million plus the number of days after August 2 times $10 million, or $A(t) = 1 + 10 \cdot t$ million dollars $= (1 + 10t)10^6$ dollars. The total fine under Penalty B would be 1 cent doubled each day after August 2, so $B(t) = 1\underbrace{(2)(2)(2)\ldots(2)}_{t \text{ times}}$ cents or

$B(t) = 1 \cdot (2)^t$ cents, or $B(t) = (0.01)2^t$ dollars.

(c) We plot $A(t) = (1 + 10t)10^6$ and $B(t) = (0.01)2^t$ on the same set of axes and observe that they intersect at $t \approx 35.032$ days. Another possible approach is to find values of $A(t)$ and $B(t)$ for different values of t, narrowing in on the value for which they are most nearly equal.

Solutions for Section 3.3

Exercises

1. (a) See Table 3.2.

   (b) For large negative values of x, $f(x)$ is close to the x-axis. But for large positive values of x, $f(x)$ climbs rapidly away from the x-axis. As x gets larger, y grows more and more rapidly. See Figure 3.3.

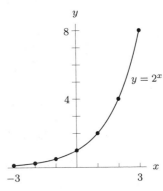

Table 3.2

x	-3	-2	-1	0	1	2	3
$f(x)$	1/8	1/4	1/2	1	2	4	8

Figure 3.3

5. Since $y = a$ when $t = 0$ in $y = ab^t$, a is the y-intercept. Thus, the function with the greatest y-intercept, D, has the largest a.

9. Graphing $y = 46(1.1)^x$ and tracing along the graph on a calculator gives us an answer of $x = 7.158$. See Figure 3.4.

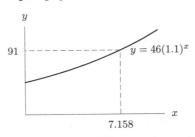

Figure 3.4

13. As t approaches $-\infty$, the value of ab^t approaches zero for any a, so the horizontal asymptote is $y = 0$ (the x-axis).

Problems

17. (a) Since the number of cases is reduced by 10% each year, there are 90% as many cases in one year as in the previous one. So, after one year there are 90% of 10000 or 10000(0.90) cases, while after two years, there are $10000(0.90)(0.90) = 10000(0.90)^2$ cases. In general, the number of cases after t years is $y = (10000)(0.9)^t$.

    (b) Setting $t = 5$, we obtain the number of cases 5 years from now

$$y = (10000) \cdot (0.9)^5 = 5904.9 \approx 5905 \text{ cases.}$$

    (c) Plotting $y = (10000) \cdot (0.9)^t$ and approximating the value of t for which $y = 1000$, we obtain $t \approx 21.854$ years.

21. As a increases, the y-intercept of the curve rises, and the point of intersection shifts down and to the left. Thus y_0 decreases. If a becomes larger than b, the point of intersection shifts to the left side of the y-axis, and the value of y_0 continues to decrease. However, y_0 will not decrease to 0, as the point of intersection will always fall above the x-axis.

25. Answers will vary, but they should mention that $f(x)$ is increasing and $g(x)$ is decreasing, that they have the same domain, range, and horizontal asymptote. Some may see that $g(x)$ is a reflection of $f(x)$ about the y-axis whenever $b = 1/a$. Graphs might resemble the following:

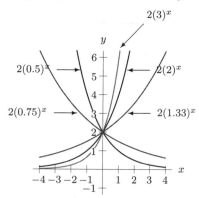

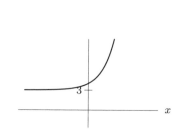

Figure 3.5 **Figure 3.6**

29. A possible graph is shown in Figure 3.6.

33. (a) $\lim_{x \to \infty} 7(0.8)^x = 0$.

(b) $\lim_{t \to -\infty} 5(1.2)^t = 0$.

(c) $\lim_{t \to \infty} 0.7(1 - (0.2)^t) = 0.7(1 - 0) = 0.7$.

37. The function, when entered as $y = 1.04\hat{\ }5x$ is interpreted as $y = (1.04^5)x = 1.217x$. This function's graph is a straight line in all windows. Parentheses must be used to ensure that x is in the exponent.

41. The domain is all possible t-values, so

Domain: all t-values.

The range is all possible Q-values. Since Q must be positive,

Range: all $Q > 0$.

Solutions for Section 3.4

Exercises

1. Using the formula $y = ab^x$, each of the functions has the same value for b, but different values for a and thus different y-intercepts.

When $x = 0$, the y-intercept for $y = e^x$ is 1 since $e^0 = 1$.
When $x = 0$, the y-intercept for $y = 2e^x$ is 2 since $e^0 = 1$ and $2(1) = 2$.
When $x = 0$, the y-intercept for $y = 3e^x$ is 3 since $e^0 = 1$ and $3(1) = 3$.

Therefore, $y = e^x$ is the bottom graph, above it is $y = 2e^x$ and the top graph is $y = 3e^x$.

5. $y = e^x$ is an increasing exponential function, since $e > 1$. Therefore, it rises when read from left to right. It matches $g(x)$.

If we rewrite the function $y = e^{-x}$ as $y = (e^{-1})^x$, we can see that in the formula $y = ab^x$, we have $a = 1$ and $b = e^{-1}$. Since $0 < e^{-1} < 1$, this graph has a positive y-intercept and falls when read from left to right. Thus its graph is $f(x)$.

In the function $y = -e^x$, we have $a = -1$. Thus, the vertical intercept is $y = -1$. The graph of $h(x)$ has a negative y-intercept.

9. We want to know when $V = 1074$. Tracing along the graph of $V = 537e^{0.015t}$ gives $t \approx 46.210$ years. See Figure 3.7.

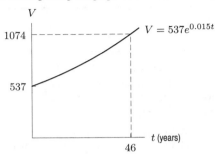

Figure 3.7

Problems

13. $\lim_{t \to \infty} (2 - 3e^{-0.2t}) = 2 - 3 \cdot 0 = 2$.

17. **(a)** For an annual interest rate of 5%, the balance B after 15 years is
$$B = 2000(1.05)^{15} = 4157.86 \text{ dollars.}$$

(b) For a continuous interest rate of 5% per year, the balance B after 15 years is
$$B = 2000e^{0.05 \cdot 15} = 4234.00 \text{ dollars.}$$

21. **(a)** The substance decays according to the formula
$$A = 50e^{-0.14t}.$$

(b) At $t = 10$, we have $A = 50e^{-0.14(10)} = 12.330$ mg.

(c) We see in Figure 3.8 that $A = 5$ at approximately $t = 16.45$, which corresponds to the year 2016.

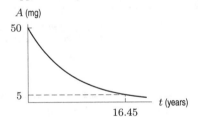

Figure 3.8

25. **(a)** A calculator or computer gives the values in Table 3.3. We see that the values of $(1 + 1/n)^n$ increase as n increases.

(b) Extending Table 3.3 gives Table 3.4. Since, correct to 6 decimal places, $e = 2.718282$, we need approximately $n = 10^7$ to achieve an estimate for e that is correct to 6 decimal places.

Table 3.3

n	$(1 + 1/n)^n$
1000	2.7169239
10,000	2.7181459
100,000	2.7182682
1,000,000	2.7182805

Table 3.4

n	$(1 + 1/n)^n$	Correct to 6 decimal places
10^5	2.71826824	2.718268
10^6	2.71828047	2.718280
10^7	2.71828169	2.718282
10^8	2.71828179	2.718282

(c) Using most calculators, when $n = 10^{16}$ the computed value of $(1 + 1/n)^n$ is 1. The reason is that calculators use only a limited number of decimal places, so the calculator finds that $1 + 1/10^{16} = 1$.

Solutions for Section 3.5

Exercises

1. **(a)** If the interest is compounded annually, there will be $500 \cdot 1.01 = \$505$ after one year.
   (b) If the interest is compounded weekly, after one year, there will be $500 \cdot (1 + 0.01/52)^{52} = \$505.02$.
   (c) If the interest is compounded every minute, after one year, there will be $500 \cdot (1 + 0.01/525{,}600)^{525{,}600} = \$505.03$.
   (d) If the interest is compounded continuously, after one year, there will be $500 \cdot e^{0.01} = \$505.03$.

5. With continuous compounding, the interest earns interest during the year, so the balance grows faster with continuous compounding than with annual compounding. Curve A corresponds to continuous compounding and curve B corresponds to annual compounding. The initial amount in both cases is the vertical intercept, \$500.

9. The value of the deposit is given by
$$V = 1000e^{0.05t}.$$
To find the effective annual rate, we use the fact that $e^{0.05t} = (e^{0.05})^t$ to rewrite the function as
$$V = 1000(e^{0.05})^t.$$
Since $e^{0.05} = 1.05127$, we have
$$V = 1000(1.05127)^t.$$
This tells us that the effective annual rate is 5.127%.

13. **(a)** The nominal rate is the stated annual interest without compounding, thus 3%.
    The effective annual rate for an account paying 1% compounded annually is 3%.
    (b) The nominal rate is the stated annual interest without compounding, thus 3%.
    With quarterly compounding, there are four interest payments per year, each of which is $3/4 = 0.75\%$. Over the course of the year, this occurs four times, giving an effective annual rate of $1.0075^4 = 1.03034$, which is 3.034%.
    (c) The nominal rate is the stated annual interest without compounding, thus 3%.
    With daily compounding, there are 365 interest payments per year, each of which is $(3/365)\%$. Over the course of the year, this occurs 365 times, giving an effective annual rate of $(1 + 0.03/365)^{365} = 1.03045$, which is 3.045%.
    (d) The nominal rate is the stated annual interest without compounding, thus 3%.
    The effective annual rate for an account paying 3% compounded continuously is $e^{0.03} = 1.03045$, which is 3.045%.

Problems

17. **(i)** Equation (b). Since the growth factor is 1.12, or 112%, the annual interest rate is 12%.
    (ii) Equation (a). An account earning at least 1% monthly will have a monthly growth factor of at least 1.01, which means that the annual (12-month) growth factor will be at least
    $$(1.01)^{12} \approx 1.1268.$$
    Thus, an account earning at least 1% monthly will earn at least 12.68% yearly. The only account that earns this much interest is account (a).
    (iii) Equation (c). An account earning 12% annually compounded semi-annually will earn 6% twice yearly. In t years, there are $2t$ half-years.
    (iv) Equations (b), (c) and (d). An account that earns 3% each quarter ends up with a yearly growth factor of $(1.03)^4 \approx 1.1255$. This corresponds to an annual percentage rate of 12.55%. Accounts (b), (c) and (d) earn less than this. Check this by determining the growth factor in each case.
    (v) Equations (a) and (e). An account that earns 6% every 6 months will have a growth factor, after 1 year, of $(1 + 0.06)^2 = 1.1236$, which is equivalent to a 12.36% annual interest rate, compounded annually. Account (a), earning 20% each year, clearly earns more than 6% twice each year, or 12.36% annually. Account (e), which earns 3% each quarter, earns $(1.03)^2 = 1.0609$, or 6.09% every 6 months, which is greater than 6%.

21. (a) The effective annual rate is the rate at which the account is actually increasing in one year. According to the formula, $M = M_0(1.07763)^t$, at the end of one year you have $M = 1.07763M_0$, or 1.07763 times what you had the previous year. The account is 107.763% larger than it had been previously; that is, it increased by 7.763%. Thus the effective rate being paid on this account each year is about 7.763%.

(b) Since the money is being compounded each month, one way to find the nominal annual rate is to determine the rate being paid each month. In t years there are $12t$ months, and so, if b is the monthly growth factor, our formula becomes

$$M = M_0 b^{12t} = M_0(b^{12})^t.$$

Thus, equating the two expressions for M, we see that

$$M_0(b^{12})^t = M_0(1.07763)^t.$$

Dividing both sides by M_0 yields

$$(b^{12})^t = (1.07763)^t.$$

Taking the tth root of both sides, we have

$$b^{12} = 1.07763$$

which means that

$$b = (1.07763)^{1/12} \approx 1.00625.$$

Thus, this account earns 0.625% interest every month, which amounts to a nominal interest rate of about $12(0.625\%) = 7.5\%$.

25. If the annual growth factor is b, then we know that, at the end of 5 years, the investment will have grown by a factor of b^5. But we are told that it has grown by 30%, so it is 130% of its original size. So

$$b^5 = 1.30$$
$$b = 1.30^{\frac{1}{5}} \approx 1.05387.$$

Since the investment is 105.387% as large as it had been the previous year, we know that it is growing by about 5.387% each year.

Solutions for Chapter 3 Review

Exercises

1. Yes. Writing the function as

$$g(w) = 2\left(2^{-w}\right) = 2\left(2^{-1}\right)^w = 2\left(\frac{1}{2}\right)^w,$$

we have $a = 2$ and $b = 1/2$.

5. Yes. Writing the function as

$$q(r) = \frac{-4}{3^r} = -4\left(\frac{1}{3^r}\right) = -4\left(\frac{1^r}{3^r}\right) = -4\left(\frac{1}{3}\right)^r,$$

we have $a = -4$ and $b = 1/3$.

9. No. The two terms cannot be combined into the form b^r.

13. We use $y = ab^x$. Since $y = 10$ when $x = 0$, we have $y = 10b^x$. We use the point $(3, 20)$ to find the base b:

$$y = 10b^x$$
$$20 = 10b^3$$
$$b^3 = 2$$
$$b = 2^{1/3} = 1.260.$$

The formula is

$$y = 10(1.260)^x.$$

17. The formula for this function must be of the form $y = ab^x$. We know that $(-2, 400)$ and $(1, 0.4)$ are points on the graph of this function, so

$$400 = ab^{-2}$$

and

$$0.4 = ab^1.$$

This leads us to

$$\begin{aligned} \frac{0.4}{400} &= \frac{ab^1}{ab^{-2}} \\ 0.001 &= b^3 \\ b &= 0.1. \end{aligned}$$

Substituting this value into $0.4 = ab^1$, we get

$$\begin{aligned} 0.4 &= a(0.1) \\ a &= 4. \end{aligned}$$

So our formula for this function is $y = 4(0.1)^x$. Since $0.1 = 10^{-1}$ we can also write $y = 4(10^{-1})^x = 4(10)^{-x}$.

Problems

21. A possible graph is shown in Figure 3.9.

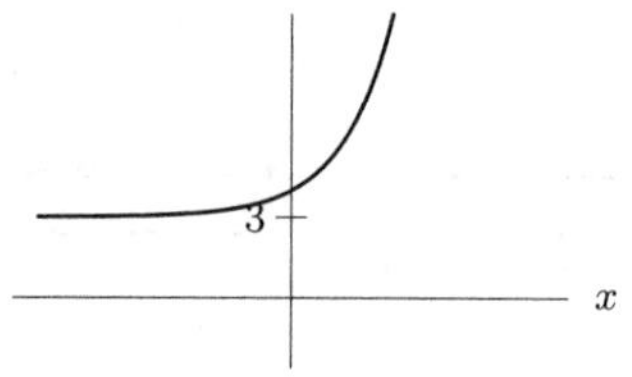

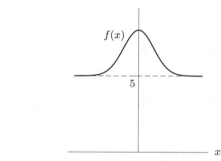

Figure 3.9

Figure 3.10

25. A possible graph is shown in Figure 3.10. There are many possible answers.

29. We have $\lim_{t \to -\infty} (21(1.2)^t + 5.1) = 21(0) + 5.1 = 5.1.$

33. We have $g(10) = 50$ and $g(30) = 25$. Using the ratio method, we have

$$\begin{aligned} \frac{ab^{30}}{ab^{10}} &= \frac{g(30)}{g(10)} \\ b^{20} &= \frac{25}{} \end{aligned}$$

$$\frac{}{50}\Big)^{1/20} \approx 0.965936.$$

Now we can solve for a:

$$\begin{aligned} a(0.965936)^{10} &= 50 \\ a &= \frac{50}{(0.965936)^{10}} \approx 70.711. \end{aligned}$$

so $Q = 70.711(0.966)^t$.

37. Let the equation of the exponential curve be $Q = ab^t$. Since this curve passes through the points $(-1, 2)$, $(1, 0.3)$, we have

$$2 = ab^{-1}$$
$$0.3 = ab^1 = ab$$

So,

$$\frac{0.3}{2} = \frac{ab}{ab^{-1}} = b^2,$$

that is, $b^2 = 0.15$, thus $b = \sqrt{0.15} \approx 0.3873$ because b is positive. Since $2 = ab^{-1}$, we have $a = 2b = 2 \cdot 0.3873 = 0.7746$, and the equation of the exponential curve is

$$Q = 0.7746 \cdot (0.3873)^t.$$

41. The starting value is $a = 2500$, and the continuous growth rate is $k = 0.042$, so $V = 2500e^{0.042t}$.

45. Testing rates of change for $S(t)$, we find that

$$\frac{6.72 - 4.35}{12 - 5} = 0.339$$

and

$$\frac{10.02 - 6.72}{16 - 12} = 0.825.$$

Since the rates of change are not the same we know that $S(t)$ is not linear.

Testing for a possible constant growth factor we see that

$$\frac{S(12)}{S(5)} = \frac{ab^{12}}{ab^5} = \frac{6.72}{4.35}$$
$$b^7 = \frac{6.72}{4.35}$$
$$b \approx 1.064$$

and

$$\frac{S(16)}{S(12)} = \frac{ab^{16}}{ab^{12}} = \frac{10.02}{6.72}$$
$$b^4 = \frac{10.02}{6.72}$$
$$b \approx 1.105.$$

Since the growth factors are different, $S(t)$ is not an exponential function.

49. **(a)** In this account, the initial balance in the account is $1100 and the effective yield is 5 percent each year.
(b) In this account, the initial balance in the account is $1500 and the effective yield is approximately 5.13%, because $e^{0.05} \approx 1.0513$.

53. In (a), we can see the y-intercept of f, which starts above g. The graph of g leaves the window in (a) to the right, not at the top, so the values of g are less than the values of f throughout the interval $0 \le x \le x_1$. Thus, the point of intersection is to the right of x_1, so x_1 is the smallest of these three values. The x-value of the point of intersection of the graphs in (b) is closer to x_3 than the x-value of the point of intersection in (c) is to x_2. Thus $x_3 < x_2$, so we have $x_1 < x_3 < x_2$.

57. **(a)** For a linear model, we assume that the population increases by the same amount every year. Since it grew by 4.14% in the first year, the town had a population increase of $0.0414(20,000) = 828$ people in one year. According to a linear model, the population in 2005 would be $20,000 + 10 \cdot 828 = 28,280$. Using an exponential model, we assume that the population increases by the same percent every year, so the population in 2005 would be $20,000 \cdot (1.0414)^{10} = 30,006$. Clearly the exponential model is a better fit.
(b) Assuming exponential growth at 4.14% a year, the formula for the population is

$$P(t) = 20,000(1.0414)^t.$$

61. (a) The data points are approximately as shown in Table 3.5. This results in $a \approx 15.269$ and $b \approx 1.122$, so $E(t) = 15.269(1.122)^t$.

Table 3.5

t (years)	0	1	2	3	4	5	6	7	8	9	10	11	12
$E(t)$ (thousands)	22	18	20	20	22	22	19	30	45	42	62	60	65

(b) In 1997 we have $t = 17$ so $E(17) = 15.269(1.122)^{17} \approx 108{,}066$.

(c) The model is probably not a good predictor of emigration in the year 2010 because Hong Kong was transferred to Chinese rule in 1997. Thus, conditions which affect emigration in 2010 may be markedly different than they were in the period from 1989 to 1992, for which data is given. In 2000, emigration was about 12,000.

65. (a) Since f is an exponential function, we can write $f(x) = ab^x$, where a and b are constants. Since the blood alcohol level of a non-drinker is zero, we know that $f(0) = p_0$. Since $f(x) = ab^x$,

$$f(0) = ab^0 = a \cdot 1 = a,$$

and so $a = p_0$ and $f(x) = p_0 b^x$. With a BAC of 0.15, the probability of an accident is $25p_0$, so

$$f(0.15) = 25p_0.$$

From the formula we know that $f(0.15) = p_0 b^{0.15}$, so

$$p_0 b^{0.15} = 25p_0$$
$$b^{0.15} = 25$$
$$(b^{0.15})^{1/0.15} = 25^{1/0.15}$$
$$b \approx 2{,}087{,}372{,}982.$$

Thus, $f(x) = p_0(2{,}087{,}372{,}982)^x$.

(b) Since

$$f(x) = p_0(2{,}087{,}372{,}982)^x,$$

using our formula, we see that $f(0.1) = p_0(2{,}087{,}372{,}982)^{0.1} \approx 8.55p_0$. This means that a legally intoxicated person is about 8.55 times as likely as a nondrinker to be involved in a single-car accident.

(c) If the probability of an accident is only three times the probability for a non-drinker, then we need to find the value of x for which

$$f(x) = 3p_0.$$

Since

$$f(x) = p_0(2{,}087{,}372{,}982)^x,$$

we have

$$p_0(2{,}087{,}372{,}982)^x = 3p_0$$

and

$$2{,}087{,}372{,}982^x = 3.$$

Using a calculator or computer, we find that $x \approx 0.051$. This is about half the BAC currently used in the legal definition.

CHECK YOUR UNDERSTANDING

1. True. If the constant rate is r then the formula is $f(t) = a \cdot (1 + r)^t$. The function decreases when $0 < 1 + r < 1$ and increases when $1 + r > 1$.

5. False. The annual growth factor would be 1.04, so $S = S_0(1.04)^t$.

9. True. The initial value means the value of Q when $t = 0$, so $Q = f(0) = a \cdot b^0 = a \cdot 1 = a$.

13. False. This is the formula of a linear function.

17. True. The irrational number $e = 2.71828\cdots$ has this as a good approximation.

21. True. The initial value is 200 and the growth factor is 1.04.

25. True. Since k is the continuous growth rate and negative, Q is decreasing.

29. True. The interest from any quarter is compounded in subsequent quarters.

Solutions to Tools for Chapter 3

1. $4^3 = 4 \cdot 4 \cdot 4 = 64$

5. $(-1)^{12} = \underbrace{(-1)(-1)\cdots(-1)}_{12\ factors} = 1$

9. $\frac{10^8}{10^5} = 10^{8-5} = 10^3 = 10 \cdot 10 \cdot 10 = 1{,}000$

13. $\sqrt{4^2} = 4$

17. Since $\dfrac{1}{7^{-2}}$ is the same as 7^2, we obtain $7 \cdot 7$ or 49.

21. The order of operations tells us to square 3 first (giving 9) and then multiply by -2. Therefore $(-2)3^2 = (-2)9 = -18$.

25. $16^{1/2} = (2^4)^{1/2} = 2^2 = 4$

29. $16^{5/2} = (2^4)^{5/2} = 2^{10} = 1024$

33. Exponentiation is done first, with the result that $(-1)^3 = -1$. Therefore $(-1)^3\sqrt{36} = (-1)\sqrt{36} = (-1)(6) = -6$.

37. $3^{-2} = \frac{1}{9}$

41. $25^{-3/2} = \dfrac{1}{(25)^{3/2}} = \dfrac{1}{(25^{1/2})^3} = \dfrac{1}{5^3} = \dfrac{1}{125}$

45. $\sqrt{y^8} = (y^8)^{1/2} = y^{8/2} = y^4$

49. $\sqrt{49w^9} = (49w^9)^{1/2} = 49^{1/2} \cdot w^{9/2} = 7w^{9/2}$

53. $\sqrt{r^4} = (r^4)^{1/2} = r^{4/2} = r^2$

57.
$$\begin{aligned}
\sqrt{48u^{10}v^{12}y^5} &= (48)^{1/2} \cdot (u^{10})^{1/2} \cdot (v^{12})^{1/2} \cdot (y^5)^{1/2} \\
&= (16 \cdot 3)^{1/2} u^5 v^6 y^{5/2} \\
&= 16^{1/2} \cdot 3^{1/2} \cdot u^5 v^6 y^{5/2} \\
&= 4\sqrt{3}u^5 v^6 y^{5/2}
\end{aligned}$$

61. First we raise $3^{x/2}$ to the second power and multiply this result by 3. Therefore $3\left(3^{x/2}\right)^2 = 3\left(3^x\right) = 3^1\left(3^x\right) = 3^{x+1}$.

65. $\sqrt{e^{2x}} = \left(e^{2x}\right)^{\frac{1}{2}} = e^{2x \cdot \frac{1}{2}} = e^x$

69. Inside the parenthesis we write the radical as an exponent, which results in
$$\left(3x\sqrt{x^3}\right)^2 = \left(3x \cdot x^{3/2}\right)^2 .$$
Then within the parenthesis we write
$$\left(3x^1 \cdot x^{3/2}\right)^2 = \left(3x^{5/2}\right)^2 = 3^2(x^{5/2})^2 = 9x^5 .$$

73. $\dfrac{4A^{-3}}{(2A)^{-4}} = \dfrac{4/A^3}{1/(2A)^4} = \dfrac{4}{A^3} \cdot \dfrac{(2A)^4}{1} = \dfrac{4}{A^3} \cdot \dfrac{2^4 A^4}{1} = 64A.$

77. First we divide within the larger parentheses. Therefore,

$$\left(\frac{35(2b+1)^9}{7(2b+1)^{-1}}\right)^2 = \left(5(2b+1)^{9-(-1)}\right)^2 = \left(5(2b+1)^{10}\right)^2.$$

Then we expand to obtain

$$25(2b+1)^{20}.$$

81. $(-625)^{3/4} = (\sqrt[4]{-625})^3$. Since $\sqrt[4]{-625}$ is not a real number, $(-625)^{3/4}$ is undefined.

85. $(-64)^{3/2} = (\sqrt{-64})^3$. Since $\sqrt{-64}$ is not a real number, $(-64)^{3/2}$ is undefined.

89. We have

$$\sqrt{4x^3} = 5$$
$$2x^{3/2} = 5$$
$$x^{3/2} = 2.5$$
$$x = (2.5)^{2/3} = 1.842.$$

93. The point of intersection occurs where the curves have the same x and y values. We set the two formulas equal and solve:

$$0.8x^4 = 5x^2$$
$$\frac{x^4}{x^2} = \frac{5}{0.8}$$
$$x^2 = 6.25$$
$$x = (6.25)^{1/2} = 2.5.$$

The x coordinate of the point of intersection is 2.5. We use either formula to find the y-coordinate:

$$y = 5(2.5)^2 = 31.25,$$

or

$$y = 0.8(2.5)^4 = 31.25.$$

The coordinates of the point of intersection are $(2.5, 31.25)$.

97. False

101. False

105. We have

$$2^x = 35$$
$$= 5 \cdot 7$$
$$= 2^r \cdot 2^s$$
$$= 2^{r+s},$$

so $x = r + s$.

109. We have

$$25^x = 64$$
$$\left(5^2\right)^x = 64$$
$$5^{2x} = 64$$
$$\left(2^a\right)^{2x} = 64$$
$$2^{2ax} = 2^6$$
$$2ax = 6$$
$$x = \frac{3}{a}.$$

CHAPTER FOUR

Solutions for Section 4.1

Exercises

1. The statement is equivalent to $19 = 10^{1.279}$.

5. The statement is equivalent to $P = 10^t$.

9. The statement is equivalent to $v = \log \alpha$.

13. We are solving for an exponent, so we use logarithms. Since the base is the number e, it makes the most sense to use the natural logarithm. Using the log rules, we have

$$e^{0.12x} = 100$$
$$\ln(e^{0.12x}) = \ln(100)$$
$$0.12x = \ln(100)$$
$$x = \frac{\ln(100)}{0.12} = 38.376.$$

17. We take the log of both sides and use the rules of logs to solve for m:

$$\log(0.00012) = \log(0.001)^{m/2}$$
$$\log(0.00012) = \frac{m}{2} \log(0.001)$$
$$\log(0.00012) = \frac{m}{2}(-3)$$
$$\frac{\log(0.00012)}{-3} = \frac{m}{2}$$
$$m = 2\frac{\log(0.00012)}{-3} = 2.614.$$

Problems

21. See Table 4.1. From the table, we see that the value of 10^n draws quite close to 3000 as n draws close to 3.47712, and so we estimate that $\log 3000 \approx 3.47712$. Using a calculator, we see that $\log 3000 = 3.4771212\ldots$.

Table 4.1

n	3	3.5	3.48	3.477	3.4771	3.47712
10^n	1000	3162.278	3019.952	2999.163	2999.853	2999.991

25. **(a)** Using the identity $\ln e^N = N$, we get $\ln e^{2x} = 2x$.
(b) Using the identity $e^{\ln N} = N$, we get $e^{\ln(3x+2)} = 3x + 2$.
(c) Since $\frac{1}{e^{5x}} = e^{-5x}$, we get $\ln\left(\frac{1}{e^{5x}}\right) = \ln e^{-5x} = -5x$.
(d) Since $\sqrt{e^x} = (e^x)^{1/2} = e^{\frac{1}{2}x}$, we have $\ln \sqrt{e^x} = \ln e^{\frac{1}{2}x} = \frac{1}{2}x$.

433

29. **(a)** Since $p = \log m$, we have $m = 10^p$.

(b) Since $q = \log n$, we have $n = 10^q$, and so

$$n^3 = (10^q)^3 = 10^{3q}.$$

(c) By parts (a) and (b), we have

$$\log(mn^3) = \log(10^p \cdot 10^{3q})$$
$$= \log(10^{p+3q})$$

Using the identity $\log 10^N = N$, we have

$$\log(mn^3) = p + 3q.$$

(d) Since $\sqrt{m} = m^{1/2}$,

$$\log \sqrt{m} = \log m^{1/2}.$$

Using the identity $\log a^b = b \cdot \log a$ we have

$$\log m^{1/2} = \frac{1}{2} \log m.$$

Since $p = \log m$

$$\frac{1}{2} \log m = \frac{1}{2} p,$$
$$\log \sqrt{m} = \frac{p}{2}.$$

33. To find a formula for S, we find the points labeled (x_0, y_1) and (x_1, y_0) in Figure 4.1. We see that $x_0 = 4$ and that $y_1 = 27$. From the graph of R, we see that

$$y_0 = R(4) = 5.1403(1.1169)^4 = 8.$$

To find x_1 we use the fact that $R(x_1) = 27$:

$$5.1403(1.1169)^{x_1} = 27$$
$$1.1169^{x_1} = \frac{27}{5.1403}$$
$$x_1 = \frac{\log(27/5.1403)}{\log 1.1169}$$
$$= 15.$$

We have $S(4) = 27$ and $S(15) = 8$. Using the ratio method, we have

$$\frac{ab^{15}}{ab^4} = \frac{S(15)}{S(4)}$$
$$b^{11} = \frac{8}{27}$$
$$b = \left(\frac{8}{27}\right)^{1/11} \approx 0.8953.$$

Now we can solve for a:

$$a(0.8953)^4 = 27$$
$$a = \frac{27}{(0.8953)^4}$$
$$\approx 42.0207.$$

so $S(x) = 42.0207(0.8953)^x$.

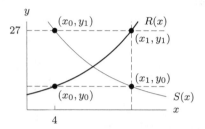

Figure 4.1

37. First, we isolate the power on one side of the equation:

$$3 \cdot 2^x = 17$$
$$2^x = \frac{17}{3}.$$

Taking the log of both sides of the equation gives

$$\log(2^x) = \log\frac{17}{3}$$
$$x \cdot \log 2 = \log\frac{17}{3}$$
$$x = \frac{\log(17/3)}{\log 2} \qquad \text{(dividing by log 2).}$$

41. Taking logs and using the log rules:

$$\log(ab^x) = \log c$$
$$\log a + \log b^x = \log c$$
$$\log a + x \log b = \log c$$
$$x \log b = \log c - \log a$$
$$x = \frac{\log c - \log a}{\log b}.$$

45.

$$58e^{4t+1} = 30$$
$$e^{4t+1} = \frac{30}{58}$$
$$\ln e^{4t+1} = \ln(\frac{30}{58})$$
$$4t + 1 = \ln(\frac{30}{58})$$
$$t = \frac{1}{4}\left(\ln(\frac{30}{58}) - 1\right).$$

49. We have $\log(2x + 5) \cdot \log(9x^2) = 0$.

In order for this product to equal zero, we know that one or both terms must be equal to zero. Thus, we will set each of the factors equal to zero to determine the values of x for which the factors will equal zero. We have

$$\log(2x + 5) = 0 \qquad \text{or} \qquad \log(9x^2) = 0$$
$$2x + 5 = 1 \qquad\qquad\qquad 9x^2 = 1$$
$$2x = -4 \qquad\qquad\qquad x^2 = \frac{1}{9}$$
$$x = -2 \qquad\qquad\qquad x = \frac{1}{3} \text{ or } x = -\frac{1}{3}.$$

Checking and substituting back into the original equation, we see that the three solutions work. Thus our solutions are $x = -2, \frac{1}{3}$, or $-\frac{1}{3}$.

53. Since $\log A < 0$, we know that $0 < A < 1$. Since $\log B > 1$, we know that $B > 10$, so $B^2 > 100$. We know that $0 < \log AB < 1$, so $1 < AB < 10$. Since $A^2 B^2 = (AB)^2$, this means that $1 < (AB)^2 < 100$. Putting all this together, we have

$$0 < A < 1 < A^2 B^2 < 100 < B^2.$$

Solutions for Section 4.2

Exercises

1. We have $a = 230$, $b = 1.182$, $r = b - 1 = 18.2\%$, and $k = \ln b = 0.1672 = 16.72\%$.

5. Writing this as $Q = 12.1(10^{-0.11})^t$, we have $a = 12.1$, $b = 10^{-0.11} = 0.7762$, $r = b - 1 = -22.38\%$, and $k = \ln b = -25.32\%$.

9. To convert to the form $Q = ae^{kt}$, we first say that the right sides of the two equations equal each other (since each equals Q), and then we solve for a and k. Thus, we have $ae^{kt} = 4 \cdot 7^t$. At $t = 0$, we can solve for a:

$$ae^{k \cdot 0} = 4 \cdot 7^0$$
$$a \cdot 1 = 4 \cdot 1$$
$$a = 4.$$

Thus, we have $4e^{kt} = 4 \cdot 7^t$, and we solve for k:

$$4e^{kt} = 4 \cdot 7^t$$
$$e^{kt} = 7^t$$
$$\left(e^k\right)^t = 7^t$$
$$e^k = 7$$
$$\ln e^k = \ln 7$$
$$k = \ln 7 \approx 1.946.$$

Therefore, the equation is $Q = 4e^{1.946t}$.

13. The continuous percent growth rate is the value of k in the equation $Q = ae^{kt}$, which is 7.

To convert to the form $Q = ab^t$, we first say that the right sides of the two equations equal each other (since each equals Q), and then we solve for a and b. Thus, we have $ab^t = 4e^{7t}$. At $t = 0$, we can solve for a:

$$ab^0 = 4e^{7 \cdot 0}$$
$$a \cdot 1 = 4 \cdot 1$$
$$a = 4.$$

Thus, we have $4b^t = 4e^{7t}$, and we solve for b:

$$4b^t = 4e^{7t}$$
$$b^t = e^{7t}$$
$$b^t = \left(e^7\right)^t$$
$$b = e^7 \approx 1096.633.$$

Therefore, the equation is $Q = 4 \cdot 1096.633^t$.

17. We want $25e^{0.053t} = 25(e^{0.053})^t = ab^t$, so we choose $a = 25$ and $b = e^{0.053} = 1.0544$. The given exponential function is equivalent to the exponential function $y = 25(1.0544)^t$. The annual percent growth rate is 5.44% and the continuous percent growth rate per year is 5.3% per year.

21. Let t be the doubling time, then the population is $2P_0$ at time t, so

$$2P_0 = P_0 e^{0.2t}$$
$$2 = e^{0.2t}$$
$$0.2t = \ln 2$$
$$t = \frac{\ln 2}{0.2} \approx 3.466.$$

25. The growth factor for Tritium should be $1 - 0.05471 = 0.94529$, since it is decaying by 5.471% per year. Therefore, the decay equation starting with a quantity of a should be:

$$Q = a(0.94529)^t,$$

where Q is quantity remaining and t is time in years. The half life will be the value of t for which Q is $a/2$, or half of the initial quantity a. Thus, we solve the equation for $Q = a/2$:

$$\frac{a}{2} = a(0.94529)^t$$
$$\frac{1}{2} = (0.94529)^t$$
$$\log(1/2) = \log(0.94529)^t$$
$$\log(1/2) = t\log(0.94529)$$
$$t = \frac{\log(1/2)}{\log(0.94529)} = 12.320.$$

So the half-life is about 12.3 years.

Problems

29. We have $g(-50) = 20$ and $g(120) = 70$. Using the ratio method, we have

$$\frac{ab^{120}}{ab^{-50}} = \frac{g(120)}{20}$$

$$b = \left(\frac{70}{20}\right)^{1/170}$$
$$\approx 1.0074.$$

Now we can solve for a:

$$a(1.0074)^{-50} = 20$$
$$a = \frac{20}{(1.0074)^{-50}}$$
$$\approx 28.9101.$$

We can also place this in the form ae^{kt} by using the fact that

$$k = \ln b = \ln(1.0074) = 0.007369,$$

so $g(t) = 28.9101e^{0.007396t}$.

33. We have $P = ab^t$ where $a = 5.2$ and $b = 1.031$. We want to find k such that

$$P = 5.2e^{kt} = 5.2(1.031)^t,$$

so

$$e^k = 1.031.$$

Thus, the continuous growth rate is $k = \ln 1.031 \approx 0.03053$, or 3.053% per year.

37. Take logarithms:

$$3^{(4\log x)} = 5$$
$$\log 3^{(4\log x)} = \log 5$$
$$(4\log x)\log 3 = \log 5$$
$$4\log x = \frac{\log 5}{\log 3}$$
$$\log x = \frac{\log 5}{4\log 3}$$
$$x = 10^{(\log 5)/(4\log 3)}.$$

41. Using $\log a + \log b = \log(ab)$, we can rewrite the equation as

$$\log(x(x-1)) = \log 2$$
$$x(x-1) = 2$$
$$x^2 - x - 2 = 0$$
$$(x-2)(x+1) = 0$$
$$x = 2 \text{ or } -1$$

but $x \neq -1$ since $\log x$ is undefined at $x = -1$. Thus $x = 2$.

45. Let $P = ab^t$ where P is the number of bacteria at time t hours since the beginning of the experiment. a is the number of bacteria we're starting with.

   (a) Since the colony begins with 3 bacteria we have $a = 3$. Using the information that $P = 100$ when $t = 3$, we can solve the following equation for b:

$$P = 3b^t$$
$$100 = 3b^3$$
$$\sqrt[3]{\frac{100}{3}} = b$$
$$b = \left(\frac{100}{3}\right)^{1/3} \approx 3.218$$

   Therefore, $P = 3(3.218)^t$.

   (b) We want to find the value of t for which the population triples, going from three bacteria to nine. So we want to solve:

$$9 = 3(3.218)^t$$
$$3 = (3.218)^t$$
$$\log 3 = \log(3.218)^t$$
$$= t\log(3.218).$$

   Thus,

$$t = \frac{\log 3}{\log(3.218)} \approx 0.940 \text{ hours.}$$

49. (a) Use $o(t)$ to describe the number of owls as a function of time. After 1 year, we see that the number of owls is 103% of 245, or $o(1) = 245(1.03)$. After 2 years, the population is 103% of that number, or $o(2) = (245(1.03)) \cdot 1.03 = 245(1.03)^2$. After t years, it is $o(t) = 245(1.03)^t$.

(b) We will use $h(t)$ to describe the number of hawks as a function of time. Since $h(t)$ doubles every 10 years, we know that its growth factor is constant and so it is an exponential function with a formula of the form $h(t) = ab^t$. In this case the initial population is 63 hawks, so $h(t) = 63b^t$. We are told that the population in 10 years is twice the current population, that is

$$63b^{10} = 126.$$

Thus,

$$b^{10} = 2$$
$$b = 2^{1/10} \approx 1.072.$$

The number of hawks as a function of time is

$$h(t) = 63(2^{1/10})^t = 63 \cdot 2^{t/10} \approx 63 \cdot (1.072)^t.$$

(c) Looking at Figure 4.2 we see that it takes about 34.2 years for the populations to be equal.

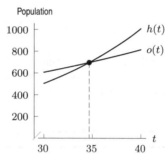

Figure 4.2

53. We have

$$Q = 0.1e^{-(1/2.5)t},$$

and need to find t such that $Q = 0.04$. This gives

$$0.1e^{-\frac{t}{2.5}} = 0.04$$
$$e^{-\frac{t}{2.5}} = 0.4$$
$$\ln e^{-\frac{t}{2.5}} = \ln 0.4$$
$$-\frac{t}{2.5} = \ln 0.4$$
$$t = -2.5 \ln 0.4 \approx 2.291.$$

It takes about 2.3 hours for their BAC to drop to 0.04.

57. (a) At time $t = 0$ we see that the temperature is given by

$$H = 70 + 120(1/4)^0$$
$$= 70 + 120(1)$$
$$= 190.$$

At time $t = 1$, we see that the temperature is given by

$$H = 70 + 120(1/4)^1$$
$$= 70 + 120(1/4)$$
$$= 70 + 30$$
$$= 100.$$

At $t = 2$, we see that the temperature is given by

$$H = 70 + 120(1/4)^2$$
$$= 70 + 120(1/16)$$
$$= 70 + 7.5$$
$$= 77.5.$$

(b) We solve for t to find when the temperature reaches $H = 90°$F:

$$70 + 120(1/4)^t = 90$$
$$120(1/4)^t = 20 \qquad \text{subtracting}$$
$$(1/4)^t = 20/120 \qquad \text{dividing}$$
$$\log(1/4)^t = \log(1/6) \qquad \text{taking logs}$$
$$t\log(1/4) = \log(1/6) \qquad \text{using a log property}$$
$$t = \frac{\log(1/6)}{\log(1/4)} \qquad \text{dividing}$$
$$= 1.292,$$

so the coffee temperature reaches $90°$F after about 1.292 hours. Similar calculations show that the temperature reaches $75°$F after about 2.292 hours.

61. Since a and b are fixed, the y-intercepts of the two graphs remain fixed. Since r increases, the growth rate of $y = ae^{rt}$ increases, and the graph of this function climbs more steeply. This will shift the point of intersection to the left unless the graph of be^{st} descends less steeply—that is, unless the value of s increases (becomes less negative/more positive).

Solutions for Section 4.3

Exercises

1. The graphs of $y = 10^x$ and $y = 2^x$ both have horizontal asymptotes, $y = 0$. The graph of $y = \log x$ has a vertical asymptote, $x = 0$.

5. (a) $10^{-x} \to 0$ as $x \to \infty$.
(b) The values of $\log x$ get more and more negative as $x \to 0^+$, so

$$\log x \to -\infty.$$

9. See Figure 4.3. The graph of $y = \log(x - 4)$ is the graph of $y = \log x$ shifted to the right 4 units.

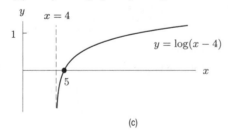

(c)

Figure 4.3

13. We know, by the definition of pH, that $13 = -\log[H^+]$. Therefore, $-13 = \log[H^+]$, and $10^{-13} = [H^+]$. Thus, the hydrogen ion concentration is 10^{-13} moles per liter.

17. We know, by the definition of pH, that $0 = -\log[H^+]$. Therefore, $-0 = \log[H^+]$, and $10^{-0} = [H^+]$. Thus, the hydrogen ion concentration is $10^{-0} = 10^0 = 1$ mole per liter.

Problems

21. The log function is increasing but is concave down and so is increasing at a decreasing rate. It is not a compliment— growing exponentially would have been better. However, it is most likely realistic because after you are proficient at something, any increase in proficiency takes longer and longer to achieve.

25. A possible formula is $y = \ln x$.

29. Since $\ln(x)$ is defined only for $x > 0$, $x > 0$.

33. (a) We are given the number of H^+ ions in 12 oz of coffee, and we need to find the number of moles of ions in 1 liter of coffee. So we need to convert numbers of ions to moles of ions, and ounces of coffee to liters of coffee. Finding the number of moles of H^+, we have:

$$2.41 \cdot 10^{18} \text{ ions} \cdot \frac{1 \text{ mole of ions}}{6.02 \cdot 10^{23} \text{ ions}} = 4 \cdot 10^{-6} \text{ ions.}$$

Finding the number of liters of coffee, we have:

$$12 \text{ oz} \cdot \frac{1 \text{ liter}}{30.3 \text{ oz}} = 0.396 \text{ liters.}$$

Thus, the concentration, $[H^+]$, in the coffee is given by

$$[H^+] = \frac{\text{Number of moles } H^+ \text{ in solution}}{\text{Number of liters solution}}$$
$$= \frac{4 \cdot 10^{-6}}{0.396}$$
$$= 1.01 \cdot 10^{-5} \text{ moles/liter.}$$

(b) We have

$$\text{pH} = -\log[H^+]$$
$$= -\log\left(1.01 \cdot 10^{-5}\right)$$
$$= -(-4.9957)$$
$$\approx 5.$$

Thus, the pH is about 5. Since this is less than 7, it means that coffee is acidic.

37. (a) We know $M_1 = \log\left(\frac{W_1}{W_0}\right)$ and $M_2 = \log\left(\frac{W_2}{W_0}\right)$. Thus,

$$M_2 - M_1 = \log\left(\frac{W_2}{W_0}\right) - \log\left(\frac{W_1}{W_0}\right)$$
$$= \log\left(\frac{W_2}{W_1}\right).$$

(b) Let $M_2 = 8.7$ and $M_1 = 7.1$, so

$$M_2 - M_1 = \log\left(\frac{W_2}{W_1}\right)$$

becomes

$$8.7 - 7.1 = \log\left(\frac{W_2}{W_1}\right)$$
$$1.6 = \log\left(\frac{W_2}{W_1}\right)$$

so

$$\frac{W_2}{W_1} = 10^{1.6} \approx 40.$$

Thus, the seismic waves of the 2005 Sumatran earthquake were about 40 times as large as those of the 1989 California earthquake.

Solutions for Section 4.4

1. Using a linear scale, the wealth of everyone with less than a million dollars would be indistinguishable because all of them are less than one one-thousandth of the wealth of the average billionaire. A log scale is more useful.

5. (a)

Table 4.2

n	1	2	3	4	5	6	7	8	9
$\log n$	0	0.3010	0.4771	0.6021	0.6990	0.7782	0.8451	0.9031	0.9542

Table 4.3

n	10	20	30	40	50	60	70	80	90
$\log n$	1	1.3010	1.4771	1.6021	1.6990	1.7782	1.8451	1.9031	1.9542

(b) The first tick mark is at $10^0 = 1$. The dot for the number 2 is placed $\log 2 = 0.3010$ of the distance from 1 to 10. The number 3 is placed at $\log 3 = 0.4771$ units from 1, and so on. The number 30 is placed 1.4771 units from 1, the number 50 is placed 1.6989 units from 1, and so on.

Figure 4.4

9. The Declaration of Independence was signed in 1776, about 225 years ago. We can write this number as

$$\frac{225}{1,000,000} = 0.000225 \text{ million years ago.}$$

This number is between $10^{-4} = 0.0001$ and $10^{-3} = 0.001$. Using a calculator, we have

$$\log 0.000225 \approx -3.65,$$

which, as expected, lies between -3 and -4 on the log scale. Thus, the Declaration of Independence is placed at

$$10^{-3.65} \approx 0.000224 \text{ million years ago} = 224 \text{ years ago.}$$

13. The figure represents populations using logs, which are exponents of 10. For instance, Greasewood, AZ corresponds to the logarithm 2.3. This means that

$$\text{Population of Greasewood} = 10^{2.3} = 200 \qquad \text{after rounding}$$

The population of the other places are in Table 4.4.

Table 4.4 *Approximate populations of eleven different localities*

Locality	Exponent	Approx. population
Lost Springs, Wy	0.6	4
Greasewood, Az	2.3	200
Bar Harbor, Me	3.4	2,500
Abilene, Tx	5.1	130,000
Worcester, Ma	5.6	400,000
Massachusetts	6.8	6,300,000
Chicago	6.9	7,900,000
New York	7.3	20,000,000
California	7.5	32,000,000
US	8.4	250,000,000
World	9.8	6,300,000,000

17.

Table 4.5

x	0	1	2	3	4	5
$y = \ln(3^x)$	0	1.0986	2.1972	3.2958	4.3944	5.4931

Table 4.6

x	0	1	2	3	4	5
$g(x) = \ln(2 \cdot 5^x)$	0.6931	2.3026	3.9120	5.5215	7.1309	8.7403

Yes, the results are linear.

21. **(a)** Table 4.7 gives values of $L = \ln \ell$ and $W = \ln w$. The data in Table 4.7 have been plotted in Figure 4.5, and a line of best fit has been drawn in. See part (b).

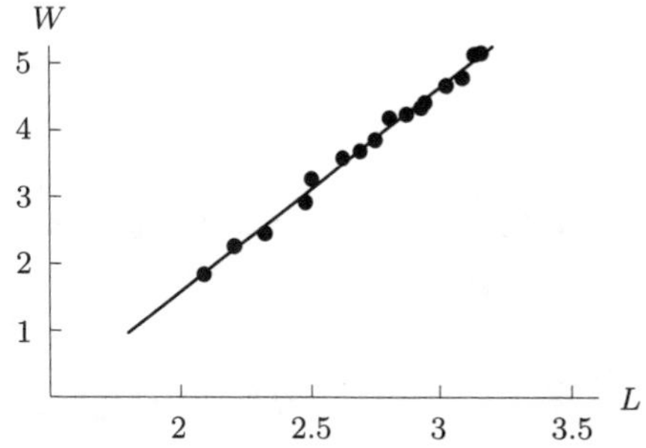

Figure 4.5: Plot of data in Table 4.7 together with line of best fit

Table 4.7 $L = \ln \ell$ and $W = \ln w$ *for 16 different fish*

Type	1	2	3	4	5	6	7	8
L	2.092	2.208	2.322	2.477	2.501	2.625	2.695	2.754
W	1.841	2.262	2.451	2.918	3.266	3.586	3.691	3.857

Type	9	10	11	12	13	14	15	16
L	2.809	2.874	2.929	2.944	3.025	3.086	3.131	3.157
W	4.184	4.240	4.336	4.413	4.669	4.786	5.131	5.155

(b) The formula for the line of best fit is $W = 3.06L - 4.54$, as determined using a spreadsheet. However, you could also obtain comparable results by fitting a line by eye.

(c) We have

$$W = 3.06L - 4.54$$
$$\ln w = 3.06 \ln \ell - 4.54$$
$$\ln w = \ln \ell^{3.06} - 4.54$$
$$w = e^{\ln \ell^{3.06} - 4.54}$$
$$= \ell^{3.06} e^{-4.54} \approx 0.011 \ell^{3.06}.$$

(d) Weight tends to be directly proportional to volume, and in many cases volume tends to be proportional to the cube of a linear dimension (e.g., length). Here we see that w is in fact very nearly proportional to the cube of ℓ.

Solutions for Chapter 4 Review

1. To convert to the form $Q = ae^{kt}$, we first say that the right sides of the two equations equal each other (since each equals Q), and then we solve for a and k. Thus, we have $ae^{kt} = 12(0.9)^t$. At $t = 0$, we can solve for a:

$$ae^{k \cdot 0} = 12(0.9)^0$$
$$a \cdot 1 = 12 \cdot 1$$
$$a = 12.$$

Thus, we have $12e^{kt} = 12(0.9)^t$, and we solve for k:

$$12e^{kt} = 12(0.9)^t$$
$$e^{kt} = (0.9)^t$$
$$\left(e^k\right)^t = (0.9)^t$$
$$e^k = 0.9$$
$$\ln e^k = \ln 0.9$$
$$k = \ln 0.9 \approx -0.105.$$

Therefore, the equation is $Q = 12e^{-0.105t}$.

5. The continuous percent growth rate is the value of k in the equation $Q = ae^{kt}$, which is -10.

To convert to the form $Q = ab^t$, we first say that the right sides of the two equations equal each other (since each equals Q), and then we solve for a and b. Thus, we have $ab^t = 7e^{-10t}$. At $t = 0$, we can solve for a:

$$ab^0 = 7e^{-10 \cdot 0}$$
$$a \cdot 1 = 7 \cdot 1$$
$$a = 7.$$

Thus, we have $7b^t = 7e^{-10t}$, and we solve for b:

$$7b^t = e^{-10t}$$
$$b^t = e^{-10t}$$
$$b^t = \left(e^{-10}\right)^t$$
$$b = e^{-10} \approx 0.0000454.$$

Therefore, the equation is $Q = 7(0.0000454)^t$.

9. We are solving for an exponent, so we use logarithms. We first divide both sides by 40 and then use logs:

$$40e^{-0.2t} = 12$$
$$e^{-0.2t} = 0.3$$
$$\ln(e^{-0.2t}) = \ln(0.3)$$
$$-0.2t = \ln(0.3)$$
$$t = \frac{\ln(0.3)}{-0.2} = 6.020.$$

13. (a) $P(t) = 51(1.03)^t = 51e^{t \ln 1.03} \approx 51e^{0.0296t}$. The population starts at 51 million with a 3 percent annual growth rate and a continuous annual growth rate of about 2.96 percent.

(b) $P(t) = 15e^{0.03t} = 15(e^{0.03})^t \approx 15(1.0305)^t$. The population starts at 15 million with an approximate 3.05% annual growth rate and a 3 percent continuous annual growth rate.

(c) $P(t) = 7.5(0.94)^t = 7.5e^{t \ln 0.94} \approx 7.5e^{-0.0619t}$. The population starts at 7.5 million with an annual percent reduction of 6% and a continuous annual decay rate of about 6.19%.

(d) $P(t) = 16e^{-0.051t} = 16(e^{-0.051})^t \approx 16(0.9503)^t$. The population starts at 16 million with an approximate 4.97% annual rate of decrease and a 5.1% continuous annual decay rate.

(e) $P(t) = 25(2^{1/18})^t = 25(e^k)^t$. Find $e^k = 2^{1/18}$, so $k = \ln(2^{1/18})$ and $P(t) \approx 25(1.0393)^t$ for an approximate annual growth rate of 3.93%, and $P(t) \approx 25e^{0.0385t}$ for an approximate continuous annual growth rate of 3.85%. (The initial population is 25 million.)

(f) Find k when $P(t) = 10((1/2)^{1/25})^t = 10(e^k)^t$. So $k = \ln((1/2)^{1/25})$ and $P(t) \approx 10(0.9727)^t$ for an approximate annual reduction of 2.73%, and $P(t) \approx 10e^{-0.0277t}$, for an approximate continuous annual decay rate of 2.77%. (The initial population is 10 million.)

17. We have

$$55e^{0.571t} = 28e^{0.794t}$$
$$\frac{e^{0.571t}}{e^{0.794t}} = \frac{28}{55}$$
$$e^{0.571t-0.794t} = e^{-0.223t} = \frac{28}{55}$$
$$-0.223t = \ln\left(\frac{28}{55}\right)$$
$$t = \frac{\ln(28/55)}{-0.223}$$
$$= 3.0275.$$

21. Rewriting both sides to the base 10 gives:

$$\left(10^{-2}\right)^x = 10^{-0.5}$$
$$10^{-2x} = 10^{-0.5}$$
$$-2x = -0.5$$
$$x = 0.25.$$

25.

$$\frac{\log x^2 + \log x^3}{\log(100x)} = 3$$
$$\log x^2 + \log x^3 = 3\log(100x)$$
$$2\log x + 3\log x = 3(\log 100 + \log x)$$
$$5\log x = 3(2 + \log x)$$
$$5\log x = 6 + 3\log x$$
$$2\log x = 6$$
$$\log x = 3$$
$$x = 10^3 = 1000.$$

To check, we see that

$$\frac{\log x^2 + \log x^3}{\log(100x)} = \frac{\log(1000^2) + \log(1000^3)}{\log(100 \cdot 1000)}$$

$$= \frac{\log(1,000,000) + \log(1,000,000,000)}{\log(100,000)}$$

$$= \frac{6 + 9}{5}$$

$$= 3,$$

as required.

29. Using the fact that $A^{-1} = 1/A$ and the log rules:

$$\ln(A + B) - \ln(A^{-1} + B^{-1}) = \ln(A + B) - \ln\left(\frac{1}{A} + \frac{1}{B}\right)$$

$$= \ln(A + B) - \ln\frac{A + B}{AB}$$

$$= \ln\left((A + B) \cdot \frac{AB}{A + B}\right)$$

$$= \ln(AB).$$

$$\frac{}{(1.052)^t} = \frac{63}{51}$$

$$\left(\frac{1.031}{1.052}\right)^t = \frac{63}{51}$$

$$\log\left(\frac{1.031}{1.052}\right)^t = \log\frac{63}{51}$$

$$t\log\left(\frac{1.031}{1.052}\right) = \log\frac{63}{51}$$

$$t = \frac{\log\frac{63}{51}}{\log\left(\frac{1.031}{1.052}\right)} = -10.480.$$

So, the populations are the same 10.5 years before 1980, in the middle of 1969.

41. (a) The number of bacteria present after 1/2 hour is

$$N = 1000e^{0.69(1/2)} \approx 1412.$$

If you notice that $0.69 \approx \ln 2$, you could also say

$$N = 1000e^{0.69/2} \approx 1000e^{\frac{1}{2}\ln 2} = 1000e^{\ln 2^{1/2}} = 1000e^{\ln\sqrt{2}} = 1000\sqrt{2} \approx 1412.$$

(b) We solve for t in the equation

$$1,000,000 = 1000e^{0.69t}$$
$$e^{0.69t} = 1000$$
$$0.69t = \ln 1000$$
$$t = \left(\frac{\ln 1000}{0.69}\right) \approx 10.011 \text{ hours.}$$

(c) The doubling time is the time t such that $N = 2000$, so

$$2000 = 1000e^{0.69t}$$
$$e^{0.69t} = 2$$
$$0.69t = \ln 2$$
$$t = \left(\frac{\ln 2}{0.69}\right) \approx 1.005 \text{ hours.}$$

If you notice that $0.69 \approx \ln 2$, you see why the half-life turns out to be 1 hour:

$$e^{0.69t} = 2$$
$$e^{t \ln 2} \approx 2$$
$$e^{\ln 2^t} \approx 2$$
$$2^t \approx 2$$
$$t \approx 1$$

45. (a) Since the drug is being metabolized continuously, the formula for describing the amount left in the bloodstream is $Q(t) = Q_0 e^{kt}$. We know that we start with 2 mg, so $Q_0 = 2$, and the rate of decay is 4%, so $k = -0.04$. (Why is k negative?) Thus $Q(t) = 2e^{-0.04t}$.

(b) To find the percent decrease in one hour, we need to rewrite our equation in the form $Q = Q_0 b^t$, where b gives us the percent left after one hour:

$$Q(t) = 2e^{-0.04t} = 2(e^{-0.04})^t \approx 2(0.96079)^t.$$

We see that $b \approx 0.96079 = 96.079\%$, which is the percent we have left after one hour. Thus, the drug level decreases by about 3.921% each hour.

(c) We want to find out when the drug level reaches 0.25 mg. We therefore ask when $Q(t)$ will equal 0.25.

$$2e^{-0.04t} = 0.25$$
$$e^{-0.04t} = 0.125$$
$$-0.04t = \ln 0.125$$
$$t = \frac{\ln 0.125}{-0.04} \approx 51.986.$$

Thus, the second injection is required after about 52 hours.

(d) After the second injection, the drug level is 2.25 mg, which means that Q_0, the initial amount, is now 2.25. The decrease is still 4% per hour, so when will the level reach 0.25 again? We need to solve the equation

$$2.25e^{-0.04t} = 0.25,$$

where t is now the number of hours since the second injection.

$$e^{-0.04t} = \frac{0.25}{2.25} = \frac{1}{9}$$
$$-0.04t = \ln(1/9)$$
$$t = \frac{\ln(1/9)}{-0.04} \approx 54.931.$$

Thus the third injection is required about 55 hours after the second injection, or about $52 + 55 = 107$ hours after the first injection.

49. At an annual growth rate of 1%, the Rule of 70 tells us this investment doubles in $70/1 = 70$ years. At a 2% rate, the doubling time should be about $70/2 = 35$ years. The doubling times for the other rates are, according to the Rule of 70,

$$\frac{70}{5} = 14 \text{ years}, \qquad \frac{70}{7} = 10 \text{ years}, \qquad \text{and} \qquad \frac{70}{10} = 7 \text{ years}.$$

To check these predictions, we use logs to calculate the actual doubling times. If V is the dollar value of the investment in year t, then at a 1% rate, $V = 1000(1.01)^t$. To find the doubling time, we set $V = 2000$ and solve for t:

$$1000(1.01)^t = 2000$$
$$1.01^t = 2$$
$$\log(1.01^t) = \log 2$$
$$t \log 1.01 = \log 2$$
$$t = \frac{\log 2}{\log 1.01} \approx 69.661.$$

This agrees well with the prediction of 70 years. Doubling times for the other rates have been calculated and recorded in Table 4.8 together with the doubling times predicted by the Rule of 70.

Table 4.8 *Doubling times predicted by the Rule of 70 and actual values*

Rate (%)	1	2	5	7	10
Predicted doubling time (years)	70	35	14	10	7
Actual doubling time (years)	69.661	35.003	14.207	10.245	

The Rule of 70 works reasonably well when the growth rate is small. The Rule of 70 does not give good estimates for growth rates much higher than 10%. For example, at an annual rate of 35%, the Rule of 70 predicts that the doubling time is $70/35 = 2$ years. But in 2 years at 35% growth rate, the $1000 investment from the last example would be not worth $2000, but only

$$1000(1.35)^2 = \$1822.50.$$

53. If $P(t)$ describes the number of people in the store t minutes after it opens, we need to find a formula for $P(t)$. Perhaps the easiest way to develop this formula is to first find a formula for $P(k)$ where k is the number of 40-minute intervals since the store opened. After the first such interval there are $500(2) = 1{,}000$ people; after the second interval, there are $1{,}000(2) = 2{,}000$ people. Table 4.9 describes this progression:

Table 4.9

k	$P(k)$
0	500
1	$500(2)$
2	$500(2)(2) = 500(2)^2$
3	$500(2)(2)(2) = 500(2)^3$
4	$500(2)^4$
$\vdots$	$\vdots$
k	$500(2)^k$

From this, we conclude that $P(k) = 500(2)^k$. We now need to see how k and t compare. If $t = 120$ minutes, then we know that $k = \frac{120}{40} = 3$ intervals of 40 minutes; if $t = 187$ minutes, then $k = \frac{187}{40}$ intervals of 40 minutes. In general,

$k = \frac{t}{40}$. Substituting $k = \frac{t}{40}$ into our equation for $P(k)$, we get an equation for the number of people in the store t minutes after the store opens:

$$P(t) = 500(2)^{\frac{t}{40}}.$$

To find the time when we'll need to post security guards, we need to find the value of t for which $P(t) = 10,000$.

$$500(2)^{t/40} = 10,000$$
$$2^{t/40} = 20$$
$$\log\left(2^{t/40}\right) = \log 20$$
$$\frac{t}{40}\log(2) = \log 20$$
$$t(\log 2) = 40\log 20$$
$$t = \frac{40\log 20}{\log 2} \approx 172.877$$

The guards should be commissioned about 173 minutes after the store is opened, or 12:53 pm.

CHECK YOUR UNDERSTANDING

1. True. If x is a positive number, $\log x$ is defined and $10^{\log x} = x$.

5. True. The value of $\log n$ is the exponent to which 10 is raised to get n.

9. True. The natural log function and the e^x function are inverses.

13. True. Since $y = \log \sqrt{x} = \log(x^{1/2}) = \frac{1}{2}\log x$.

17. True. Divide both sides of the first equation by 50. Then take the log of both sides and finally divide by $\log 0.345$ to solve for t.

21. False. Since $\frac{1}{4} = \frac{1}{2}^2$, it takes only two half-life periods. That is 10 hours.

25. True. For example, astronomical distances.

29. False. The fit will not be as good as $y = x^3$ but an exponential function can be found.

Solutions to Tools for Chapter 4

1. $\log(\log 10) = \log(1) = 0$.

5. $\dfrac{\log 100^6}{\log 100^2} = \dfrac{6\log 100}{2\log 100} = \dfrac{6}{2} = 3$.

9. $\sqrt{\log 10,000} = \sqrt{\log 10^4} = \sqrt{4\log 10} = \sqrt{4} = 2$.

13. The equation $10^{0.477} = 3$ is equivalent to $\log 3 = 0.477$.

17. The equation $\log 0.01 = -2$ is equivalent to $10^{-2} = 0.01$.

21. Rewrite the logarithm of the product as a sum, $\log 2x = \log 2 + \log x$.

25. The logarithm of a quotient and the power property apply, so

$$\log\left(\frac{x^2+1}{x^3}\right) = \log(x^2+1) - \log x^3$$
$$= \log(x^2+1) - 3\log x.$$

29. In general the logarithm of a difference cannot be simplified. In this case we rewrite the expression so that it is the logarithm of a product.

$$\log(x^2 - y^2) = \log((x+y)(x-y)) = \log(x+y) + \log(x-y).$$

33. Rewrite the sum as $\ln x^3 + \ln x^2 = \ln(x^3 \cdot x^2) = \ln x^5$.

37. Rewrite with powers and combine,

$$
\begin{aligned}
\frac{1}{3}\log 8 - \frac{1}{2}\log 25 &= \log 8^{1/3} - \log 25^{1/2} \\
&= \log 2 - \log 5 \\
&= \log \frac{2}{5}.
\end{aligned}
$$

41. Rewrite as $10^{-\log 5x} = 10^{\log(5x)^{-1}} = (5x)^{-1}$.

45. Rewrite as $t \ln e^{t/2} = t(t/2) = t^2/2$.

49. Rewrite as $\ln \sqrt{x^2 + 16} = \ln(x^2 + 16)^{1/2} = \frac{1}{2}\ln(x^2 + 16)$.

53. Taking logs of both sides we get

$$\log(4^x) = \log 9.$$

This gives

$$x \log 4 = \log 9$$

or in other words

$$x = \frac{\log 9}{\log 4} \approx 1.585.$$

57. Taking natural logs of both sides we get

$$\ln(e^x) = \ln 8.$$

This gives

$$x = \ln 8 \approx 2.079.$$

61. Taking logs of both sides we get

$$\log 12^{5x} = \log(3 \cdot 15^{2x}).$$

This gives

$$
\begin{aligned}
5x \log 12 &= \log 3 + \log 15^{2x} \\
5x \log 12 &= \log 3 + 2x \log 15 \\
5x \log 12 - 2x \log 15 &= \log 3 \\
x(5 \log 12 - 2 \log 15) &= \log 3 \\
x &= \frac{\log 3}{5 \log 12 - 2 \log 15} \approx 0.157.
\end{aligned}
$$

65. We first re-arrange the equation so that the log is alone on one side, and we then convert to exponential form:

$$
\begin{aligned}
4 \log(9x + 17) - 5 &= 1 \\
4 \log(9x + 17) &= 6 \\
\log(9x + 17) &= \frac{3}{2} \\
10^{\log(9x+17)} &= 10^{3/2} \\
9x + 17 &= 10^{3/2} \\
9x &= 10^{3/2} - 17 \\
x &= \frac{10^{3/2} - 17}{9} \approx 1.625.
\end{aligned}
$$

CHAPTER FIVE

Solutions for Section 5.1

Exercises

1. (a)

x	-1	0	1	2	3
$g(x)$	-3	0	2	1	-1

The graph of $g(x)$ is shifted one unit to the right of $f(x)$.

(b)

x	-3	-2	-1	0	1
$h(x)$	-3	0	2	1	-1

The graph of $h(x)$ is shifted one unit to the left of $f(x)$.

(c)

x	-2	-1	0	1	2
$k(x)$	0	3	5	4	2

The graph $k(x)$ is shifted up three units from $f(x)$.

(d)

x	-1	0	1	2	3
$m(x)$	0	3	5		2

The graph $m(x)$ is shifted one unit to the right and three units up from $f(x)$.

5. See Figure 5.1.

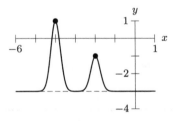

Figure 5.1

9. (a) The translation $f(x) + 5$ moves the graph up 5 units. The x-coordinate is not changed, but the y-coordinate is $-4 + 5 = 1$. The new point is $(3, 1)$.
   (b) The translation $f(x + 5)$ shifts the graph to the left 5 units. The y-coordinate is not changed, but the x-coordinate is $3 - 5 = -2$. The new point is $(-2, -4)$.
   (c) This translation shifts both the x and y coordinates; 3 units right and 2 units down resulting in $(6, -6)$.

13. $m(n+1) = \frac{1}{2}(n+1)^2 = \frac{1}{2}n^2 + n + \frac{1}{2}$

To sketch, shift the graph of $m(n) = \frac{1}{2}n^2$ one unit to the left, as in Figure 5.2.

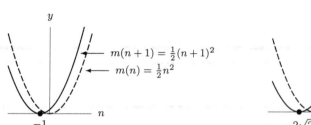

$$m(n+1) = \frac{1}{2}(n+1)^2$$
$$m(n) = \frac{1}{2}n^2$$

Figure 5.2

$$m(n+2\sqrt{2}) = \frac{1}{2}(n+2\sqrt{2})^2$$
$$m(n) = \frac{1}{2}n^2$$

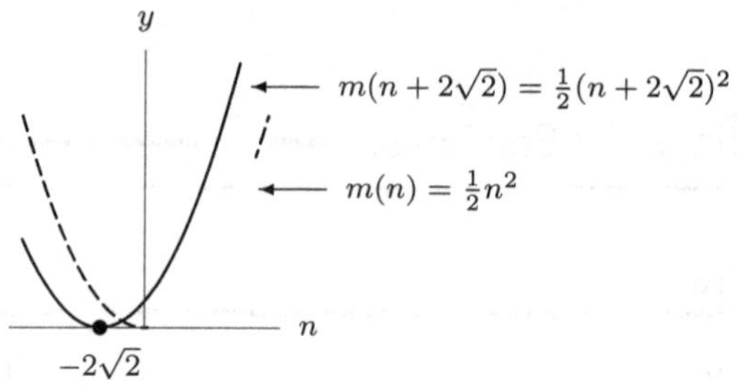

Figure 5.3

17. $m(n+2\sqrt{2}) = \frac{1}{2}(n+2\sqrt{2})^2 = \frac{1}{2}n^2 + 2\sqrt{2}n + 4$

To sketch, shift the graph of $m(n) = \frac{1}{2}n^2$ by $2\sqrt{2}$ units to the left, as in Figure 5.3.

21. $k(w-3) = 3^{w-3}$

To sketch, shift the graph of $k(w) = 3^w$ to the right by 3 units, as in Figure 5.4.

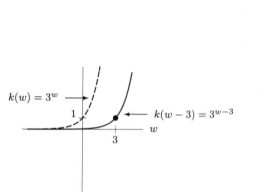

$k(w) = 3^w$
$k(w-3) = 3^{w-3}$

Figure 5.4

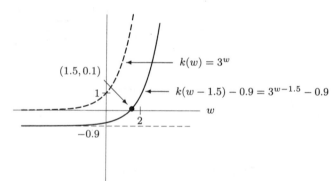

$k(w) = 3^w$

$k(w-1.5) - 0.9 = 3^{w-1.5} - 0.9$

$(1.5, 0.1)$

Figure 5.5

25. $k(w-1.5) - 0.9 = 3^{w-1.5} - 0.9$

To sketch, shift the graph of $k(w) = 3^w$ to the right by 1.5 units and down by 0.9 units, as in Figure 5.5.

Problems

29. (a) $P(t) + 100$ describes a population that is always 100 people larger than the original population.

(b) $P(t + 100)$ describes a population that has the same number of people as the original population, but the number occurs 100 years earlier.

33. Since the $+3$ is an outside change, this transformation shifts the entire graph of $q(z)$ up by 3 units. That is, for every z, the value of $q(z) + 3$ is three units greater than $q(z)$.

37. From the inside change, we know that the graph is shifted b units to the left. From the outside change, we know that it is shifted a units down. So, for any given z value, the graph of $q(z + b) - a$ is b units to the left and a units below the graph of $q(z)$.

41. (a) If

$$H(t) = 68 + 93(0.91)^t$$

then $\quad H(t+15) = 68 + 93(0.91)^{(t+15)} = 68 + 93(0.91)^{t+15}$

and $\quad H(t) + 15 = (68 + 93(.91)^t) + 15 = 83 + 93(0.91)^t$

(b)

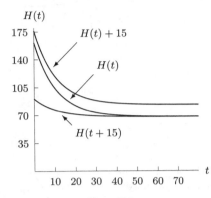

Figure 5.6

(c) $H(t+15)$ is the function $H(t)$ shifted 15 units to the left. This function could describe the temperature of the cup of coffee if it had been brought to class fifteen minutes earlier. $H(t) + 15$ is the function $H(t)$ shifted upward 15 units, or $15°F$. This function could describe the temperature of the coffee if it had been brought into a warmer classroom.

(d) As t gets very large, both $H(t+15)$ and $H(t)$ approach a final temperature of $68°F$. In contrast, $H(t)+15$ approaches $68°F + 15°F = 83°F$.

45. Since $g(x) = 5e^x$ and $g(x) = f(x - h) = e^{x-h}$, we have

$$5e^x = e^{x-h}.$$

Solve for h by taking the natural log of both sides

$$\ln(5e^x) = \ln(e^{x-h})$$
$$\ln 5 + x = x - h$$
$$h = -\ln 5.$$

Solutions for Section 5.2

Exercises

1. (a) The y-coordinate is unchanged, but the x-coordinate is the same distance to the left of the y-axis, so the point is $(-2, -3)$.

(b) The x-coordinate is unchanged, but the y-coordinate is the same distance above the x-axis, so the point is $(2, 3)$.

5. To reflect about the x-axis, we make all the y-values negative, getting $y = -e^x$ as the formula.

9. The graph of $y = -g(x) = -(1/3)^x$ is the graph of $y = g(x)$ reflected across the x-axis. See Figure 5.7.

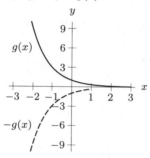

Figure 5.7

13.

$$y = -m(-n) + 3 = -(-n)^2 + 4(-n) - 5 + 3$$
$$= -n^2 - 4n - 2.$$

To graph this function, first reflect the graph of m across the y-axis, then reflect it across the n-axis, and finally shift it up by 3 units.

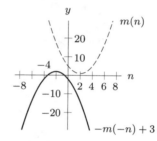

Figure 5.8: $y = -m(-n) + 3$

17.

$$y = -k(w - 2) = -3^{w-2}$$

To graph this function, first reflect the graph of k across the w-axis, then shift it to the right by 2 units.

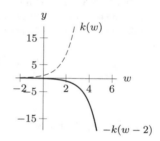

Figure 5.9: $y = -k(w - 2)$

21. The definition of an odd function is that $f(-x) = -f(x)$. Since $f(-x) = 4(-x)^7 - 3(-x)^5 = -4x^7 + 3x^5$, we see that $f(-x) = -f(x)$, so the function is odd.

Problems

25. (a) See Figure 5.10.
    (b) See Figure 5.10.

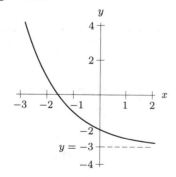

Figure 5.10: $y = 2^{-x} - 3$

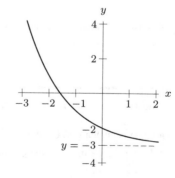

Figure 5.11: $y = 2^{-x} - 3$

(c) The two functions are the same in this case. Note that you will not always obtain the same result if you change the order of the transformations.

29. The answers are

(i) c   (ii) d   (iii) e

(iv) f   (v) a   (vi) b

33. See Figure 5.12.

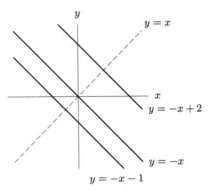

Figure 5.12: The graphs of $y = -x + 2$, $y = -x$, and $y = -x - 1$ are all symmetric across the line $y = x$.

Any straight line perpendicular to $y = x$ is symmetric across $y = x$. Its slope must be -1, so $y = -x + b$, for an arbitrary constant b, is symmetric across $y = x$.

Also, the line $y = x$ is symmetric about itself.

37. Because $f(x)$ is an odd function, $f(x) = -f(-x)$. Setting $x = 0$ gives $f(0) = -f(0)$, so $f(0) = 0$. Since $c(0) = 1$, $c(x)$ is not odd. Since $d(0) = 1$, $d(x)$ is not odd.

41. Suppose $f(x)$ is both even and odd. If $f(x)$ is even, then

$$f(-x) = f(x).$$

If $f(x)$ is odd, then

$$f(-x) = -f(x).$$

Since $f(-x)$ equals both $f(x)$ and $-f(x)$, we have

$$f(x) = -f(x).$$

Add $f(x)$ to both sides of the equation to get

$$2f(x) = 0$$

or

$$f(x) = 0.$$

Thus, the function $f(x) = 0$ is the only function which is both even and odd. There are no *nontrivial* functions that have both symmetries.

Solutions for Section 5.3

Exercises

1. To increase by a factor of 10, multiply by 10. The right shift of 2 is made by substituting $x - 2$ for x in the function formula. Together they give $y = 10f(x - 2)$.

5. See Figure 5.13.

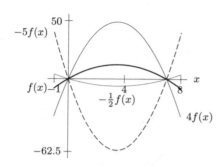

Figure 5.13

9. (a)

Table 5.1

x	-4	-3	-2	-1	0	1	2	3	4
$f(-x)$	13	6	1	-2	-3	-2	1	6	13

(b)

Table 5.2

x	-4	-3	-2	-1	0	1	2	3	4
$-f(x)$	-13	-6	-1	2	3	2	-1	-6	-13

(c)

Table 5.3

x	-4	-3	-2	-1	0	1	2	3	4
$3f(x)$	39	18	3	-6	-9	-6	3	18	39

(d) All three functions are even.

13. Since $g(x) = x^2$, $-g(x) = -x^2$. The graph of $g(x)$ is flipped over the x-axis. See Figure 5.14.

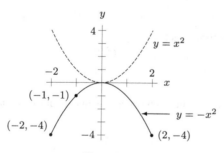

Figure 5.14

17. (i) i: The graph of $y = f(x)$ has been stretched vertically by a factor of 2.
   (ii) c: The graph of $y = f(x)$ has been stretched vertically by $1/3$, or compressed.
   (iii) b: The graph of $y = f(x)$ has been reflected over the x-axis and raised by 1.
   (iv) g: The graph of $y = f(x)$ has been shifted left by 2, and raised by 1.
   (v) d: The graph of $y = f(x)$ has been reflected over the y-axis.

Problems

21. The graph of $f(t-3)$ is the graph of $f(t)$ shifted to the right by 3 units. See Figure 5.15.

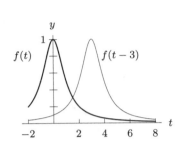

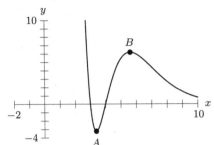

Figure 5.15

Figure 5.16

25. (a) (iii)   The number of gallons needed to cover the house is $f(A)$; two more gallons will be $f(A) + 2$.
   (b) (i)   To cover the house twice, you need $f(A) + f(A) = 2f(A)$.
   (c) (ii)   The sign is an extra 2 ft^2 so we need to cover the area $A + 2$. Since $f(A)$ is the number of gallons needed to cover A square feet, $f(A + 2)$ is the number of gallons needed to cover $A + 2$ square feet.

29. See Figure 5.16. The graph is shifted to the right by 3 units.

33. See Figure 5.17. The graph is vertically flipped, horizontally shifted left by 5 units, and vertically shifted up by 5 units.

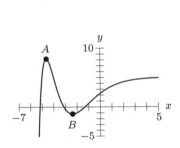

Figure 5.17

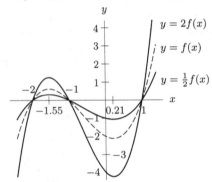

Figure 5.18: The graph of $y = 2f(x)$ and $y = \frac{1}{2}f(x)$ compared to the graph of $f(x)$

37. Figure 5.18 gives a graph of a function $y = f(x)$ together with graphs of $y = \frac{1}{2}f(x)$ and $y = 2f(x)$. All three graphs cross the x-axis at $x = -2, x = -1$, and $x = 1$. Likewise, all three functions are increasing and decreasing on the same intervals. Specifically, all three functions are increasing for $x < -1.55$ and for $x > 0.21$ and decreasing for $-1.55 < x < 0.21$.

   Even though the stretched and compressed versions of f shown by Figure 5.18 are increasing and decreasing on the same intervals, they are doing so at different rates. You can see this by noticing that, on every interval of x, the graph of $y = \frac{1}{2}f(x)$ is less steep than the graph of $y = f(x)$. Similarly, the graph of $y = 2f(x)$ is steeper than the graph of $y = f(x)$. This indicates that the magnitude of the average rate of change of $y = \frac{1}{2}f(x)$ is less than that of $y = f(x)$, and that the magnitude of the average rate of change of $y = 2f(x)$ is greater than that of $y = f(x)$.

Solutions for Section 5.4

Exercises

1. The graph is compressed horizontally by a factor of $1/2$ so the transformed function gives an output of 3 when the input is 1. Thus the point $(1, 3)$ lies on the graph of $g(2x)$.

5. The graph in Figure 5.19 of $n(x) = e^{2x}$ is a horizontal compression of the graph of $m(x) = e^x$. The graph of $p(x) = 2e^x$ is a vertical stretch of the graph of $m(x) = e^x$. All three graphs have a horizontal asymptote at $y = 0$. The y-intercept of $n(x) = e^{2x}$ is the same as for $m(x)$, but the graph of $p(x) = 2e^x$ has a y-intercept of $(0, 2)$.

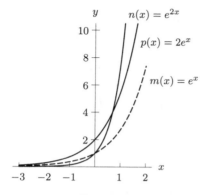

Figure 5.19

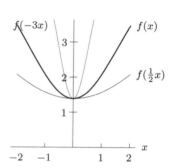

Figure 5.20

9. See Figure 5.20.

Problems

13. The stretch away from the y-axis by a factor of d requires multiplying the x-coordinate by $1/d$, and the upward translation requires adding c to the y-coordinate. This gives $(a/d, b + c)$.

17. If profits are $r(t) = 0.5P(t)$ instead of $P(t)$, then profits are half the dollar level expected. If profits are $s(t) = P(0.5t)$ instead of $P(t)$, then profits are accruing half as fast as the projected rate.

21. The function f has been reflected over the x-axis and the y-axis and stretched horizontally by a factor of 2. Thus, $y = -f(-\frac{1}{2}x)$.

25. Temperatures in this borehole are the same as temperatures 5 meters deeper in the Belleterre borehole. See Table 5.4.

Table 5.4

d	20	45	70	95	120	145	170	195
$h(d)$	5.5	5.2	5.1	5.1	5.3	5.5	5.75	6

29. Temperatures in this borehole are 2°C warmer than temperatures 50% higher than temperatures at the same depth in the Belleterre borehole. See Table 5.5.

Table 5.5

d	25	50	75	100	125	150	175	200
$q(d)$	10.25	9.8	9.65	9.65	9.95	10.25	10.63	11

Solutions for Section 5.5

Exercises

1. By comparing $f(x)$ to the vertex form, $y = a(x - h)^2 + k$, we see the vertex is $(h, k) = (1, 2)$. The axis of symmetry is the vertical line through the vertex, so the equation is $x = 1$. The parabola opens upward because the value of a is positive

3.

5. Since the coefficient of x^2 is not 1, we first factor out the coefficient of x^2 from the formula. This gives

$$w(x) = -3\left(x^2 + 10x - \frac{31}{3}\right).$$

We next complete the square of the expression in parentheses. To do this, we add $\left(\frac{1}{2} \cdot 10\right)^2 = 25$ inside the parentheses:

$$w(x) = -3(\underbrace{x^2 + 10x + 25}_{\text{completing the square}} - \underbrace{25}_{\text{compensating term}} - 31/3).$$

Thus,

$$w(x) = -3((x+5)^2 - 106/3)$$
$$w(x) = -3(x+5)^2 + 106$$

so the vertex of the graph of this function is $(-5, 106)$, and the axis of symmetry is $x = -5$. Also, since $a = -3$ is negative, the graph is a downward opening parabola.

9. Since the vertex is $(4, 7)$, we use the form $y = a(x - h)^2 + k$, with $h = 4$ and $k = 7$. We solve for a, substituting in the second point, $(0, 4)$.

$$y = a(x - 4)^2 + 7$$
$$4 = a(0 - 4)^2 + 7$$
$$-3 = 16a$$
$$-\frac{3}{16} = a.$$

Thus, an equation for the parabola is

$$y = -\frac{3}{16}(x - 4)^2 + 7.$$

13. We know there are zeros at $x = -6$ and $x = 2$, so we use the factored form:

$$y = a(x + 6)(x - 2)$$

and solve for a. At $x = 0$, we have

$$5 = a(0 + 6)(0 - 2)$$
$$5 = -12a$$
$$-\frac{5}{12} = a.$$

Thus,

$$y = -\frac{5}{12}(x + 6)(x - 2)$$

or

$$y = -\frac{5}{12}x^2 - \frac{5}{3}x + 5.$$

17. Using the vertex form $y = a(x - h)^2 + k$, where $(h, k) = (2, 5)$, we have

$$y = a(x - 2)^2 + 5.$$

Since the parabola passes through $(1, 2)$, these coordinates must satisfy the equation, so

$$2 = a(1 - 2)^2 + 5.$$

Solving for a gives $a = -3$. The formula is:

$$y = -3(x - 2)^2 + 5.$$

Problems

21. We have $(h, k) = (4, 2)$, so $y = a(x - 4)^2 + 2$. Solving for a, we have

$$a(11 - 4)^2 + 2 = 0$$
$$49a = -2$$
$$a = -\frac{2}{49},$$

so $y = (-2/49)(x - 4)^2 + 2$. We can verify this formula using the other zero:

$$(-2/49)(-3 - 4)^2 + 2 = (-2/49)(-7)^2 + 2 = -2 + 2 = 0,$$

as required.

25. The graph of $y = x^2 - 10x + 25$ appears to be the graph of $y = x^2$ moved to the right by 5 units. See Figure 5.21. If this were so, then its formula would be $y = (x - 5)^2$. Since $(x - 5)^2 = x^2 - 10x + 25$, $y = x^2 - 10x + 25$ is, indeed, a horizontal shift of $y = x^2$.

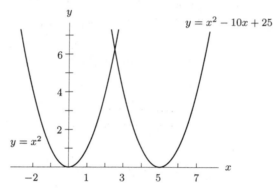

Figure 5.21

29. Yes, we can find the function. Because the vertex is $(1, 4)$, $f(x) = a(x - 1)^2 + 4$ for some a. To find a, we use the fact that $x = -1$ is a zero, that is, the fact that $f(-1) = 0$. We can write $f(-1) = a(-1 - 1)^2 + 4 = 0$, so $4a + 4 = 0$ and $a = -1$. Thus $f(x) = -(x - 1)^2 + 4$.

33. The distance around any rectangle with a height of h units and a base of b units is $2b + 2h$. See Figure 5.22. Since the string forming the rectangle is 50 cm long, we know that $2b + 2h = 50$ or $b + h = 25$. Therefore, $b = 25 - h$. The area, A, of such a rectangle is

$$A = bh$$
$$A = (25 - h)(h).$$

The zeros of this quadratic function are $h = 0$ and $h = 25$, so the axis of symmetry, which is halfway between the zeros, is $h = 12.5$. Since the maximum value of A occurs on the axis of symmetry, the area will be the greatest when the height is 12.5 and the base is also 12.5 ($b = 25 - h = 25 - 12.5 = 12.5$).

Figure 5.22

If the string were k cm long, $2b + 2h = k$ or $b + h = \frac{k}{2}$, so $b = \frac{k}{2} - h$. $A = bh = \left(\frac{k}{2} - h\right) h$. The zeros in this case are $h = 0$ and $h = \frac{k}{2}$, so the axis of symmetry is $h = \frac{k}{4}$. If $h = \frac{k}{4}$ $\quad \frac{k}{2} - h = \frac{k}{2} - \frac{k}{4} = \frac{k}{4}$. So the dimensions for maximum area are $\frac{k}{4}$ by $\frac{k}{4}$; in other words, the rectangle with the maximum area is a square whose side measures $\frac{1}{4}$ of the length of the string.

Solutions for Chapter 5 Review

Exercises

1. (a) The input is $2x = 2 \cdot 2 = 4$.
   (b) The input is $\frac{1}{2}x = \frac{1}{2} \cdot 2 = 1$.
   (c) The input is $x + 3 = 2 + 3 = 5$.
   (d) The input is $-x = -2$.

5. A function is odd if $a(-x) = -a(x)$.

$$a(x) = \frac{1}{x}$$
$$a(-x) = \frac{1}{-x} = -\frac{1}{x}$$
$$-a(x) = -\frac{1}{x}$$

Since $a(-x) = -a(x)$, we know that $a(x)$ is an odd function.

9. A function is even if $b(-x) = b(x)$.

$$b(x) = |x|$$
$$b(-x) = |-x| = |x|$$

Since $b(-x) = b(x)$, we know that $b(x)$ is an even function.

13. The function has zeros at $x = -1$ and $x = 3$, and appears quadratic, so it could be of the form $y = a(x + 1)(x - 3)$. Since $y = -3$ when $x = 0$, we know that $y = a(0 + 1)(0 - 3) = -3a = -3$, so $a = 1$. Thus $y = (x + 1)(x - 3)$ is a possible formula.

Problems

17. The graph is the graph of f shifted to the left by 2 and up by 2. See Figure 5.23.

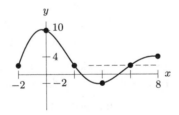

Figure 5.23

21. (a) $D(225)$ represents the number of iced cappuccinos sold at a price of \$2.25.
    (b) $D(p)$ is likely to be a decreasing function. The coffeehouse will probably sell fewer iced cappuccinos if they charge a higher price for them.
    (c) p is the price the coffeehouse should charge if they want to sell 180 iced cappuccinos per week.
    (d) $D(1.5t)$ represents the number of iced cappuccinos the coffeehouse will sell if they charge one and a half times the average price. $1.5D(t)$ represents 1.5 times the number of cappuccinos sold at the average price. $D(t + 50)$ is the number of iced cappuccinos they will sell if they charge 50 cents more than the average price. $D(t) + 50$ represents 50 more cappuccinos than the number they can sell at the average price.

461

25. **(a)** Using the formula for $d(t)$, we have

$$d(t) - 15 = (-16t^2 + 38) - 15$$
$$= -16t^2 + 23.$$

$$d(t - 1.5) = -16(t - 1.5)^2 + 38$$
$$= -16(t^2 - 3t + 2.25) + 38$$
$$= -16t^2 + 48t + 2.$$

(b)

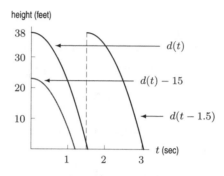

Figure 5.24

(c) $d(t) - 15$ represents the height of a brick which falls from $38 - 15 = 23$ feet above the ground. On the other hand, $d(t - 1.5)$ represents the height of a brick which began to fall from 38 feet above the ground at one and a half seconds after noon.

(d) (i) The brick hits the ground when its height is 0. Thus, if we represent the brick's height above the ground by $d(t)$, we get

$$0 = d(t)$$
$$0 = -16t^2 + 38$$
$$-38 = -16t^2$$
$$t^2 = \frac{38}{16}$$
$$t^2 = 2.375$$
$$t = \pm\sqrt{2.375} \approx \pm 1.541.$$

We are only interested in positive values of t, so the brick must hit the ground 1.541 seconds after noon.

(ii) If we represent the brick's height above the ground by $d(t) - 15$ we get

$$0 = d(t) - 15$$
$$0 = -16t^2 + 23$$
$$-23 = -16t^2$$
$$t^2 = \frac{23}{16}$$
$$t^2 = 1.4375$$
$$t = \pm\sqrt{1.4375} \approx \pm 1.199.$$

Again, we are only interested in positive values of t, so the the brick hits the ground 1.199 seconds after noon.

(e) Since the brick, whose height is $d(t - 1.5)$, begins falling 1.5 seconds after the brick whose height is $d(t)$, we expect the brick whose height is $d(t - 1.5)$ to hit the ground 1.5 seconds after the brick whose height is $d(t)$. Thus, the brick should hit the ground $1.5 + 1.541 = 3.041$ seconds after noon.

29. The graph appears to have been shifted to the left 6 units, compressed vertically by a factor of 2, and shifted vertically by 1 unit, so

$$y = \frac{1}{2}h(x + 6) + 1.$$

33.

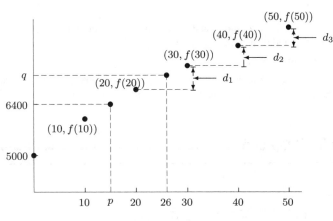

Figure 5.25

37. There is a vertical stretch of 3 so

$$y = 3h(x).$$

41. Figure 5.26 shows a graph of the basketball player's trajectory for $T = 1$ second. Since this is the graph of a parabola, the maximum height occurs at the t-value which is halfway between the zeros, 0 and 1. Thus, the maximum occurs at $t = 1/2$ second. The maximum height is $h(1/2) = 4$ feet, and 75% of 4 is 3. Thus, when the basketball player is above 3 feet from the ground, he is in the top 25% of his trajectory. To find when he reaches a height of 3 feet, set $h(t) = 3$. Solving for t gives $t = 0.25$ or $t = 0.75$ seconds. Thus, from $t = 0.25$ to $t = 0.75$ seconds, the basketball player is in the top 25% of his jump, as indicated in Figure 5.26. We see that he spends half of the time at the top quarter of the height of this jump, giving the impression that he hangs in the air.

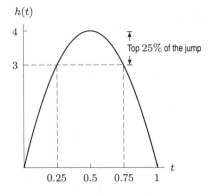

Figure 5.26: A graph of $h(t) = -16t^2 + 16Tt$ for $T = 1$

CHECK YOUR UNDERSTANDING

1. True. The graph of $g(x)$ is a copy of the graph of f shifted vertically up by three units.

5. True. The reflection across the x-axis of $y = f(x)$ is $y = -f(x)$.

9. True. Any point (x, y) on the graph of $y = f(x)$ reflects across the y-axis to the point $(-x, y)$, which lies on the graph of $y = f(-x)$.

13. False. If $f(x) = x^2$, then $f(x+1) = x^2 + 2x + 1 \neq x^2 + 1 = f(x) + 1$.

17. True.

21. False. Consider $f(x) = x^2$. Shifting up first and then compressing vertically gives the graph of $g(x) = \frac{1}{2}(x^2 + 1) = \frac{1}{2}x^2 + \frac{1}{2}$. Compressing first and then shifting gives the graph of $h(x) = \frac{1}{2}x^2 + 1$.

25. True. This is the definition of a vertex.

29. True. Transform $y = ax^2 + bx + c$ to the form $y = a(x - h)^2 + k$ where it can be seen that if $a < 0$, then the value of y has a maximum at the vertex (h, k), and the parabola opens downward.

Solutions to Tools for Chapter 5

1. $x^2 + 8x = x^2 + 8x + 16 - 16 = (x + 4)^2 - 16$

5. $s^2 + 6s - 8 = s^2 + 6s + 9 - 9 - 8 = (s + 3)^2 - 17$

9. We add and subtract the square of half the coefficient of the c-term, $\left(\frac{3}{2}\right)^2 = \frac{9}{4}$, to get

$$
\begin{aligned}
c^2 + 3c - 7 &= c^2 + 3c + \frac{9}{4} - \frac{9}{4} - 7 \\
&= \left(c^2 + 3c + \frac{9}{4}\right) - \frac{9}{4} - 7 \\
&= \left(c + \frac{3}{2}\right)^2 - \frac{37}{4}.
\end{aligned}
$$

13. Completing the square yields

$$x^2 - 2x - 3 = (x^2 - 2x + 1) - 1 - 3 = (x - 1)^2 - 4.$$

17. Complete the square and write in vertex form.

$$
\begin{aligned}
y &= x^2 + 6x + 3 \\
&= x^2 + 6x + 9 - 9 + 3 \\
&= (x + 3)^2 - 6.
\end{aligned}
$$

The vertex is $(-3, -6)$.

21. Complete the square and write in vertex form.

$$
\begin{aligned}
y &= -x^2 + x - 6 \\
&= -(x^2 - x + 6) \\
&= -\left(x^2 - x + \frac{1}{4} - \frac{1}{4} + 6\right) \\
&= -\left(\left(x - \frac{1}{2}\right)^2 - \frac{1}{4} + 6\right) \\
&= -\left(x - \frac{1}{2}\right)^2 - \frac{23}{4}.
\end{aligned}
$$

The vertex is $(1/2, -23/4)$.

25. Complete the square and write in vertex form.

$$y = 2x^2 - 7x + 3$$
$$= 2\left(x^2 - \frac{7}{2}x + \frac{3}{2}\right)$$
$$= 2\left(x^2 - \frac{7}{2}x + \frac{49}{16} - \frac{49}{16} + \frac{3}{2}\right)$$
$$= 2\left(\left(x - \frac{7}{4}\right)^2 - \frac{49}{16} + \frac{3}{2}\right)$$
$$= 2\left(x - \frac{7}{4}\right)^2 - \frac{25}{8}.$$

The vertex is $(7/4, -25/8)$.

29. Complete the square using $(-2/2)^2 = 1$, take the square root of both sides and solve for p.

$$p^2 - 2p = 6$$
$$p^2 - 2p + 1 = 6 + 1$$
$$(p - 1)^2 = 7$$
$$p - 1 = \pm\sqrt{7}$$
$$p = 1 \pm \sqrt{7}.$$

33. Get the variables on the left side, the constants on the right side and complete the square using $\left(\frac{5}{2}\right)^2 = \frac{25}{4}$.

$$2s^2 + 10s = 1$$
$$2\left(s^2 + 5s\right) = 1$$
$$2\left(s^2 + 5s + \frac{25}{4}\right) = 2\left(\frac{25}{4}\right) + 1$$
$$2\left(s + \frac{5}{2}\right)^2 = \frac{25}{2} + 1$$
$$2\left(s + \frac{5}{2}\right)^2 = \frac{27}{2}.$$

Divide by 2, take the square root of both sides and solve for s.

$$\left(s + \frac{5}{2}\right)^2 = \frac{27}{4}$$
$$s + \frac{5}{2} = \pm\sqrt{\frac{27}{4}}$$
$$s + \frac{5}{2} \qquad \frac{27}{2}$$
$$s = -\frac{5}{2} \pm \frac{\sqrt{27}}{2}.$$

37. With $a = 1$, $b = -4$, and $c = -12$, we use the quadratic formula,

$$n = \frac{-b \pm \sqrt{b^2 - 4ac}}{2a}$$
$$= \frac{4 \pm \sqrt{(-4)^2 - 4 \cdot 1 \cdot (-12)}}{2 \cdot 1}$$

$$= \frac{4 \pm \sqrt{16 + 48}}{2}$$

$$= \frac{4 \pm \sqrt{64}}{2}$$

$$= \frac{4 \pm 8}{2}.$$

So, $n = 6$ or $n = -2$.

41. Set the equation equal to zero, $z^2 + 4z - 6 = 0$. With $a = 1$, $b = 4$, and $c = -6$, we use the quadratic formula,

$$z = \frac{-b \pm \sqrt{b^2 - 4ac}}{2a}$$

$$= \frac{-4 \pm \sqrt{4^2 - 4 \cdot 1 \cdot (-6)}}{2 \cdot 1}$$

$$= \frac{-4 \pm \sqrt{16 + 24}}{2}$$

$$= \frac{-4 \pm \sqrt{40}}{2}$$

$$= \frac{-4 \pm 2\sqrt{10}}{2}$$

$$= -2 \pm \sqrt{10}.$$

45. Rewrite the equation to equal zero, and factor.

$$n^2 + 4n - 5 = 0$$
$$(n + 5)(n - 1) = 0.$$

So, $n + 5 = 0$ or $n - 1 = 0$, thus $n = -5$ or $n = 1$.

49. Set the equation equal to zero, and use the quadratic formula with $a = 25$, $b = -30$, and $c = 4$.

$$u = \frac{30 \pm \sqrt{(-30)^2 - 4 \cdot 25 \cdot 4}}{2 \cdot 25}$$

$$= \frac{30 \pm \sqrt{900 - 400}}{50}$$

$$= \frac{30 \pm \sqrt{500}}{50}$$

$$= \frac{30 \pm 10\sqrt{5}}{50}$$

$$= \frac{3 \pm \sqrt{5}}{5}.$$

53. Set the equation equal to zero and use factoring.

$$2w^3 - 6w^2 - 8w + 24 = 0$$
$$w^3 - 3w^2 - 4w + 12 = 0$$
$$w^2(w - 3) - 4(w - 3) = 0$$
$$(w - 3)(w^2 - 4) = 0$$
$$(w - 3)(w - 2)(w + 2) = 0.$$

So, $w - 3 = 0$ or $w - 2 = 0$ or $w + 2 = 0$ thus, $w = 3$ or $w = 2$ or $w = -2$.

CHAPTER EIGHT

Solutions for Section 8.1

Exercises

1. To construct a table of values for r, we must evaluate $r(0), r(1), \ldots, r(5)$. Starting with $r(0)$, we have

$$r(0) = p(q(0)).$$

Therefore

$$r(0) = p(5) \qquad \text{(because } q(0) = 5\text{)}$$

Using the table given in the problem, we have

$$r(0) = 4.$$

We can repeat this process for $r(1)$:

$$r(1) = p(q(1)) = p(2) = 5.$$

Similarly,

$$r(2) = p(q(2)) = p(3) = 2$$
$$r(3) = p(q(3)) = p(1) = 0$$
$$r(4) = p(q(4)) = p(4) = 3$$
$$r(5) = p(q(5)) = p(8) = \text{ undefined.}$$

These results have been compiled in Table 8.1.

Table 8.1

x	0	1	2	3	4	5
$r(x)$	4	5	2	0	3	–

5. Using substitution we have $h(k(x)) = 2^{k(x)} = 2^{x^2}$ and $k(h(x)) = (h(x))^2 = (2^x)^2 = 2^{2x} = 4^x$.

9. Replacing the x's in the formula for $f(x)$ with $\sqrt{x}$ gives $(\sqrt{x})^2 + 1 = x + 1$.

13. The inside function is $f(x) = \sin x$.

17. The inside function is $f(x) = 5 + 1/x$.

Problems

21. The function $t(f(H))$ gives the time of the trip as a function of temperature, H.

25. **(a)** We have $f(1) = 2$, so $f(f(1)) = f(2) = 4$.
  (b) We have $g(1) = 3$, so $g(g(1)) = g(3) = 1$.
  (c) We have $g(2) = 2$, so $f(g(2)) = f(2) = 4$.
  (d) We have $f(2) = 4$, so $g(f(2)) = g(4) = 0$.

29. Reading values of the graph, we make an approximate table of values; we use these values to sketch Figure 8.1.

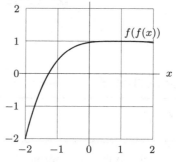

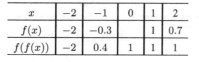

x	-2	-1	0	1	2
$f(x)$	-2	-0.3		1	0.7
$f(f(x))$	-2	0.4	1	1	1

Figure 8.1: Graph of $f(f(x))$

33. (a) See Figures 8.2 and 8.3.

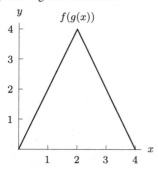

Figure 8.2

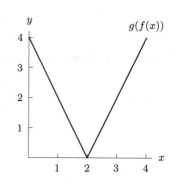

Figure 8.3

(b) From the graph, we see that $f(g(x))$ is increasing on the interval $0 < x < 2$.

(c) From the graph, we see that $g(f(x))$ is increasing on the interval $2 < x < 4$.

37. Substitute $q(p(t)) = \log(p(t))^2$ and solve:

$$\log(p(t))^2 = 0$$
$$\log(10(0.01)^t)^2 = 0$$
$$\log(10^2 \cdot (0.01)^{2t}) = 0$$
$$\log 10^2 + \log(0.01^{2t}) = 0$$
$$2 + 2t \log(0.01) = 0$$
$$2 + 2t(-2) = 0$$
$$2 - 4t = 0$$
$$t = \frac{1}{2}$$

41. First we calculate

$$f(x+h) - f(x) = \frac{1}{x+h} - \frac{1}{x} = \frac{x}{x(x+h)} - \frac{x+h}{x(x+h)}$$
$$= \frac{x - (x+h)}{x(x+h)} = \frac{-h}{x(x+h)}$$

Then

$$\frac{f(x+h) - f(x)}{h} = \frac{\dfrac{-h}{x(x+h)}}{h} = \frac{-h}{x(x+h)} \cdot \frac{1}{h} = \frac{-1}{x(x+h)}$$

45. Since $k(f(x)) = e^{f(x)}$, we have $e^{f(x)} = x$. Taking the natural log of both sides, we obtain the formula $f(x) = \ln x$.

49. (a) Since $u(x) = 2x$ and y can be written as $y = 2 \cdot 2^x$, we take $v(x) = 2^x$.
   (b) Since $v(x) = -x$ and y can be written $y = 2^{1-(-x)}$, we take $u(x) = 2^{1-x}$.

53. One possible solution is $g(x) = u(v(x))$ where $v(x) = x^2$ and $u(x) = \sin x$.

57. One possible solution is $G(x) = u(v(x))$ where $u(x) = \frac{2}{x}$ and $v(x) = 1 + \sqrt{x}$.

61. (a) The function f represents the exchange is dollars to yen, and 1 dollar buys 114.64 yen. Thus, each of the x dollars buys 114.64 yen, for a total of $114.64x$ yen. Therefore,

$$f(x) = 114.64x.$$

Referring to the table, we see that 1 dollar purchases 0.829 European Union euros. If x dollars are invested, each of the x dollars will buy 0.829 euros, for a total of $0.829x$ euros. Thus,

$$g(x) = 0.829x.$$

Finally, we see from the table that 1 yen buys 0.00723 euros. Each of the x yen invested buys 0.00723 euros, so $0.00723x$ euros can be purchased. Therefore,

$$h(x) = 0.00723x.$$

   (b) We evaluate $h(f(1000))$ algebraically. Since $f(1000) = 114.64(1000) = 114{,}640$, we have

$$\begin{aligned}
h(f(1000)) &= h(114{,}640) \\
&= 0.00723(114{,}640) \\
&= 828.8472.
\end{aligned}$$

To interpret this statement, we break the problem into steps. First, we see that $f(1000) = 114{,}640$ means 1000 dollars buy 114,640 yen. Second, we see that $h(114{,}640) = 828.8472$ means that 114,640 yen buys 828.8472 euros. In other words, $h(f(1000)) = 828.8472$ represents a trade of \$1000 for 114,640 yen which is subsequently traded for 828.8472 euros (Of course, a direct trade of \$1000 would yield 828.8472 euros).

Solutions for Section 8.2

Exercises

1. It is not invertible.

5. It is not invertible.

9. One way to check that these functions are inverses is to make sure they satisfy the identities $g(g^{-1}(x)) = x$ and $g^{-1}(g(x)) = x$.

$$\begin{aligned}
g(g^{-1}(x)) &= 1 - \frac{1}{\left(1 + \dfrac{1}{1-x}\right) - 1} \\
&= 1 - \frac{1}{\left(\dfrac{1}{1-x}\right)} \\
&= 1 - (1 - x) \\
&= x.
\end{aligned}$$

Also,

$$g^{-1}(g(x)) = 1 + \cfrac{1}{1 - \left(1 - \cfrac{1}{x-1}\right)}$$

$$= 1 + \cfrac{1}{\cfrac{1}{x-1}}$$

$$= 1 + x - 1 = x.$$

So the expression for g^{-1} is correct.

13. Check using the two compositions

$$f(f^{-1}(x)) = e^{f^{-1}(x)/2} = e^{(2\ln x)/2} = e^{\ln x} = x$$

and

$$f^{-1}(f(x)) = 2\ln f(x) = 2\ln e^{x/2} = 2(x/2) = x.$$

They are inverses of one another.

17. Start with $x = k(k^{-1}(x))$ and substitute $y = k^{-1}(x)$. We have

$$x = k(y)$$
$$x = 3e^{2y}$$
$$\frac{x}{3} = e^{2y}$$
$$\ln\frac{x}{3} = \ln e^{2y} = 2y$$
$$\frac{\ln\frac{x}{3}}{2} = y$$

So $y = k^{-1}(x) = \dfrac{\ln\frac{x}{3}}{2}$.

21. Solve for x in $y = h(x) = \sqrt{x}/(\sqrt{}$

$$\frac{\overline{x}}{\sqrt{x+1}}$$
$$\sqrt{x} = y(\sqrt{x}+1)$$
$$\sqrt{x} = y\sqrt{x} + y$$
$$\sqrt{x} - y\sqrt{x} = y$$
$$\sqrt{x}(1-y) = y \qquad \text{(factoring)}$$
$$\sqrt{x} = \frac{y}{1-y}$$
$$x = h^{-1}(y) = \left(\frac{y}{1-y}\right)^2.$$

Writing h^{-1} in terms of x gives

$$h^{-1}(x) = \left(\frac{x}{1-x}\right)^2.$$

25. Solving $y = f(x)$ for x gives:

$$y = \ln\left(1 + \frac{1}{x}\right)$$
$$e^y = 1 + \frac{1}{x}$$
$$\frac{1}{x} = e^y - 1$$
$$x = \frac{1}{e^y - 1},$$

so $f^{-1}(x) = \dfrac{1}{e^x - 1}$.

Problems

29. (a) The compositions are

$$p(q(t)) = p(\log t) = 10^{\log t} = t \quad \text{and} \quad q(p(t)) = q(10^t) = \log 10^t = t.$$

Thus, the two functions are inverses of one another.

(b) The graph of the two functions is symmetric about the line $y = t$. See Figure 8.4.

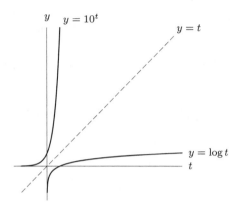

Figure 8.4

33. Solving for I gives

$$N = 10 \log \left(\frac{I}{I_0} \right)$$
$$\frac{N}{10} = \log \left(\frac{I}{I_0} \right)$$
$$\frac{I}{I_0} = 10^{N/10}$$
$$I = I_0 10^{N/10}.$$

The inverse function $f^{-1}(N) = I_0 10^{N/10}$ gives the intensity of a sound with a decibel rating of N.

37. We take the exponential function to both sides since the exponential function is the inverse of logarithm:

$$\ln(x + 3) = 1.8$$
$$x + 3 = e^{1.8}$$
$$x = e^{1.8} - 3.$$

41. Reading the values from the graph, we get:

$$f(0) = 1.5, \quad f^{-1}(0) = 2.5, \quad f(3) = -0.5, \quad f^{-1}(3) = -5.$$

Ranking them in order from least to greatest, we get:

$$f^{-1}(3) < f(3) < 0 < f(0) < f^{-1}(0) < 3.$$

45. (a) $A = \pi r^2$

(b) The graph of the function in part (a) is in Figure 8.5.

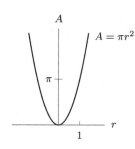

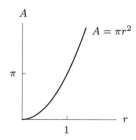

Figure 8.5   Figure 8.6

(c) Because a circle cannot have a negative radius, the domain is $r \geq 0$. See Figure 8.6.

(d) Solve the formula $A = f(r) = \pi r^2$ for r in terms of A:

$$r^2 = \frac{A}{\pi}$$

$$r = \pm\sqrt{\frac{A}{\pi}}$$

The range of the inverse function is the same as the domain of f, namely non-negative real numbers. Thus, we choose the positive root, and $f^{-1}(A) = \sqrt{\dfrac{A}{\pi}}$.

(e) We rewrite both functions to be y in terms of x, and graph. See Figure 8.7.

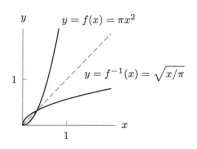

Figure 8.7

(f) Yes. If the function $A = \pi r^2$ refers to radius and area, its domain must be $r \geq 0$. On this domain the function is invertible, so radius is also a function of area.

49. (a) Her maximum height is approximately 36 m.

(b) She lands on the trampoline approximately 6 seconds later.

(c) The graph is a parabola, and hence is symmetric about the vertical line $x = 3$ through its vertex. We choose the right half of the parabola, whose domain is the interval $3 \leq t \leq 6$. See Figure 8.8.

(d) The gymnast is part of a complicated stunt involving several phases. At 3 seconds into the stunt, she steps off the platform for the high wire, 36 meters in the air. Three seconds later (at $t = 6$) she lands on a trampoline at ground level.

(e) See Figure 8.9. As the gymnast falls, her height decreases steadily from 36 m to 0 m. In other words, she occupies each height for one moment of time only, and does not return to that height at any other time. This means that each value of t corresponds to a single height, and therefore time is a function of height.

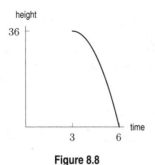

Figure 8.8

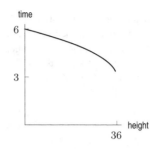

Figure 8.9

53. Since f is assumed to be an increasing function, its inverse is well-defined. This is an amount of caffeine: the amount predicted to give a pulse 20 bpm higher than r_c, that is, 20 bpm higher than the pulse of a person having 1 serving of coffee.

57. Since f is assumed to be an increasing function, its inverse is well-defined. This is an amount of caffeine. We know that $1.1f(q_c) = 1.1r_c$ is 10% higher than the pulse of a person who has had 1 serving of coffee. This makes $f^{-1}(1.1f(q_c))$ is the amount of caffeine that will lead to a pulse 10% higher than will a serving of coffee.

Solutions for Section 8.3

Exercises

1. (a) We have $f(x) + g(x) = x + 1 + 3x^2 = 3x^2 + x + 1$.
   (b) We have $f(x) - g(x) = x + 1 - 3x^2 = -3x^2 + x + 1$.
   (c) We have $f(x)g(x) = (x + 1)(3x^2) = 3x^3 + 3x^2$.
   (d) We have $f(x)/g(x) = (x + 1)/(3x^2)$.

5. (a) We have $f(x) + g(x) = x^3 + x^2$.
   (b) We have $f(x) - g(x) = x^3 - x^2$.
   (c) We have $f(x)g(x) = (x^3)(x^2) = x^5$.
   (d) We have $f(x)/g(x) = (x^3)/(x^2) = x$.

9. To find $h(x)$, we multiply $n(x)$ and $o(x)$, giving $n(x)o(x) = 2x \cdot \sqrt{x + 2}$.

13. We have $f(x) = e^x(2x + 1) = 2xe^x + e^x$.

17. $f(x) + g(x) = \sin x + x^2$.

21. $g(f(x)) = g(\sin x) = \sin^2 x$.

Problems

25. (a) See Table 8.2.

Table 8.2

t (yrs)	0	1	2	3	4	5
$f(t)$ ($)	109,366	111,958	111,581	114,931	119,162	122,499
$g(t)$	13.61	13.68	13.03	13.42	13.73	13.63

   (b) f is the dollar difference between the cutoff income for a household in the 95th percentile and a household in the 10th percentile. In other words, f tells us how much more money a household at the top of the higher income bracket makes than a house at the top of the lower income bracket. In contrast, g is the ratio of these incomes. Notice that the dollar difference in incomes is rising for every year shown by the table, ending (in 1998) with a difference of $122,499. In contrast, the ratio is much steadier, remaining close to 13.5 (except during 1995, when it fell to almost 13). This means that while the dollar gap between rich and poor households grew considerably during this time period (from about $110,000 to about $122,500), the rich households earned about 13.5 times the income of the poor households, with slight variation.

29. Since $f(a) = g(a)$, $h(a) = g(a) - f(a) = 0$. Similarly, $h(c) = 0$. On the interval $a < x < b$, $g(x) > f(x)$, so $h(x) = g(x) - f(x) > 0$. As x increases from a to b, the difference between $g(x)$ and $f(x)$ gets greater, becoming its greatest at $x = b$, then gets smaller until the difference is 0 at $x = c$. When $x < a$ or $x > b$, $g(x) < f(x)$ so $g(x) - f(x) < 0$. Subtract the length e from the length d to get the y-intercept. See Figure 8.10.

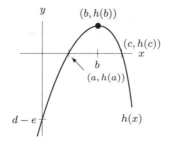

Figure 8.10

33. **(a)** A formula for $h(x)$ would be

$$h(x) = f(x) + g(x).$$

To evaluate $h(x)$ for $x = 3$, we use this equation:

$$h(3) = f(3) + g(3).$$

Since $f(x) = x + 1$, we know that
$$f(3) = 3 + 1 = 4.$$

Likewise, since $g(x) = x^2 - 1$, we know that

$$g(3) = 3^2 - 1 = 9 - 1 = 8.$$

Thus, we have

$$h(3) = 4 + 8 = 12.$$

To find a formula for $h(x)$ in terms of x, we substitute our formulas for $f(x)$ and $g(x)$ into the equation $h(x) = f(x) + g(x)$:

$$h(x) = \underbrace{f(x)}_{x+1} + \underbrace{g(x)}_{x^2-1}$$
$$h(x) = x + 1 + x^2 - 1 = x^2 + x.$$

To check this formula, we use it to evaluate $h(3)$, and see if it gives $h(3) = 12$, which is what we got before. The formula is $h(x) = x^2 + x$, so it gives

$$h(3) = 3^2 + 3 = 9 + 3 = 12.$$

This is the result that we expected.

(b) A formula for $j(x)$ would be

$$j(x) = g(x) - 2f(x).$$

To evaluate $j(x)$ for $x = 3$, we use this equation:

$$j(3) = g(3) - 2f(3).$$

We already know that $g(3) = 8$ and $f(3) = 4$. Thus,

$$j(3) = 8 - 2 \cdot 4 = 8 - 8 = 0.$$

To find a formula for $j(x)$ in terms of x, we again use the formulas for $f(x)$ and $g(x)$:

$$j(x) = \underbrace{g(x)}_{x^2 - 1} - 2\underbrace{f(x)}_{x + 1}$$
$$= (x^2 - 1) - 2(x + 1)$$
$$= x^2 - 1 - 2x - 2$$
$$= x^2 - 2x - 3.$$

We check this formula using the fact that we already know $j(3) = 0$. Since we have $j(x) = x^2 - 2x - 3$,

$$j(3) = 3^2 - 2 \cdot 3 - 3 = 9 - 6 - 3 = 0.$$

This is the result that we expected.

(c) A formula for $k(x)$ would be

$$k(x) = f(x)g(x).$$

Evaluating $k(3)$, we have

$$k(3) = f(3)g(3) = 4 \cdot 8 = 32.$$

A formula in terms of x for $k(x)$ would be

$$k(x) = \underbrace{f(x)}_{x + 1} \cdot \underbrace{g(x)}_{x^2 - 1}$$
$$= (x + 1)(x^2 - 1)$$
$$= x^3 - x + x^2 - 1$$
$$= x^3 + x^2 - x - 1.$$

To check this formula,

$$k(3) = 3^3 + 3^2 - 3 - 1 = 27 + 9 - 3 - 1 = 32,$$

which agrees with what we already knew.

(d) A formula for $m(x)$ would be

$$m(x) = \frac{g(x)}{f(x)}.$$

Using this formula, we have

$$m(3) = \frac{g(3)}{f(3)} = \frac{8}{4} = 2.$$

To find a formula for $m(x)$ in terms of x, we write

$$m(x) = \frac{g(x)}{f(x)} = \frac{x^2 - 1}{x + 1}$$
$$= \frac{(x + 1)(x - 1)}{(x + 1)}$$
$$= x - 1 \text{ for } x \neq -1$$

We were able to simplify this formula by first factoring the numerator of the fraction $\dfrac{x^2 - 1}{x + 1}$. To check this formula,

$$m(3) = 3 - 1 = 2,$$

which is what we were expecting.

(e) We have

$$n(x) = (f(x))^2 - g(x).$$

This means that

$$
\begin{aligned}
n(3) &= (f(3))^2 - g(3) \\
&= (4)^2 - 8 \\
&= 16 - 8 \\
&= 8.
\end{aligned}
$$

A formula for $n(x)$ in terms of x would be

$$
\begin{aligned}
n(x) &= (f(x))^2 - g(x) \\
&= (x+1)^2 - (x^2 - 1) \\
&= x^2 + 2x + 1 - x^2 + 1 \\
&= 2x + 2.
\end{aligned}
$$

To check this formula,

$$n(3) = 2 \cdot 3 + 2 = 8,$$

which is what we were expecting.

37. In order to evaluate $h(3)$, we need to express the formula for $h(x)$ in terms of $f(x)$ and $g(x)$. Factoring gives

$$h(x) = C^{2x}(kx^2 + B + 1).$$

Since $g(x) = C^{2x}$ and $f(x) = kx^2 + B$, we can re-write the formula for $h(x)$ as

$$h(x) = g(x) \cdot (f(x) + 1).$$

Thus,

$$
\begin{aligned}
h(3) &= g(3) \cdot (f(3) + 1) \\
&= 5(7 + 1) \\
&= 40.
\end{aligned}
$$

41. (a) Since the initial amount was 316.75 and the growth factor is 1.004, we have $A(t) = 316.75(1.004)^t$.
(b) Since the CO_2 level oscillates once per year, the period is 1 year. The amplitude is 3.25 pm, so one possible answer is $V(t) = 3.25\sin(2\pi t)$. Any sinusoidal function with the same amplitude and period could describe the variation.
(c) The graph of $y = 316.75(1.004)^t + 3.25\sin(2\pi t)$ is in Figure 8.11.

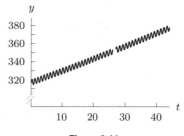

Figure 8.11

Solutions for Chapter 8 Review

Exercises

1. Since $g(x) = 9x - 2$, we substitute $9x - 2$ for x in $r(x)$, giving us $r(g(x)) = \sqrt{3(9x - 2)}$, which simplifies to $r(g(x)) = \sqrt{27x - 6}$.

5. Since $f(x) = 3x^2$, we substitute $3x^2$ for x in $m(x)$, giving us $m(f(x)) = 4(3x^2)$, which simplifies to $m(f(x)) = 12x^2$, which we then substitute for x in $g(x)$, giving $g(m(f(x))) = 9(12x^2) - 2$, which simplifies to $g(m(f(x))) = 108x^2 - 2$.

9. $g(f(x)) = g(e^x) = 2e^x - 1$

13. $f(g(x)) = f(2x - 1) = e^{2x-1}$, so $f(g(x))h(x) = \sqrt{x}e^{2x-1}$.

17. Find the two composite functions

$$u(v(x)) = u(e^x) = \frac{1}{1 + (e^x)^2} = \frac{1}{1 + e^{2x}}$$

and

$$w(v(x)) = w(e^x) = \ln(e^x) = x$$

to obtain

$$u(v(x)) \cdot w(v(x)) = \frac{1}{1 + (e^x)^2} \cdot x = \frac{x}{1 + (e^x)^2} = \frac{x}{1 + e^{2x}}.$$

21. Evaluate the two parts of the subtraction

$$h(g(x)) = \tan\left(2\left(\frac{(3x - 1)^2}{4}\right)\right) = \tan\frac{(3x - 1)^2}{2} \quad \text{and} \quad f(9x) = (9x)^{3/2} = 9^{3/2} \cdot x^{3/2} = 27x^{3/2}$$

and subtract

$$h(g(x)) - f(9x) = \tan\left(\frac{(3x - 1)^2}{2}\right) - 27x^{3/2}.$$

25. Start with $x = h(h^{-1}(x))$ and substitute $y = h^{-1}(x)$. We have

$$x = h(y)$$
$$x = \frac{2y + 1}{3y - 2}$$
$$x(3y - 2) = 2y + 1$$
$$3yx - 2x = 2y + 1$$
$$3yx - 2y = 2x + 1$$
$$y(3x - 2) = 2x + 1 \quad \text{(factor out a } y\text{)}$$
$$y = \frac{2x + 1}{3x - 2}$$

Therefore,

$$h^{-1}(x) = \frac{2x + 1}{3x - 2}.$$

29. We start with $f(f^{-1}(x)) = x$ and substitute $y = f^{-1}(x)$. We have

$$f(y) = x$$
$$\cos\sqrt{y} = x$$
$$\sqrt{y} = \arccos x$$
$$y = (\arccos x)^2.$$

Thus

$$f^{-1}(x) = (\arccos x)^2.$$

Problems

33. $g(x) = x^2$ and $h(x) = x + 3$

37.

$$f(g(65)) = f(50) \quad \text{Because } g(65) = 50$$
$$= 65.$$

41. See Figure 8.12.

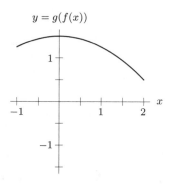

$$y = g(f(x))$$

Figure 8.12

45. **(a)** From the definitions of the functions, we have:

$$u(x) = \frac{1}{12 - 4x}.$$

So the domain of u is all reals x, such that $x \neq 3$.

(b) From the definitions of the functions, we have:

$$u(x) = \sqrt{(12 - 4x) - 4} = \sqrt{8 - 4x}.$$

Since the quantity under the radical must be nonnegative, we require

$$8 - 4x \geq 0$$
$$8 \geq 4x$$
$$2 \geq x.$$

Thus the domain of u is all reals x such that $x \leq 2$.

49.

$$q(x) = p(u(x))$$
$$\underbrace{\sqrt{x} - 3}_{q(x)} = \underbrace{2u(x) - 3}_{p(u(x))}$$
$$\sqrt{x} = 2u(x)$$
$$u(x) = 0.5\sqrt{x}.$$

53. (a) $N(20{,}000)$ is the number of units the company will sell if $20,000 is spent on advertising. This amount is $5,000 less than $25,000; thus, the company will sell 20 fewer units than when it spends $25,000, or 380 units total. Therefore, $N(20{,}000) = 380$.

(b) It costs $5,000 to sell an additional 20 units, or $250 to sell an additional unit. This means that $N(x)$ will increase by 1 when x increases by 250. In other words, the slope of $N(x)$ is $\dfrac{1}{250}$

$$\frac{1}{250}(x - 25{,}000)$$
$$N(x) = 400 + \frac{1}{250}x - 100$$
$$N(x) = \frac{1}{250}x + 300.$$

(c) The slope of $N(x)$ is $1/250$, which means that an additional $250 must be spent on advertising to sell an additional unit. The y-intercept of $N(x)$ is 300, which means that even if the company spends no money on advertising, it will still sell 300 units. The x-intercept is $-75{,}000$, which represents a negative amount of money spent on advertising. This has no obvious interpretation.

(d) $N^{-1}(500)$ is the advertising expenditure required to sell 500 units, or 100 units more than when it spends $25,000. Since the company needs to spend an additional $5,000 to sell an additional 20 units, it must spend an additional $25,000 to sell 500 units, or $50,000 total. Thus, $N^{-1}(500) = 50{,}000$.

(e) If only $2000 in profits are made on the sale of ten units, then the per-unit profit, before advertising costs are accounted for, is $200. Thus, the company makes an additional $200 for each unit sold. However, it must spend $250 on ads to sell an additional unit. Thus, the company must spend more on advertising to sell an additional unit than it makes on the sale of that unit. Therefore, it should discontinue its advertising campaign, or, at the very least, find an effective way to lower its per-unit advertising expenditure.

57. Since $2x$ represents twice as much office space as x, the cost of building twice as much space is $f(2x)$. The cost of building x amount of space is $f(x)$, so twice this cost is $2f(x)$. Thus, the contractors statement is expressed

$$f(2x) < 2f(x).$$

61. The inequality $h(f(x)) < x$ tells us that Space can build fewer than x square feet of office space with the money Ace needs to build x square feet. You get more for your money with Ace.

65. This is an increasing function, because if $g(x)$ is a decreasing function, then $-g(x)$ will be an increasing function. Since $f(x) - g(x) = f(x) + [-g(x)]$, $f(x) - g(x)$ can be written as the sum of two increasing functions, and is thus increasing.

CHECK YOUR UNDERSTANDING

1. False, since $f(4) + g(4) = \frac{1}{4} + \sqrt{4}$ but $(f + g)(8) = \frac{1}{8} + \sqrt{8}$.

5. True, since $g(f(x)) = g\left(\dfrac{1}{x}\right) = \sqrt{\dfrac{1}{x}}$.

9. True. Evaluate $\dfrac{f(3) + g(3)}{h(3)} = \dfrac{\frac{1}{3} + \sqrt{3}}{3 - 5}$ and simplify.

13. False. As a counterexample, let $f(x) = x^2$ and $g(x) = x + 1$. Then $f(g(x)) = (x + 1)^2 = x^2 + 2x + 1$, but $g(f(x)) = x^2 + 1$.

17. False. $f(x + h) = \dfrac{1}{x + h} \neq \dfrac{1}{x} + \dfrac{1}{h}$.

21. False. If $f(x) = ax^2 + bx + c$ and $g(x) = px^2 + qx + r$, then

$$f(g(x)) = f(px^2 + qx + r) = a(px^2 + qx + r)^2 + b(px^2 + qx + r) + c.$$

Expanding shows that $f(g(x))$ has an x^4 term.

25. True, since $g(f(2)) = g(1) = 3$ and $f(g(3)) = f(1) = 3$.

29. True. The function g is not invertible if two different points in the domain have the same function value.

33. True. Each x value has only one y value.

37. True. The inverse of a function reverses the action of the function and returns the original value of the independent variable x.

CHAPTER NINE

Solutions for Section 9.1

Exercises

1. Yes. Writing the function as

$$g(x) = \frac{(-x^3)^3}{6} = \frac{(-1)^3(x^3)^3}{6} = \frac{-x^9}{6} = -\frac{1}{6}x^9,$$

we have $k = -1/6$ and $p = 9$.

5. Yes. Writing the function as

$$T(s) = (6s^{-2})(es^{-3}) = 6es^{-2}s^{-3} = 6es^{-5},$$

we have $k = 6e$ and $p = -5$.

9. Since the graph is symmetric about the origin, the power function is odd.

13. We use the form $y = kx^p$ and solve for k and p. Using the point $(1, 2)$, we have $2 = k1^p$. Since 1^p is 1 for any p, we know that $k = 2$. Using our other point, we see that

$$17 = 2 \cdot 6^p$$
$$\frac{17}{2} = 6^p$$
$$\ln\left(\frac{17}{2}\right) = p\ln 6$$
$$\frac{\ln(17/2)}{\ln 6} = p$$
$$1.194 \approx p.$$

So $y = 2x^{1.194}$.

17. Substituting into the general formula $c = kd^2$, we have $45 = k(3)^2$ or $k = 45/9 = 5$. So the formula for c is

$$c = 5d^2.$$

When $d = 5$, we get $c = 5(5)^2 = 125$.

21. Solve for $g(x)$ by taking the ratio of (say) $g(4)$ to $g(3)$:

$$\frac{g(4)}{g(3)} = \frac{-32/3}{-9/2} = \frac{-32}{3} \cdot \frac{-2}{9} = \frac{64}{27}.$$

We know $g(4) = k \cdot 4^p$ and $g(3) = k \cdot 3^p$. Thus,

$$\frac{g(4)}{g(3)} = \frac{k \cdot 4^p}{k \cdot 3^p} = \frac{4^p}{3}\Big)^p = \frac{64}{27}.$$

Thus $p = 3$. To solve for k, note that $g(3) = k \cdot 3^3 = 27k$. Thus, $27k = g(3) = -\frac{9}{2}$. Thus, $k = -\frac{9}{54} = -\frac{1}{6}$. This gives $g(x) = -\frac{1}{6}x^3$.

Problems

25. The graphs are shown in Figure 9.1.

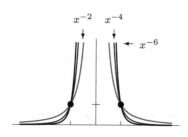

Figure 9.1

Some observations we can make are:

- All three curves pass through the points $(-1, 1)$ and $(1, 1)$.
- All three curves have asymptotes at $x = 0$ and $y = 0$.
- All three curves have even symmetry and the same overall shape.
- x^{-4} approaches its horizontal asymptote more rapidly than x^{-2}, and x^{-6} approaches its horizontal asymptote more rapidly than x^{-4}.
- for x-values close to zero, x^{-6} climbs more rapidly than x^{-4}, which in turn climbs more rapidly than x^{-2}.

29. (a) The power function will be of the form $g(x) = kx^p$, and from the graph we know p must be odd and k must be negative. Using $(-1, 3)$, we have

$$3 = k(-1)^p,$$

so $\quad 3 = -k \quad$ (since p is odd)

or $\quad k = -3.$

We do not have enough information to solve for p, since any odd p will work. Therefore, we have $g(x) = -3x^p$, p odd.

(b) Since the function is of the form $g(x) = -3x^p$, with p odd, we know that the the graph of this function is symmetric about the origin. This implies that if (a, b) is a point on the graph, then $(-a, -b)$ is also a point on the graph. Thus the information that the point $(1, -3)$ is on the graph does not help us.

(c) Since we know that the function is symmetric about the origin it will follow that the points $(-2, 96)$ and $(0, 0)$ also lie on the graph. To get other points lying on the graph, we can find the formula for this function. We know that

$$g(x) = -3x^p$$

so plugging in the point $(2, -96)$ we get

$$-96 = -3(2)^p.$$

Solving for p

$$-96 = -3(2)^p$$
$$32 = 2^p$$
$$p = 5.$$

Thus the formula for the function is given by

$$g(x) = -3x^5.$$

Any values satisfying this formula will describe points on the graph: e.g. $(3, -729)$ or $(-0.1, 0.00003)$ or $(\sqrt{7}, -147\sqrt{7})$ etc.

33. Calories are directly proportional to ounces because as the amount of beef, x, increases, the number of calories, c, also increases. Substituting into the general formula $c = kx$, we have $245 = k(3)$ or $k = 81.67$. So the formula is

$$c = 81.67x.$$

When $x = 4$, $c = 81.67(4) = 326.68$. Therefore, 4 ounces of hamburger contain 326.68 calories.

37. The map distance is directly proportional to the actual distance (mileage), because as the actual distance, x, increases, the map distance, d, also increases.

Substituting the values given into the general formula $d = kx$, we have $0.5 = k(5)$, so $k = 0.1$, and the formula is

$$d = 0.1x.$$

When $d = 3.25$, we have $3.25 = 0.1(x)$ so $x = 32.5$. Therefore, towns which are separated by 3.25 inches on the map are 32.5 miles apart.

41. We are given that $V = k\sqrt{w/a}$ where $V =$ stall velocity, $w =$ weight, $a =$ wing area. If the wing area is twice a and all other conditions are the same, then

$$V = k\sqrt{\frac{w}{2a}}$$
$$= \frac{1}{\sqrt{2}}\left(k\sqrt{\frac{w}{a}}\right)$$
$$\approx 0.70711\left(k\sqrt{\frac{w}{a}}\right) = 70.711\% \cdot \text{Original } V.$$

Thus, the stall velocity decreases to 70.711% of what it was; that is, it decreases by 29.289%.

45. (a) We have
$$f(x) = g\left(h(x)\right) = 16x^4.$$

Since $g(x) = 4x^2$, we know that

$$g\left(h(x)\right) = 4\left(h(x)\right)^2 = 16x^4$$
$$\left(h(x)\right)^2 = 4x^4.$$
$$\text{Thus,} \qquad h(x) = 2x^2 \text{ or } -2x^2.$$

Since $h(x) \le 0$ for all x, we know that
$$h(x) = -2x^2.$$

(b) We have
$$f(x) = j\left(2g(x)\right) = 16x^4, \qquad j(x) \text{ a power function.}$$

Since $g(x) = 4x^2$, we know that
$$j\left(2g(x)\right) = j(8x^2) = 16x^4.$$

Since $j(x)$ is a power function, $j(x) = kx^p$. Thus,

$$j(8x^2) = k(8x^2)^p = 16x^4$$
$$k \cdot 8^p x^{2p} = 16x^4.$$

Since $x^{2p} = x^4$ if $p = 2$, letting $p = 2$, we have

$$k \cdot 64x^4 = 16 \cdot x^4$$
$$64k = 16$$
$$k = \frac{1}{4}$$

Thus, $j(x) = \frac{1}{4}x^2$.

Solutions for Section 9.2

Exercises

1. This is a polynomial of degree one (since $x = x^1$).

5. Since $y = 4x^2 - 7x^{9/2} + 10$ and $9/2$ is not a nonnegative integer, this is not a polynomial.

9. Since $2x^2/x^{-7} = 2x^9$, we can rewrite this polynomial as $y = 2x^9 - 7x^5 + 3x^3 + 2$. Since the leading term of the polynomial is $2x^9$, the value of y goes to infinity as $x \to \infty$. The graph resembles $y = 2x^9$.

Problems

13. The graph of $y = g(x)$ is shown in Figure 9.2 on the window $-5 \le x \le 5$ by $-20 \le y \le 10$. The minimum value of g occurs at point B as shown in the figure. Using either a table feature or trace on a graphing calculator, we approximate the minimum value of g to be -16.543 (to three decimal places).

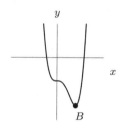

Figure 9.2

17. To find the x-intercept for $y = 2x - 4$ let $y = 0$. We have

$$0 = 2x - 4$$

$$2x = 4$$

$$x = 2.$$

When $x = 0$ on $y = x^4 - 3x^5 - 1 + x^2$, then $y = -1$. This gives the y-intercept for $y = x^4 - 3x^5 - 1 + x^2$. Thus, we have the points $(2, 0)$ and $(0, -1)$. The line through these points will have the same y-intercept, so the linear function is of the form

$$y = mx - 1.$$

The slope, m, is found by taking

$$\frac{0 - (-1)}{2 - 0} = \frac{1}{2}.$$

Thus,

$$y = \frac{1}{2}x - 1$$

is the line through the required points.

21. (a) A graph of V is shown in Figure 9.3 for $0 \le t \le 5, 0 \le V \le 1$.

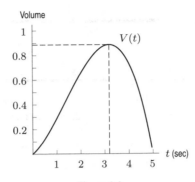

Figure 9.3

(b) The maximum value of V for $0 \leq t \leq 5$ occurs when $t \approx 3.195$, $V \approx .886$. Thus, at just over 3 seconds into the cycle, the lungs contain ≈ 0.88 liters of air.

(c) The volume is zero at $t = 0$ and again at $t \approx 5$. This indicates that at the beginning and end of the 5 second cycle the lungs are empty.

25. Yes. For the sake of illustration, suppose $f(x) = x^2 + x + 1$, a second-degree polynomial. Then

$$f(g(x)) = (g(x))^2 + g(x) + 1$$
$$= g(x) \cdot g(x) + g(x) + 1.$$

Since $f(g(x))$ is formed from products and sums involving the polynomial g, the composition $f(g(x))$ is also a polynomial. In general, $f(g(x))$ will be a sum of powers of $g(x)$, and thus $f(g(x))$ will be formed from sums and products involving the polynomial $g(x)$. A similar situation holds for $g(f(x))$, which will be formed from sums and products involving the polynomial $f(x)$. Thus, either expression will yield a polynomial.

29. (a)

$$p(1) = 1 + 1 + \frac{1^2}{2} + \frac{1^3}{6} + \frac{1^4}{24} + \frac{1^5}{120} \approx 2.71666\ldots.$$

This is accurate to 2 decimal places, since $e \approx 2.718$.

(b) $p(5) \approx 91.417$. This is not at all close to $e^5 \approx 148.4$.

(c) See Figure 9.4. The two graphs are difficult to tell apart for $-2 \leq x \leq 2$, but for x much less than -2 or much greater than 2, the fit gets worse and worse.

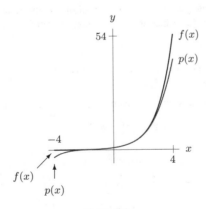

Figure 9.4

Solutions for Section 9.3

Exercises

1. Zeros occur where $y = 0$, at $x = -3$, $x = 2$, and $x = -7$.

5. The graph shows that $g(x)$ has zeros at $x = -2$, $x = 0$, $x = 2$, $x = 4$. Thus, $g(x)$ has factors of $(x + 2)$, x, $(x - 2)$, and $(x - 4)$, so

$$g(x) = k(x + 2)x(x - 2)(x - 4).$$

Since $g(x) = x^4 - 4x^3 - 4x^2 + 16x$, we see that $k = 1$, so

$$g(x) = x(x + 2)(x - 2)(x - 4).$$

9. Factoring f gives $f(x) = -5(x + 2)(x - 2)(5 - x)(5 + x)$, so the
x intercepts are at $x = -2, 2, 5, -5$.
The y intercept is at: $y = f(0) = -5(2)(-2)(5)(5) = 500$.

   The polynomial is of fourth degree with the highest powered term $5x^4$. Thus, both ends point upward. A graph of $y = f(x)$ is shown in Figure 9.5.

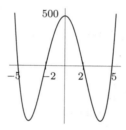

Figure 9.5

Problems

13. First, the viewing window $0 \le x \le 5$, $-25 \le y \le 25$ shows that p has zeros at approximately $x = 1$ and at $x = 3$. Also, since this view of p suggests that the graph of p "bounces off" the x-axis at $x = 1$, we guess that the factorization of $p(x)$ contains a positive even power of $(x - 1)$. Next, the viewing window $-20 \le x \le 10$, $-10000 \le y \le 10000$ indicates another zero at approximately $x = -15$. Putting all of this information together and noting that p is a fourth degree polynomial, we guess that the factorization of $p(x)$ must contain $(x - 3)$, $(x - 1)^2$, and $(x + 15)$. Thus, we have

$$p(x) = k(x + 15)(x - 1)^2(x - 3),$$

where k is some constant. Since the leading coefficient of p must equal 1, we take $k = 1$. We check this factorization by expanding the product to obtain $p(x)$.

17. To pass through the given points, the polynomial must be of at least degree 2. Thus, let f be of the form

$$f(x) = ax^2 + bx + c.$$

Then using $f(0) = 0$ gives

$$a(0)^2 + b(0) + c = 0,$$

so $c = 0$. Then, with $f(2) = 0$, we have

$$a(2)^2 + b(2) + 0 = 0$$
$$4a + 2b = 0$$
$$\text{so} \quad b = -2a.$$

Using $f(3) = 3$ and $b = -2a$ gives

$$a(3)^2 + (-2a)(3) + 0 = 3$$

so

$$9a - 6a = 3$$
$$3a = 3$$
$$a = 1.$$

Thus, $b = -2a$ gives $b = -2$. The unique polynomial of degree ≤ 2 which satisfies the given conditions is $f(x) = x^2 - 2x$.

21. The points $(-3, 0)$ and $(1, 0)$ indicate two zeros for the polynomial. Thus, the polynomial must be of at least degree 2. We could let $p(x) = k(x + 3)(x - 1)$ as in the previous problems, and then use the point $(0, -3)$ to solve for k. An alternative method would be to let $p(x)$ be of the form

$$p(x) = ax^2 + bx + c$$

and solve for a, b, and c using the given points.

The point $(0, -3)$ gives

$$a \cdot 0 + b \cdot 0 + c = -3,$$
$$\text{so} \quad c = -3.$$

Using $(1, 0)$, we have

$$a(1)^2 + b(1) - 3 = 0$$
$$\text{which gives} \quad a + b = 3.$$

The point $(-3, 0)$ gives

$$a(-3)^2 + b(-3) - 3 = 0$$
$$9a - 3b = 3$$
$$\text{or} \quad 3a - b = 1.$$

From $a + b = 3$, substitute

$$a = 3 - b$$

into

$$3a - b = 1.$$

Then

$$3(3 - b) - b = 1$$
$$9 - 3b - b = 1$$
$$-4b = -8$$
$$\text{so} \quad b = 2.$$

Then $a = 3 - 2 = 1$. Therefore,

$$p(x) = x^2 + 2x - 3$$

is the polynomial of least degree through the given points.

25. The shape of the graph suggests an odd degree polynomial with a positive leading term. Since the graph crosses the x-axis at 0, -2, and 2, there are factors of x, $(x + 2)$ and $(x - 2)$, giving $y = ax(x + 2)(x - 2)$. To find a we use the fact that at $x = 1$, $y = -6$. Substituting:

$$-6 = a(1)(1 + 2)(1 - 2)$$
$$-6 = -3a$$
$$2 = a.$$

Thus, a possible polynomial is $y = 2x(x + 2)(x - 2)$.

29. We use the position of the "bounce" on the x-axis to indicate a repeated zero at that point. Since there is not a sign change at those points, the zero is repeated an even number of times. Letting

$$y = k(x + 2)^2(x)(x - 2)^2$$

represent (c), we use the point $(1, -3)$ to get

$$-3 = f(1) = k(3)^2(1)(-1)^2,$$

so

$$-3 = 9k,$$

$$k = -\frac{1}{3}.$$

Thus, a possible is

$$y = -\frac{1}{3}(x + 2)^2(x)(x - 2)^2.$$

33. We see that g has zeros at $x = -2$, $x = 2$ and at $x = 0$. The zero at $x = 0$ is at least double, so let $g(x) = k(x + 2)(x - 2)x^2$. We have $g(1) = k(1 + 2)(1 - 2)(1)^2 = k \cdot 3(-1)(1)^2 = -3k$. Since $g(1) = 1$, $-3k = 1$, so $k = -\frac{1}{3}$ and

$$g(x) = -\frac{1}{3}(x + 2)(x - 2)x^2$$

is a possible formula for g.

37. Factoring $y = x^2 + 5x + 6$ gives $y = (x + 2)(x + 3)$. Thus $y = 0$ for $x = -2$ or $x = -3$.

41. By using the quadratic formula, we find that $y = 0$ if

$$x = \frac{3 \pm \sqrt{9 - 4(2)(-3)}}{4} = \frac{3 \pm \sqrt{33}}{4}.$$

45. We express the volume as a function of the length, x, of the square's side that is cut out in Figure 9.6.

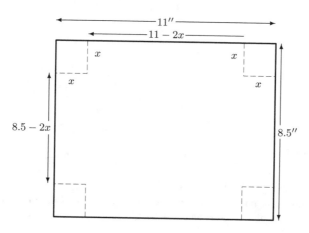

Figure 9.6

Since the sides of the base are $(11 - 2x)$ and $(8.5 - 2x)$ inches and the depth is x inches, the volume, $V(x)$, is given by

$$V(x) = x(11 - 2x)(8.5 - 2x).$$

The graph of $V(x)$ in Figure 9.7 suggest that the maximum volume occurs when $x \approx 1.585$ inches. (A good viewing window is $0 \le x \le 5$ and $0 \le y \le 70$.) So one side is $x = 1.585$, and therefore the others are $11 - 2(1.585) = 7.83$ and $8.5 - 2(1.585) = 5.33$.

The dimensions of the box are 7.83 by 5.33 by 1.585 inches.

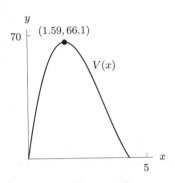

Figure 9.7

49. (a) Never true, because $f(x) \to -\infty$ as $x \to \pm\infty$, which means $f(x)$ must be of even degree.
   (b) Sometimes true, since f could be an even-degree polynomial without being symmetric to the y-axis.
   (c) Sometimes true, since f could have a multiple zero.
   (d) Never true, because f must be of even degree.
   (e) True, because, since f is of even degree, $f(-x)$ must have the same long-run behavior as $f(x)$.
   (f) Never true, because, since $f(x) \to -\infty$ as $x \to \pm\infty$, f will fail the horizontal-line test.

Solutions for Section 9.4

Exercises

1. This is a rational function, as we can put it in the form of one polynomial divided by another:

$$f(x) = \frac{x^2}{2} + \frac{1}{x} = \frac{x^3}{2x} + \frac{2}{2x} = \frac{x^3 + 2}{2x}.$$

5. This is a rational function, as we can put it in the form of one polynomial divided by another:

$$f(x) = \frac{x^2}{x-3} - \frac{5}{x-3} = \frac{x^2 - 5}{x-3}.$$

9. As $x \to \pm\infty$, $1/x \to 0$, so $f(x) \to 1$. Therefore $y = 1$ is the horizontal asymptote.

Problems

13. (a) If $\lim_{x \to \infty} r(x) = 0$, then the degree of the denominator is greater than the degree of the numerator, so $n > m$.
   (b) If $\lim_{x \to \infty} r(x) = k$, with $k \ne 0$, the degree of the numerator and denominator must be equal, so $n = m$.

17. (a) Since g is the average of x and $2/x^2$:

$$g(x) = \frac{1}{2}\left(x + \frac{2}{x^2}\right) = \frac{x^3 + 2}{2x^2}.$$

(b)

Table 9.1

x	$g(x)$
1.26	1.2598816
1.2598816	1.2599408
1.2599408	1.2599112
1.2599112	1.2599260
1.2599260	1.2599186
1.2599186	1.2599223

Table 9.1 shows the estimates for six iterations of using g to estimate $\sqrt[3]{2}$. Since $\sqrt[3]{2} = 1.25992105\ldots$, the last estimate is accurate to five decimal places. However, note that the fifth decimal place has been hopping back and forth some since the third iteration. To be assured that the fifth decimal place has settled down (i.e., all new activity taking place beyond the fifth decimal), we might want to execute another iteration (or so).

21. (a) (i) $C(1) = 5050$ means the cost to make 1 unit is $5050.
  (ii) $C(100) = 10{,}000$ means the cost to make 100 units is $10,000.
  (iii) $C(1000) = 55{,}000$ means the cost to make 1000 units is $55,000.
  (iv) $C(10000) = 505{,}000$ means the cost to make 10,000 units is $505,000.
(b) (i) $a(1) = C(1)/1 = 5050$ means that it costs $5050/unit to make 1 unit.
  (ii) $a(100) = C(100)/100 = 100$ means that it costs $100/unit to make 100 units.
  (iii) $a(1000) = C(1000)/1000 = 55$ means that it costs $55/unit to make 1000 units.
  (iv) $a(10000) = C(10000)/10000 = 50.5$ means that it costs $50.50/unit to make 10,000 units.
(c) As the number of units increases, the average cost per unit gets closer to $50/unit, which is the unit (or marginal) cost. This makes sense because the fixed or initial $5000 expenditure becomes increasingly insignificant as it is averaged over a large number of units.

Solutions for Section 9.5

Exercises

1. The zero of this function is at $x = -3$. It has a vertical asymptote at $x = -5$. Its long-run behavior is: $y \to 1$ as $x \to \pm\infty$. See Figure 9.8.

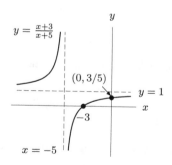

Figure 9.8

5. The x-intercept is $x = 2$; the y-intercept is $y = -2/(-4) = 1/2$; the horizontal asymptote is $y = 1$; the vertical asymptote is $x = 4$.

9. (a)

x	2	2.9	2.99	3	3.01	3.1	4
$f(x)$	-1	-10	-100	undefined	100	10	1

As x approaches 3 from the left, $f(x)$ takes on very large negative values. As x approaches 3 from the right, $f(x)$ takes on very large positive values.

(b)

x	5	10	100	1000
$f(x)$	0.5	0.143	0.010	0.001

x	-5	-10	-100	-1000
$f(x)$	-0.125	-0.077	-0.010	-0.001

For $x > 3$, as x increases, $f(x)$ approaches 0 from above. For $x < 3$, as x decreases, $f(x)$ approaches 0 from below.

(c) The horizontal asymptote is $y = 0$ (the x-axis). The vertical asymptote is $x = 3$. See Figure 9.9.

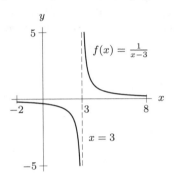

Figure 9.9

Problems

13. (a) To estimate

$$\lim_{x \to 5^+} \frac{x}{5 - x},$$

we consider what happens to the function when x is slightly larger than 5. The numerator is positive and the denominator is negative and is approaching 0 as x approaches 5. We suspect that $\dfrac{x}{5 - x}$ gets more and more negative as x approaches 5 from the right. We can also use either a graph or a table of values as in Table 9.2 to estimate this limit. We see that

$$\lim_{x \to 5^+} \frac{x}{5 - x} = -\infty.$$

Table 9.2

x	5.1	5.01	5.001	5.0001
$f(x)$	-51	-501	-5001	-50001

(b) To estimate

$$\lim_{x \to 5^-} \frac{x}{5 - x},$$

we consider what happens to the function when x is slightly smaller than 5. The numerator is positive and the denominator is positive and is approaching 0 as x approaches 5. We suspect that $\dfrac{x}{5 - x}$ gets larger and larger as x approaches 5 from the left. We can also use either a graph or a table of values to estimate this limit. We see that

$$\lim_{x \to 5^-} \frac{x}{5 - x} = +\infty.$$

17. (a) $y = -\dfrac{1}{(x-5)^2} - 1$ has a vertical asymptote at $x = 5$, no x intercept, horizontal asymptote $y = -1$: (iii)

(b) vertical asymptotes at $x = -1, 3$, x intercept at 2, horizontal asymptote $y = 0$: (i)

(c) vertical asymptotes at $x = 1$, x intercept at $x = -2$, horizontal asymptote $y = 2$: (ii)

(d) $y = \dfrac{x - 3 + x + 1}{(x+1)(x-3)} = \dfrac{2x - 2}{(x+1)(x-3)}$ has vertical asymptotes at $x = -1, 3$, x intercept at 1, horizontal asymptote at $y = 0$: (iv)

(e) $y = \dfrac{(1+x)(1-x)}{x-2}$ has vertical asymptote at $x = 2$, two x intercepts at ± 1: (vi)

(f) vertical asymptote at $x = -1$, x intercept at $x = \frac{1}{4}$, horizontal asymptote at $y = -2$: (v)

21. (a) The graph of $y = -f(-x) + 2$ will be the graph of f flipped about both the x-axis and the y-axis and shifted up 2 units . The graph is shown in Figure 9.10.

(b) The graph of $y = \frac{1}{f(x)}$ will have vertical asymptotes $x = -1$ and $x = 3$. As $x \to +\infty$, $\frac{1}{f(x)} \to -\frac{1}{2}$ and as $x \to -\infty$, $\frac{1}{f(x)} \to 0$. At $x = 0$, $\frac{1}{f(x)} = \frac{1}{2}$, and as $x \to -1$ from the left, $\frac{1}{f(x)} \to -\infty$; as $x \to -1$ from the right, $\frac{1}{f(x)} \to +\infty$; as $x \to 3$ from the left, $\frac{1}{f(x)} \to +\infty$; and as $x \to 3$ from the right, $\frac{1}{f(x)} \to -\infty$.

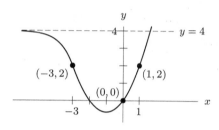

Figure 9.10

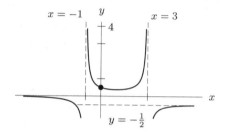

Figure 9.11

25. (a) The graph appears to be $y = 1/x^2$ shifted 3 units to the right and flipped across the x-axis. Thus,

$$y = -\frac{1}{(x-3)^2}$$

is a possible formula for it.

(b) The equation $y = -1/(x-3)^2$ can be written as

$$y = \frac{-1}{x^2 - 6x + 9}.$$

(c) Since y can not equal zero if $y = -1/(x^2 - 6x + 9)$, the graph has no x-intercept. The y-intercept occurs when $x = 0$, so $y = \frac{-1}{(-3)^2} = -\frac{1}{9}$. The y-intercept is at $(0, -\frac{1}{9})$.

29. (a) The table indicates translation of $y = 1/x$ because the values of the function are headed in opposite directions near the vertical asymptote.

(b) The data points in the table indicate that $y \to \frac{1}{2}$ as $x \to \pm\infty$. The vertical asymptote does not appear to have been shifted. thus, we might try

$$y = \frac{1}{x} + \frac{1}{2}.$$

A check of x-values shows that this formula works. To express as a ratio of polynomials, we get a common denominator. Then

$$y = \frac{1(2)}{x(2)} + \frac{1(x)}{2(x)}$$
$$y = \frac{2 + x}{2x}$$

33. We see that the graph has a double zero at $x = 0$, and zeros at $x = -3$ and $x = 2$. So let

$$y = f(x) = kx^2(x + 3)(x - 2).$$

Since $y = f(-2) = -1$, we have

$$y = f(-2) = k(-2)^2(-2 + 3)(-2 - 2) = -16k$$

which gives

$$-16k = -1,$$

or $k = 1/16$. Thus a possible formula is

$$y = f(x) = \frac{1}{16}x^2(x + 3)(x - 2).$$

37. We try $(x+3)(x-1)$ in the numerator in order to get zeros at $x = -3$ and $x = 1$. There is only one vertical asymptote at $x = -2$, but in order to have the horizontal asymptote of $y = 1$, the numerator and denominator must be of same degree. Thus, try

$$y = \frac{(x + 3)(x - 1)}{(x + 2)^2}.$$

Note that this answer gives the correct y-intercept of $(0, -\frac{3}{4})$ and $y \to 1$ as $x \to \pm\infty$.

41. The vertical asymptotes indicate a denominator of $(x + 2)(x - 3)$. The horizontal asymptote of $y = 0$ indicates that the degree of the numerator is less than the degree of the denominator. To get the point $(5,0)$ we need $(x - 5)$ as a factor in the numerator. Therefore, try

$$g(x) = \frac{(x - 5)}{(x + 2)(x - 3)}.$$

Solutions for Section 9.6

Exercises

1. The function fits neither form. If the expression in the parentheses expanded, then $m(x) = 3(9x^2 + 6x + 1) = 27x^2 + 18x + 3$.

5. The function fits an exponential, because $r(x) = 2 \cdot 3^{-2x} = 2(3^{-2})^x = 2(\frac{1}{9})^x$.

9. (a)

Table 9.3

x	$f(x)$	$g(x)$
-3	1/27	
	1/9	-8
-1	1/3	-1
0	1	0
1	3	1
2	9	8
3	27	27

(b) As $x \to -\infty$, $f(x) \to 0$. For f, large negative values of x result in small $f(x)$ values because a large negative power of 3 is very close to zero. For g, large negative values of x result in large negative values of $g(x)$, because the cube of a large negative number is a larger negative number. Therefore, as $x \to -\infty$, $g(x) \to -\infty$.

As $x \to \infty$, $f(x) \to \infty$ and $g(x) \to \infty$. For $f(x)$, large x-values result in large powers of 3; for $g(x)$, large x values yield the cubes of large x-values. f and g both climb *fast*, but f climbs faster than g (for $x > 3$).

13. As $x \to \infty$, we know x^3 dominates x^2. Multiplying by a positive constant a or b, does not change the outcome, so $y = ax^3$ dominates.

Problems

17. (a) Let $f(x) = ax + b$. Then $f(1) = a + b = 18$ and $f(3) = 3a + b = 1458$. Solving simultaneous equations gives us $a = 720, b = -702$. Thus $f(x) = 720x - 702$.

(b) Let $f(x) = a \cdot b^x$, then

$$\frac{f(3)}{f(1)} = \frac{ab^3}{ab} = b^2 = \frac{1458}{18} = 81.$$

Thus,

$$b^2 = 81$$
$$b = 9 \qquad \text{(since } b \text{ must be positive)}$$

Using $f(1) = 18$ gives

$$a(9)^1 = 18$$
$$a = 2.$$

Therefore, if f is an exponential function, a formula for f would be

$$f(x) = 2(9)^x.$$

(c) If f is a power function, let $f(x) = kx^p$, then

$$\frac{f(3)}{f(1)} = \frac{k(3)^p}{k(1)^p} = (3)^p$$

and

$$\frac{f(3)}{f(1)} = \frac{1458}{18} = 81.$$

Thus,

$$3^p = 81 \qquad \text{so} \qquad p = 4.$$

Solving for k, gives

$$18 = k(1^4) \qquad \text{so} \qquad k = 18.$$

Thus, a formula for f is

$$f(x) = 18x^4.$$

21. Note: $\frac{5}{7} > \frac{9}{16} > \frac{3}{8} > \frac{3}{11}$, and we know that for $x > 1$, the higher the exponent, the more steeply the graph climbs, so

$$A \text{ is } kx^{5/7}, \quad B \text{ is } kx^{9/16}, \quad C \text{ is } kx^{3/8}, \quad D \text{ is } kx^{3/11}.$$

25. Since the denominator has highest power of t^6, which dominates t^2, the ratio tends to 0. Thus, $y \to 0$ as $t \to \infty$ or $t \to -\infty$.

29. For large positive t, the value of $3^{-t} \to 0$ and $4^t \to \infty$. Thus, $y \to 0$ as $t \to \infty$.

For large negative t, the value of $3^{-t} \to \infty$ and $4^t \to 0$. Thus,

$$y \to \frac{\text{Very large positive number}}{0 + 7} \qquad \text{as } t \to -\infty.$$

So $y \to \infty$ as $t \to -\infty$.

33. Since e^t and t^2 both dominate $\ln|t|$, we have $y \to \infty$ as $t \to \infty$.

For large negative t, the value of $e^t \to 0$, but t^2 is large and dominates $\ln|t|$. Thus, $y \to \infty$ as $t \to -\infty$,

37. (a) If $y = a \cdot r^{3/4}$, the function is concave down—i.e., values increase at a slower and slower rate as r increases. The data for g demonstrates this type of increase. For $y = b \cdot r^{5/4}$, function values will increase at a faster rate as r increases. Thus, $h(r) = b \cdot r^{5/4}$.

(b) Using any data point from the table, we find $a \approx 8$ and $b \approx 3$. Reasonable models for g and h are

$$g(r) = 8r^{3/4} \qquad \text{and} \qquad h(r) = 3r^{5/4}.$$

Solutions for Section 9.7

Exercises

1. $f(x) = ax^p$ for some constants a and c. Since $f(1) = 1 = a(1)^p$, it follows that $a = 1$. Also, $f(2) = 2^p = c$. Solving for p we have $p = \ln c / \ln 2$. Thus, $f(x) = x^{\ln c / \ln 2}$

5. (a) Regression on a calculator returns the power function $f(x) = 201.353x^{2.111}$, where $f(x)$ represents the total dry weight (in grams) of a tree having an x cm diameter at breast height.

(b) Using our regression function, we obtain $f(20) = 201.535(20)^{2.111} = 112{,}313.62$ gm.

(c) Solving $f(x) = 201.353x^{2.111} = 100{,}000$ for x we get

$$x^{2.111} = \frac{100{,}000}{201.353}$$

$$x = \left(\frac{100{,}000}{201.353} \right)^{1/2.111} = 18.930 \text{ cm.}$$

9. The slope of this line is $\frac{2-0}{5-0} = 0.4$. The vertical intercept is 0. Thus $\ln y = 0.4x$, and $y = e^{0.4x}$.

Problems

13. (a) The FM band appears linear, because the FM frequency always increases by 4 as the distance increases by 10. See Figure 9.12.

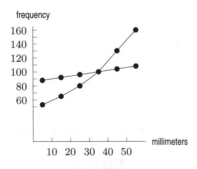

Figure 9.12

(b) The AM band is increasing at an increasing rate. These data could therefore represent an exponential relation.

(c) We recall that any linear function has a formula $f(x) = b + mx$. Since the rate of change, m, is the change in frequency, 4, compared to the change in length, 10, then $m = \frac{4}{10} = 0.4$. So

$$y = b + 0.4x.$$

But the table tells us that $f(5) = b + 0.4(5) = b + 2 = 88$. Therefore, $b = 86$, and

$$y = 86 + 0.4x.$$

We could have also used a calculator or computer to determine the coefficients for the linear regression.

(d) Since the data for the AM band appear exponential, we wish to plot the natural log of the frequency against the length. Table 9.4 gives the values of the AM station numbers, y, and the natural log, $\ln y$, of those station numbers as a function of their location on the dial, x.

Table 9.4

x	5	15	25	35	45	55
y	53	65	80	100	130	160
$\ln y$	3.97	4.17	4.38	4.61	4.87	5.08

The $(x, \ln y)$ data are very close to linear. Regression gives the coefficients for the linear equation $\ln y = b + mx$, yielding

$$\ln y = 3.839 + 0.023x.$$

Solving for y gives:

$$e^{\ln y} = e^{3.839 + 0.023x}$$
$$y = e^{3.839 + 0.023x} \quad \text{(since } e^{\ln y} = y\text{)}.$$
$$y = e^{3.839} e^{0.023x} \quad \text{(since } a^{x+y} = a^x a^y\text{)}$$

Since $e^{3.839} \approx 46.5$,

$$y = 46.5 e^{0.023x}.$$

17. (a) Use a calculator or computer to find an exponential regression function starting with $t = 0$ for 1985, $C(t) = 664.769(1.388)^t$. Answers may vary.

(b) From the equation, the growth factor is 1.388, so cellular subscriptions are increasing by 38.8% per year.

(c) Although the number of cell subscriptions may continue to increase, we eventually expect slower growth. The graph would become concave down.

21. (a) The formula is $N = 1271.2 e^{0.3535t}$. See Figure 9.13.

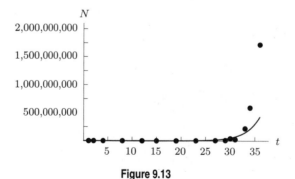

Figure 9.13

(b) The doubling time is given by $\ln 2 / 0.3534 \approx 1.961$. This is consistent with *Moore's Law*, which states that the number of transistors doubles about once every two years. Dr. Gordon E. Moore is Chairman Emeritus of Intel Corporation According to the Intel Corporation, "Gordon Moore made his famous observation in 1965, just four years after the first planar integrated circuit was discovered. The press called it 'Moore's Law' and the name has stuck. In his original paper, Moore observed an exponential growth in the number of transistors per integrated circuit and predicted that this trend would continue."

25. (a) We take the log of both sides and make the substitution $y = \ln N$ to obtain

$$y = \ln N = \ln\left(at^p\right)$$
$$= \ln a + \ln t^p$$
$$= \ln a + p \ln t.$$

We make the substitution $b = \ln a$, so the equation becomes

$$y = b + p \ln t.$$

Notice that this substitution does not result in y being a linear function of t. However, if we make a second substitution, $x = \ln t$, we have

$$y = b + px.$$

So $y = \ln N$ *is* a linear function of $x = \ln t$.

(b) If a power function fits the original data, the points lie on a line. If the points do not lie on a line, a power function does not fit the data well.

29. (a) Using a computer or calculator, we find that $t = 8966.1 H^{-2.3}$. See Figure 9.14.

(b) Using a computer or calculator, we find that $r = 0.0124H - 0.1248$. See Figure 9.15.

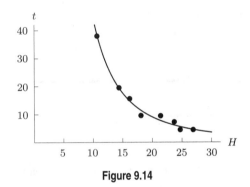

Figure 9.14   **Figure 9.15**

(c) From part (a), we see that $t \to \infty$ as $H \to 0$, and since $r = 1/t$, we have $r \to 0$ as $H \to 0$. From part (b), we can solve for the value of H making $r = 0$ as follows:

$$0.0124H - 0.1248 = 0$$
$$0.0124H = 0.1248$$
$$H \approx 10.1.$$

Thus, the first model predicts that the development rate will fall to $r = 0$ only at $H = 0°C$ (the freezing point of water), whereas the second model predicts that r will reach 0 at around $10°C$ (or about $50°F$). The latter prediction seems far more reasonable: certainly weevil eggs (or any other eggs) would not grow at temperatures near freezing.

Solutions for Chapter 9 Review

Exercises

1. While $y = 6x^3$ is a power function, when we add two to it, it can no longer be written in the form $y = kx^p$, so this is not a power function.

5. Although y is a power function of $(x + 7)$, it is not a power function of x and cannot be written in the form $y = kx^p$.

9. Since $f(1) = k \cdot 1^p = k$, we know $k = f(1) = \frac{3}{2}$

Since $f(2) = k \cdot 2^p = \frac{3}{8}$, and since $k = \frac{3}{2}$, we know

$$\left(\frac{3}{2}\right) \cdot 2^p = \frac{3}{8}$$

which implies

$$2^p = \frac{3}{8} \cdot \frac{2}{3} = \frac{1}{4}.$$

Thus $p = -2$, and $f(x) = \frac{3}{2} \cdot x^{-2}$.

13. $y = 1 - 2x^4 + x^3$ is a fourth degree polynomial with three terms. Its long-run behavior is that of $y = -2x^4$: as $x \to \pm\infty, y \to -\infty$.

17. This is a rational function, as we can put it in the form of one polynomial divided by another:

$$f(x) = \frac{x^3}{2x^2} + \frac{1}{6} = \frac{x}{2} + \frac{1}{6} = \frac{3x}{6} + \frac{1}{} \quad \underline{}_{6}.$$

21. We have

$$\lim_{x \to \infty} \left(2x^{-3} + 4\right) = \lim_{x \to \infty} \left(2/x^3 + 4\right) = 0 + 4 = 4.$$

Problems

25. We have $-0.1 \le x \le 0.1, 0 \le y \le f(0.1)$ or $0 \le y \le 0.011$.

29. Graph (i) looks periodic with amplitude of 2 and period of 2π, so it best corresponds to function J,

$$y = 2\sin(0.5x).$$

Graph (ii) appears to decrease exponentially with a y-intercept < 10, so it best corresponds to function L,

$$y = 2e^{-0.2x}.$$

Graph (iii) looks like a rational function with two vertical asymptotes, no zeros, a horizontal asymptote at $y = 0$ and a negative y-intercept, so it best corresponds to function O,

$$y = \frac{1}{x^2 - 4}.$$

Graph (iv) looks like a logarithmic function with a negative vertical asymptote and y-intercept at $(0,0)$, so it best corresponds to function H,

$$y = \ln(x + 1).$$

33. Let $h(x) = k(x + 2)(x + 1)(x - 1)^2(x - 3)$, since h has zeros at $x = -2$, -1, 3 and a double zero at $x = 1$. To solve for k, use $h(2) = -1$. Since, $h(2) = k(2 + 2)(2 + 1)(2 - 1)^2(2 - 3) = k(4)(3)(1)(-1) = -12k$, then $-12k = -1$, or $k = \frac{1}{12}$. Thus

$$h(x) = \frac{1}{12}(x + 2)(x + 1)(x - 1)^2(x - 3)$$

is a possible choice.

37. One way to approach this problem is to consider the graphical interpretations of even and odd functions. Recall that if a function is even, its graph is symmetric about the y-axis. If a function is odd, its graph is symmetric about the origin.

(a) The function $f(x) = x^2 + 3$ is $y = x^2$ shifted three units up. Note that $y = x^2$ is symmetric about the y-axis. An upward shift will not affect the symmetry. Therefore, f is even.

(b) We consider $g(x) = x^3 + 3$ as an upward shift (by three units) of $y = x^3$. However, although $y = x^3$ is symmetric about the origin, the upward-shifted function will not have that symmetry. Therefore, $g(x) = x^3 + 3$ is neither even nor odd.

(c) The function $y = \frac{1}{x}$ is symmetric about the origin (odd). The function $h(x) = \frac{5}{x}$ is merely a vertical stretch of $y = \frac{1}{x}$. This would not affect the symmetry of the function. Therefore, $h(x) = \frac{5}{x}$ is odd.

(d) If $y = |x|$, the graph is symmetric about the y-axis. However, a shift to the right by four units would make the resulting function symmetric to the line $x = 4$. The graph of $j(x) = |x - 4|$ is neither even nor odd.

(e) The function $k(x) = \log x$ is neither even nor odd. Since k is not defined for $x \leq 0$, clearly neither type of symmetry would apply for $k(x) = \log x$.

(f) If we take $l(x) = \log(x^2)$, we have now included $x < 0$ into the domain of l. For $x < 0$, the graph looks similar to $y = \log x$ flipped about the y-axis. Thus, $l(x) = \log(x^2)$ is symmetric about the y-axis. —It is even.

(g) Clearly $y = 2^x$ is neither even nor odd. Likewise, $m(x) = 2^x + 2$ is neither even nor odd.

(h) We have already seen that $y = \cos x$ is even. Note that the graph of $n(x) = \cos x + 2$ is the cosine function shifted up two units. The graph will still be symmetric about the y-axis. Thus, $n(x) = \cos x + 2$ is even.

41. (a) Since $p = kd^{3/2}$ where k in this case is given by

$$k = \frac{365}{(93)^{3/2}}, \qquad \text{(in millions)}$$

so

$$p = \frac{365}{(93)^{3/2}} \cdot d^{3/2} = 365 \left(\frac{d}{93}\right)^{3/2}.$$

If p is twice the earth's period, $p = 2(365)$, so

$$2(365) = 365 \left(\frac{d}{93}\right)^{3/2}$$

$$2(93)^{3/2} = d^{3/2}$$

$$d^{3/2} \approx 1793.719$$

$$d \approx 147.628 \text{ million miles.}$$

(b) Yes, Mars orbits approximately 141 million miles from the sun.

45. (a) If $y = f(x)$, then $x = f^{-1}(y)$. Solving $y = f(x)$ for x, we have

$$y = \frac{x}{x + 5}$$
$$y(x + 5) = x$$
$$yx + 5y = x$$
$$yx - x = -5y$$
$$x(y - 1) = -5y$$
$$x = \frac{-5y}{y - 1} = \frac{5y}{1 - y}.$$

Thus, $f^{-1}(x) = 5x/(1 - x)$.

(b) $f^{-1}(0.2) = \frac{5(0.2)}{(1 - 0.2)} = \frac{1}{0.8} = 1.25$. This means that 1.25 gallons of alcohol must be added to give an alcohol concentration of .20 or 20%.

(c) $f^{-1}(x) = 0$ means that $\frac{5x}{1 - x} = 0$ which means that $x = 0$. This means that 0 gallons of alcohol must be added to give a concentration of 0%.

(d) The horizontal asymptote of $f^{-1}(x)$ is $y = -5$. Since x is a concentration of alcohol, $0 \leq x \leq 1$. Thus, the regions of the graph for which $x < 0$ and $x > 1$ have no physical significance. Consequently, since $f^{-1}(x)$ approaches its asymptote only as $x \to \pm\infty$, its horizontal asymptote has no physical significance.

49. Let $h(x) = j(x) + 7$ where $j(x)$ has zeros at $x = -5, -1, 4$. Since j has zeros at these x-values, h has "sevens" there—that is, the value of h equals 7 at these x-values. A formula for $j(x) = k(x+5)(x+1)(x-4)$, so $h(x) = k(x+5)(x+1)(x-4) + 7$. Solving for k, we have

$$h(0) = 3$$
$$k(5)(1)(-4) + 7 = 3$$
$$-20k = -4$$
$$k = \frac{1}{5}.$$

Thus, $h(x) = (1/5)(x+5)(x+1)(x-4) + 7$.

53. (a) See Figure 9.16.

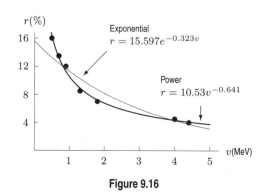

Figure 9.16

(b) The value of r tends to go down as v increases. This means that the telescope is better able to distinguish between high-energy gamma ray photons than low-energy ones.

(c) The first curve is a power function given by $r = 10.53v^{-0.641}$. The second is an exponential function given by $r = 15.597e^{-0.323v}$. The power function appears to give a better fit.

(d) The power function predicts that $r \to \infty$ as $v \to 0$, and so is most consistent with the prediction that the telescope gets rapidly worse and worse at low energies. In contrast, exponential function predicts that r gets close to 15.6% as E gets close to 0.

CHECK YOUR UNDERSTANDING

1. False. The quadratic function $y = 3x^2 + 5$ is not of the form $y = kx^n$, so it is not a power function.

5. True. All positive even power functions have an upward opening U shape.

9. True. The x-axis is an asymptote for $f(x) = x^{-1}$, so the values approach zero.

13. False. As x grows very large the exponential decay function g approaches the x-axis faster than any power function with a negative power.

17. False. For example, the polynomial $x^2 + x^3$ has degree 3 because the degree is the highest power, not the first power, in the formula for the polynomial.

21. True. The graph crosses the y-axis at the point $(0, p(0))$.

25. True. We can write $p(x) = (x-a) \cdot C(x)$. Evaluating at $x = a$ we get $p(a) = (a-a) \cdot C(a) = 0 \cdot C(a) = 0$.

29. True. This is the definition of a rational function.

33. True. The ratio of the highest degree terms in the numerator and denominator is $2x/x^2 = 2/x$, so for large positive x-values, y approaches 0.

37. False. The ratio of the highest degree terms in the numerator and denominator is $3x^4/x^2 = 3x^2$. So for large positive x-values, y behaves like $y = 3x^2$.

41. True. At $x = -4$, we have $f(-4) = (-4 + 4)/(-4 - 3) = 0/(-7) = 0$, so $x = -4$ is a zero.

45. False. If $p(x)$ has no zeros, then $r(x)$ has no zeros. For example, if $p(x)$ is a nonzero constant or $p(x) = x^2 + 1$, then $r(x)$ has no zeros.

Solutions to Tools for Chapter 9

1. $\dfrac{3}{5} + \dfrac{4}{7} = \dfrac{3 \cdot 7 + 4 \cdot 5}{35} = \dfrac{21 + 20}{35} = \dfrac{41}{35}$

5. $\dfrac{-2}{yz} + \dfrac{4}{z} = \dfrac{-2z + 4yz}{yz^2} = \dfrac{-2 + 4y}{yz} = \dfrac{-2(1 - 2y)}{yz}$

9. $\dfrac{\frac{3}{4}}{\frac{7}{20}} = \dfrac{3}{4} \cdot \dfrac{20}{7} = \dfrac{60}{28} = \dfrac{15}{7}$

13. $\dfrac{13}{x - 1} + \dfrac{14}{2x - 2} = \dfrac{13}{x - 1} + \dfrac{14}{2(x - 1)} = \dfrac{13 \cdot 2 + 14}{2(x - 1)} = \dfrac{40}{2(x - 1)} = \dfrac{20}{x - 1}$

17. $\dfrac{8y}{y - 4} + \dfrac{32}{y - 4} = \dfrac{8y + 32}{y - 4} = \dfrac{8(y + 4)}{y - 4}$

21.
$$\dfrac{8}{3x^2 - x - 4} - \dfrac{9}{} \qquad \dfrac{8}{(x + 1)(3x - 4)} - \dfrac{9}{x + 1}$$
$$= \dfrac{8 - 9(3x - 4)}{(x + 1)(3x - 4)}$$
$$= \dfrac{-27x + 44}{(x + 1)(3x - 4)}$$

25. If we rewrite the second fraction $-\dfrac{1}{1 - x}$ as $\dfrac{1}{x - 1}$, the common denominator becomes $x - 1$. Therefore,
$$\dfrac{x^2}{x - 1} - \dfrac{1}{1 - x} = \dfrac{x^2}{x - 1} + \dfrac{1}{x - 1} = \dfrac{x^2 + 1}{x - 1}.$$

29. The common denominator is e^{2x}. Thus,
$$\dfrac{1}{e^{2x}} + \dfrac{1}{e^x} = \dfrac{1}{e^{2x}} + \dfrac{e^x}{e^{2x}} = \dfrac{1 + e^x}{e^{2x}}.$$

33. $\dfrac{8y}{y - 4} - \dfrac{32}{y - 4} = \dfrac{8y - 32}{y - 4} = \dfrac{8(y - 4)}{y - 4} = 8$

37. We write this complex fraction as a multiplication problem. Therefore,
$$\dfrac{\frac{w+2}{2}}{w + 2} = \dfrac{w + 2}{2} \cdot \dfrac{1}{w + 2} = \dfrac{1}{2}.$$

41. We expand within the first brackets first. Therefore,
$$\dfrac{[4 - (x + h)^2] - [4 - x^2]}{h} = \dfrac{[4 - (x^2 + 2xh + h^2)] - [4 - x^2]}{h}$$
$$= \dfrac{[4 - x^2 - 2xh - h^2] - 4 + x^2}{h} = \dfrac{-2xh - h^2}{h}$$
$$= -2x - h.$$

45. We simplify the second complex fraction first. Thus,

$$p - \frac{q}{\frac{p}{q} + q} \qquad \frac{\frac{p^2+q^2}{qp}}{} = p - q \cdot \frac{qp}{p^2 + q^2}$$

$$= \frac{p(p^2 + q^2) - q^2 p}{p^2 + q^2} = \frac{p^3}{p^2 + q^2}.$$

49. Write

$$\frac{\frac{1}{2}(2x - 1)^{-1/2}(2) - (2x - 1)^{1/2}(2x)}{(x^2)^2} = \frac{\frac{1}{(2x-1)^{1/2}} - \frac{2x(2x-1)^{1/2}}{1}}{(x^2)^2}.$$

Next a common denominator for the top two fractions is $(2x - 1)^{1/2}$. Therefore we obtain,

$$\frac{\frac{1}{(2x-1)^{1/2}} - \frac{2x(2x-1)}{(2x-1)^{1/2}}}{x^4} = \frac{1 - 4x^2 + 2x}{(2x - 1)^{1/2}} \cdot \frac{1}{x^4} = \frac{-4x^2 + 2x + 1}{x^4 \sqrt{2x - 1}}.$$

53. The denominator $p^2 + 11$ is divided into each of the two terms of the numerator. Thus,

$$\frac{7 + p}{p^2 + 11} = \frac{7}{p^2 + 11} + \frac{p}{p^2 + 11}.$$

57. The numerator $q - 1 = q - 4 + 3$. Thus,

$$\frac{q - 1}{q - 4} = \frac{(q - 4) + 3}{q - 4} = 1 + \frac{3}{q - 4}.$$

61.

$$\frac{1 + e^x}{e^x} = \frac{1}{e^x} + \frac{e^x}{e^x} = \frac{1}{e^x} + 1 = 1 + \frac{1}{e^x}$$

65. False

INDEX

0^+ notation, 168
σ, 496
$\rightarrow$ notation, 123, 168
e, the number, 130, 131
    infinite series, 135
$e^{i\theta}$, 344
i, the number, 342
    powers of, 343
n-dimensional vector, 459
x-component of vector, 457
x-intercept, 399
y-axis, symmetry about, 205
y-component of vector, 457
y-intercept, 20

Aaron, Henry, 49
Absolute value function, 76
Acceleration, 28
Acidity, chemical, 170
Acoustic beats, 333
Acute angle, 308
Addition
    of complex numbers, 342
    of fractions, 441
    of vectors, 450
        properties, 454
Advertising expenditure, 183
Afghanistan, population, 25
African elephant, body mass, 183, 394
AIDS, 428, 432
Albatross, body mass, 183
Alcohol concentration, 372
Alternating current, 249, 270
Alternating sequence, 488
AM signal, 335
Ambiguous case, Law of Sines, 311
Ampicillin, 510
Amplitude
    cosine function, 269
    exponentially decreasing, 331
    sine function, 269
    trigonometric function, 265, 269, 272
    definition, 247
Analog radio dial, 432
Andromeda Galaxy, 175
Angle
    acute, 308

obtuse, 312
Angle measure
    conversion between degrees and radians, 259
    on unit circle, 250
    radian, 258
    reference angle, 290, 291
    special angles, 252, 301
Angular frequency, 270
Annual growth factor, 109
Apollonius of Perga (262–190 BC), 538
Approximate solution, 56
Approximation
    cube root, 414
    of e, 135
    polynomial, 401
Arc length, 257, 260
Arccosine, 287
Archimedean spiral, 338, 521
Archimedes, 548
Arcsine, 289
Arctangent, 289
Area
    circle, 11, 62
    square, 25, 69
Arithmetic sequence, 489
Arithmetic series, 494
    sum of, 494
Associative property
    vector operations, 454
Astronomical unit (AU), 539
Astronomy
    astronomical distances, 175
    planetary motion, 395
    sunspots, 16
Asymptote
    exponential function, 123
    horizontal, 123, 169
    hyperbola, 544
    logarithmic function, 167
    power function, 391
    rational function, 413, 417, 418
    vertical, 169, 280
Atenolol, 505
Atmospheric pressure, 128
Average
    cost of production, 409, 414
    income, Canada, 381

rate of change, 11
    as slope, 13
    function notation for, 13
    weighted, 414
Axis of symmetry, 226
    parabola, 227

Ballet dancer, vertical jump, 232
Base e, 131
Base change, exponential function, 163
Baseball diamond, 313
Baseball, height function, 89, 229
Basketball player, slam-dunk jump, 237
Ben, 198
Biology
    blood stream concentration, 143
    calories, 16, 48, 72
    carbon-14 decay, 12, 16, 107, 125
    circulation time, 394
    deer population, 48
    epidemic, 95
    genetic distance, 473
    hand strength, 49
    metabolic rate, 179
    oxygen consumption, 28, 31, 48
    respiratory cycle, 401
    snowy tree cricket, 2
Black bear population, 122
Black rhinoceros, body mass, 394
Blood alcohol content, 144
Blood pressure, 277
Blood sugar level, 51
Blue whale, body mass, 183, 394
Body mass, various animals, 183, 394
Bonds, 510
Bone mass, 186
Boston telephone directory, 73
Boston, temperature, 278
Botswana, population, 144
Branches of hyperbola, 534, 544, 554
Break-even point, 34
British Airways, ferris wheel, 244
Bronze alloy, 73, 414
Bullet, velocity, 33

Calories, 16, 48, 72
Capacitor, 124
Capture cross-section, 439
Car rental agencies, comparison, 37

Carbon-14, 12, 16, 107, 111, 125, 159, 162, 166, 186
Cardioid, 341
Cartesian
    coordinates, 336
    plane, 2
Causation, 47
Celsius, 26
Change
    average rate of, 11
    inside, 197
    outside, 197
Charlotte, North Carolina, daylight hours, 234
Chemical acidity, 170
Chicago O'Hare airport, rainfall, 5, 69, 72
Circle, 526
    area, 11, 62
    conic section, 526
    coordinates, 253
    geometric definition, 539
    implicit equation, 527
    parametric equation, 527
    standard form, 527
    unit circle, 250
Circulation time, 394
Closed form, 502
Coefficient, 398
Combination of functions, 373
    difference, 373, 374
    product, 376
    quotient, 376, 377
    sum, 374
Comet, Halley's, 538, 551
Common
    denominator, 442
    logarithmic function, 152
Commutative property
    dot product, 469
    vector operations, 454
Compact discs, 15, 180, 435
Completing the square, 227, 239, 528
Complex
    fraction, 443
    number, 341
        addition of, 342
        conjugate, 342
        definition, 342
        division of, 343
        multiplication of, 343
        polar coordinates and, 344
        polar form, 345

polar representation, 344, 345
        powers of, 346
        powers of i, 343
        roots of, 346
        subtraction of, 342
    plane, 344
    power, 345
Component of vector, 456, 457
    notation, 461
Composition of functions, 79, 355
    decomposition, 357
    using formulas, 355
    using graphs, 357
Compound interest, 136
    balance formula, 137
    continuous, 138
        balance formula, 138
Compression
    horizontal, 221
    vertical, 212
Computer graphics
    in films, 465
    vector, 449
Concave
    down, 85, 86
    up, 84, 86
Concavity, 84, 86
Concentration, 372, 414, 438
Conic sections, 526, 538
Conjugate, complex number, 342
Constant
    percent growth rate, 106
    percent rate of change, 106
    rate of change, 21
    term, 398
Consumption vector, 463
Continuous
    compounding, 138
    growth rate, 131
Coordinates
    Cartesian, 336
    polar, 336
    relation between Cartesian and polar, 336
Correlation, 47
    causation and, 47
    coefficient of, 47
Cosecant function, 282
Cosh function, 552
    identities, 554
    properties, 552
Cosine function
    amplitude, 269, 272

definition, 251
    graph, 264
    horizontal shift, 272
    hyperbolic, 552
    inverse, 285, 287, 370
    Law of Cosines, 308
    midline, 272
    period, 270, 272
    special angles, 252, 264, 301
    triangle definition, 301
Cost
    average, 409, 414
    fixed, 53, 409
    marginal, 512
    total, 414
    unit, 53
    variable, 409
Cotangent function, 282
Coulomb's Law, 467
Coupon, of bond, 510
Credit multiplier, 513
Cricket
    snowy tree, 2, 4
    thermometer, 2, 4
Crime rates, 377
Crow's nest, on ship's mast, 294
Cube
    surface area formula, 83
    volume formula, 83
Cube root approximation, 414
Cubic polynomial, 398
Currency exchange rates, 361
Cylinder
    surface area formula, 97
    volume formula, 97

Damped oscillation, 329
    formula, 331
Data
    fitting exponential functions, 116, 181
    fitting linear functions, 44, 116
    fitting power functions, 429
    linearization, 180
    transformed, 181
Deceleration, 28
Decibel, 171
Decimal
    repeating, 510
    writing as fraction, 510
Decomposition of functions, 357
    trivial, 358
Decreasing function, 11, 107, 109

exponential vs. power, 425

graph of, 12
Degree, 398
conversion to radians, 259
Degree-day model, 34
Demand, 34, 372
Denominator, common, 442
Density, 401
Dependence, 2
Dependent variable, 4
Depreciation
exponential, 122
linear, 19, 25, 43
Difference
function, 130
of functions, 373
using graphs, 374
of squares, factoring, 101
quotient, 361
table of differences, 115
Difference-of-angle formula, 323, 346
Direction of vector, 449
Directrix
parabola, 546, 547
Discrete set, 30
Displacement
net, 448
vector, 459
vs. distance, 448
Distance vs. displacement, 448
Distributive property
dot product, 469
real numbers, 99
vector operations, 454
Division
of fractions, 441
of complex numbers, 343
Domain, 69
for real situation, 69
from formula, 71
from graph, 70
inverse cosine, 287, 370
inverse function, 367
inverse sine, 289, 370
inverse tangent, 289, 370
logarithmic function, 167
restriction, 369
Dot product, 468
geometric interpretation, 471
properties, 469
Double ferris wheel, 335
Double-angle
cosine, 317

sine, 317
tangent, 317
Double-angle identities, 315, 316
Doubling time, 161
rule of seventy, 187
Drug level, 503
equilibrium, 506

Earning power, 144
Earth
distance from sun, 395
formation of, 177
latitude, 297
radius
computing, 263
Economics
average cost of production, 409, 414
bonds, 510
break-even point, 34
budget constraint, 485
compound interest, 137
consumption, 485
continuous compound interest, 138
credit multiplier, 513
demand, 34, 372
depreciation, 122
economies of scale, 385
marginal cost, 512
models of investment, 136
profit, 34
revenue vector, 463
straight-line depreciation, 19
total cost of production, 20, 53
vector, 449
Economies of scale, 385
Effective
annual yield, 139
rate, 136
yield, 136
Eiffel Tower, 312
Eigenvalue, 482
Eigenvector, 482
Elimination and simultaneous equations, 56
Ellipse, 526, 529
conic section, 526
focal point, 539, 542
focus, 539, 542
general formula, 530
geometric definition, 539
implicit equation, 530

major axis, 530
minor axis, 530
parametric equation, 529
reflective properties, 542
Elliptical orbit, 538
EPA, 17
Equation
exponential
algebraic solution, 154, 159
graphical solution, 125
graphing in polar coordinates, 338
logarithmic
algebraic solution, 154
parametric, 517
quadratic
completing the square, 239
factoring, 89
quadratic formula, 240
simultaneous, 36, 56
solution by factoring, 101
solving, 63
trigonometric
algebraic solution, 285
graphical solution, 285
reference angles and, 290
Eudoxus, 301
Euler's
formula, 344
identities and, 346
identity, 345
Euler, Leonhard, 131
European euro, exchange rate, 361
Evaluating a function, 62
Even
function, 205
power function, 390
symmetry, 205, 207
Exact solution, 56
Exchange rates, currency, 361
Explicitly defined function, 525
Exponent
relation to logarithm, 153
Exponential
decay, 107, 111
equation
algebraic solution, 154, 159
graphical solution, 125
function
base change, 163
compound interest, 136
continuous compounding, 138
continuous growth rate, 131
decreasing, 107, 109

definition, 106

doubling time, 161
effective yield, 136
fitting to data, 181
from a table, 115
general formula, 110
graph, 168
growth factor, 109
half-life, 162
horizontal asymptote, 123
increasing, 108
inverse of logarithm, 153, 155
nominal interest rate, 136
parameters, 110, 131
parameters and graph, 123
percent rate of change, 106
ratio method, 116
vs. linear, 115, 117
vs. power function, 424
growth, 118
Exponential regression, 126
Extrapolation, 45, 434
Eyewall wind profile, 8, 68

Factored formula
polynomial function, 403
and zeros, 404
quadratic function, 89
Factoring, 89
algebraic expressions, 99
difference of squares, 101
formula of function, 376
perfect squares, 101
quadratic expressions, 100
solving equation, 101
Fahrenheit, 26
Fairbanks, AL, temperature, 298
Falling objects, 497
False-positive, 439
Family of functions
exponential, 106
quadratic, 227
rational, 410
Ferris wheel function, 244, 248, 254
graph, 245, 266
Fibonacci sequence, 68
Financial models, 19
Fitting data
exponential function, 181
linear function, 44
power function, 429
regression, 44
Fixed cost, 53, 409

Focal point, 539, 543
ellipse, 542
hyperbola, 544
Focus, 548
ellipse, 539, 542
hyperbola, 543, 544
parabola, 546–548
Food supply, per capita, 376
Food surplus, per capita, 373
Football, motion of, 232
Force
gravitational, 437
normal, 484
sliding, 484
vector, 449
Formula
arc length, 260
area
square, 69
circle, 62
balance
compound interest, 137
continuous compound interest, 138
composite functions, 355
coordinates on a circle, 253
cosine function, 272
damped oscillation, 331
difference of squares, 101
difference-of-angle, 323
double-angle
cosine, 316
sine, 316
tangent, 316
Euler's, 344
exponential function, 110
ratio method, 116
for a function
definition, 3
inside changes, 197
outside changes, 197
horizontal line, 39
inverse function, 80, 363
linear function
from graph, 28
from verbal description, 29
general, 20
point-slope, 31
parametric, 517
perfect square, 101
polynomial function, 398
from graph, 405
power function, 389

from graph, 392
quadratic, 240
quadratic function, 89, 227
from graph, 228, 229
rational function
from graph, 418
sine function, 272
sum-of-angle, 320, 323
surface area
cube, 83
cylinder, 97
transformation
horizontal compression, 221
horizontal reflection, 204
horizontal shift, 195, 196
horizontal stretch, 221
vertical compression, 212
vertical reflection, 204
vertical shift, 195, 196
vertical stretch, 212
vertical line, 39
volume
cube, 83
cylinder, 97
Fraction
arithmetic of, 441
complex, 443
reducing, 442
Frequency, 270
angular, 270
fusion, 184
piano notes, 333
Fuel consumption, 52
Function
absolute value, 76
average rate of change, 11
combination, 373
composition, 79, 355
concave down, 85, 86
concave up, 84, 86
cosecant, 282
cosh, 552
cosine, 251
cotangent, 282
cricket, 2, 4, 63
domain and range, 69
inverse, 81
decomposition, 357
decreasing, 11
definition, 2
dependent variable, 4
difference, 130, 373
domain, 69

evaluating, 62

even, 205
explicitly defined, 525
exponential, 106
    general formula, 110
    graph, 168
    vs. linear, 115, 117
    vs. power, 424
ferris wheel, 244
    graph, 245
formula for, 3
graph of, 2
implicitly defined, 525
increasing, 11
independent variable, 4
input, 2, 4, 62, 63
inside, 79
inside change, 197
inverse, 80, 362
inverse cosine, 287
inverse sine, 289
inverse tangent, 289
invertible, 80, 362
linear
    definition, 17, 19
    general formula, 20
    graph, 19, 36
    point-slope form, 31
    slope-intercept form, 31
    standard form, 31
    table, 21, 27
    vs. exponential, 115, 117
logarithmic
    common, 152
    graph, 168
    natural, 155
logistic, 70
maximum value, 229
minimum value, 229
noninvertible, 365
notation, 4, 62
odd, 206
output, 2, 4, 62
outside, 79
outside change, 197
parametric equation, 517
periodic, 246, 247
polynomial, 396
polynomial approximation, 401
power, 389
    vs. exponential, 424
quadratic, 89, 227
range, 69

rational, 410
representations of, 2
secant, 282
sine, 251
sinh, 552
sinusoidal, 269
table representation, 2
tangent, 279
transformation
    combined, 198, 207, 215
    compression, 212, 221
    reflection, 204
    shift, 196
    stretch, 212, 221
trigonometric
    cosecant, 282
    cosine, 251
    cotangent, 282
    inverse cosine, 287
    inverse sine, 289
    inverse tangent, 289
    secant, 282
    sine, 251
    tangent, 279
verbal representation, 2
vertical line test, 6
zero, 89
Fusion frequency, 184

Gain, 211
Galileo, 450
Garbage production, 17
Gas mileage, 72
Gateway Arch, St. Louis, MO, 305
General formula
    cosine function, 272
    ellipse, 530
    exponential function, 110
    hyperbola, 554
    linear function, 20
    polynomial function, 398
    power function, 389
    sine function, 272
General term
    of sequence, 488
Genetic distance, 473
Geometric sequence, 490
Geometric series, 502
    infinite, 506
        sum of, 507
    sum of, 502
Geometry, Riemannian, 537
Golden ratio, 438, 492

Gore Mountain, NY, 78
Grapefruit, velocity, 27
Graph
    cosine function, 264
    exponential function, 168
    finding input and output, 64
    function, 2
    hyperbolic cosine function, 552
    hyperbolic sine function, 552
    inverse function, 367
        $\ln x$ and e^x, 168
        $\log x$ and 10^x, 168
    linear function, 19
        y-intercept, 36
        slope, 36
    logarithmic function, 168
    natural logarithmic function, 169
    polynomial function, 398
    power function, 389
    rational function, 417
    sine function, 264
    tangent function, 279
Gravitation, 437
    Newton's Law of, 464
Gravitational force, 437
Growth
    exponential vs. linear, 118
    linear, 17
Growth factor, 108
    annual, 109
    formula, 110
Growth rate
    constant percent, 106
    continuous, 131
Gwendolyn, 232

Half-life, 162
Halley's comet, 538, 551
Hand strength, 49
Harry Potter, film, 463
Hawk, body mass, 183
Heart rate, 28
    effect of drug on, 354
Heating schedule, 194
Heating, Newton's Law of, 208
Hertz, 249
Hippopotamus, body mass, 183, 394
Holes in rational functions, 419
Home run record, 49
Horizontal
    asymptote, 123, 169
        rational function, 413, 418
    compression, 221

line
    slope, 39
    test, 365
    reflection, 202, 204
    shift, 194, 196
        sinusoidal function, 271, 272
    stretch, 221
Horse, body mass, 183, 394
Housepainting, 62, 69, 197, 217
Human, body mass, 183, 394
Hummingbird, body mass, 183
Hurricane, 8, 68
Hyperbola, 526, 533
    asymptote, 544
    conic section, 526
    focal point, 543, 544
    focus, 543, 544
    general formula, 554
    geometric definition, 543
    implicit equation, 535
    parametric equation, 534, 554
    reflective properties, 545
Hyperbolic function, 552
    cosh, 552
    identities, 554
    properties, 552
    sinh, 552
Hyperbolic orbit, 538

Identities
    and solving equations, 314
    derivation of, 323
    Euler's, 345
    Euler's formula and, 346
    hyperbolic function, 554
    tangent, 314
    trigonometric, 281, 313
        difference of two cosines, 323
        difference of two sines, 323
        difference-of-angle, 323
        double-angle, 315, 316
        negative-angle, 317
        Pythagorean, 314
        sum of sine and cosine, 322
        sum of two cosines, 323
        sum of two sines, 323
        sum-of-angle, 320, 323
    vector operations, 454
Imaginary
    number, 342
    part, of complex number, 342
    power, 345
Implicit, 525

Implicitly defined function, 525
Income tax, 68
Increasing function, 11, 108
    exponential vs. power, 424
    graph of, 12
Independent variable, 4
Infinite geometric series, 506
    sum of, 507
Inflation, 113, 144, 166
Influenza epidemic, 95
Input, 2, 4, 62
    as independent variable, 4
    from graph, 65
    from table, 64
Inside change, 197
    to a formula, 197
Inside function, 79
Intensity
    light, 219
    sound, 171
Intercept, 3, 20
    x-axis, 399
    vertical, 20
Interest rate
    compound, 136, 138
    effective, 136
    nominal, 136
Interpolation, 45, 434
Intersection of graphs, 56
    lines, 36
Inverse function, 80
    cosine, 285, 287, 370
    definition, 362
    domain, 367
    domain restriction, 369
    evaluating graphically, 365
    formula, 363
    graph, 367
        $\ln x$ and e^x, 168
        $\log x$ and 10^x, 168
    notation, 80
    property, 368
    range, 367
    sine, 288, 289, 370
    tangent, 288, 289, 370
Inverse proportionality, 388
Invertible, 80, 362
IQ, 48
Ireland, population, 96
Ironman triathlon, 75

Japanese yen, exchange rate, 361
Jonah, 197

Jupiter, distance from sun, 395

Kepler, Johannes (1571–1630), 395, 537

Lampshade, 551
Latitude, 297
Law
    of Cosines, 308
    of planetary motion, 395
    of Sines, 310
        ambiguous case, 311
    Torricelli's, 392
Leading term, 398
Least-squares line, 46
Letterman, David, 52
Leukemia, 250
Lewis, Carl, 17
Lexus, depreciation, 122
Light intensity, 219
Lighthouse beacon, 219
Limit, 123, 168
Linear depreciation, 19, 25, 43
Linear extrapolation, 45
Linear factor, 404
Linear function
    definition, 17, 19
    extrapolation, 45
    fitting to data, 44
    from a table, 115
    graph, 19, 36
    interpolation, 45
    point-slope form, 31
    regression, 44
    slope-intercept form, 31
    standard form, 31
    table, 21, 27
    vs. exponential, 115, 117
Linear growth, 17, 118
Linear interpolation, 45
Linear regression, 44
    assumptions, 45
    correlation, 47
    least squares, 46
Linear scale, 175
Linearize data, 180
Lion, body mass, 183
Lissajous figure, 522
Lithotripsy, 542
Log
    function, 152
    of large numbers, 176
    of small numbers, 177
Log-log scale, 179

Logarithm

exponential equation, solution to, 154, 159

is an exponent, 153

Logarithmic

equation

algebraic solution, 154

function

common, 152

domain, 167

graph, 168

inverse of exponential, 153, 155

misconceptions, 156

natural, 155

properties, 154, 156

range, 167

undoes exponentiation, 153

vertical asymptote, 167

vs. power function, 425

scale, 176, 180

order of magnitude, 170

Logistic function, 70

London ferris wheel, 244, 248

Long playing records, 15

Long-run behavior

power function, 423

Long-run behavior

polynomial function, 399

rational function, 411, 417

LORAN, 545, 551

Magnetic field

vector, 449

Magnitude of vector, 449

notation, 450

Major axis

ellipse, 530

Malthus, Thomas, 118, 373

Marginal cost, 512

Mars Pathfinder, 516

Mars, orbit, 537

Mass, 395

bone, 186

various animals, 183, 394

Mathematical model, 3

Maximum function value, 229

Meal plan, cost, 33

Melting time, 96

Metabolic rate, 179

Mexico, population, 23, 107, 111

Midline

cosine function, 269

sine function, 269

trigonometric function, 269, 272

definition, 247, 266

Milky Way, 175

Minimum function value, 229

Minor axis

ellipse, 530

Misconceptions, logarithmic functions, 156

Model

financial, 19

investment, 136

involving trigonometric functions, 327

linear growth, 18

mathematical, 3

stock value, 334

Monk, Timothy, 52

Multiple zero, 405

Multiplication

of complex numbers, 343

of fractions, 441

scalar, 453

properties, 454

vector dot product, 468

properties, 469

National Football League, 64

Natural base, 131

Natural logarithmic function, 154

definition, 155

graph, 169

properties, 155

NCAA basketball playoffs, 114

Negative stretch factor, 212

Negative-angle identities, 317

New England population, 461, 468

Newton's Law of

Gravitation, 464

Heating, 208

Nominal rate, 136

Noninvertible function, 365

Normal force, 484

Notation

function, 4, 62

inverse function, 80

sigma, 496

summation, 496

vector components, 461

vector magnitude, 450

Notes, frequency, 333

Number

e, 130, 131

i, 342

Oak tree, water consumption, 234

Obtuse angle, 312

Odd

function, 206

power function, 390

symmetry, 207

Orbit, 437, 537

elliptical, 538

hyperbolic, 538

Mars, 537

Pluto, 539

Order of magnitude, 170

Origin, symmetry about, 206

Orwoll, Dr. Eric, 186

Oscillation, 249

damped, 329

rising midline, 331

Osgood, Charles, 9

Output, 2, 4, 62

as dependent variable, 4

from graph, 65

from table, 64

Outside change

to a formula, 197

Outside function, 79

Oxygen consumption, 28, 31, 48

Parabola, 225

axis of symmetry, 226, 227

conic section, 526

directrix, 546, 547

focus, 546–548

formula, 227

function, 228

geometric definition, 546

reflective properties, 548

symmetry, 226

vertex, 225, 227

Parallel lines, slope, 39

Parameter, 516

exponential function, 123, 131

linear function, 20, 35

effect on graph, 36

power function

k, 423

p, 389

p vs. k, 423

special cases, 389

Parameters, 110

Parametric curve, 521

Parametric equation, 517

of a circle, 527

of a hyperbola, 534, 555

of an ellipse, 529

Partial sum, 493, 506
Pearl Harbor, film, 463
Percent growth rate
    constant, 106
    continuous, 132
Percent rate of change, 106
Perfect square, factoring, 101
Period, 246
    cosine function, 270
    sine function, 270
    tangent function, 280
    trigonometric function, 272
        definition, 247
Periodic function, 246, 247
Perpendicular lines, slope, 39, 40
Petroleum imports, US, 278
PH, 170, 174
Phase shift
    trigonometric function, 272, 275
Physics
    electrical circuit, 124
    normal force, 484
    planetary motion, 395
    projectile motion, 88, 229
    sliding force, 484
    work, 471
Piano note frequency, tuning, 333
Piecewise defined functions, 73
Plane
    Cartesian, 2
    complex, 344
Planetary motion, law of, 395
Plumb bob, 263
Pluto, orbit, 539
Point-slope form, 31
Polar coordinates, 336
    Archimedean spiral, 338
    cardioid, 341
    circle, 338
    complex number and, 344
    graphing equations, 338
Polar form of a complex number, 345
Poltrack, David, 52
Polynomial
    approximation, 401
    cubic, 398
    function
        coefficients, 398
        constant term, 398
        definition, 396
        degree, 398
        factored form, 403

formula from graph, 405
    general formula, 398
    graphs of, 398
    leading term, 398
    long-run behavior, 399
    multiple zero, 405
    short-run behavior, 402
    standard form, 398
    turns, 404
    zero, 399, 404
    quadratic, 398
    quartic, 398
    quintic, 398
Population
    Afghanistan, 25
    black bear, 122
    Botswana, 144
    deer, 48
    exponential growth, 107, 118
    foxes, 66
    foxes and rabbits, 5, 522
    Ireland, 96
    island rabbit, 73
    linear growth, 18
    Malthus, Thomas, 373
    Mexico, 23, 107, 111
    New England, 461, 468
    owl and hawk, 166
    rabbit, 274, 332
    Somerville, MA, 278
    Sri Lanka, 25
    turtle, 116
    United States, 217
    vector, 449
    Washington, 165
Position vector, 465
Power function, 388
    comparison of powers, 423
    even power, 390
    first quadrant behavior, 423
    fitting to data, 429
    formula from graph, 392
    fractional power, 391
    graphs, 389
    long-run behavior, 423
    negative power, 390
    odd power, 390
    parameter k, 423
    parameter p, 389
    parameter p vs. k, 423
    special cases, 389
    transformation, 418
    vs. exponential function, 424

vs. log function, 425
Power, complex, imaginary, 345
Present value, 507, 508
Price vector, 463
Principal, of bond, 510
Product of functions, 376
Production vector, 479
Profit, 34
Projectile motion, 88, 229
Propeller thrust, 395
Properties
    hyperbolic functions, 552
    inverse function, 368
    logarithm, 154
        justification, 156
    natural logarithm, 155
    scalar multiplication, 454
    vector addition, 454
Property
    associativity, 454
    commutative, 454
    distributive, 99, 454
Proportional to, 21
    a power, 388
    inversely, 388
Proportionality, definition
    inverse, 388
    power of a variable, 388
Prosperity, measure of, 373, 376
Proxima Centauri, 175
Pyramids, construction of, 178
Pythagorean identity, 314

Quadratic
    equation
        completing the square, 239
        factoring, 89
        quadratic formula, 240
    formula, 240
    function, 89, 227
        axis of symmetry, 227
        completing the square, 227, 239
        factored formula, 89
        max/min applications, 229
        standard form, 227
        vertex, 225
        vertex form, 227, 358
    polynomial, 398
Quartic polynomial, 398
Quintic polynomial, 398
Quotient of functions, 376, 377

Radian, 257

calculating arc length, 260

conversion to degrees, 259

Radio dial, analog, 432

Radioactive decay, 12, 16, 107, 111, 125, 159, 162, 166

Rainfall, Chicago O'Hare airport, 5, 69, 72

Range, 69

for real situation, 69

from formula, 71

from graph, 70

inverse cosine, 287

inverse function, 367

inverse sine, 289

inverse tangent, 289

logarithmic function, 167

Rate of change, 10

average, 11

function notation for, 13

concavity and, 84

constant, 21

constant percent, 106

linear function, 19

reflection and, 208

stretch of graph and, 214, 215

Ratio

golden, 438

method for exponential formula, 116

table of ratios, 115

Rational function, 410

asymptote, 413

horizontal, 413, 418

vertical, 417

formula from graph, 418

graph, 417

holes, 419

long-run behavior, 411, 417

short-run behavior, 415

transformation of power function, 418

zero, 415, 417

Real part, of complex number, 342

Reciprocal, trigonometric function, 282

Recognition memory, 184

Recurrence relation, 492

Reference angle, 290, 291

Reflection

across $y = x$, 367

horizontal, 202, 204

rate of change and, 208

vertical, 202, 204

Reflective properties

ellipse, 542

hyperbola, 545

parabola, 548

Regression

assumptions, 45

exponential, 126

fitting data, 44

least squares, 46

line, 44

correlation, 47

Relief package, motion of, 93

Repeating decimal, 510

Representations

emphases of, 3

of functions, 2

Resolving vectors, 457

Respiratory cycle, 401

Revenue vector, 463

Richter scale, 174, 187

Riemannian geometry, 537

Right triangle, 301

Riverfront park, area, 230

Robin, body mass, 183

Rodriguez, Alex, 507, 508

Roses, 339

Rule of seventy, 187

Saks Fifth Avenue, 187

Salary raises, 106

SAT, 7

Scalar, 449

multiplication, 453

properties, 454

rules of, 454

Scale

linear, 175

log-log, 179

logarithmic, 176, 180

models, 437

Richter, 187

Scanning law, 78

Scatter plot, 44

Seattle, tides, 201

Secant function, 282

Sequence, 488

n^{th} term, 489

alternating, 488

arithmetic, 489

Fibonacci, 68

geometric, 490

terms of, 488

Series, 493

arithmetic, 494

sum of, 494

geometric, 502

infinite, 506

sum of, 502

partial sum, 493

Shift

formulas for, 195

horizontal, 194, 196

trigonometric function, 271

vertical, 196

Short-run behavior

polynomial function, 402

rational functions, 415

Shrek, film, 463

Sigma notation, 496

Signature, 78

Simultaneous equations, 36, 56

Sine function

amplitude, 269, 272

definition, 251

graph, 264

horizontal shift, 272

hyperbolic, 552

inverse, 288, 289, 370

Law of Sines, 310

midline, 272

period, 270, 272

special angles, 252, 264, 301

triangle definition, 301

Sinh function, 552

identities, 554

properties, 552

Sinusoidal function, 269, 272

Sliding force, 484

Slope

as average rate of change, 13

horizontal line, 39

of a line, 20

parallel lines, 39

perpendicular lines, 39, 40

vertical line, 39

Slope-intercept form, 31

Snowy tree cricket, 2, 4

Sojourner, 516

Solid waste production, 43

Solow, Robert, 52

Solution, approx. vs. exact, 56

Somerville, MA, population, 278

Sound intensity, 171

Spanned by, arc length, 257

Special angles, 252, 264, 301

Spiral, Archimedean, 338, 521

Square

area, 25, 69
perimeter, 25
Sri Lanka, population, 25
Stall velocity, 395
Standard form
circle, 527
linear function, 31
quadratic function, 227
Stereo amplifier, 211
Stock value, model of, 334
Stone Age man, 166
Straight-line depreciation, 19
Stretch
horizontal, 221
rate of change and, 214, 215
vertical, 212
Substitution and simultaneous equations, 56
Subtraction
of complex numbers, 342
of vectors, 451
Sum
arithmetic series, 494
geometric series
infinite, 507
of functions, 374
partial, 506
Sum-of-angle formula, 320, 323, 346
Summation notation, 496
Sunspots, 16
Super Bowl XL, commercials, 394
Surface area
cube, 83
cylinder, 97
Surplus vector, 479
Surveying
transit, 305, 350
Swimming, world records, 49
Symmetry
y-axis, 205
about $y = x$, 211
axis of, 226
even, 205, 207
odd, 207
origin, 206
System of equations, 56

Table
exponential function, 115
finding input and output, 64
linear function, 21, 27, 115
of function values, 2
Tangent function, 279

graph, 279
inverse, 288, 289, 370
period, 280
triangle definition, 301
Tangent identity, 314
Tax, income, 68
Taxi fare, 77, 224
Telephone calling plans, comparison, 43
Temperature
Boston, 278
conversion, 26
Fairbanks, AL, 298
New York City, 8
Term
of polynomial, 398
of sequence, 488
Tesh, John, 174
Test
horizontal line, 365
vertical line, 6
Texas Rangers, 507
The Mummy Returns, film, 463
Theophylline concentration, 143
Thermometer cricket, 2, 4
Thermostat, 298
Thrust, propeller, 395
Torricelli's Law, 392
Trading
at discount, 510
at premium, 510
Transformation
combined, 198, 207, 215, 272
horizontal
compression, 221
reflection, 202, 204
shift, 194, 196
stretch, 221
power function, 418
reflection across $y = x$, 367
translation, 196
trigonometric functions, 272
vertical
compression, 212
reflection, 202, 204
shift, 196
stretch, 212
Transformed data, 181
Transistor, failure, 166
Transit, 305, 350
Translation, 196
Triangle
adjacent side, 301
opposite side, 301

right, 301
trigonometric definitions, 301
trigonometry
Law of Cosines, 308
Law of Sines, 310
Triathlon, Ironman, 75
Trigonometric
equation, 285
algebraic solution, 285
graphical solution, 285
reference angles and, 290
function
amplitude, 247, 265, 272
angular frequency, 272
cosecant, 282
cosine, 251
cotangent, 282
graph, 264
horizontal shift, 271, 272
inverse cosine, 287
Law of Cosines, 308
Law of Sines, 310
midline, 247, 266, 272
period, 247, 272
phase shift, 272, 275
reciprocal, 282
secant, 282
sine, 251
special angles, 252, 264, 301
tangent, 279
identities, 281, 313
difference of two cosines, 323
difference of two sines, 323
difference-of-angle, 323
double-angle, 315, 316
negative-angle, 317
Pythagorean, 314
sum of sine and cosine, 322
sum of two cosines, 323
sum of two sines, 323
sum-of-angle, 320, 323
tangent, 314
Trigonometry, 301
Trivial decomposition, 358
True-positive, 439
Tuition cost, 26

Unit circle, 250
Unit cost, 53
Unit vector, 456
United States, population, 217
US dollar, exchange rates, 361

Variable, 2

dependent, 4
independent, 4
Variable cost, 409
Vector
n-dimensional, 459
x-component, 457
y-component, 457
addition, 450
properties, 454
applications
computer graphics, 449, 465
consumption vector, 463
economics, 449, 485
force, 449
magnetic fields, 449
population, 449
price vector, 463
revenue vector, 463
velocity, 449
work, 471
component, 456, 457
notation, 461
definition, 448
direction, 449
displacement vector, 459
identities, 454
magnitude, 449

notation, 450
multiplication
dot product, 468
position vector, 465
scalar multiplication, 453
properties, 454
subtraction, 451
unit vector, 456
zero vector, 454
Velocity
stall, 395
vector, 449
Vertebrates, appearance of, 177
Vertex, 225, 227
form of quadratic function, 227
Vertical
asymptote, 169
logarithmic function, 167
rational function, 417
tangent function, 280
compression, 212
intercept, 20
line
slope, 39
test, 6
reflection, 202, 204
shift, 196
stretch, 212
Video games, sales, 335

Videodisc players, 92
Viscosity, 44
Volcano, sound of explosion, 395
Volume
cube, 83
cylinder, 97
Von Bertalanffy growth model, 373
Voyager, 450

Washington, population, 165
Water filtration, 113
Weight, 395
Weighted average, 414
Whispering gallery, 542
White rhinoceros, body mass, 394
Work, in physics, 471

Yam, temperature, 208, 213
Yonkers, NY, 111, 122, 125
Yugo, 22

Zero
multiple, 405
of a function, 89
polynomial function, 399
and factors, 404
number of, 404
rational function, 415, 417
vector, 454

Practice Questions
for the Final

Practice Questions to Review for the MA 153 Final

Bring the following items to the final:
- ✓ **your graphing calculator**
- ✓ **Number 2 pencils**
- ✓ **ID Number** (You can get this on OASIS after logging into **http://my.ipfw.edu**. You can also get it from your instructor.)

The final exam will evaluate how well you meet the course goals of MA 153:
- Highlight the link of mathematics to the real world.
- Develop a wide base of mathematical knowledge, including
  - o basic skills and concepts,
  - o a functional view of mathematics, including graphical, analytical, numerical, and contextual viewpoints (Note: using these four representations is the *Rule of Four*),
  - o properties and applications of some of the basic families of functions,
  - o geometric visualization,
  - o problem solving, predicting, critical thinking, and generalizing.
- Incorporate the use of general academic skills such as
  - o communicating mathematics concepts,
  - o understanding and using technology.

Just like the chapter exams throughout the semester, this exam tests your ability to interpret detailed, precisely worded directions. Be sure to read the directions carefully and do all that is asked.

Format of the exam: The actual final exam will consist of both multiple-choice questions and open ended (constructed response) questions. Include units in your answers whenever appropriate. You may certainly use your calculator (but not its manual). In fact, some questions will *require* a graphing calculator.

> ## NO formula sheets, notes, books, or other external sources may be used.

For the open ended questions, you will need to show all of your work. If you are basing your reasoning on a graph, then sketch a labeled graph, with numerical values on the axes. If you base your reasoning from a table, you must include the table, which consists of at least five sets of entries. If using an equation, write out the steps you used to solve the equation. Remember you the solution to the problem is not simply the *end result*, but showing the *process* that you used to justify your claim.

Be careful when explaining your reasoning. This is more than simply restating the question. For example:
Three long distance phone plans are represented by the graphs shown, where *x* gives the number of minutes used per month and Y_A, Y_B, and Y_C are the monthly charges, in dollars, using Company A, B, and C, respectively. Which plan is best? Explain your reasoning using the graph

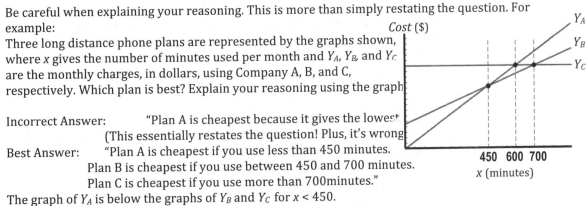

Incorrect Answer: "Plan A is cheapest because it gives the lowest (This essentially restates the question! Plus, it's wrong

Best Answer: "Plan A is cheapest if you use less than 450 minutes.
Plan B is cheapest if you use between 450 and 700 minutes.
Plan C is cheapest if you use more than 700minutes."
The graph of Y_A is below the graphs of Y_B and Y_C for $x < 450$.
The graph of Y_B is below the graphs of Y_A and Y_C for $450 < x < 700$.
The graph of Y_C is below the graphs of Y_A and Y_B for $x > 700$.

How to prepare for the exam: Some of the practice questions that follow are from previous final exams over this material. Note that the exam will NOT look exactly like these questions, so you should also review previous homework assignments, *eHW*, quizzes, and tests, as well as material worked on during class meetings. **Topics from the last chapter on *Polynomial and Rational Functions* will receive more of an emphasis than earlier chapters.** Keep the *Rule of Four* in mind when solving problems, just as you have done throughout the semester.

Sample Questions for the Final Exam

1. Suppose you and Charlie are working together in a group to determine the long run behavior of $f(x) = 60 - 8x + 15x^2 + 25x^3 - 4x^4 + 40x^5 + x^6$. Charlie uses his graphing calculator in the window $-10 \leq x \leq 10$ and $-10 \leq y \leq 100$ and sees the graph shown. Charlie concludes that the long run behavior is as follows:
As $x \to -\infty$, then $y \to -\infty$; as $x \to \infty$, then $y \to \infty$. . How should you respond?

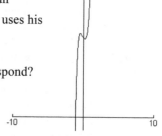

   A. "Good job, Charlie!"
   B. "Sorry, Charlie!
   As $x \to -\infty$, then $y \to \infty$; as $x \to \infty$, then $y \to \infty$."
   C. "Sorry, Charlie!
   As $x \to -\infty$, then $y \to -\infty$; as $x \to \infty$, then $y \to -\infty$."
   D. "Sorry, Charlie!
   As $x \to -\infty$, then $y \to \infty$; as $x \to \infty$, then $y \to -\infty$."
   E. "Sorry, Charlie!
   As $x \to 0^+$, then $y \to -\infty$; as $x \to 0^+$, then $y \to \infty$."

$-10 \leq x \leq 10 \quad -10 \leq y \leq 100$

For **Questions 2-3**, $P(t)$ is a polynomial of degree 3 whose graph is shown.

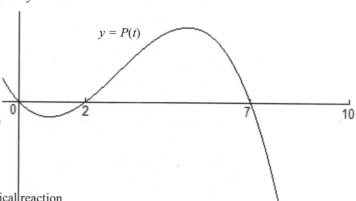

$y = P(t)$

2. For $0 \leq t \leq 10$, $P(t)$ describes the temperature of a certain chemical reaction in degrees Celcius, t seconds after the reaction began. Suppose the temperature reached -1 degree Celcius exactly 1 second after the reaction began.

   Determine the formula for $P(t)$.
   Then find the minimum temperature that the chemical reaction reaches in the first 10 seconds after it began.
   A. $-1\,°C$ B. $-10\,°C$ C. $-20\,°C$ D. $-40\,°C$ E. None of these

3. A certain power function $Q(t)$ has the same long run behavior as $P(t)$, so much that $Q(t)$ and $P(t)$ look nearly indistinguishable if you graph both of these functions with technology and zoom out for very large values of x. This tells us that it would not be sensible to use $P(t)$ to model the temperature of the reaction for *all* $t \geq 0$. What is the formula for $Q(t)$?
   A. $Q(t) = -t^3$ B. $Q(t) = t^3$ C. $Q(t) = -\frac{1}{6}t^3$ D. $Q(t) = \frac{1}{6}t^3$ E. None of these.

4. Graphs of $y = 100x^2$, $y = x^4$, and $y = 2^x$ are shown. Assume the viewing window shows their **long run behavior**.

   (a) Which function corresponds to which?
   A. $y_1 = 100x^2$ $y_2 = x^4$ $y_3 = 2^x$
   B. $y_1 = x^4$ $y_2 = 100x^2$ $y_3 = 2^x$
   C. $y_1 = 2^x$ $y_2 = 100x^2$ $y_3 = x^4$
   D. $y_1 = 2^x$ $y_2 = x^4$ $y_3 = 100x^2$
   E. None of these

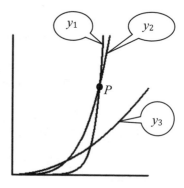

   (b) Give the coordinates of P, where the graphs of y_1 and y_2 intersect.
   Hint: A table feature on a graphing calculator may be helpful.

Questions 5-7

The EDI pharmaceutical company has recently acquired the abandoned but historic Rotting Hill building and has decided to move its employees into this renovated building one month at a time. The table gives the number, $E(t)$, of EDI employees who have moved to the Rotting Hill building t months after the building was acquired.

t	$E(t)$
0	0
1	30
2.02	48
2.83	60

5. The data for $E(t)$ is modeled by a power function.
   Find the formula for $E(t)$. Which of the following would be closest to the value of $E(7)$?
   A. 100   B. 110   C. 120   D. 130   E. 210

6. Unfortunately, many of the employees of EDI who have their offices located in the Rotting Hill building have contracted a mysterious disease which incapacitates them for weeks at a time. The table gives the number, $S(t)$, of EDI employees who have their offices located in the Rotting Hill building *and* are sick t months after the initial acquisition of the building.

t	$S(t)$
0	0
1.05	6
2.05	15
2.98	25

   The data for $S(t)$ is modeled by a power function. Find the formula for $S(t)$. Which of the following would be closest to the value of $S(11)$?
   A. 30   B. 70   C. 110   D. 120   E. 150

7. When the ratio of number of sick employees in a building to total number of employees in a building is greater than 0.75 the building is declared to have sick building syndrome and is closed down for health inspection. How many months after the Rotting Hill building is first acquired by EDI will it be closed for health inspection? Select the one closest to your answer.
   A. 10 days   B. 2 months   C. 5 months   D. 7 months   E. 16 months

8. The population (in hundreds) of the town *Polynomia* grows according to $P(t) = t^3 - 6t^2 + 8t + 4$, where $t = 0$ corresponds to January 1, 1970.

The population (in hundreds) of the town *Exponentia* is given by $E(t)$, where again $t = 0$ corresponds to January 1, 1970. The town initially has 4 hundred people when $t = 0$ and it increases by 20% each year.

The graph shows the populations over the first five years. If the population follows these mathematical models, which of the following must be true? Select the best response.

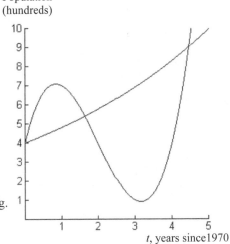

Population (hundreds)

A. The population of *Polynomia* is always more than 90 people.

B. After 1974 the populations of both towns are always increasing.

C. The population graphs will intersect a total of four times. The population of *Exponentia* will overtake and exceed the population of *Polynomia* sometime after the year 2028.

D. Both A and B are true.

E. All of the above are true.

519

Questions 9-10

The volume of pollutants (in millions of cubic feet) in Smirch Reservoir is given by

$$P(t) = 360 + 9t$$

where t is in years. The total volume of Smirch Reservoir (which includes both pollutants and water and also in millions of cubic feet) is gradually increasing and is given by

$$R(t) = 12,000 + 12t$$

Let $C(t)$ be the fraction of the reservoir's total volume that consists of pollutants.

Write an expression for $C(t) = \dfrac{P(t)}{R(t)}$ in terms of t and use your expression to answer the questions below.

9. In year $t = 0$, what percent of the reservoir's total volume consists of pollutants?
   A. 0.3%   B. 3%   C. $33\frac{1}{3}$ %   D. $66\frac{2}{3}$ %   E. None of these

10. According to the mathematical model, if these trends were to continue for many, many years, about what percentage of Smirch Reservoir's total volume would eventually consist of pollutants?
    A. 0.3%   B. 3%   C. $33\frac{1}{3}$ %   D. $66\frac{2}{3}$ %   E. None of these

Questions 11-13

The formula $E = 7.4Lh^2$ is used by marine geologists to find the energy, E (in foot-pounds) delivered by an ocean wave with length L (feet) and height h (feet).

11. Write a function which describes the relationship between E and L for a 10-foot high wave. Sketch a graph of the function $E(L)$.

A.   B.   C.   D.   E.
    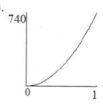   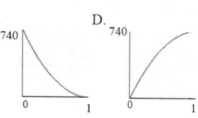   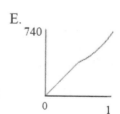

12. Write a function which describes the relationship between E and h for a 100-foot long wave. Sketch a graph of the function $E(h)$.

A.   B.   C.   D.   E.

13. Approximate the height of a 100-foot long wave if it delivers 60,000 foot-pounds of energy.
    A. 0.81 feet   B. 9 feet   C. 81 feet   D. 86 feet   E. None of these.

Questions 14-19

Peter grows peppers. The yield, P, of peppers (in pecks) he picks is a function of the amount, m, of fertilizer (in pounds) used, so we have $P = f(m)$. See the graph below.

14. The statement $f(30) = 450$ means
    A. The yield ranges from 30 to 450 pecks of peppers.
    B. When 30 lb of fertilizer is applied, the yield is 450 pecks of peppers.
    C. For every 30 lb of fertilizer added to the orchard, you increase the yield by 450 pecks.
    D. When 450 lb of fertilizer is applied, the yield is 30 pecks of peppers.
    E. You apply 30 to 450 pounds of fertilizer to the orchard.

15. The vertical intercept for the graph represents:
    A. The maximum yield of the orchard.
    B. The amount of fertilizer that must be applied to produce a maximum yield.
    C. The yield without applying any fertilizer at all.
    D. The initial amount of fertilizer applied to the orchard.
    E. The amount of fertilizer that will kill all the trees and produce no yield at all.

16. Use the graph of the function to estimate the range.
    A. $0 \le f(m) \le 70$
    B. $200 \le f(m) \le 450$
    C. $70 \le f(m) \le 200$
    D. $70 \le f(m) \le 450$
    E. $0 \le f(m) \le 450$

17. For what values of m is the function increasing?
    A. $200 < m < 450$
    B. $0 < m < 450$
    C. $0 < m < 30$
    D. $30 < m < 70$
    E. None of these

18. For what values of m is the function concave up?
    A. $200 < m < 450$
    B. $0 < m < 450$
    C. $0 < m < 30$
    D. $0 < m < 70$
    E. None of these

19. For what values of m is $Y > 200$?
    A. $200 < m < 450$
    B. $60 < m < 450$
    C. $60 < m < 70$
    D. $0 < m < 60$
    E. None of these

20. In year $t = 0$, the balance of an account is \$2200. The account earns 3.82% annual interest, compounded quarterly. Find the amount in year t.
    A. $2200(1.382)^{4t}$ B. $2200(1+\frac{3.82}{4})^{4t}$ C. $2200(1+\frac{0.0382}{4})^{4t}$ D. $2200(1+\frac{3.82}{4})^{t}$ E. $2200(1+\frac{0.382}{4})^{4t}$

21. In year $t = 0$, the balance of an account is \$2200. The account earns 3.82% annual interest, compounded continuously. Find the amount in year t.
    A. $2200e^{1.382t}$ B. $2200e^{1.0382t}$ C. $2200(e \cdot 1.382)^{t}$ D. $2200e^{0.382t}$ E. None of these

22. In the year 2000 the population P of a town was 11,500. It grew by 275 people every year.
In the year 2000 the population Q of a town was 2,000. The town grew by 20% every 5 years.
Find when the population of Q overtakes the population of P.
Select the response which is closest to the answer.
   A. 1.97 years   B. 10.33 years   C. 76.5 years   D. 314.6 years   E. Q will never overtake P.

Questions 23-24

The amount Q of drug present in a person's body is $Q = 20(0.4)^t$,
where Q is in milligrams at time t, and t is in hours.

23. What percent of the drug is lost per hour?
   A. 4%   B 20%   C. 40%   D. 6%   E. 60%   F. 80%

24. What is the growth factor?
   A. 0.4   B. 4.0   C. 6.0   D. 20   E. 60   F. 80

Questions 25-26

The graph gives the balance, P,
of an investment in year t.
Find a possible formula
for $P = f(t)$ assuming the
balance grows exponentially.

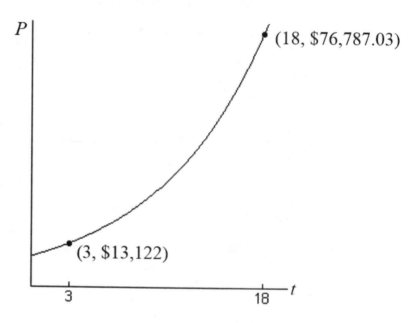

25.   Which amount is closest to
   the initial balance?
   A. $5,424
   B. $5,454
   C. $9,216
   D. $10,122
   E. $11,664
   F. $41,812

26.   What annual interest rate
   does the account pay?
   A. 1.125%
   B. 11.25%
   C. 12.5%
   D. 34%
   E. 112.5%
   F. 125%

27. <u>Good news!</u> ☺: You win a contest to have dinner at the home of NCIS* director Mark D. Clookie!
<u>Bad news!</u> ☹:   When given a tour of the premises, his butler is discovered in the wine cellar,
sprawled dead on the floor.
Special Agent Clookie has with him a temperature probe, which he uses to find the body temperature of the
butler. At 6:00 pm, he determines that the body temperature is 85°F.
Two hours later, after dinner, he takes another temperature reading to find the body has cooled to 79.36°F.

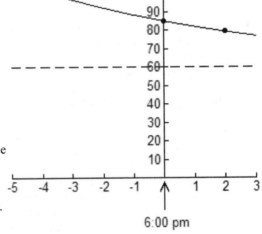

(a) Clookie shares that he keeps his wine cellar at a
constant temperature of 60°F.
Because of this, butler's body temperature will decay
exponentially**.
He sketches the graph shown on a paper napkin.
The graph has the model $y = ab^t + 60$.
Give the constants a and b.
Which is true? Select one:

A. $a = 25$ G. A and D   M. C and D
B. $a = 60$ H. A and E   N. C and E
C. $a = 85$ I. A and F   O. C and F
D. $b \approx -2.82$ J. B and D   P. None of these
E. $b \approx 0.478$ K. B and E
F. $b \approx 0.88$ L   B and F

6:00 pm

(b) Another possibility is to use the equation $y = He^{kt} + 60$.
Give the constants H and k.
Which is true? Select one:

A. $H = 25$ G. A and D   M. C and D
B. $H = 60$ H. A and E   N. C and E
C. $H = 85$ I. A and F   O. C and F
D. $k \approx -1.04$ J. B and D   P. None of these
E. $k \approx -0.74$ K. B and E
F. $k \approx -0.128$ L   B and F

(c) Clookie recalls that his niece restocked his wine cellar earlier that day. House records show that
she arrived at 2:45 p.m. It is also known that his butler had a reputation of good health - his body
temperature was 98.6°F. Was the butler already dead when his niece delivered the wine?
When was the time of death? Explain your reasoning.

* NCIS is the Naval Criminal Investigative Service
**The effect to which Clookie refers is known as *Newton's Law of Cooling*.

28. The monthly charge for a waste collection service is $32 for 100 kilograms of waste and is $48 for
180 kilograms of waste.
(a) Find a linear formula for the cost, C, of waste collection as a function of
the number of kilograms of waste, w.
(b) What is the slope of the line found in part **(a)**?
Give units and interpret your answer in terms of the cost of waste collection.
(c) What is the vertical intercept of the line found in part **(a)**?
Give units and interpret your answer in terms of the cost of waste collection.

29. A research facility on an island off of Costa Rica has 900 gallons of fresh water for a two-month period.

   (a) There are 4 members of the research team and each is allotted 3 gallons of water per day for cooking and drinking. Find a formula for $f(t)$, the amount of fresh water left on the island after t days has elapsed, assuming that each member of the team uses their total allotment of water each day.

   (b) Evaluate and interpret the following expressions

      (i) $f(0)$

      (ii) $f^{-1}(0)$

30. In a second hand clothing store in Kampala, Uganda, the table* shown is used to exchange U.S. dollars for shillings. The function is linear.

U.S. dollars	Shillings
$1.00	2200
$2.50	5500
$3.00	6600

   (a) What is the y-intercept of the graph of this function?

   (b) A pair of trousers cost 4000 shillings. How much is this in U.S. dollars?

   (c) If you have $4.00 U.S, can you afford a coat which sells for 8500 shillings?

*Based on a December 2005 Associated Press report.

31. A summer amusement park, charges $10.00 for admission. An average of 10,000 people visit the park each day it is open. Consultants predict that for each $1.00 increase in the entrance price, the park would lose an average of 500 daily customers.

   (a) Construct a table of values which shows the entrance price, p, and number of tickets sold, N. Your table should have at least five entries.

   (b) Let $N = f(p)$. Find a formula for this function.

   (c) Add a third column to your table in part **(a)** which gives the daily revenue, R, for each entrance price p. (The *revenue* is the total amount received by the park before any costs are deducted.)

   (d) Let $R = g(p)$. Find a formula for this function.

   (e) Find the axis intercepts of $N = f(p)$. Interpret what each means to the staff at the amusement park.

   (f) Find and interpret the axis intercepts of the revenue function $R = g(p)$.

   (g) What ticket price maximizes the revenue?

   (h) Sketch graphs of $N = f(p)$ and $R = g(p)$ on the same set of axes. Be sure your sketch is properly labeled with the values found in parts **(e)**, **(f)**, and **(g)**.

32. A power function passes through $(-5, -40)$ and $(10, 5)$.

   Find a possible formula. Show work to receive any credit

33. For each of the scenarios below, decide which graph (or graphs) are most appropriate.

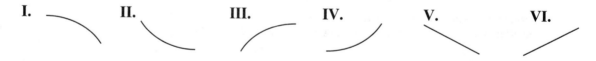

   (a) "Even though the child's temperature is still rising, the penicillin seems to be taking effect."

   (b) "Your distance from the Atlantic Ocean, in kilometers per minute, increases at a constant rate."

   (c) "The interest on your savings plan is compounded annually.

   (d) "At first your balance grows slowly, but its rate of growth continues to increase."

   (e) "The annual profit is decreasing at a higher rate each year."

   (f) The function has a positive rate of change and the rate of change is decreasing.

   (g) "The price of memory chips isn't decreasing as quickly it used to be."

   (h) The function is concave down.

   (i) The function is decreasing.

34. Indicate which graph matches the statements. Note the choice of axes.

a. A train pulls into a station and lets off passengers.

I.

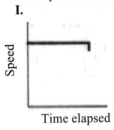

II.

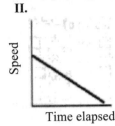

III.

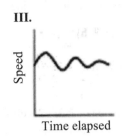

IV.

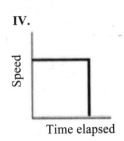

b. I start to walk to class at a slow steady rate. I hear the clock chimes and walk faster and faster.

I.

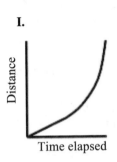

II.

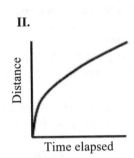

III.

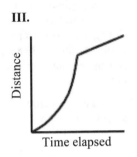

IV.

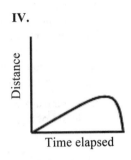

c. I climb a hill at a steady pace and then start to run down one side.

I.

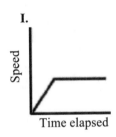

II.

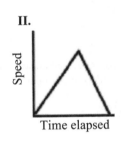

III.

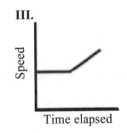

IV.

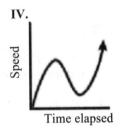

d. I ride on a ferris wheel.

I.

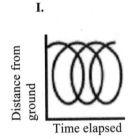

II.

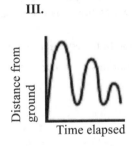

III.

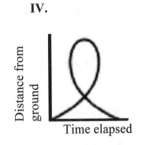

IV.

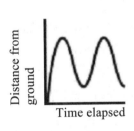

e. A child climbs up a slide and then slides down.

I.

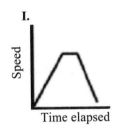

II.

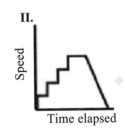

III.

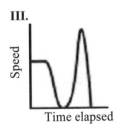

IV.

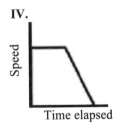

35. One description best fits each function. Decide which one, and write its letter in the corresponding blank.

    i. _____ $P(t) = 300 - 2t$ ii. _____ $Q(t) = 300e^{0.02t}$

    iii. _____ $R(t) = 300(0.98)^t$ iv. _____ $S(t) = -\tfrac{4}{3}t^2 + 300$

A. The population, which began at 300, declines at a constant rate, becoming extinct in 15 years.
B. The population increases exponentially at first and then levels off.
C. The population, which began at 300, is growing at the continuous rate of 2 percent each year.
D. In one year, 98 percent of the population is lost.
E. The population, which was originally at 300, has been increasing at a rate of 98 percent.
F. The population starts at 300 and has dropped to 250 after 25 years.
G. The population, which began at 300, decreases faster and faster.
H. The population, originally at 300, has been decreasing at the annual rate of 2 percent.
I. The population, which was originally at 300, undergoes explosive logarithmic growth, increasing at the annual rate of 2 percent.

36. Determine any x- and y-intercepts and vertical and horizontal asymptotes of each. If none, state so. (Sole use of a graphing calculator may not be the most practical approach for this problem.)

    (i) $f(x) = \dfrac{5x^2 - 5}{8000x - 80}$ (ii) $f(x) = \dfrac{5x^2 + 5}{8000x^2 - 80}$ (ii) $f(x) = \dfrac{5x - 5}{8000x^2 + 80}$

37. Short Questions:

  (a) Suppose you put \$1000 in a bank account at 5% interest compounded continuously. Compute the amount you have at the end of one year, rounded to the nearest cent.

  (b) Find log 10. Does log 20 = log 10 + log 10?

  (c) Simplify as much as possible: $e^{\ln x^2 + \ln 5}$

  (d) If f is a function, describe how the graph of $2f(x + 4) + 3$ is related to that of $f(x)$. Be sure that the order in which the transformations are applied is clear.

  (e) Show that $x = 2$ is a solution to the equation $4x + 8 = 4^x$. Then find all values of x which solve $4x + 8 > 4^x$. (Report your answer accurate to 3 decimal places.)

38. Which of the following functions has its domain identical with its range?

  A. $f(x) = x^2$ B. $g(x) = \log x$ C. $h(x) = x^3$ D. $i(x) = |x|$ E. None of these.

39. For the graphs in this problem assume all global behavior is shown.

a. Find a possible formula of least possible degree for the function $y = f(x)$. Then use your formula to find $f(3)$.

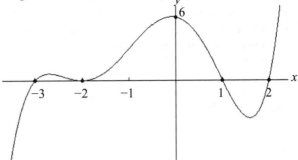

    A. 30
    B. 75
    C. 306
    D. 501
    E. None of these

b. Find the formula for $f(x)$. Using your formula, determine which of the following must be true.

    A. $f(-1) = f(0)$
    B. $f(-7) = f(6)$
    C. $f(-3) = f(2)$
    D. Choices A, B and C are true.
    E. None of these is true

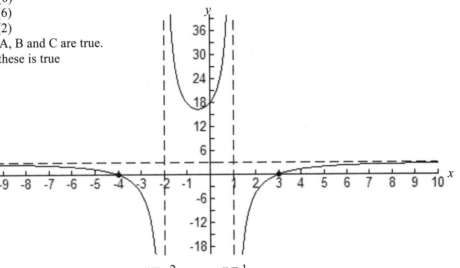

c. Find the formula for $f(x)$. Using your formula, determine which of the following must be true.
    A. $f(-1) = -4$
    B. $f(1) = 1$
    C. $f(-6) = 2.25$
    D. Choices A and C are true.
    E. None of these is true

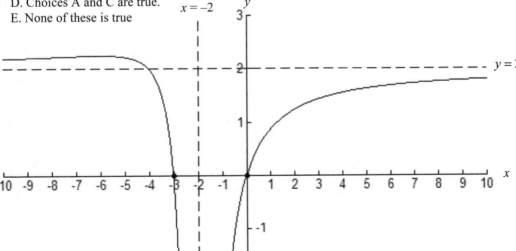

40. A rational function $y = f(x)$ has the following properties:
- there is only one zero at 4,
- the short run behavior near that zero looks like ⟋ or ⟍ (as opposed to ⌣ or ⌢)
- there is one vertical asymptote at $x = 2$,
- the short run behavior near the vertical asymptote looks like ⊣⌄ or ⌃
- the degree of the denominator is the lowest degree possible,
- there is a horizontal asymptote of $y = 0$, and
- $f(0) = -8$

Find the formula for $f(x)$. Then use your formula to find $f(3)$.

    A. −16
    B. −8
    C. −4
    D. 8
    E. 16

41. Assume a, b, c, and d are positive real numbers.
The rational function $f(x)$ graphed below has the following properties:

- <u>short run behavior</u>:
  - zeros are at a, c
  - vertical asymptotes are at $x = b$ and $x = d$

- <u>long run behavior</u>:
  as $x \to -\infty$, $y \to -\infty$
  as $x \to \infty$, $y \to \infty$

  Consequently, there is no horizontal asymptote.

Assume k is some positive real number. Which could be its equation?

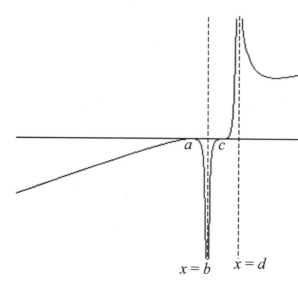

A. $f(x) = \dfrac{k(x-a)^2(x-c)^3}{(x-b)^2(x-d)^4}$

B. $f(x) = \dfrac{k(x-a)^2(x-c)^3}{(x-b)^2(x-d)^2}$

C. $f(x) = \dfrac{k(x-a)^2(x-c)^3}{(x-b)^2(x-d)}$

D. $f(x) = \dfrac{k(x-a)^4(x-c)^3}{(x-b)^3(x-d)^4}$

E. $f(x) = \dfrac{k(x-a)^2(x-c)^3}{(x-b)(x-d)^3}$

42. For each of the graphs below, select the formula beneath the graph which best fits the behavior of the graph. In each case, assume that A, B, and C are positive real numbers. (Circle your choice.)
Scales are not shown on the axes, so the graphs may not have a true geometric perspective.

(I)

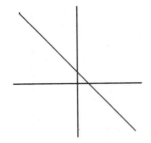

(a) $y = Ax + B$

(b) $y = -Ax - B$

(c) $y = B - Ax$

(d) $y = \dfrac{x + A}{x + A}$

(II)

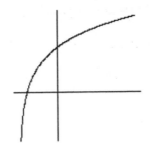

(a) $y = e^{-Ax}$

(b) $y = \log(x - A)$

(c) $y = \log(x + A)$

(d) $y = A^{(x+B)}$

(III)

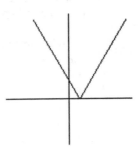

(a) $y = |x - A|$

(b) $y = |x + A|$

(c) $y = |x| - A$

(d) $y = |x| + A$

(IV)

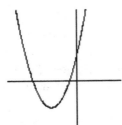

(a) $y = Ax^2 - B$

(b) $y = C - A(x + B)^2$

(c) $y = A(x + B)^2 - C$

(d) $y = A(x - B)^2 - C$

(V)

(a) $y = -Ax^5 + B$

(b) $y = Ax^3 + B$

(c) $y = -A(x + B)^5 + C$

(d) $y = A(x + B)^5 + C$

(VI)

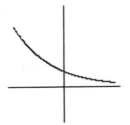

(a) $y = -\ln(x + A)$

(b) $y = -(1/A)^x$

(c) $y = -A^x$

(d) $y = (1/A)^x$

(VII)

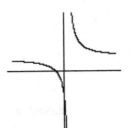

(a) $y = \dfrac{A(x - B)}{x + C}$

(b) $y = -\dfrac{A(x - B)}{x + C}$

(c) $y = \dfrac{A(x + B)}{x - C}$

(d) $y = \dfrac{-A(x + B)}{x - C}$

(VIII)

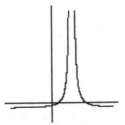

(a) $y = \dfrac{A}{(x - B)^2} - C$

(b) $y = \dfrac{A}{(x + B^2)} - C$

(c) $y = \dfrac{A}{(x - B)} - C$

(d) $y = \dfrac{-A}{(x - B)} - C$

43. A line with slope $-\frac{2}{3}$ passes through the point (60, 30). Find the <u>x-intercept</u> of the line.

   A. 105   B. 70   C. 60   D. 30   E. None of these

44. The graph of the function is a translation of $y = 5x^2$, shifted left 3 and up 1. What is the **range** of the graph?

   A. all real numbers
   B. $y \geq 1$
   C. $y \geq -3$
   D. $y \geq -1$
   E. $y \leq 1$

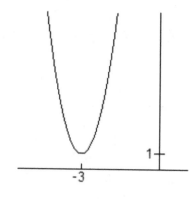

45. Assuming x, y, and w are positive real numbers, which of the following is $\log \dfrac{x^3 y^2}{\sqrt{w}}$?

   A. $x^3 + y^2 - \sqrt{w}$ B. $\frac{1}{3}\log x + \frac{1}{2}\log y - 2\log w$ C. $3\log x + 2\log y - \frac{1}{2}\log w$

   D. $\dfrac{3\log x + 2\log y}{\frac{1}{2}\log w}$ E. None of these

46. Solve for x to the nearest hundredth: $25^x = 3^{600}$
   (Most calculators are unable to solve this numerically or graphically due to overflow problems.)
   A. 409.56   B. 530.44   C. 204.78   D. No solution   E. None of these

47. Find the vertex of the parabola: $y = 4x^2 + 8x + 100$.
   A. $(-2, 100)$ B. $(1, 130)$ C. $(0, 100)$ D. $(-1, 96)$ E. None of these

48. Find all the zeros of the polynomial function: $f(x) = 7(x^3 - 3x^2 - 4x)$.
   A. $-1, 4$ B. $-4, 1$ C. $-1, 0, 4$ D. $-1, 0, 4, 7$ E. None of these

49. Find all possible values of x for which $9x^2(x+6)(x-6)^2 \geq 0$.
   Support your reason graphically.
   A. $-6 \leq x \leq 6$ B. $-6 \leq x \leq 0$ or $x \geq 6$ C. $x \geq -6$ D. $x \leq 6$ E. None of these

50. An initial deposit of \$4000 is made in a savings account for which the interest is compounded continuously. If the interest rate is 7.3%, how long will it take, to the nearest 0.01 year, for the investment to triple? Use $A = Pe^{rt}$.
   A. 0.15 years   B. 2.79 years   C. 6.54 years   D. 15.05 years   E. None of these

51. Given $f(x) = \dfrac{1}{x^2}$ and $g(x) = \sqrt{x^2 + 4}$, find $f(g(x))$.

   A. $f(g(x)) = \dfrac{1}{x^2 + 4}$ B. $f(g(x)) = \dfrac{1}{\sqrt{x^2 + 4}}$ C. $f(g(x)) = x^2 + 4$ D. $f(g(x)) = \dfrac{1}{x^2\sqrt{x^2 + 4}}$

52. Which of the following is true about the graph of $y = f(x) = b^x$? List **all** correct answers.

    I.   It increases if $b > 1$
    II. It decreases if $b < 0$
    III. It has y-intercept $(0, 1)$ if $b > 0$.

    A. I, II and III   B. I and II   C. II and III   D. I and III   E. III only.

53. Use what you know about transformations and the graph of $y = \log x$ to answer the following about the graph of $f(x) = 2 + \log (x - 1)$. Which are true? List **all** correct answers.
The graph of $f(x) = 2 + \log (x - 1)$

    I. increases for all values of x in its domain.
    II. crosses the x-axis at 1
    III. never touches the y-axis
    IV. passes through the point $(2, 2)$.

    Note: Don't be misled by technology when answering this question.
    A. I, II and III   B. I and II   C. II and IV   D. I and IV   E. I, III and IV only.

54. A function passes through the origin and has a vertical asymptote at $x = a$, where $a > 0$. It has the graph shown. Which could be its equation?

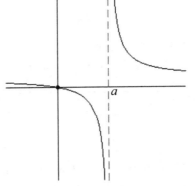

    A. $f(x) = \dfrac{1}{x - a}$ B. $f(x) = \dfrac{1}{x + a}$ C. $f(x) = \dfrac{x}{x - a}$

    D. $f(x) = \dfrac{x}{x + a}$ E. $f(x) = \dfrac{x}{(x - a)^2}$

55. Let a be some constant.

    Which is true about $f(x) = \dfrac{2ax}{(x - a)^2}$?

    A. Its horizontal asymptote is $y = 2a$.   D. Its horizontal asymptote is $y = 0$.
    B. Its horizontal asymptote is $y = 2$.   E. It has no horizontal asymptote.

    C. Its horizontal asymptote is $y = \dfrac{2a}{x}$.

56. The relationship of pH to the hydrogen ion concentration, C is pH $= -\log C$.
If the pH is 2.1, what is the hydrogen ion concentration?
    A. 0.74   B. 0.008   C. 125.89   D. −0.322   E. −125.89

Questions 57-58:

57. Which of the following is an acceptable first step to solve the equation $\ln 2x^3 = 5$?
    A. $3\ln 2x = 5$ B. $2x^3 = e \cdot 5$ C. $2x^3 = \dfrac{5}{\ln}$ D. $2x^3 = e^5$ E. $\ln 2x^3 = \ln 5$

58. What is the correct **exact** solution to the equation $\ln 2x^3 = 5$?
    A. $\sqrt[3]{\dfrac{5}{2\ln}}$ B. $\sqrt[3]{\dfrac{5e}{2}}$ C. $\sqrt[3]{\dfrac{e^5}{2}}$ D. $\sqrt[3]{\dfrac{5}{2}}$ E. $\frac{1}{2}e^{5/3}$

Questions 59-60:

The graph of $y = f(x)$ is shown.

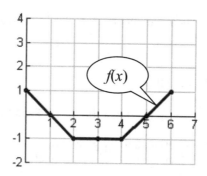

59. The function $y = g(x)$ shown below is a transformation of $f(x)$.
Write a rule for $g(x)$ in terms of $f(x)$.

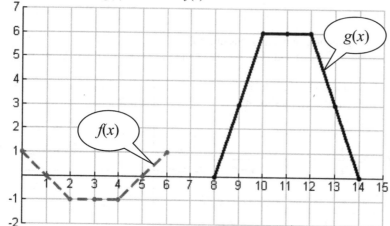

A. $g(x) = -3f(x-8)$

B. $g(x) = -3f(x+8)$

C. $g(x) = -6f(x-8)$

D. $g(x) = -6f(x+8)$

E. $g(x) = -3f(x-8)+3$

60. The function $y = h(x)$ shown below is a transformation of $f(x)$.
Write a rule for $h(x)$ in terms of $f(x)$.

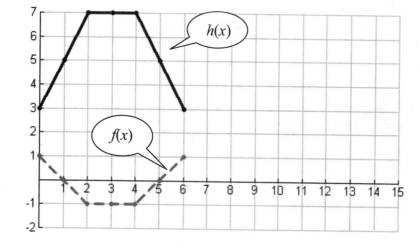

A. $h(x) = -2f(x)+6$

B. $h(x) = -4f(x)+4$

C. $h(x) = -2f(x)+5$

D. $h(x) = -4f(x)+3$

E. $h(x) = -2f(x)+4$

1. For positive or negative large values of x, $f(x) = 60 - 8x + 15x^2 + 25x^3 - 4x^4 + 40x^5 + x^6$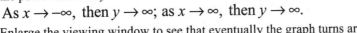

   look like
   the power function $y = x^6$. We can describe its long run behavior as follows:
   As $x \to -\infty$, then $y \to \infty$; as $x \to \infty$, then $y \to \infty$.
   Enlarge the viewing window to see that eventually the graph turns around.
   Choice **B**.

   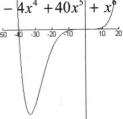

   $-50 \le x \le 20$
   $-300{,}000{,}000 \le y \le 100{,}000{,}000$

2. There are zeros at 0, 2, and 7. Therefore:

   $y = kt(t-2)(t-7)$ passes through $(1,-1)$:

   $-1 = k(1)(1-2)(1-7)$

   $-1 = k(-1)(-6)$

   $k = -\dfrac{1}{6}$

   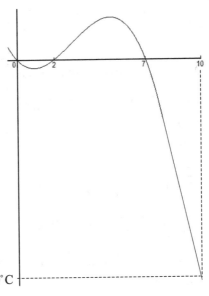

   The minimum value of $P(t)$ in the first ten seconds must
   be $P(10) = -40°\,C$.
   This can be found using a graph or table or by
   evaluating $P(t) = -\frac{1}{6}t(t-2)(t-7)$ for $t = 10$.

   $P(10) = -\frac{1}{6}(10)(10-2)(10-7) = -\frac{1}{6}(10)(8)(3) = -40$

   Choice **D**.

3. $Q(t) = -\frac{1}{6}t^3$ since

   $P(t) = -\frac{1}{6}t(t-2)(t-7) = -\frac{1}{6}t^3 + \text{remaining terms of lower degree}$

   Therefore, $P(t)$ and $Q(t)$ look very much alike for large values of t. (Note that the $-\frac{1}{6}$ is not optional.)

4. **(a)** Since all global behavior is shown, notice in the long run that
   graph y_1 is above graph y_2 which is above graph y_3.

   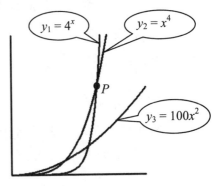

   Exponential functions eventually outpace power functions, so
   the graph of $y = 2^x$ will be above graphs of $y = 100x^2$ and $y = x^4$.
   This means that y_1 must be the graph of $y = 2^x$.

   Power functions with greater degree will outpace
   those of lower degree, so the graph of $y = x^4$ must be above
   the graph of $y = 100x^2$ after some point.
   Therefore y_2 must be the graph of $y = x^4$ and
   y_3 must be the graph of $y = 100x^2$.
   Choice **D**.

   (b) The point P is where the graphs of $y_1 = 4^x$ and $y_2 = x^4$ intersect. We must solve the equation $4^x = x^4$.
   This equation cannot be solved using logarithms. However, if you enter both equations into a graphing
   calculator and use a table feature, you can find they intersect at the point $(16, 65536)$.
   This also can help you find a suitable viewing window, such as $0 \le x \le 20$ and $0 \le y \le 100{,}000$

5. $E(t) = 30t^{0.668}$.　　　To find $y = kt^p$, notice $E(1) = 30$ so if $t = 1$, then $y = 30$.

Therefore we have $k = 30$, since $30 = k(1)^p = k(1) = k$.

Now use another point to find p for $y = 30t^p$. We used (2.02, 48).

$$48 = 30(2.02)^p$$

$$\frac{48}{30} = (2.02)^p$$

$$1.6 = (2.02)^p \quad \text{So } p = \frac{\ln 1.6}{\ln 2.02} \approx 0.668.$$

This means $E(t) = 30x^{0.67}$ and $E(7) = 30(7)^{0.67} \approx 110$.　Choice **B**.

6. $S(t) = 5.61x^{1.37}$.　　To find $y = kt^p$, use two points. We used (2.05, 15) and (2.98, 25).

$$\frac{25}{15} = \frac{k(2.98)^p}{k(2.05)^p}$$

$$\frac{5}{3} = (\tfrac{2.98}{2.05})^p$$

$$p = \frac{\ln(5/3)}{\ln(2.98/2.05)} \approx 1.3655$$

$y = kt^{1.366}$　　Now use any other point to find k. We used (1.05, 6)

$6 = k(1.05)^{1.366}$

$k \approx 5.61$

$S(t) = 5.61x^{1.37}$　　　Choice **E**.

7. $E(t) = 30x^{0.67}$

$S(t) = 5.61x^{1.37}$

$$\frac{S}{E} = \frac{5.61x^{1.37}}{30x^{0.67}} = 0.187x^{0.7}$$

Solve $0.187x^{0.7} > 0.75$ by graphing $y = 0.187x^{0.7}$ and the target line $y = 0.75$

Perform an INTERSECTION routine or solve $0.187x^{0.7} = 0.75$ to find the first time after which

the ratio $\dfrac{S}{E}$ is above 0.75. This is about 7.3 months.　　Choice **D**.

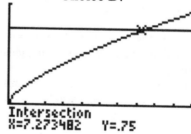

Window: $0 \leq x \leq 10$, $-0.25 \leq y \leq 1$

Note: You could also just enter

```
Y₁≣5.61X^1.37/(30X^.67)
Y₂≣.75
```

in a grapher, but the parentheses are crucial on a TI-83 or TI-83 Plus.

For example, you would NOT get the same function if you just typed

```
Y₁≣5.61X^1.37/ 30X^.67
Y₂≣.75
```

That would give you $y = \dfrac{5.61x^{1.37}}{30} \cdot x^{0.67}$

which is not what you want at all.

8. The town of *Polynomia* always exceeds 90 people.
A population of 90 people = 0.9 hundred.
Use a graphing calculator to sketch
$y = x^3 - 6x^2 + 8x + 4$ and the line $y = 0.9$
in a viewing window such as
$0 \le x \le 5$ and $0 \le y \le 2$
The polynomial never falls below the line.
You could also use a calculator routine to determine
the minimum value of the polynomial in this window,
which is (3.1547, 0.920799).
For $t > 0$ the lowest value of this town's population is
a mere 92 people!

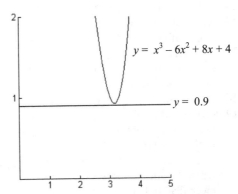

$P(t) = t^3 - 6t^2 + 8t + 4$ has the same long run behavior as $y = x^3$, so it will continually increase after $t = 4$ or after 1974. Since the town of *Exponentia* begins initially with 400 people and grows by 20% each year, the formula for $E(t) = 4(1.2)^t$. The graph of this function increases for all t. Exponential functions will eventually outpace polynomial functions, so the graphs must cross more than three times. Using graphing technology, we can find that $E(t)$ will intersect $P(t)$ again about 58.88 years after 1970, or in the year 2028. To check this, sketch the difference function $D(t) = E(t) - P(t)$ on a grapher and find when it is zero.

The correct response is Choice **E**, all of the above are true.

9. We have $C(t) = \dfrac{P(t)}{R(t)} = \dfrac{360 + 9t}{12,000 + 12t}$. Therefore $C(0) = \dfrac{360 + 9(0)}{12,000 + 12(0)} = \dfrac{360}{12,000} = 0.03$ or 3%.

Choice **B**.

10. As t gets larger and larger, the function $C(t) = \dfrac{360 + 9t}{12,000 + 12t}$ approaches the ratio of the leading terms,

namely $\dfrac{9t}{12t} = 0.75$. Eventually 75% of the reservoir's total volume would consist of pollutants. This can be confirmed with a graph of the function or a view of its table for large values of t. Choice **E**.

11. If $h = 10$, then $E(L) = 7.4(L)(10)^2 = 740L$
The graph is a line through the origin with slope 740.
It passes through the point (1, 740). Choice **A**.

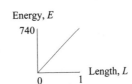

12. If $L = 100$, then $E(h) = 7.4(100)h^2 = 740h^2$

The graph is a parabola
through the origin also passing through (1, 740). Choice **B**.

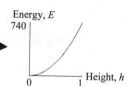

13. Find h if $L = 100$ and $E = 60{,}000$ ft-lb.

$$740h^2 = 60{,}000$$

$$h^2 = \tfrac{60{,}000}{740}$$

$$h = \sqrt{\tfrac{6000}{74}} \approx 9.005 \quad \text{The wave would be about 9 ft. tall. Choice } \mathbf{B}.$$

14. 30 lb of fertilizer produces a maximum yield of 450 pecks of peppers. Choice **B**.

15. Without applying any fertilizer at all, we see from the graph that the orchard will produce 200 pecks of peppers. Choice **C**.

16. The range is $0 \leq f(m) \leq 450$. Note: You can also write [0, 450]. Choice **E**.

17. The function $f(m)$ is **increasing** for $0 < m < 30$. Choice **C**.
Note: The function f(m) is **decreasing** for $30 < m < 70$.

18. The function $f(m)$ is never **concave up** and is **concave down** for $0 < m < 70$. Choice **E**.

19. $f(m) > 200$ for $0 < m < 60$.
Determine where the graph of $y = f(m)$
is above the line $y = 200$.
The yield is more than 200 pecks of peppers
when the amount of fertilizer applied is
more than 0 lb and less than 60 lb.
Choice **D**.

20. Choice **C**.

21. Choice **E**. It should be $2200e^{0.0382t}$

22. $P = 11500 + 275t$ and $Q = 2000(1.2)^{t/5}$
Set the equations equal to each other and solve using
technology. They intersect at $t = 76.5$ years. Choice **C**.

23. $Q = 20(0.4)^t = 20(1 - 0.6)^t$, so 60% of the drug is lost per hour. Choice **E**.

24. Choice **A**.

25. The equation is $P = 9216(1.125)^t$. The initial amount when $t = 0$ is \$9,216. Choice **C**.

26. Since the equation is $P = 9216(1.125)^t = 9216(1 + \underline{\mathbf{0.125}})^t$, the growth rate is 12.5%. Choice **C**.

27. (a) We have been given that the equation is of the form $y = ab^t + 60$ and we must find a and b.
When $t = 0$, $y = 85\ ^\circ$F:

$85 = ab^0 + 60$

$85 = a + 60$

$a = 85 - 60 = 25.$

Note this is the initial temperature difference
between the butler and the room temperature.

We have $y = 25b^t + 60$ and need b.
When $t = 2$, $y = 79.36\ ^\circ$F:

$79.36 = 25b^2 + 60$

$19.36 = 25b^2$

$b^2 = \dfrac{19.36}{25} = 0.7744$

$b = \sqrt{0.7744} = 0.88$

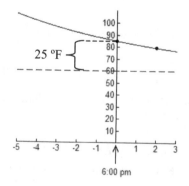

The model is $y = 25(0.88)^t + 60$. Check with a grapher or resubstitute the points. Choice **I**.

(b) We must write $y = 25(0.88)^t + 60$ as $y = He^{kt} + 60$.

We can simplify this to writing $25(0.88)^t$ as He^{kt} for some constants H and k.

The constant H is 25.

To find k, set $e^k = 0.88$

so $k = \ln e^k = \ln(0.88)$

To 3 decimal places, $k = \ln(0.88) = -0.128$ and we have $y = 25e^{-0.128t} + 60$.

Again we can check with a grapher or resubstitute the points. Choice **I**.

(c) When his body temperature, y, is 98.6°F, we will assume the butler was alive.

Set $y = 25(0.88)^t + 60$ and $y = 98.6$ equal to each other to find the time of death.

(From the graph, we expect a negative number.)

Algebraic solution:

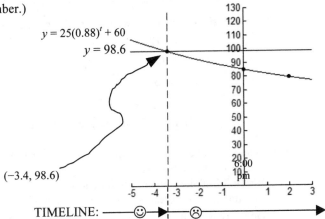

$y = 25(0.88)^t + 60$
$y = 98.6$

$$25(0.88)^t + 60 = 98.6$$

$$25(0.88)^t = 38.6$$

$$(0.88)^t = \tfrac{38.6}{25}$$

$$\ln(0.88)^t = \ln \tfrac{38.6}{25}$$

$$t\ln(0.88) = \ln(38.6/25)$$

$$t = \tfrac{\ln(38.6/25)}{\ln(0.88)} \approx -3.4 \qquad (-3.4,\ 98.6)$$

Notice the timeline on the graph:

He died 3.4 hours before 6:00 pm.

<Before death, butler is 98.6°F >< Butler starts to cool.>

This is 3 hours and $0.4 \cdot 60 = 24$ minutes before 6:00 pm

(or 24 minutes prior to 3:00 pm) which is 2:36 pm. Since the house records indicate that the niece arrived at 2:45 pm., the butler was already dead when she arrived.

Note: You could have also have used the equation involving e as shown below.

Since $\ln(0.88) = -0.128$, you reach the same answer:

$$25e^{-0.128t} + 60 = 98.6$$

$$25e^{-0.128t} = 38.6$$

$$e^{-0.128t} = \tfrac{38.6}{25}$$

$$\ln e^{-0.128t} = \ln \tfrac{38.6}{25}$$

$$-0.128t = \ln(38.6/25)$$

$$t = \tfrac{\ln(38.6/25)}{-0.128} \approx -3.4$$

28. (a) It might be helpful to plot the points and organize the information in a table.

The slope is positive:

$$m = \frac{\Delta C}{\Delta w} = \frac{\$48 - \$32}{180 - 100} = \frac{16}{80} = 0.2$$

w	C
100	$32
180	$48

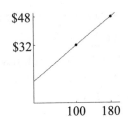

We have $C = b + 0.2w$

Substitute $w = 100$, $C = \$32$: $32 = b + 0.2(100)$

$$32 = b + 20$$

$$b = 12$$

Therefore $C = 12 + 0.2w$.

(b) The slope is $0.20 per kg, which is the monthly rate that the service charges for waste collection.

(c) The vertical intercept is (0, $12). When no waste is collected, the service charges a fixed charge of $12.

29. (a) Since we start with 900 gallons of fresh water, the vertical intercept is (0, 900). Each day we lose 12 gallons of water so the equation is $f(t) = 900 - 12t$.

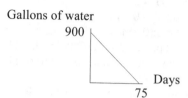

(b) (i) $f(0) = 900$.

Initially we have 900 gallons of water.

(ii) To find $f^{-1}(0) = t$, we must find the time t when the team has 0 gallons of fresh water.

$$0 = 900 - 12t$$

$$12t = 900$$

$$t = \tfrac{900}{12} = 75$$

Thus $f^{-1}(0) = 75$ days.

It will take 75 days before the team has 0 gallons of water remaining.

30. (a) When we have zero U.S. dollars, we have zero shillings: the y-intercept is (0, 0).

(b) We need an equation for $y = f(x)$.

We first find the slope of the function.

The function is increasing so we expect a positive slope.

One way is to find the slope is to compute Δy and Δx.

We want $\dfrac{\Delta y}{\Delta x} = \dfrac{3300 \,\text{shillings}}{\$1.50} = 2200$

	U.S. dollars	Shillings	
Δx	$1.00	2200	Δy
$1.50	$2.50	5500	3300
$0.50	$3.00	6600	1100

Check that this is also the same as $\dfrac{1100 \,\text{shillings}}{\$0.50} = 2200$ shillings per U.S. dollar.

Since the y-intercept is (0, 0), the equation is $y = 2200x$.

Check: The equation passes through the point (1, 2200), as well as the other points in the table.

If $y = 4000$ shillings, then $4000 = 2200x$ so $x = \tfrac{4000}{2200} \approx \$1.82$. The trousers cost $1.82.

(Recall these are second-hand items in the Kampala market.)

(c) If we have $x = \$4.00$, then we can exchange it for $y = 2200x = 2200 \cdot 4 = 8800$ shillings, so we can afford the 8500 shilling coat.

31. (a) We know that when the price $p = \$10$, the number of customers N who will come to the park is 10,000. For each $1.00 increase in the entrance price p, the park would lose an average of 500 daily customers:

p	N
$10.00	10,000
$11.00	9,500
$12.00	9,000
$13.00	8,500
$14.00	8,000

(b) $N = f(p)$ is linear. When $\Delta p = \$1$, then $\Delta N = -500$.

The slope is $\dfrac{\Delta N}{\Delta p} = \dfrac{-500}{\$1} = -500$ and it passes through ($10, 10,000).

We have $N = b - 500p$. Substitute $p = 10$, $N = 10,000$:

$$10,000 = b - 500(10)$$

$$10,000 = b - 5,000$$

$$b = 15,000$$

p	N	$R = p \cdot N$
$10.00	10,000	$100,000
$11.00	9,500	$104,500
$12.00	9,000	$108,000
$13.00	8,500	$110,500
$14.00	8,000	$112,000

Therefore $N = f(p) = 15,000 - 500p$. *TIP:* Check the formula using the table feature of a grapher.

(c) If 10,000 customers pay $10 each, the revenue is
$10,000 \cdot \$10 = \$100,000$. Do this for each row to
complete the table. Notice revenue increases due to the
ticket price increase, although N decreases.

(d) In general, R is the product of the first two columns,
so $R = p \cdot N$. Since $N = 15,000 - 500p$, we have $R = p \cdot N = p \cdot (15,000 - 500p)$.
Check the formula using the table feature of a grapher.

(e) To find the N-intercept of $N = 15,000 - 500p$, set $p = 0$. By inspection it is (0, 15,000).
Interpretation: If the tickets were free, the amusement park would have 15,000 customers.
To find the p-intercept of $N = f(p)$, set $N = 0$ and solve for p:

$$N = 15000 - 500p$$
$$0 = 15000 - 500p$$
$$500p = 15000$$
$$p = 30$$

The p-intercept is (30, 0).
Interpretation: If the ticket price was $30, no customer would purchase one.

(f) Find any p-intercepts by solving $R = p \cdot (15,000 - 500p) = 0$
Set each factor equal to 0: we know $R = 0$ when $p = 0$ and $15,000 - 500p = 0$.
From part **(e)**, $15,000 - 500p = 0$ when $p = 30$ so the p-intercepts are (0, 0) and (30, 0).
Interpretation:
(0, 0): If the tickets were free,
there would be no revenue (even though 15000 customers would come).
(30, 0): If the tickets were $30, there would be no revenue (since no customers would buy them.)

To find all the R-intercepts, set $p = 0$ in the equation $R = g(p) = p \cdot (15,000 - 500p)$.
$R = g(0) = 0 \cdot 15,000 = 0$.
The only R-intercept is the point (0, 0), interpreted previously.

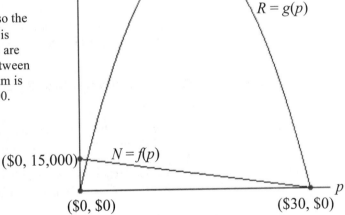

(g) $15 since the maximum is at (15, 112,500).
There are several strategies to get the maximum of
$R(x) = x(15,000 - 500x) = -500x^2 + 15000x$

1. The coefficient of the x^2 term is negative, so the
parabola is concave down. Since a parabola is
symmetric about its maximum, and its zeros are
at $x = 0$ and 30, the maximum is midway between
at $x = 15$. The y= coordinate of the maximum is
$R = g(15) = 15 \cdot (15,000 - 500 \cdot 15) = 112,500$.
2. Use the maximum feature.
3. Use the table feature.

(h) See the graph at the right.

32. The formula for the power function is $y = 5000x^{-3}$.

For $y = kx^p$, we have $-40 = k(-5)^p$ and $5 = k(10)^p$. Take ratios.

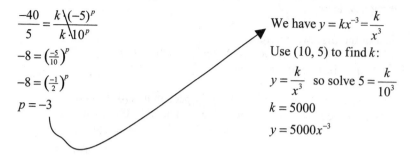

$$\frac{-40}{5} = \frac{k(-5)^p}{k\,10^p}$$

$$-8 = \left(\tfrac{-5}{10}\right)^p$$

$$-8 = \left(\tfrac{-1}{2}\right)^p$$

$$p = -3$$

We have $y = kx^{-3} = \dfrac{k}{x^3}$

Use (10, 5) to find k:

$y = \dfrac{k}{x^3}$ so solve $5 = \dfrac{k}{10^3}$

$k = 5000$

$y = 5000x^{-3}$

The formula for the power function is $y = 5000x^{-3}$ or $y = \dfrac{5000}{x^3}$.

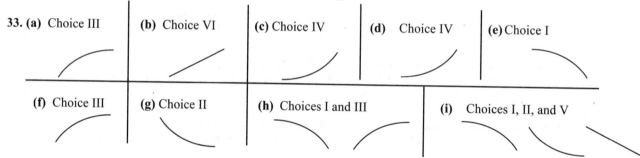

33. (a) Choice III **(b)** Choice VI **(c)** Choice IV **(d)** Choice IV **(e)** Choice I

(f) Choice III **(g)** Choice II **(h)** Choices I and III **(i)** Choices I, II, and V

34. a. Choice II. The train's speed slows to a stop (speed is 0).

   b. Choice I. My rate is constant at first, so the graph appears linear.
   Once the chimes ring, my rate increases so the graph is concave up.

   c. Choice III. First my speed is constant, or flat. The graph appears horizontal.
   When I run, my speed increases.

   d. Choice II. The ferris wheel car climbs to its highest point, then descends, then climbs again.

   e. Choice III. As the child climbs up the slide her speed is steady and constant.
   When she stops at the top of the slide, her speed is 0.
   Once she slides down her speed increases, exceeding the
   speed she had when she was climbing the slide.
   At the bottom of the slide, her speed is 0 when she stops.

35. (i) $P(t) = 300 - 2t$ is Choice **F** since $300 - 2t = 250$ when $t = 25$.

The population starts at 300 and has dropped to 250 after 25 years.
It is not Choice **A** since, even though $P(t) = 300 - 2t$ declines at a constant rate,
$P(t)$ becomes 0 in 150 years, not 15.

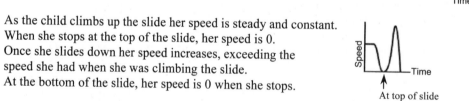

(ii) $Q(t) = 300e^{0.02t}$ is Choice **C**.

The population, which began at 300, is growing at the continuous rate of 2 percent each year.

(iii) $R(t) = 300(0.98)^t$ is Choice **H**.

The population, originally at 300, has been decreasing at the annual rate of 2 percent.

(iv) $S(t) = -\frac{4}{3}t^2 + 300$ is Choice **G**.

The population, which began at 300, decreases faster and faster.

36. (i) $f(x) = \dfrac{5x^2 - 5}{8000x - 80}$

x-intercepts: $(1, 0)$ and $(-1, 0)$.

The x-intercepts occur when $y = f(x) = 0$, which is when the numerator $5x^2 - 5 = 0$. Solve $5x^2 = 5$

$$x^2 = 1$$
$$x = 1, -1$$

y-intercept: $(0, \frac{1}{16})$.

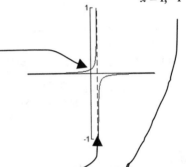

Set $x = 0$. $\quad y = \dfrac{5x^2 - 5}{8000x - 80} = \dfrac{5(0)^2 - 5}{8000(0) - 80} = \dfrac{-5}{-80} = \dfrac{1}{16}$

vertical asymptote: $x = 0.01$
Solve $8000x - 80 = 0$

$$8000x = 80$$

$$x = \frac{80}{8000} = 0.01$$

horizontal asymptote: None.

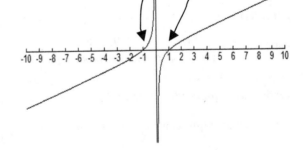

As $x \to \infty, f(x) = \dfrac{5x^2 - 5}{8000x - 80} \to \dfrac{5x^2}{8000x} = \dfrac{5x}{8000} = \dfrac{5}{1600}x$

For large values of x the function looks very much like the linear function $y = \frac{1}{1600}x$.

Note: Graphs are not expected, but shown here to confirm the algebraic reasoning. None of these graphs show the complete behavior of the function by themselves.

(ii) $f(x) = \dfrac{5x^2 + 5}{8000x^2 - 80}$

x-intercepts: None

The *x*-intercepts occur when $y = f(x) = 0$, which is when the numerator $5x^2 + 5 = 0$.

However, $5x^2 + 5$ is never 0, so there are no *x*-intercepts.

y-intercept: $\left(0, -\frac{1}{16}\right)$.

Set $x = 0$. $\quad y = \dfrac{5x^2 + 5}{8000x^2 - 80} = \dfrac{5(0)^2 + 5}{8000(0)^2 - 80} = \dfrac{5}{-80} = -\dfrac{1}{16}$

vertical asymptotes: $x = \frac{1}{10}, x = -\frac{1}{10}$

Set the denominator equal to 0.

$8000x^2 - 80 = 0$

$\quad 8000x^2 = 80$

$\qquad x^2 = \frac{80}{8000} = \frac{1}{100}$

$\qquad x = \pm\frac{1}{10}$

horizontal asymptote: $y = \frac{1}{1600}$

As $x \to \infty$, $f(x) = \dfrac{5x^2 + 5}{8000x^2 - 80} \to \dfrac{5x^2}{8000x^2} = \dfrac{5}{8000} = \dfrac{1}{1600}$

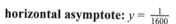

(iii) $f(x) = \dfrac{5x - 5}{8000x^2 + 80}$

x-intercept: $(1, 0)$

The *x*-intercept occurs when $y = f(x) = 0$, which is when the numerator $5x - 5 = 0$ or when $x = 1$.

y-intercept: $\left(0, -\frac{1}{16}\right)$.

Set $x = 0$. $\quad y = \dfrac{5x - 5}{8000x^2 + 80} = \dfrac{5(0)^2 - 5}{8000(0) + 80} = \dfrac{-5}{80} = -\dfrac{1}{16}$

vertical asymptotes: None, since $8000x^2 + 80$ is never 0.

horizontal asymptote: $y = 0$ since as $x \to \infty$, $f(x) = \dfrac{5x - 5}{8000x^2 + 80} \to \dfrac{5x}{8000x^2} = \dfrac{5}{8000x} \to 0$.

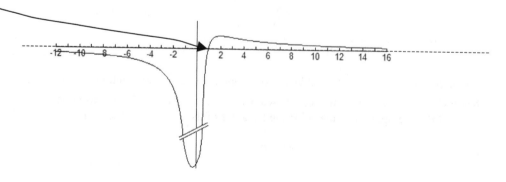

37. (a) $1000e^{(0.05 \cdot 1)} \approx \$1051.27$

(b) No since $\log 10 = 1$.

(c) Simplify as much as possible: $e^{\ln x^2 \,+\, \ln 5} = e^{\ln 5 \,+\, \ln x^2} = e^{\ln 5}\, e^{\ln x^2} = 5x^2$

(d) First, the graph of $f(x)$ is shifted to the left by 4 units, then (second) it is stretched vertically by a factor of 2, and then (third) it is shifted upward by 3 units.

(e) $x = 2$ is a solution to the equation $4x + 8 = 4^x$ since

$$4x + 8 = 4^x$$
$$4(2) + 8 = 4^2$$
$$8 + 8 = 16$$

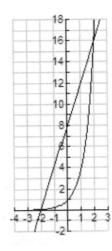

To solve $4x + 8 > 4^x$, we must find all solutions to $4x + 8 = 4^x$, which can only be solved graphically or numerically. The solutions are $x = -1.98403$ and $x = 2$.

From the graph, the solution to $4x + 8 > 4^x$ are the values of x when the graph of $y = 4x + 8$ is **above** the graph of $y = 4^x$, which is $-1.98403 < x < 2$.

38. Choice **C**. $h(x) = x^3$ The domain and range are all real numbers.

39. (a) The polynomial has formula $y = \frac{1}{4}(x-2)(x-1)(x+3)(x+2)^2$

Because the function has single zeros at -3, 1, and 2 and a double zero at -2 we can write $y = a(x-2)(x-1)(x+3)(x+2)^2$ Now substitute the point $(0,6)$:

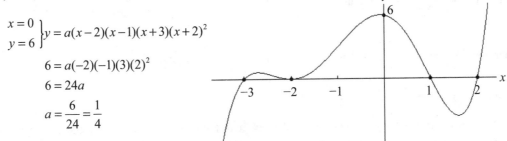

$$\left.\begin{array}{l} x = 0 \\ y = 6 \end{array}\right\} y = a(x-2)(x-1)(x+3)(x+2)^2$$

$$6 = a(-2)(-1)(3)(2)^2$$
$$6 = 24a$$
$$a = \frac{6}{24} = \frac{1}{4}$$

Therefore, the polynomial is $f(x) = \frac{1}{4}(x-2)(x-1)(x+3)(x+2)^2$

To find $f(3)$, let $x = 3$: $f(3) = \frac{1}{4}(3-2)(3-1)(3+3)(3+2)^2 = \frac{1}{4}(1)(2)(6)(5)^2 = 75$

You could also use the table feature of a graphing calculator. Choice **B**.
Important: You should check with a graphing calculator to be sure that the function is correct.

(b) The rational function has the formula $y = \dfrac{3(x-3)(x+4)}{(x-1)(x+2)}$

Because the zeros of the function are 3 and -4, the factors of the numerator are $(x-3)(x+4)$, since the function is 0 when the numerator is 0.

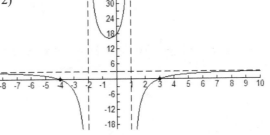

Since the vertical asymptotes are $x = -2$ and $x = 1$, the factors of the denominator are $(x-1)(x+2)$. (The vertical asymptotes are found where the denominator is 0 and the numerator is not).

So we can write $y = \dfrac{a(x-3)(x+4)}{(x-1)(x+2)}$.

Since the horizontal asymptote is $y = 3$ and it is found by the ratio of the leading terms, we must have $a = 3$. Therefore the function must be $y = \dfrac{3(x-3)(x+4)}{(x-1)(x+2)}$. Check that when $x = 0$, you have $y = 18$. Use a table feature to find Choice **D** is correct.

(c) The rational function has the formula $y = \dfrac{2x(x+3)}{(x+2)^2}$.

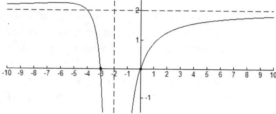

Because the zeros of the function are 0 and -3, the factors of the numerator are $x(x+3)$, since the function is 0 when the numerator is 0.

There is one vertical asymptote at $x = -2$, so $(x + 2)$ is a factor of the denominator. However, the short run behavior near this asymptote looks like $y = k/x^2$ (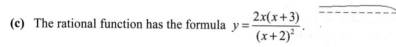) so the factor must have a power of 2. We can write $y = \dfrac{ax(x+3)}{(x+2)^2}$. Since the horizontal asymptote is $y = 2$, we must have $a = 2$.

Note: $y = \dfrac{ax(x+3)}{(x+2)^2} \approx \dfrac{ax^2}{x^2} = a$ as $x \to \pm\infty$ so $a = 2$.

Therefore, the rational function has the formula $y = \dfrac{2x(x+3)}{(x+2)^2}$. Choice **D** is correct.

40. The equation is $y = \dfrac{8(x-4)}{(x-2)^2}$

Because there is a horizontal asymptote of $y = 0$, the degree of the numerator is less than the degree of the denominator. The numerator has a factor of $(x-4)^1$ since it has a single zero. Because the short run behavior

near the vertical asymptote looks like ⎯⫯⎯ or ⎯⫯⎯

the lowest degree possible for the denominator must be 2. So it has a factor of $(x-2)^2$. It has the form $y = \dfrac{a(x-4)}{(x-2)^2}$, and we can find a if we use the fact that when $x = 0$, $y = -8$: $-8 = \dfrac{a(0-4)}{(0-2)^2}$

$$-8 = \tfrac{-4}{4}a$$
$$a = 8$$

So $f(x) = \dfrac{8(x-4)}{(x-2)^2}$. To find $f(3)$, we let $x = 3$ and find y. $f(3) = \dfrac{8(3-4)}{(3-2)^2} = \dfrac{8(-1)}{1} = -8$

Choice **B**.